Handbook for Teaching and Learning in Geography

Edited by

Helen Walkington

Oxford Brookes University, UK

Jennifer Hill

University of the West of England (UWE Bristol), UK

Sarah Dyer

University of Exeter, UK

EE **Edward Elgar**
PUBLISHING

Cheltenham, UK • Northampton, MA, USA

Published by
Edward Elgar Publishing Limited
The Lypiatts
15 Lansdown Road
Cheltenham
Glos GL50 2JA
UK

Edward Elgar Publishing, Inc.
William Pratt House
9 Dewey Court
Northampton
Massachusetts 01060
USA

A catalogue record for this book
is available from the British Library

Library of Congress Control Number: 2019915301

This book is available electronically in the **Elgar**online
Social and Political Science subject collection
DOI 10.4337/9781788116497

MIX
Paper from
responsible sources
FSC
www.fsc.org   FSC® C013056

ISBN 978 1 78811 648 0 (cased)
ISBN 978 1 78811 649 7 (eBook)

Typeset by Servis Filmsetting Ltd, Stockport, Cheshire

Printed and bound in Great Britain by TJ International Ltd, Padstow, Cornwall

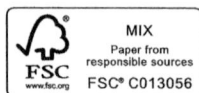

Contents

Figures

Tables

Boxes

Contributors

Colin Arrowsmith has recently retired as Associate Professor in Geospatial Science in the School of Science at RMIT University. He is now a visiting professor at the University of South Australia and Flinders University. He holds a Doctor of Philosophy from RMIT as well as two masters' degrees and a bachelor's degree from the University of Melbourne, and a Graduate Diploma of Education from Hawthorn Institute of Education. Colin has authored more than 80 refereed publications and eight book chapters in the fields of GIS, tourism analysis and film studies. Colin's research interests include geospatial science education, the application of spatial information systems, including geographic information systems (GIS), to investigating the impact of tourism on nature-based tourist destinations, tourist behaviour, as well as investigating the issue of managing micro-historical data within GIS utilising cinema data. Colin is a member of the Surveying and Spatial Sciences Institute of Australia and a Fellow of the Royal Geographical Society.

Karen Barton, PhD, is a Professor of Geography at the University of Northern Colorado where she teaches resource management, African studies, and global environmental change. She has received the NCGE teaching award, several Fulbright fellowships, and the National Endowment for the Humanities Senior Fellow Award for her engaged scholarship in rural communities. She is currently completing a book manuscript on 'Africa's Greatest Shipwreck' for Lexington Press.

Shauna Brail is Associate Professor, Teaching Stream, in the Urban Studies Program, and a Senior Associate in the Innovation Policy Lab at the Munk School of Global Affairs, University of Toronto. She holds a BA in Urban Studies/Geography (UofT), an MA in Urban Planning (UBC), and a PhD in Geography (UofT). As an economic geographer, her research focuses on the transformation of cities as a result of economic, social and cultural change. She has led the development of academic internships and community engaged learning in the Urban Studies Program for over a decade, working with students, university administrators and partners at urban-focused organizations across the city. Shauna is the author or co-author of articles about experiential learning and community partnerships in the following: *Journal of Geography*, *Journal of Geography in Higher Education*, *Canadian Journal of Higher Education* and the *International Journal of Teaching and Learning in Higher Education*.

Joanna Bullard, PhD, PFHEA, is Professor of Physical Geography and Associate Dean (Teaching) for the School of Social Sciences and Humanities at Loughborough University, UK. Throughout her career she has had a sustained interest in, and commitment to, how high-quality teaching and learning can be provided, developed and encouraged in higher education. She was a member of the Editorial Board of the *Journal of Geography in Higher Education* from 1997 to 2007 and has ten publications in the field of pedagogy focusing on teaching geosciences and academic development. She is a Principal Fellow of the Higher Education Academy and is currently Chair of the Royal Geographical Society (with Institute of British Geographers) programme accreditation panel (2016–19).

Graham Butt is Professor in Education, Co-Director of Research and Co Post Graduate Research Tutor at the School of Education, Oxford Brookes University. He is a founding member of the Geography Education Research Collective (GEReCo). Graham's research is predominantly in the field of geography education, although he has also published on assessment, teacher workload and modernisation of the teaching workforce. His books include *Modernising Schools* (2007, with Helen Gunter), *Lesson Planning* (3rd edition) (2008), *Making Assessment Matter* (2010), *Geography Education Research: Retrospect and Prospect* (2018) and, as editor, *Geography, Education and the Future* (2011), *MasterClass in Geography Education* (2015) and *The Power of Geographical Thinking* (2017) (with Clare Brooks and Mary Fargher). Graham is a long-established member of the Geographical Association and an invited member of the UK Committee of the International Geographical Union (IGU).

William Cartwright is Professor of Cartography in the School of Science at RMIT University. His major research interest is integrated media and cartography, and the exploration of different metaphorical approaches to the depiction of geographical information. He was President of the International Cartographic Association, past Chair of the Joint Board of Geospatial Information Societies – JBGIS (now UN-GGIM: Geospatial Societies). He is co-editor of the *International Journal of Cartography*. He holds a Doctor of Philosophy and a Doctor of Education. He has six other university qualifications – in the fields of cartography, applied science, education, media studies, information and communication technology, and graphic design. He is the author of over 300 academic papers. In 2013 he was made a Member of the Order of Australia for 'significant service to cartography and geospatial science as an academic, researcher and educator'. In 2017 he was made an Honorary Fellow of the International Cartographic Association.

Lucy Clarke, PhD, is a geomorphologist, specialising in river processes, natural flood management and using GIS (Geographic Information Systems) and image analysis to evaluate landform change. She is a Senior Lecturer in Physical Geography at the University of Gloucestershire in the UK, where she teaches a range of undergraduate modules spanning research methods and field skills, environmental processes, GIS and river science and management. She was awarded the University of Gloucestershire University Teaching Fellowship in 2015 for her use of digital technologies in enhancing student learning. Fieldwork has been an important component of both her research and teaching, and she has experience of undertaking fieldwork in a variety of different environments across the World, including sites in Europe, Canada, New Zealand and South Africa.

David Conradson teaches human geography at the University of Canterbury in New Zealand. He has professional qualifications in geography and psychotherapy, and together these trainings have alerted him to the complex ways in which relational conditions, past and present, can both enable and inhibit learning. From this perspective, he has become interested in the co-creation of supportive learning environments for university students.

Michael DeMers, PhD, GISP, is Professor of Geography in the Department of Geography at New Mexico State University where he focuses on Geographic Information Science, Landscape Ecology and Geography Education, especially GIS education. He holds the James R. Anderson Medal of Honor in Applied Geography, given by the

Applied Geography Specialty Group of the American Association of Geographers, and the Wheeler Peak Lifetime Achievement Award given by the New Mexico Geographic Information Council.

Sarah Dyer is an Associate Professor in Human Geography at the University of Exeter, UK. She is a member of the editorial board of the *Journal of Geography in Higher Education* and is author of 'Appreciate: cards to support appreciative partnership learning' (available to download from the Advance HE website). Her research explores various connections between work and higher education, including academics' working lives and narratives of student employment and employability.

James Esson, PhD, is Lecturer in Human Geography in the Department of Geography and Environment at Loughborough University, and head of the RGS-IBG RACE's Learning and Teaching subcommittee. The RGS-IBG's Race, Culture and Equality Working Group (RGS-IBG RACE) was established in 2015, with the aim of encouraging and undertaking geographical research, curriculum development and positive action for change on issues around race and racism.

Matt Finn, PhD, FHEA, is a Senior Lecturer in Human Geography. He explores the contemporary conditions of education as a geographer through approaches which include participatory action research (PAR). He is interested in childhood and young people's lives and has researched how the rise of data changes the way people think about themselves and are governed in educational settings. He is a member of the editorial collective of *Geography*, the Geographical Association's international journal for lecturers, teachers and students in post-16 geography.

Derek France, PhD, NTF, FHEA, teaches physical geography in the Department of Geography and International Development at University of Chester. He was awarded a UK National Teaching Fellowship in 2008 and Professor of *Pedagogy in Geographical Sciences* in 2009. He was the recipient of the 2013 RGS-IBG Taylor and Francis Award for Excellence in Teaching and Learning Higher Education Geography. Derek is co-editor of the *Journal of Geography in Higher Education* and has research interests in the pedagogy of fieldwork and mobile learning. In 2018, he received national recognition for the work of the Enhancing Fieldwork Learning team through a national Collaborative Award for Teaching Excellence (CATE).

Erin H. Fouberg is Professor of Geography and Director of the Honors Program at Northern State University in Aberdeen, South Dakota, USA. Dr Fouberg is a broadly trained human geographer with expertise in political geography and geography education. Dr Fouberg won the Biennial Award for Teaching and Learning from the *Journal of Geography in Higher Education*. She serves on the board of the National Council for Geographic Education. Dr Fouberg co-authors two college level textbooks: *Understanding World Regional Geography* and *Human Geography: People, Place, and Culture*, both published by Wiley.

Ian C. Fuller, PhD, FHEA, is Professor of Physical Geography in the School of Agriculture and Environment at Massey University in New Zealand, where he was awarded a 2015 Vice Chancellor's Teaching Excellence Award for Sustained Commitment to Teaching Excellence and nominated for the National Tertiary Teaching Excellence Award. He is a sub-editor of the *Journal of Geography in Higher Education* and researches the pedagogy of fieldwork. Completing his doctorate in 1995, his teaching career began as a tutor in Aberystwyth, prior to a lectureship at Northumbria in 1996, before moving to Massey in 2003. Beyond teaching, his research focuses on fluvial geomorphology at multiple spatial and temporal scales.

Amy L. Griffin is a Senior Lecturer in Geospatial Sciences in the School of Science at RMIT University in Melbourne, Australia. She has taught in a multidisciplinary school for 15 years and is an active researcher in both geospatial science and pedagogical practice in Geography. She serves on the editorial board of the *Journal of Geography in Higher Education*.

Martin Haigh, PhD, NTF, SFHEA, is Emeritus Professor of Geography, Department of Social Sciences, Oxford Brookes University, UK and a former editor of the *Journal of Geography in Higher Education*. In 2010, he was awarded the Royal Geographical Society's 'Taylor and Francis Award for Excellence in Geography Teaching (Higher Education)'. His special interests include environmental education for a sustainable future, dharmic pedagogies, the internationalisation of university curricula and applied environmental reconstruction, especially in Uttarakhand, India and Wales, UK. In 2016, Martin was GIAN teaching fellow at the University of Nagaland, India, and from 2017 to 2019, Board of Directors' Thematic Moderator for Geography in the AOPDA-SAARC-ASEAN Postdoc Academia.

Ruth L. Healey, PhD, SFHEA, NTF, is an Associate Professor in Pedagogy in Higher Education at the University of Chester, UK. In 2016, she also joined Healey HE Consultants. Her wide range of pedagogic research interests include teaching for social transformations, debates, ethics, and students as partners. She is on the editorial board of the *Journal of Geography in Higher Education* and is one of the inaugural editors of the *International Journal for Students as Partners*.

Jennifer Hill, PhD, is an Associate Professor in Teaching and Learning at the University of the West of England, Bristol, UK, where she teaches, researches, and develops curricula and practice in geography and cognate disciplines. Jenny is a Chartered Geographer, Fellow of the Royal Geographical Society, a National Teaching Fellow and a Principal Fellow in the UK Professional Standards Framework. Jenny's educational enquiry has focused on student partnership, assessment and feedback, the development of graduate attributes, learning spaces, and the teaching–research dialectic. She has published over 90 journal articles, book chapters and co-edited books. Jenny has chaired the RGS-IBG Higher Education Research Group and is currently a member of the international editorial boards for *Journal of Geography in Higher Education, Higher Education Pedagogies and GEOverse.*

Richard Hodgkins, PhD, SFHEA, is a Senior Lecturer in Physical Geography at Loughborough University, Director of Studies in the School of Social Sciences and Humanities, Senior Fellow of the HEA, and External Examiner for the Open University Earth and Environmental Science modules. He has 20 years' teaching experience across four institutions at both undergraduate and postgraduate levels. His research concerns the hydrology and meteorology of Arctic, glacier-dominated environments, and he has published 42 peer-reviewed research papers to date. He is a member of the UK Arctic–Antarctic Partnership Steering Group.

Peter Hopkins is Professor in Social Geography at Newcastle University where he has taught for over ten years. Peter's research interests focus upon: young people's geographies; the geographies of race, ethnicity and religion; and the intersections between masculinities and ethnicities. He is author of *Young People, Place and Identity*, a Routledge textbook for a third-year module of the same name that he has taught at Newcastle for five years. With Simon Tate, Peter has developed a strong interest in student transitions, in particular the transitions of students to university. Before working at Newcastle, Peter taught at Lancaster and Edinburgh Universities and so has experience in working with students in different university systems. Peter has served as external examiner for Geography at Dundee and Exeter and for Geography and Planning at Cardiff. Being an external examiner has provided him with insights into the challenges that first-year geography students face nationally and these inform the writing of this chapter.

Michael Horswell is Senior Lecturer in Applied GIS and Spatial Analysis at the University of the West of England, Bristol. He teaches GIS and remote sensing across all levels, both as core and optional elements of the geography programmes. He also teaches philosophy of science to post-graduate research students. He is a UWE Learning and Teaching Fellow, in recognition of his implementation of longitudinal curricula and explicit incorporation of graduate dispositional development into GIS teaching. He has been involved in developing and delivering international residential field trips, and most recently has led an advanced geographic expedition to South Africa, with Lisa Mol.

Alice Hovorka is Dean and Professor in the Faculty of Environmental Studies at York University in Toronto, Canada. She is an award-winning instructor who has taught courses on gender and environment, animal geographies, human–environment relations, research methods, and contemporary geographic thought at graduate and undergraduate levels. She is active in the scholarship of teaching and learning, exploring issues related to experiential learning, capstone courses, student participation, and student emotional responses to course content.

Annie Hughes, PhD, is a geographer and developed her interest in inclusive academic practices in higher education during her tenure as Director of Geography programmes at Kingston University. She has published on the ways in which normative practice in geographical education act to exclude or disadvantage some groups of students. In her current role as Head of the Learning and Teaching Enhancement Centre in the Directorate of Student Achievement at Kingston University, she is responsible for ensuring that academic learning and teaching practices are inclusive and ensure an equality of opportunity for all students. With Nona McDuff, Annie developed Kingston University's Inclusive Curriculum Framework. Her work has had a significant impact on the educational mission of her institution and the sector more broadly. The Inclusive Curriculum Framework was awarded the Guardian Award for Teaching Excellence in 2017. Annie's research has been supported by Kingston University, as well as AdvanceHE, the Office for Students and the ESRC. She is a Principal Fellow of the Higher Education Academy and is a National Teaching Fellow.

Niem Tu Huynh, PhD, PPCC, FRCGS, is a geographer, multipotentialite and calculated risk taker. Her interest in supporting students in searching for meaningful careers was ignited by her own journey. Professional work took her to Texas, for an Assistant Professor position, and this was followed by a research role in a non-profit organization in Washington, DC. Feeling like the Canada goose, she traced her roots back to Canada where she has since enjoyed working with students as a career advisor (McGill University) and manager of graduate recruitment (Concordia University). Today, Niem explores entrepreneurship through private practice as a Professional and Personal Life Coach as well as an inspirational speaker. She has published chapters about navigating employment prospects for new graduates in the geospatial sciences, geography learning and career readiness.

Joseph Kerski, PhD, GISP, is a geographer who believes that spatial analysis through digital mapping can transform education and society through better decision-making using the geographic perspective. He has served as geographer and cartographer at NOAA, the US Census Bureau, and the US Geological Survey. He teaches online and face-to-face courses at primary and secondary schools, through MOOCs, and universities. Joseph serves as GIS instructor for the University of Denver and Education Manager for Esri, focused on thought leadership in geospatial technology education. This work includes curriculum development, research in the effectiveness of GIS in education, professional development for educators, and fostering partnerships to support GIS in education at all levels, internationally. Joseph holds three degrees in geography, has authored 4,000 videos, 1,000 blog essays, over 100 articles and chapters, and seven books, and is passionate about people and the planet.

Phil Klein, PhD, is Professor in the Department of Geography, GIS, and Sustainability at the University of Northern Colorado (USA), where he is also chair of its Hewit Institute for History and Social Science Education. He has been involved in several major geography instructional-materials development projects since the 1990s, including *Geographic Issues into Global Inquiry* (GIGI) and the AAG's *Center for Global Geography Education* (CGGE). In addition, he works with several local school districts, K-12 teachers, and publishers to create online geography materials.

Pauline E. Kneale, PhD, PFHEA and National Teaching Fellow (2002), is an Emeritus Professor at the University of Plymouth. She has moved from hydrology and geomorphology research to focus on student skills, Masters level teaching, inclusive assessment, students' experience of university and the position of pedagogic research in REF2014. Career highlights include directing the White Rose Centre for Excellence in Teaching and Learning of Enterprise, University of Leeds 2005–10, and the Higher Education Academy Subject Centre for Geography, Earth and Environmental Sciences 2009–11. In 2010 Pauline was appointed Professor and Pro Vice-Chancellor for Teaching and Learning at the University of Plymouth, where she established and directed the Pedagogic Research Institute and Observatory (PedRIO).

Angela Last is Lecturer in Human Geography in the Department of Geography at the University of Leicester, and Treasurer of the RGS-IBG RACE. The RGS-IBG's Race, Culture and Equality Working Group (RGS-IBG RACE) was established in 2015, with the aim of encouraging and undertaking geographical research, curriculum development and positive action for change on issues around race and racism.

Jieun Lee, PhD, is Assistant Professor in the Department of Geography, GIS, and Sustainability at the University of Northern Colorado. An urban geographer specializing in transportation, urban design and land use planning and policy, her research focuses on gender, socioeconomic, racial and health disparities in marginalized communities. Dr Lee has published in diverse urban studies and public health journals and co-authored several book chapters on global urban health. Currently she is analysing determinants of health and health-care accessibility in Colorado, having been previously involved in community-based research on urban pollution and public health in New York.

Avril Maddrell, PhD, is Professor of Social and Cultural Geography at the University of Reading. She is a feminist geographer, with research interests in spaces, landscapes and practices of death, mourning and remembrance; pilgrimage and sacred mobilities; and gendered historiography. She is co-editor of *Social and Cultural Geography*, author of *Complex Locations. Women's Geographical Work in the UK 1850–1970* (2009, Wiley-Blackwell/RGS), co-author of *Christian Pilgrimage, Landscape and Heritage* (Routledge, 2015), *Charity Shops* (Routledge, 2002), and co-editor of *Consolationscapes . . .* (Routledge, 2019), *Deathscapes. Spaces for Death, Dying, Mourning and Remembrance* (Ashgate, 2010), *Memory, Mourning, Landscape* (Rodopi, 2010), *Sacred Mobilities* (Ashgate, 2015), and *Contemporary Encounters in Gender and Religion* (Palgrave, 2017).

Nona McDuff is Director of Student Achievement at Kingston University, UK. Nona is a panel member on the UK's Teaching Excellence Framework (TEF) and Chair of the Higher Education Race Action Group. With Dr Annie Hughes, Nona developed the Inclusive Curriculum Framework (Guardian Teaching Excellence Award 2017) to ensure students have a relevant and accessible learning experience within and beyond the classroom. Nona has also promoted diversity in staff in higher education and her work was recognised in 2012 by the Guardian Award for Diversity. Nona's research has been supported by Kingston University and the Leadership Foundation for HE. Nona is currently leading the Office for Students' catalyst project to disseminate Kingston's work on the Value Added Metric and the Inclusive Curriculum Framework across five other UK higher education institutions. Nona is a Principal Fellow of the Higher Education Academy and was awarded an OBE in the 2017 Honours List for services to Higher Education.

Gill Miller, FRGS, is Senior Lecturer Emerita in the Department of Geography and International Development at the University of Chester. She is an experienced A-level Chief Examiner and author of textbooks and journal articles for A-level students, and advises on the preparation of A-level Geography papers.. She led the GEES *Transitions Special Interest Group Report* (HEA, 2012) with S. Brace and H. Walkington. She is Vice President of the Geographical Association (President 2019–2020) and has two GA Awards for Excellence in 2013 and 2017.

Lisa Mol, PhD, is a geomorphologist, specialising in rock deterioration processes. The interdisciplinary nature of her work has taken her across the world, working in environments as diverse as the Arctic and the high veld of southern Africa. She completed a BSc in Geography at Durham University, as well as an MSc and DPhil at Oxford University. After working at Cardiff University as a lecturer, she took up a lectureship at UWE Bristol where she teaches subjects ranging from Environmental Challenges to Research Skills and Earth Science. She continues to undertake research, primarily the Heritage in the Cross-Fire project which is funded by the Leverhulme Trust, and other heritage-based projects such as the damage to the Glasgow School of Art. She also works in the natural environment, researching the impacts of climate change on rock deterioration in the Arctic and complex lithology weathering in the Karoo, South Africa.

Niamh Moore-Cherry, PhD, PFHEA, is Vice-Principal for Teaching and Learning at the College of Social Sciences and Law, University College Dublin. She is also Associate Professor of Urban Governance and Development in the School of Geography. Her research is focused on understanding how cities are governed; how urban policy is developed; and with what impacts. She is the author of *Dublin Docklands Reinvented* (Four Courts Press, 2008), has co-edited three books and has papers published in national and international journals. Her current work focuses on the spaces and practices of metropolitan governance, and the implications for spatial planning. Niamh has a strong research and teaching interest in student transitions and students as partners and has co-authored a number of papers on these topics. She is a member of: the Social Sciences Committee, Royal Irish Academy; the IGU Urban Commission Steering Group; and is past-President of the Geographical Society of Ireland.

Carrie Mott is currently an Assistant Professor in the Department of Geography and Geosciences at the University of Louisville after serving two years as an Instructor at Rutgers with the department of Geography. Her research explores the dynamics of racialized difference in the United States. Her present research investigates the processes of settler colonialism and white supremacy in the US Pacific Northwest by looking to reclamation projects throughout the Columbia River Basin. This project builds upon her dissertation work on the racialized dynamics of social justice movements in the US/ Mexico borderlands. She also has published on topics related to knowledge production in geography, looking at teaching as well as practices of citation and research.

Ash Parton, PhD, is a Senior Lecturer in the Department of Social Sciences at Oxford Brookes University, and a Lecturer at Mansfield College, Oxford where he has taught Physical and Environmental Geography for the past four years at both undergraduate and postgraduate levels. He is a palaeoenvironmental scientist and geoarchaeologist with interests in the dynamics and periodicity of long-term climate change in drylands and the potential effects of such changes on human populations and has published over 40 peer-reviewed research papers to date.

Eric Pawson is Emeritus Professor of Geography at the University of Canterbury, New Zealand. His teaching and research interests focus on global environmental issues, environmental history and management, and active learning. He is a national tertiary teaching award winner, and author or editor of about a dozen books. Recent publications include 'What sort of geographical education for the Anthropocene?', *Geographical Research*, 2015 and 'Classrooms without borders: new spaces and places of learning', *Journal of Geography in Higher Education*, 2016, as well as two essays in the *International Encyclopedia of Geography* (AAG/Wiley-Blackwell, 2017) on ecological imperialism and environmental history respectively. He is a registered academic auditor with the Academic Quality Agency, Wellington.

Mark Poskitt graduated with a BSc in Geography and Philosophy from the University of Canterbury, New Zealand, in 2017. He is now studying a Masters in Community and

Regional Planning at the University of British Columbia, Canada. His interests include urban design, health geographies, the ethics of everyday life, and the philosophy of language and meaning. Mark enjoys open, discussion-based learning, as well as finding things out independently for himself. He participated in the Australasian Conference for Undergraduate Research in Adelaide in 2017, presenting a paper based on voluntary research into urban resilience in post-earthquake Christchurch undertaken over the preceding year. This has been published in the open access journal *Macquarie Matrix*.

Kamalini Ramdas is Senior Lecturer at the Department of Geography, National University of Singapore. Her research focuses primarily on feminist care ethics and the geographies of familyhood and community. She is particularly interested in how community politics and activism by marginalised groups produce alternative spaces of care and possibility. Kamalini obtained her PhD degree from the National University of Singapore in May 2013. Prior to joining the Department of Geography, she worked with the Asia Research Institute and The Economist Intelligence Unit. She has published in *Environment and Planning A*, *Environment and Planning D: Society and Space*, *Gender Place and Culture*, *Geoforum* and has also co-edited *Untying the Knot: Marriage and Reality in Asian Marriage* (with Gavin Jones; Singapore: NUS Press, 2004) and *Changing Landscapes of Singapore: Old Tensions, New Discoveries* (Singapore: NUS Press, 2013). Kamalini is on the editorial board of *Gender, Place and Culture* and is also co-Chair of the IGU Gender Commission's Young and Emerging Scholars Taskforce (YES!). She has also volunteered with non-governmental groups such AWARE and Action for AIDS Singapore. She continues to volunteer with Sayoni, a local LBTQ group in Singapore.

Chris Ribchester, PhD, SFHEA, is an Associate Professor: Learning and Teaching in the Centre for Excellence in Learning and Teaching at the University of Derby, UK having previously been an Academic Practice Advisor at the University of Birmingham, UK. Prior to this, he was a lecturer in human geography for over 20 years, and has led and collaborated with others on research projects exploring different dimensions of the student experience, focusing on both discipline-specific pedagogies (for example fieldwork) as well as more generic topics (for example, induction and the transition to university, employability, assessment feedback).

Bradley Rink, PhD, is Senior Lecturer in the Department of Geography, Environmental Studies & Tourism at the University of the Western Cape (UWC) in Cape Town, South Africa, where he focuses his research and teaching on mobilities, tourism and urban place-making. His recent outputs have been published in leading journals within his field, including *Mobilities, Transfers, Tourism Geographies, Urban Forum*, as well as various edited collections. He is the recipient of the 2017 UWC *Faculty of Arts Teaching & Learning Award*, as well as the 2017 CHE-HELTASA *National Excellence in Teaching and Learning Award*.

Zoe P. Robinson, NTF, PFHEA, is Professor of Sustainability in Higher Education and Director of Education for Sustainability at Keele University, UK. Zoe is a Principal Fellow of the Higher Education Academy and a National Teaching Fellow for her work in the area of Education for Sustainable Development. Zoe's teaching and research focuses on the broad area of sustainability in higher education with particular research emphasis on educational approaches, covering the development of sustainability as a field of research and study, supporting interdisciplinary learning, and activist learning for sustainability. In the spirit of interdisciplinarity inherent as a geographer, Zoe continues to research in glacial environments focusing on the interaction and dynamics between geomorphology, hydrology, ecology and biogeochemical cycles.

Jessica Salo, PhD, is an Associate Professor in the Department of Geography, GIS, and Sustainability at the University of Northern Colorado (USA), where she teaches various courses related to geospatial technology and landscape ecology. Her research focuses on the interaction between rivers and surrounding ecosystems. Currently, she is investigating historic river channel migration and its impact on adjacent cottonwood forests in eastern Colorado. Dr Salo is engaged in several local research and professional activities, allowing her to provide research positions to undergraduate students and promote student involvement in their own professional growth.

David M. Schultz, SFHEA, is Professor of Synoptic Meteorology in the School of Earth and Environmental Sciences, University of Manchester. He has been awarded the university's Teaching Excellence Award twice, in 2014 and 2017. He led the development of two eLearning tools for climate (BuildYourOwnEarth.com) and weather (ManUniCast.com) and developed and taught a Coursera MOOC on Earth science 'Our Earth'. He is the author of *Eloquent Science: A Practical Guide to Becoming a Better Writer, Speaker, and Atmospheric Scientist*.

Ifan D.H. Shepherd is Professor of GeoBusiness at Middlesex University Business School, where he is Director of its DBA programme. During the early years of his career in a geography department, he developed an abiding interest in the application of ICT to teaching and learning, for which he was awarded the Royal Geographical Society prize in 2001. This early work grew to embrace GIS, remote sensing and data visualization and, more recently, to the application of videogame and augmented reality technologies to geographical information analysis. More recently, he has published a book on the transfer of learning, developed courses in GIS for Business and Geodemographics, and established the first MA in e-Business course in the UK. Ifan has been involved in numerous government-funded research projects, both nationally and internationally, and his recent publications have addressed the problems of 3D data visualization, the convergence of videogame and GIS technology, data analytics and transdisciplinarity.

Michael Solem, PhD, is Co-Director of the National Center for Research in Geography Education. He holds a joint appointment at Texas State University (Professor of Geography) and the American Association of Geographers (Senior Adviser for Geography Education). His publications include articles in the *Annals of the Association of American Geographers*, *The Professional Geographer*, *Research in Higher Education*, *Education About Asia*, *The Geography Teacher*, *Journal of Geography in Higher Education*, and the edited books *Aspiring Academics*, *Teaching College Geography*, *Practicing Geography*, and *Learning Progressions for Maps, Geospatial Technology and Spatial Thinking: A Research Handbook*. Michael has twice received the *Journal of Geography in Higher Education*'s award for promoting excellence in teaching and learning for his research on faculty development and graduate education in geography. He is the 2015 recipient of the AAG Gilbert Grosvenor Honors in Geographic Education.

Rachel Spronken-Smith is a Professor in Higher Education and Geography and Dean of the Graduate Research School at the University of Otago, New Zealand. She did her PhD in Geography at the University of British Columbia, and then lectured in Geography at the University of Canterbury, NZ for nine years. Rachel completed a Postgraduate Diploma in Tertiary Teaching in 2002, and moved into Higher Education at the University of Otago. Rachel has led national projects on inquiry-based learning and graduate attributes and also has research interests in doctoral education. She has won teaching awards at the University of Canterbury and the University of Otago, and in 2015 she was awarded a national tertiary teaching award for sustained excellence in teaching. In 2016 she won the TERNZ-HERDSA medal for Sustained Contribution to the Research Environment in NZ, and gained a Fulbright Scholar Award for research on PhD education and graduate outcomes.

Simon Tate is a Senior Lecturer in Geography and the Director of Excellence in Learning and Teaching for the School of Geography, Politics and Sociology at Newcastle University. As well as producing academic outputs on the issue of student transitions, in 2012 he co-authored (with Peter Hopkins) a report on the issue for the HEA. Subsequently, Simon was appointed as an academic consultant by several exam boards, advising on ways to improve the transition from A-level to degree-level geography. Simon is also a member of the Royal Geographical Society's Accreditation Panel for Undergraduate Degree Programmes and in 2018 he won Newcastle University's Vice-Chancellor's Education Excellence Award in recognition of his impact upon the experience of students at Newcastle University and beyond. Simon's other academic interest is the geopolitics of the Anglo-American Special Relationship. In January 2012 his single-authored monograph, *A Special Relationship? British Foreign Policy in the Era of American Hegemony*, was published by Manchester University Press.

Timothy Vowles, PhD, is an adjunct professor of geography at the University of Northern Colorado, where he teaches both undergraduate and graduate classes. He has been on the faculty of several different institutions with wide ranging educational missions in the United States and New Zealand. Tim has directed the Advanced Placement Program Summer Institute at UNC, helping prepare high school educators to teach the AP Human Geography course. He is also a multi-time winner of the First-Year Scholars' Outstanding Faculty Award at the University of Northern Colorado.

Helen Walkington, PhD, NTF, PFHEA, is Professor of Higher Education in the Department of Social Sciences at Oxford Brookes University, UK where she teaches geography and carries out research into higher education pedagogy. She has written and presented widely on the research–teaching nexus, research-based learning strategies and research mentoring excellence, particularly at undergraduate level. Helen initiated and managed a university-wide student experience project called *Get Published!* and supports students in publishing their work through the national undergraduate research journal GEO*verse*. In 2018 she received the Taylor and Francis Award from the RGS-IBG for sustained contributions to teaching and learning in Higher Education. She is on the editorial boards of the *Journal of Geography in Higher Education*, *Higher Education Pedagogies* and *Scholarship and Practice of Undergraduate Research*.

Richard I. Waller, SFHEA, is a Senior Lecturer in Physical Geography in the School of Geography, Geology and the Environment at Keele University. He teaches on the Geography, Geology and Natural Science programmes and in addition to his active research in cold environments, works with schools, colleges, the Geographical Association and the Royal Geographical Society (with IBG) to support student transitions. Along with his co-authors, he published an article for Teaching Geography on information literacy that received the GA Award for Excellence in Leading Geography in 2017.

Kate Whalen is a PhD candidate in the School of Geography & Earth Sciences at McMaster University. Kate holds an MA from McMaster University. Her Masters research was published in *Transportation Research Part A: Policy and Practice, Urban Studies* and *The Journal of Transport Geography*. Recent interests include exploring the extensive history of geography education in providing a platform to foster human and environment interactions and experiential learning. Kate is currently working to understand the role of experience in the learning process with a focus on reflection as a tool for teaching and learning. Kate previously developed and managed McMaster's Office of Sustainability before spearheading the development and management of McMaster's Academic Sustainability Programs Office starting in 2014, where she currently works to provide students with interdisciplinary, student-led, community-based and experiential learning opportunities focused on addressing real-world sustainability problems in the Hamilton community.

Edward Wigley is currently a Staff Tutor at the Open University. He completed his PhD at the University of the West of England, Bristol, UK and then worked as a Post-Doctoral Research Associate on the ESRC-funded project *Smart Cities in the Making: Learning from Milton Keynes* based at the Open University. He has taught on a range of topics within social, cultural and urban geographies. Recent journal contributions have been published in *Cultural Geographies* (2019), *Social and Cultural Geography* (2016, 2018, 2019), *Mobilities* (2018) and *Globalizations* (2018).

Peter Wolf is a higher education consultant with over 25 years' experience in educational development, administration and advocacy. He is an award-winning educational leader with recognized expertise in curriculum development processes, educational technology and learning spaces. Peter is also active in the scholarship of teaching and learning, exploring issues with the goal of enhancing teaching practices and approaches.

Nancy Worth, PhD, is an Assistant Professor in Geography & Environmental Management at the University of Waterloo. She is a feminist economic geographer who is interested in work, social reproduction, inequalities, age and generations, and social theory. Dr Worth's research agenda as a whole takes an identities approach to focus on issues of social justice and equity. Recent publications include *Intergenerational Space* with Robert Vanderbeck (Routledge 2015), research with young adults on work and precarity (*Environment and Planning D* 2016, *Gender, Place & Culture* 2016, *Social & Cultural Geography* 2018 and *The Journal of Cultural Economy* 2018) and a chapter on intergenerational transfers in *The Millennial City: Trends, Implications, and Prospects for Urban Planning and Policy* (Routledge 2017). Her pedagogical research examines how students experience learning, through student-led seminars (*PLANET* 2013) and student focused assessment criteria (*Journal of Geography in Higher Education* 2014).

1. Introduction to the *Handbook for Teaching and Learning in Geography*

Helen Walkington, Jennifer Hill and Sarah Dyer

THE AIM OF THIS HANDBOOK

This handbook is an original reference work designed to provide a broad overview of knowledge on the teaching of geography in higher education and its practical application. The chapters present expert scholarly analysis from a wide range of teaching contexts internationally and offer a vital reference point for further research that can inform and enhance practice. Our aim was to present a mixture of chapters based on new synthesis of published work, evidence-based practice and personal reflections, providing an overview and insight into the extensive range of issues relating to teaching geography in contemporary higher education. Taken as a whole, this volume conveys a wide-ranging picture of the current state of knowledge in the field of higher education pedagogy in the discipline, although, of course, it is not exhaustive. This chapter briefly outlines the values that underpin the handbook and its structure, then provides a flavour of each chapter in turn, so the reader has a sense of the breadth of coverage, before delving further into the specifics. In our final chapter we draw out salient themes from the handbook as a whole, in a synthesis that speaks to current educational thinking and debates.

The handbook is written for people teaching geography in a higher education setting as well as those supporting them. Chapters are written in an accessible manner so that early career geographers and those who are new to teaching can easily engage with the material. Equally, contributions cater for colleagues who are mid-career as well as those with very significant experience by offering new ways of thinking about issues and providing insights and ideas for developing educational practice. Academic staff developers, as well as others who support teaching and learning, including library and careers staff, and those with responsibility for curriculum and programme development, will also benefit immensely from reading the handbook. The authors and our intended audience are international so nation-specific terminology is clearly explained.

Ethos

The chapters of the handbook have been written with a diverse student body in mind, and ideas about inclusivity are embedded throughout, as well as recognition that internationalisation of the student body, through greater student mobility, requires ongoing curriculum internationalisation. There is also recognition that resource constraints are part and parcel of many university and college contexts, despite more people accessing higher education. Partially in response to this, but also as a result of ongoing innovations, the utility of technology for reaching larger numbers of students also permeates the book. Student engagement is central to all chapters and a wide range of learning contexts

1

relevant to the breadth of spaces and places in which geography teaching takes place are used to provide examples of how this can be enhanced. In addition, case study sections provide context from a range of sub-disciplinary approaches. The authors and editors of this handbook have given their time to developing chapters aimed at sharing good practice, based on the belief that reading about each other's practice is an important step in reflecting on one's own teaching and approaches to supporting student learning.

This handbook is important because it provides a comprehensive evidence base through a mix of literature and empirical data, as well as reflections on practitioners' own teaching practice, supported with authentic case studies and exemplars. All the submissions represent 'original' research, either in terms of a new synthesis of the literature and ideas, or inclusion of the authors' own empirical findings relating to geography higher education pedagogy (of course many do both). Individual chapters present expert scholarly analysis and offer a vital reference point for further research that can inform and enhance practice. Taken as a whole, the handbook conveys a wide-ranging picture of the current state of knowledge in the field of teaching and learning in geography in higher education. We hope that it will provide an invaluable and innovative tool for academic geographers globally.

Structure

The structure of the book is threefold. Part I explores the pedagogies to ease the transition into higher education geography. Topics in this section include fieldwork and group work as transition pedagogies, student engagement and active learning in large classes, and threshold concepts in the discipline. Part II discusses pedagogies for independent learning and how to inspire 'thinking as a geographer' as well as ensuring all learners are included. We cover a range of approaches which encourage students to make the transition to more autonomous, participatory and self-directed learning, including through fieldwork and the use of specialist technology. Part III focuses on future-oriented pedagogies to develop self-efficacy and self-authorship. It features partnership learning, experiential learning, innovative capstone projects, work-based and service learning, developing graduate attributes and preparing for careers.

We chose transitions as the organising framework for the handbook to acknowledge that student needs at different times in a programme may require different pedagogic approaches. Learners coming into higher education are not the same as those about to graduate. Student identities, learning approaches, capabilities, competencies and preoccupations vary significantly throughout the student journey within higher education, and our pedagogic approaches can help to support the transitions that students go through.

Each chapter extends what has previously been published on the topic. Some chapters do this by providing a theoretical rationale or literature review as context to the author's empirical research or pre-existing case studies, to provide an evidence base for what works. All the chapters include some references or links to further resources at the end, which will be useful for readers who wish to follow up the material in the chapter. Each chapter concludes with key messages for the reader about the implications for their educational practice.

PART I: PEDAGOGIES TO SUPPORT TRANSITION INTO HIGHER EDUCATION

In Part I we examine the support that students need to make a successful transition to higher education. Chapters examine themes that will be familiar to those who teach students during their transition to university. One of these themes is the importance of acknowledging 'the whole person' who is becoming a student; someone who is experiencing social and identity, as well as academic, transitions. Authors explore how this acknowledgement should inform the ways we design learning experiences and teach. Another theme in this section is the role of transition teaching in preparing students to be successful throughout their degrees. This requires students to have the appropriate skills and approaches to learning. It requires that they be willing to engage meaningfully with geography, challenging their existing understanding of the world and their place in it. The final couple of themes examine the contexts in which transition teaching often takes place. First, a number of our authors explore effective teaching of 'large cohorts', examining lecturing, assessing, and fieldwork. Extending these discussions the final theme examines how contexts such as teaching by teams and in multi- and interdisciplinary departments can be done well. Taken together these chapters extend our understanding of geography education during transition to higher education. They offer geography educators approaches to improve their own practice.

Part I begins with Chapter 2, in which **Simon Tate** and **Peter Hopkins** explore the social and academic transitions new geography undergraduates are confronted with as they start their degrees. Their chapter extends discussion about the academic transitions students encounter, using research which indicates a symbiotic relationship between these academic and social transitions that students face. Their research also suggests that, while the transition to university is one of the 'critical moments' in a young person's life course, university can be more usefully conceptualised as a process of transitioning to, and through, university, rather than as a distinct event. They include practical and pedagogical ideas for university educators to help students negotiate these academic and social transitions successfully throughout their degree.

In Chapter 3 **Graham Butt** discusses the known 'gap' between the expected skills and curricular content of school and undergraduate geography courses. He draws on reviews of geography education globally to provide a comparative perspective across jurisdictions (see Butt and Lambert, 2014). He provides a case study of the impact of recent education policy shifts in England, which have required university academics to help revise the content of geography 'A' (advanced) levels. It highlights the convergence and divergence of content and skills in schools and universities. The English case study is designed to highlight common issues and to suggest how similar transition problems might be addressed in different national contexts. His approach enables the reader to make comparisons with educational situations in other countries. He discusses the implications for the effective transfer of students from school to university geography courses and perennial concerns about the range of geography content taught to pre-university students are considered.

In Chapter 4 **Matt Finn** and **Carrie Mott** focus on the demands of lecturing to large groups. Lectures retain a key place in the timetables of many sites of higher education, despite common critiques of lectures as unhelpful for learning, detrimental for student engagement and alienating for students and academics alike. Finn and Mott argue that being attentive to the specificities of context can focus our understanding about the challenges and possibilities of large lectures. Through looking at the context of the university, student community, and that of the respective educators themselves, they offer an understanding of the ways teaching and learning are embodied experiences which necessarily develop differently depending on the person in question, and the dynamics of place. Rather than characterising large classes solely through their pitfalls, they consider a range of strategies available to those teaching large lectures, emphasising the potentials for student engagement that are possible.

In Chapter 5 **Bradley Rink** turns our attention to assessment in the context of large groups. He reflects on teaching practices within undergraduate geography courses at the University of the Western Cape in Cape Town, South Africa. With learning goals which focus on understanding the complex relationships between people, the natural environment, and the non-human world, and the challenge of limited resources, the undergraduate curriculum requires students to demonstrate their learning through a variety of assessment tasks ranging from tests, essays, reflective journals, tutorial and practical work. In this chapter he demonstrates that assessment for large classes can be based on best practice and be applicable in low-resourced environments in order to support critical learning goals for students. This chapter discusses strategies such as peer evaluation, scaffolding, and both diagnostic and formative assessment using a variety of on-line learning platforms.

Erin H. Fouberg writes about the importance of curriculum design in Chapter 6. She explores the importance of 'threshold concepts', arguing that integrating threshold concepts into the curriculum will not, in itself, help students into liminal space which enables them to grapple with troublesome concepts and learn to think in a discipline. Curricula should be designed to create learning spaces where deep learning and integration of concepts can occur. This chapter qualitatively examines survey results and reflective essays of first-year students in an introductory 'world regional geography' class in the United States. Fouberg proposes the combination of integrating threshold concepts, establishing a learning space that encourages uncertainty and liminality, and formative feedback and assessment which gives students the conditions to actively engage, build, and refine their schemata.

Chapter 7 sees **Kamalini Ramdas** discuss fieldwork as a transition pedagogy. It builds on her experience of a module, 'Changing Landscapes of Singapore', in which students are immersed in an experiential learning environment through fieldwork. The purposes of this chapter are two-fold. First, it shares strategies for how fieldwork can be used as a transition pedagogy to promote a spirit of discovery, networking and peer learning, as well as acquire soft skills that students can take with them as they progress to higher level modules and beyond the university. Second, the chapter compares the outcomes of different models of fieldwork employed over the years in iterations of the module. In particular Ramdas compares lecturer-guided 'look and see' fieldwork and self-guided field work using student feedback from the module.

In Chapter 8 **David Conradson** explores the nature, significance and creation of supportive learning environments for students who are beginning university. The chapter begins by outlining several aspects of the transition to university, before exploring the nature of supportive learning environments in both conceptual and practical terms. Particular attention is given to the significance of welcome, interpersonal recognition, and attunement, which are viewed as elements of a more general relational hospitality. The discussion then moves to consider how supportive learning environments might be fostered within undergraduate geography programmes through the pedagogical practices of residential fieldtrips, group work, and alternative modes of assessment.

Amy L. Griffin discusses the challenges of teaching in a multidisciplinary context in Chapter 9. She argues that few university geography teaching staff are strangers to multi- and interdisciplinary research. While problems such as inconsistencies in language and epistemology present challenges, geographers are well placed to overcome these challenges because of the breadth of perspectives in the discipline and the myriad contexts to which geographical thinking is applied. She explores the increasing phenomenon of geographers finding themselves operating in a multi- or interdisciplinary context in their teaching as well as in their research. This chapter uses a model, developed to describe successful interdisciplinary research collaboration, to identify pedagogical implications for teaching university students the skills needed for multi- and interdisciplinary thinking. Further, it identifies a number of practical strategies that teachers can use to support students in developing these skills as well as key challenges associated with teaching in multi- and interdisciplinary contexts.

In Chapter 10 **Sarah Dyer** discusses teaching as part of a team. She discusses the impact that the collaborations between educators have on student learning. In first-year units the number and the diversity of such collaborations is often great. They include team-taught units, units delivered across geography's sub-disciplines and with other disciplines, and units taught with Graduate Teaching Assistants (GTAs) and faculty who have recently been appointed. These collaborations are not generally discussed in geography or education literature. In this chapter Dyer forefronts these education collaborations and proposes the idea of co-pedagogy as a sensitising concept, which calls attention to the impact they have on student learning. The chapter examines different models of teaching together, to highlight their challenges and affordances.

In Chapter 11 **Ruth L. Healey** and **Chris Ribchester** argue that teaching ethics needs to begin early in undergraduate degrees. Ethical issues are an example of 'supercomplexity', whereby 'the very frameworks by which we orientate ourselves to the world are themselves contested' (Barnett, 2000, p. 257). Reflecting on ethical issues develops practical, critical thinking skills for dealing with such 'supercomplexity', as the frameworks students use to analyse ethical issues may be challenged and are likely to change over time. Yet, despite the wide-ranging potential, teaching ethics is often marginalised and segregated in the geographical curriculum, with ethics frequently being limited to prescriptive research considerations. This chapter offers a holistic approach to how ethical thinking might be embedded within geography programmes through a set of key principles related to recognising, reviewing and responding to ethical issues. This framework enables tutors to work with students to address ethical thinking and problems both inside and outside the curriculum, as well as to prepare students for their futures, including in the graduate-level workplace. Healey and Ribchester suggest that encouraging students to reflect on 'everyday' ethical problems may sometimes act as a helpful first step prior to addressing ethical challenges within the content and practice of the discipline.

In the final chapter in this part, Chapter 12, **Richard Waller, Gill Miller** and **David M. Schultz** discuss the importance of information literacy in students' transition. Information literacy encapsulates the varied skills or behaviours required to make effective use of information resources. From the perspective of learning and teaching in geography, information literacy skills allow students to work more independently, to engage with the research 'cutting edge', to appreciate the plural and contested nature of the subject, and to place their own work within its broader academic context. Whilst recent technological developments have been beneficial, the limited development of information literacy skills within secondary education can pose significant problems for learners making the transition into higher education. This chapter considers the key conceptual frameworks, the challenges faced by students, and the practical strategies than can help students to engage effectively within academic research literature.

PART II: PEDAGOGIES TO FACILITATE MORE AUTONOMOUS LEARNING

In Part II we focus on pedagogies to facilitate students becoming more autonomous learners, that is pedagogies for independent learning and thinking as a geographer. Topics in this section include pedagogies for research-based learning, for values education, for broadening participation and the range of approaches which encourage students to make the transition to more autonomous, participatory and self-directed learning, including through fieldwork and the use of specialist technology. The chapters in Part II also focus on embedded aspects of the geography curriculum such as sustainability and internationalisation, which are not specific to our discipline, as many disciplines try to make their curricula more imbued with sustainability literacy, and more international, but the important work of doing this through the discipline of geography is critically engaged with and exemplified by experts in these fields.

In Chapter 13 **Annie Hughes** and **Nona McDuff** focus on inclusivity in the curriculum. They take as their starting point differential student outcomes, a major challenge for higher education. They acknowledge that the causes of long-standing differences in students' attainment are clearly multi-dimensional and complex (HEFCE, 2015) but critique the pervasive model of student-deficit to 'explain away' these gaps, where students from particular backgrounds are perceived not to have the appropriate facility to do well in higher education. Using student data they report that factors such as the user-friendliness of curricula, and the extent to which students feel supported and encouraged in their daily interactions, also play an important part (Mountford-Zimdars et al., 2015). This chapter argues that to ensure an equality of opportunity for all students in higher education, teaching staff in academic disciplines like geography must reflect more robustly on the inclusiveness of their own curriculum and the (unwritten) assumptions they bring to their teaching and learning practice (Hughes, 2016). The authors argue that an 'inclusive' curriculum is crucial in ensuring that all students are connected to their learning and therefore more likely to succeed. In their chapter these authors apply an 'Inclusive Curriculum Framework' based upon three principles of inclusivity, to a case study of rural geography teaching and provide evidence of its efficacy.

In Chapter 14 **Helen Walkington** describes a 'student-researcher' pedagogy outlining facilitating teaching practices, the contexts in which it can be adopted, and levels of student engagement that can be achieved in terms of participation and ownership of the research process. She argues that disseminating results is an integral part of the research process in which students should be involved. The chapter provides empirical data contrasting the student learning gains from writing for a national undergraduate research journal, GEOverse, with presenting and participating at student research conferences. This is the first time that the two research dissemination formats have been compared empirically and differences in the student engagement and potential for each format to promote self-authorship are described. The chapter provides suggestions for linking and scaffolding research experiences and dissemination opportunities through a programme-level approach. The chapter closes with a discussion of the academic staff (faculty) role in the supervision and mentoring of student research and begins to explore the characteristics of effective research mentors.

Richard Hodgkins and **Joanna Bullard** describe the challenge of keeping lecture material up to date in very rapidly evolving fields within geography in Chapter 15, taking the example of glaciology. Their chapter discusses how students can be co-producers of up-to-date content, rather than recipients of content mediated by a lecturer, through enabling them to evaluate accessible sources such as online commentaries and explainers as pathways into the specialist literature. They argue that communication of complex and changing science is a key skill, of particular importance in geography, which, as an integrating subject, draws its strength from rendering specialist material relevant and accessible to wider fields and audiences. An assessment-based case study is presented, in which students examine and present an account of a contemporary issue at the interface of environmental change and societal impact, from perspectives of escalating specialism and detail.

Phil Klein, Karen Barton, Jessica Salo, Jieun Lee and **Timothy Vowles** start Chapter 16 by focussing on teaching geographic concepts through issues-based inquiry with the premise that part of becoming a geographer is learning the discipline's conceptual framework. Their chapter illustrates several inquiry-based activities designed to help geography students develop understanding of essential disciplinary concepts and perspectives. The methods employ varieties of a structured, issues-based inquiry pedagogy, in which short in-class activities present essential concepts through analysis and interpretation of diverse forms of geographic data. Their examples show that as supplements to lectures, such brief inquiry activities can help students make connections among geographic concepts and foster development of a geographical perspective. They also reveal the diversity of attainable issues-based approaches within introductory and advanced geography courses. The central argument of the chapter is that designing effective inquiry activities necessitates situating them within the local geographic context (cultures, politics, environments, and economics) of the university and its students. Informal responses from students indicate consistent approval of these types of activities as memorable and effective ways to learn new concepts and link theory to practical applications. Inquiry activities help make geographic conceptual structures relatable for students, connecting them to their own local experiences as well as to their future professional development.

Writing on behalf of the RACE working group of the Royal Geographical Society with institute of British Geographers (RGS-IBG), **James Esson** and **Angela Last** demonstrate how learning and teaching about race can both further understanding about racial inequality within geography and improve disciplinary knowledge about the history and spatiality of racism as it intersects with wider structural inequalities. Through doing so, Chapter 17 contributes to longstanding and more recent debates over how geography curricula are shaped by and perpetuate subjectivities, epistemologies and practices underpinned by racist logic. The authors illustrate how insights from decolonial approaches, and Critical Race Theory (CRT) perspectives, can support geographers in creating degree programmes that address and counteract the perpetuation of 'white geographies', that is the racist and colonial assumptions that are normalised and circulated through our institutional arrangements and practices. They conclude by calling on geographers to embrace a 'curriculum against domination', which rejects learning, teaching and knowledge production that perpetuates hierarchies of superiority and inferiority.

Chapter 18 sees **Avril Maddrell** and **Edward Wigley** write on the topic of teaching emotionally challenging material. They use a case study of teaching a module entitled 'the geography of death' to students. Adopting a highly active learning style with scaffolded group discussions, field visits and with creative practices embedded into the assessment, their reflections are especially valuable in framing how particular pedagogic approaches support the teaching of challenging content.

In Chapter 19 **Zoe P. Robinson** takes the stance that geography teaching comes with a set of responsibilities, using sustainability as a lens to explore this concept. Her chapter explores the ways in which geography educators have a responsibility to think about the impact of what we teach and how we teach it on wider society, ensuring our students are equipped to become knowledgeable and engaged actors within sustainability debates, with the skills to educate and influence others, and the agency to enact change. She argues that this responsibility includes reflecting on the ways we engage with sustainability in our teaching, the use of active and experiential pedagogies, and the provision of opportunities and support for students to practically explore sustainability without fear of failure. Her contribution also acknowledges that we also have a collective responsibility for geography as a subject, to ensure that tensions between human and physical geography do not preclude the discipline from an important role in the growing interdisciplinary arenas of sustainability education and research. Sustainability and internationalisation share similar agendas with regard to being values based and with institutional directives often encouraging their embedding in whole programmes.

Ash Parton and **Martin Haigh** write on the topic of internationalisation in Chapter 20 and consider the question: 'what does internationalisation of the curriculum really mean for my teaching?' They explore two contrasting curricula that explore ways of adapting a geography curriculum to develop, simultaneously, both key geographical concepts and, through internationalisation of the curriculum, 'graduate attributes', such as global citizenship. The first case study uses geographical content as a vehicle to explore global, international and intercultural concepts and to develop a conscious and critical awareness of Western mind-sets. The second adapts Asian 'dharmic' pedagogies and methods to explore subjects of geographical concern from a perspective that places the learner's 'self' centre stage. Geographical education for global citizenship is presented as both a process for constructing transformative moral cosmopolitanism and a means for creating more ethically-aware, conative and affective learning.

In Chapter 21 **Michael DeMers** takes GIS as a lens to explore online learning and personalised learning, combined with conditions of self-determined learning or 'heutagogy'. He describes how Geographical Information Systems (GIS) and Science have evolved from programming and development to include application and modelling, design and institutional implementation, yet notes that the need for specialised, career-specific instruction has increased and diversified. He argues that the traditional college/university approach of formal GIS instruction is proving outmoded and insufficient to satisfy the needs of a widening set of learners. His chapter describes how a heutagogic approach might be achieved with existing technology and approaches.

Also looking at technology in learning, but this time in fieldwork, **Ian C. Fuller** and **Derek France** take a critical look at fieldwork pedagogy in Chapter 22. They explore how particular forms of practice can support more independent learning with examples of fieldwork practice which enable students to develop as independent learners. The authors discuss a range of field-based approaches in a variety of settings, with a view to developing learner independence and encouraging students to take ownership of their work. Two foci towards developing learner independence are presented: utilising digital technologies in fieldwork; and the use of field-based research. The authors use case studies to suggest that both approaches foster a range of key skills at different levels and for a range of contexts to cultivate independent learning.

PART III: CAPSTONE AND BRIDGING PEDAGOGIES FOR THE FINAL YEAR

Part III features a range of high impact pedagogies for being successful in honours level study and transitioning from university into the world of further study or employment. These include: pedagogic partnerships; active, experiential learning through fieldwork, group work, studio activities, inquiry- and research-based studies, and work- and community-based projects; developing graduate attributes; and preparing for careers. Authentic approaches to assessment are discussed and exemplified, supporting geography undergraduates to behave as reflective practitioners and developing their skills for lifelong learning.

Recognising that geographers have been among the most vocal advocates for, and early adopters of, partnership working within teaching and learning, in Chapter 23, **Niamh Moore-Cherry** examines pedagogical partnerships, identity building and self-authorship in geography higher education. She notes that in the last decade, as the higher educational landscape has shifted, 'partnership working' has become an aspirational goal for institutions, policymakers, educators and student representative bodies. She highlights that partnerships can vary in nature and scale, including academic staff, students and professional staff in a variety of combinations and collaborating on a range of curricular, extra-curricular and co-curricular activities. Moore-Cherry references international literature, which suggests that while meaningful partnership working can raise significant challenges for stakeholder groups, it has a transformative capacity. An ethos and culture of partnership in higher education can impact positively on student engagement by supporting the development of an enhanced student identity and sense of institutional belonging. The chapter focuses particularly on pedagogical partnerships and their role in supporting the student journey towards self-authorship. It offers case studies from a variety of international contexts to highlight the diversity of approaches to partnership working within the geography discipline, and the specific impacts on student engagement and learning. The chapter concludes by reflecting on how a partnership approach to pedagogical practice might be progressed to become a more mainstream pedagogy in 21st-century geography programmes.

The chapter co-authored by **Eric Pawson** and **Mark Poskitt** (Chapter 24) focuses on the theme of 'taking ownership', that is, the assumption of responsibility for one's own learning. Their approach combines the reflections of a current student and staff member to give a novel perspective on how students and teachers alike can participate at a deeper level with the learning process. These authors highlight that taking ownership of learning demands significant commitment but has the potential to reap many benefits in terms of motivation and student engagement, which, in turn, may lead to greater understanding and enhanced learning. The authors develop their argument in four parts, starting by exploring the subversion of traditional hierarchical structures, drawing out the distinction between teaching and learning, constructivism and the creation of knowledge. The authors go on to examine the implications of taking ownership for the student as subject, for the lecturer as tutor and mentor, and for the construction and use of learning spaces. Next, they illustrate the discussion with three case studies of specific learning practices to encourage those who wish to develop their own classroom practices: problem-based learning; undergraduate research; and living laboratories. Finally, by drawing the threads together to show how taking ownership enables lifelong learning and encourages the elastic and creative thinking skills required for navigating the challenges of a human-dominated planet in the Anthropocene, the authors discuss the implications of assuming joint ownership of their chapter as a combined student and staff writing team.

In Chapter 25, **Shauna Brail** and **Kate Whalen** highlight the value of experiential learning in undergraduate education, focusing on the potential for multi-faceted learning for senior undergraduate students. They begin their chapter by introducing experiential learning opportunities connected to curricular learning as an important means through which provide students with a set of skills and a knowledge base to become knowledgeable geographers, engaged learners and active citizens. A literature review highlights both pedagogical theory and best practice case studies, helping to inform and advise on the meaning and value of the synergistic relationship developed by connecting classroom learning to experiential learning. The authors progress to explore three types of academic courses that connect learning inside and outside the classroom: 1) placement courses, 2) studio courses and 3) field study courses. Through an examination of these different yet complementary approaches to experiential learning, the authors highlight ways in which course and assignment design – combined with various approaches to experiential learning – enrich and extend student learning beyond the classroom.

Lisa Mol, **Michael Horswell** and **Lucy Clarke** (Chapter 26) examine how final year fieldwork in the undergraduate geography curriculum can develop graduate skills. They note that field-based disciplines like geography have long used time in the field as an educational tool. Usually, this experience concerns using the field location as a locus for teaching and practicing technical skills and for improving group identity in support of better learning outcomes. This work can take the form of students working independently in a field location, students working alongside staff, or students following a staff-led itinerary in a larger group, including geographic expeditions. All three forms of fieldwork carry with them unique benefits for pedagogy and academic, personal and professional development, but also risks related to physical safety and mental wellbeing which need to be managed carefully. The authors note that this is particularly important if students are working in difficult circumstances, such as areas of high poverty, poor access to health care and absence of easily navigable infrastructure. They reference the wider literature and personal case studies to explore the benefits and potential issues associated with all three forms of student fieldwork, comparing examples in order to evaluate the role of fieldwork in the curriculum.

The chapter co-authored by **Jennifer Hill** and **Nancy Worth** (Chapter 27) aims to guide readers to develop assessment and feedback practices that will support geography undergraduate students to behave as reflective practitioners, developing skills for lifelong learning. The chapter begins by outlining why approaches to assessment and feedback in higher education should be reconsidered. Key theories and concepts are introduced that encourage readers to think of assessment as part of learning rather than a summative conclusion about performance. The concepts examined are authenticity, liminality, dialogue, learner responsibility, self-regulation and self-efficacy. Two case studies are presented to exemplify a social constructivist approach to assessment, where students find assessment meaningful and 'real'. The first case study shares formative and summative assessments that involve students contributing to contemporary debates about the geographies of citizenship. The second case study explores student perceptions of dialogic feedforward and charts the resulting impact on student behaviour, achievement and transferable skills. The authors highlight the challenges inherent in authentic assessment approaches and how they might be mitigated, and conclude with wider recommendations for practice.

The aim of Chapter 28, co-authored by **Alice Hovorka** and **Peter Wolf**, is to offer a range of ideas and approaches regarding capstones in geography that challenge students to demonstrate mastery, as well as synthesise and reflect on their learning, particularly as applicable for the wider world. For geography students, a capstone experience offers an opportunity to 'pull it all together' and consider geographical knowledge, skills and values as a whole. It also offers students an opportunity to integrate and critically assess their undergraduate experiences, make sense and meaning of those experiences, and look forward to building upon them for the future. The authors begin the chapter by setting out the broader context of capstones in geography, highlighting what they seek to do and noting the common formats and approaches taken. Singled out for examination are residential field courses, independent research projects and courses featuring historical disciplinary overviews. The authors continue by emphasising that capstones in geography can be conceived of and delivered in various and innovative ways, which may resonate with increasingly diverse groups of undergraduate students working towards successful engagement with an increasingly complex world. To this end, the chapter details capstones focused on re-conceptualising the field, re-framing the dissertation, and re-imagining disciplinary contributions to enhance the meaning and relevance of culminating experiences for students, and to address broader geography program learning outcomes.

Ifan D.H. Shepherd explores the interplay between the world of learning and the world of work (Chapter 29). He notes that geography as a discipline, and geography as represented in higher education curricula, straddles the spectrum between vocational at one end and non-vocational at the other. In recent decades, the relationship between the university as a place of learning and the workplace as an environment for learning has become increasingly complex. Shepherd explores how learning and work are inter-related, and how individuals can learn from both contexts in a mutually beneficial way. Based on a review of the literature, he presents a model that defines five levels of student engagement with work and the workplace during their undergraduate studies. At the lowest level, students engage in familiarisation activities about the world of work, while at the highest level, they learn about the world of work first hand, as temporary employees on placements or internships. A number of case studies are used to illustrate the various kinds of learning experience provided in both university and work environments, which are designed to provide geography students with opportunities to become aware of, and prepared for, employment after graduation. The chapter presents a critical examination of these recent and current practices, and highlights unresolved issues and challenges.

The chapter by **Colin Arrowsmith** and **William Cartwright** (Chapter 30) is written from the perspective of teaching in an institution that historically has a focus on the development of curricula that accord to, and are in concert with, the needs of industry. The Royal Melbourne Institute of Technology (RMIT University) values its close links with industry and encourages active participation of industry in program development and review. The institution also promotes engagement between academics and students with industry in solving real-world problems. With this background of university–industry co-operation, curriculum design considers, as a matter of course, embedding employability skills in teaching. The authors review undergraduate programs in geospatial science and surveying, as well as postgraduate masters and doctoral programs taught at RMIT. They begin with a summary of the employability skills required by the geospatial sciences industry and follow this with an overview of the requirements and accreditation standards specified by national and international professional organisations and accreditation boards and authorities. They detail selected case studies, as exemplars of university–industry engagement, before making general observations about the skills acquired through undergraduate and postgraduate partnership with industry, recognised within the broad constraints of these partnerships.

In Chapter 31, **Rachel Spronken-Smith** examines the what, why and how of graduate attributes in geography higher education. She begins her chapter by providing definitions of graduate attributes, considering capabilities, as well as discipline-specific versus generic graduate attributes. She also provides a rationale for why we should consider graduate attributes when designing courses and curricula, moving beyond compliance to sound pedagogical design. The chapter continues with a synthesis of recent literature to identify which attributes or capabilities are relevant for geography graduates in terms of discipline-specific knowledge and skills, and transferable skills. It also points to the need for consultation with stakeholders (students, staff and employers) to determine contextually-relevant transferable skills (for example in New Zealand the need for strong understanding of bicultural issues). The chapter progresses to outline practical guidelines concerning how to design geography curricula to foster graduate attributes, covering aspects such as an outcomes-based approach to curriculum design, and teaching and learning activities and assessment tasks. Key mechanisms to embed graduate attributes in geography curricula include curriculum mapping to ensure all attributes are taught and assessed, and the use of high impact educational practices and signature pedagogies to develop the attributes. However, the author notes that implementing graduate attributes can be challenging, so it is important to seek support from colleagues and educational developers.

In Chapter 32, **Michael Solem**, **Niem Tu Huynh** and **Joseph Kerski** examine the unique challenge of educating geography students about career opportunities. They highlight that it is rather uncommon for an employer to advertise an opening for a 'geographer' per se, even in cases where a job entails applications of geographic knowledge, skills, and technologies. At the same time, many employers are simply unfamiliar with what a person with a geography degree knows and is able to do. While this may at first glance seem to put geography students at a disadvantage, the authors note that the professional possibilities awaiting geography graduates are bountiful and extensive, and very likely to remain so well into the future. They go on to say that our responsibility as educators and advisers in this context is to engage students in a process of thinking about the significance and potential of their academic preparation in geography and what it means to be and become a professional geographer. The authors introduce three model activities that are designed to help geography students identify and understand the range of career options available to them. The pedagogical approach they advocate goes beyond the 'nuts-and-bolts' of helping students write cover letters, format resumes, design portfolios and improve their interviewing skills. Rather these authors highlight ways of preparing students to think analytically about the broader industry trends shaping the future economy, and how their disciplinary expertise connects to the evolving needs of business, government and non-profit employer organisations. The authors conclude that from this approach, students stand to gain valuable research skills and a newfound appreciation of the broader value of geography in a wide array of professional settings.

In Chapter 33, **Pauline E. Kneale** examines the tensions that exist in designing final year programmes to meet the needs of employers, whilst also satisfying learners and meeting their expectations. In undergraduate teaching the promotion of active learning, problem-based learning, enquiry-based learning, and expedition and fieldwork pedagogies are likely to involve group-based project work, which develop skills of networking, discussion and collaborative writing that have currency in many early stages of employment. But these group approaches are at odds with a final year ethos of students demonstrating what they can do alone, through individual research projects, the dissertation and independent assignments. The author develops the argument that students find this change in ethos confusing and it can disrupt their developmental preparation to be effective, team-based researchers in workplace or academic settings. As such, Kneale considers the argument for increasing group-based research challenges in the final undergraduate year. She argues that challenging team-based projects, extending over a semester, offer appropriate development, demonstrate progression, embed research and reporting skills through serious practical experience, and enable exploration into contemporary issues in geography that are relevant, exciting and motivating.

Finally, in Chapter 34 **Jennifer Hill**, **Helen Walkington** and **Sarah Dyer** synthesise the themes from the book as a whole, identifying four principles that together build a solid foundation for successful teaching, learning and assessment of geography in higher education. These principles are: 1) entering the pedagogic borderlands; 2) embracing partnership working; 3) acknowledging the whole student; and 4) adopting courageous pedagogy. The nature and meaning of each of these principles is outlined, along with their affordances and challenges. The chapter demonstrates that entering the pedagogic borderlands and working in partnership to legitimate emotions as part of holistic and meaningful academic exploration can help reveal to students our disciplinary ways of knowing the world. Being courageous in our pedagogy, taking calculated risks, and working creatively within time constraints and workload pressures, we can ultimately establish more meaningful connections and deeper ways of knowing in our classrooms, over our campuses, in local communities and across the world. Consulting the mass of knowledge presented in this collection, we hope that colleagues will feel more supported in working with students to develop the geocapabilities for responsible global citizenship, both now and into the future.

REFERENCES

Barnett, R. (2000) 'Supercomplexity and the curriculum', *Studies in Higher Education*, 25 (3), pp. 255–265.

Butt, G. and Lambert, D. (2014) 'International perspectives on the future of geography education and the role of national standards', *International Research in Geographical and Environmental Education*, 23(1), pp. 1–12.

Higher Education Funding Council (HEFCE) (2015) *Differences in Degree Outcomes: The Effect of Subject and Student Characteristics.* Issue paper 2015/21. Bristol. Available at: http://www.hefce.ac.uk/media/HEFCE2014/Content/Pubs/2015/201521/HEFCE2015_21.pdf (accessed 12 May 2017).

Hughes, A. (2016) 'Exploring normative whiteness: ensuring inclusive pedagogic practice in undergraduate fieldwork teaching and learning', *Journal of Geography in Higher Education*, 40(3), pp. 1–18.

Mountford-Zimdars, A., Sabri, D., Moore, J., Sanders, J., Jones, S. and Higham, L. (2015) 'Causes of differences in student outcomes', Report to HEFCE by King's College London, ARC Network and The University of Manchester.

PART I

PEDAGOGIES TO SUPPORT TRANSITION INTO HIGHER EDUCATION

2. Student perspectives on the importance of both academic and social transitions to and through their undergraduate geography degree
Simon Tate and Peter Hopkins

INTRODUCTION

Debates amongst geographers around their students' transition to university education have re-emerged periodically since at least the 1970s (Morgan, 2002) and speak to central issues about geography's definition and purpose as an academic subject. The latest round of this debate, since the late 2000s, has focussed on the fact that 'university and pre-university geography in [the UK] are like distant relations: there is a family connection but it is fairly weak' (Castree, Fuller and Lambert, 2007, p. 130). Amongst geographers, interest in this 'distant' relationship has fallen into several strands, with discussions ranging in focus from the content of pre-university curricula (Stannard, 2003; Castree, Fuller and Lambert, 2007; Marriott, 2007; Prykett and Smith, 2009), via discussions of the importance of improved dialogue between teachers and lecturers (Birnie, 1999; Jeffrey, 2003; Imrie and Cowling, 2006; Barnes et al., 2011); to more fundamental questions about the nature of contemporary geography (Bonnett, 2008), and the different theoretical perspectives from which curricula are developed (Huckle, 2002; Lambert, 2011).

We have been researching students' transitions for several years, motivated by a combination of our own backgrounds, experiences, and research interests. It seems to us that three things are too often absent from these transitions debates: first, it is our contention that, as university educators, we need to listen more carefully to the voices of our students. In this chapter we aim to highlight the top-down nature of much of the current literature on transitions to university and to explore why it is important to listen to, and include, our students' voices as a more central part of these debates. Second, we argue that the transition to studying university geography is not just an academic challenge for students to negotiate. Instead, the process presents a complex and symbiotic relationship between academic challenges and personal and social development. Our contention is that focusing on one or the other of these in isolation will not help to 'solve' the transitions 'problem' between pre-university and university geography, and that if we, as university educators, focus too heavily on academic transitions we risk ignoring the often challenging social transitions with which many of our students are grappling (see also Conradson, Chapter 8 in this volume, on supportive learning environments). Third, we argue that the focus of transitions debates is often placed too heavily on transitions *to* university at the expense of transitions *to* and *through* university. Focusing upon transitions both to and through university is important as it places the emphasis squarely on the idea that these transitions are an ongoing process, rather than a one-off event. Finally, in making these three points we hope to highlight some practical steps we can all consider to help address these challenges. More importantly, we hope to reinvigorate all of us, as university educators, to continue to think actively about innovative ways to improve our students' transitions to and through university.

STUDENT PERSPECTIVES ON THE ACADEMIC TRANSITION TO STUDYING UNIVERSITY GEOGRAPHY

With a handful of notable (and somewhat dated) exceptions, overlooked within most of the work on transitions is the way in which geography students understand and negotiate the step up from studying pre-university geography to beginning their degree-level geography course (see, as notable exceptions: Bryson, 1997; Haigh and Kilmartin, 1999; Maguire, Evans and Dyas, 2001; Marriott, 2007; Holdsworth, 2006, 2009a, 2009b; Barnes et al., 2011; Tate and Swords, 2013). Our view is that only if we empower students to speak much more loudly in transitions debates and discourses can we answer questions such as: Do they perceive the new subject knowledge required at university to be the most problematic transition that they are faced with as new undergraduates? Are the skills that academics expect from their new geography undergraduates a more significant problem? What do students think is the best way to resolve these transitional issues within geography?

An insight into why it is important to allow student voices the space to ask and answer these questions is provided by a project we ran in 2009 and 2010. Through a series of lectures, seminars and workshops, we asked two cohorts of first-year undergraduate students to explore the relationship between pre-university and university geography. To do this, we asked the students to write a report, which required them to evaluate critically the relationship between one particular pre-university geography syllabus and our university's first-year geography syllabus. Students were required to make changes to one or both of their chosen syllabi and to justify why their changes would improve their own experience of the academic transition to university. The assessment was, in effect, a variant of the traditional first-year undergraduate essay asking 'what is geography?' As a follow-up, we conducted nine focus groups with a total of 53 students (five focus groups in the first year of data collection and four in the following year). Twenty-five of these students self-identified as being primarily physical geographers, the rest self-identified as primarily human geographers. These focus groups, along with the students' original reports, formed the core of our data collection. To preserve anonymity, we identified students only using pseudonyms.

Following the message from the literature on transitions, we expected students to highlight either gaps in their knowledge, or differences in their knowledge depending on the pre-university syllabus they had studied, as an issue when arriving at university. However, it immediately became obvious from the students' revised syllabuses that they were less concerned with the perceived disjuncture in subject content between university and pre-university geography than we had expected. For example, few students felt the need to introduce aspects of degree-level geography at pre-university level (or *vice versa*) as a means of improving the transition. Likewise, few students seemed to expect, or want, degree-level geography to be a continuation of pre-university geography in terms of the content they were taught. Unlike so much of the academic literature discussed above, these were not major concerns for the students (cf. Castree, Fuller and Lambert, 2007;

Standish, 2008). In contrast, the students were far more concerned with the different geographical skills and more generic study skills required to study for a geography degree, and whether they were adequately prepared for the challenges that lay ahead. Indeed, students expressed a range of emotions from disappointment through to anger and fear at how inadequately prepared for university they considered themselves to be. For example, Donna said '*students are unprepared for the massive change in approach to the study of geography at university*'. As Michael put it, '*there needs to be a fundamental change in the geography curriculum to allow a move from a spoon-fed learning experience*'. Others – such as Rachel – placed the blame squarely at the exam boards: '*students on the [exam board name redacted] course are left with no idea of the university curriculum ahead*'.

Despite this, as they neared the end of their first year, the students were able to reflect upon their experiences and, in many cases, were able to suggest innovative and progressive ideas to improve the preparation of future cohorts. This was demonstrated most clearly by the number of students who wanted degree-level study skills to be taught as part of pre-university courses, and the number who suggested a return to prominence of skills (such as extended essay writing) which have been increasingly side-lined by the successive restructuring of pre-university syllabuses:

> *My proposal, in an attempt to eradicate this problem, is to introduce a 'Geographical Study Skills' module, in which school students will be required to write critical essays using a range of academic sources.* (Harvey)

> *School students go from using a small selection of text books to using massive amounts of literature spanning journals, books, and research papers. It makes the transition to university a time-consuming battle. It would be more efficient and more productive for the students to have already experienced this method of learning before reaching higher education.* (Jessica)

> *. . . at [school] nowhere in the curriculum does it encourage students to challenge what they are being told, and this is what more radical geography would bring to the school curriculum if it were studied in more detail.* (Louis)

In addition to more generic study skills, a further skill-set which the students felt they were lacking at the start of their degree were those practical skills learnt on fieldwork, in laboratories and through IT. In relation to fieldwork, this translated into the difficulties the students experienced with knowing what a fieldwork notebook was, how to keep effective notes in the field, and reflexive approaches to recording and understanding data:

> *fieldwork is fundamental, not only as a learning process for students to rely on their own knowledge and research, but also as an introduction to the process of self-taught learning that universities rely on.* (Trevor)

While a minority of the students had been fortunate enough to have been taught by someone with, for example, GIS skills, the majority felt they were at a disadvantage and were playing 'catch-up', as Jenny observed. They appreciated the time, resource, and cost pressures faced by schools and colleges when trying to provide fieldtrips, laboratory work, and IT resources, and the structural hindrances on how such skills-based assessments could be marked; nonetheless, they frequently called for advanced geographical skills to feature more prominently in pre-university level geography syllabuses.

As academics, this disjuncture between what we expected to hear from students and their actual experience of making the transition to studying university geography convinced us of the need to place students' perceptions of pedagogical issues more centrally in contemporary teaching and learning debates. While cautious of formal student feedback mechanisms, which tend to reduce the student voice to a series of metrics, our contention is that student–staff committee representatives, student societies, informal focus groups, and in-class discussions all have an important role to play in allowing students to express their voices and experiences clearly (see Tate and Swords, 2013 for full discussion of this project; see also Bryson, 2013, for further discussion of academics working with students as partners in the design of teaching and learning). That said, while providing fresh and useful insights into the transitions debate, student perspectives cannot provide all the answers. For example, we can reflect upon the fact that it is a weakness of many first-year undergraduate courses that, rather than embedding geographical and study skills in all modules, they are too often expunged into a separate, generic first-year 'skills module'. Yet, many students suggested replicating this approach by creating 'geography skills classes' as part of their pre-university courses. Therefore, rather than accepting wholesale the thoughts of students, we are suggesting that our role as educators is to mediate between these and established pedagogical ideas and debates. In so doing, common ground can be found in the work of Hirsch (2007) and Lambert (2011) who view a 'good education' as a symbiotic relationship between core knowledge and skills. In other words, what transforms critical-thinking and other skills into 'general all-purpose abilities is a person's possession of general all-purpose knowledge' (Hirsch, 2007, p. 12). We agree with this, for it provides the renewed focus on skills which students were asking for, while reinforcing the importance of developing skills in a useful way, related to (rather than divorced from) subject content.

Finally, it is worth noting Ferreira's (2018) conclusion that, whether we ask teachers, students, or university educators, all agree that a sizeable chunk of the responsibility for helping students through their transition to university lies with higher education staff. With this in mind, listening to the voices of our own students will be incredibly helpful to us in the coming years, to identify what academic support they need from us to transition into effective university learners. For example, following on from our study in 2009 and 2010, we asked our undergraduate representatives on the student–staff committee to explore what more we could do to improve their peers' experience of the academic transition to degree-level geography. As a response they came up with the idea of an 'extended induction' to university; in other words, extending the length of the induction period offered to first-year students and incorporating student voices into the induction process, so as to create a supportive geographic community of undergraduates, postgraduates, and staff (see Pain (2004) and Hopkins (2006) for discussion of the importance of bringing the voice of existing students into the induction process for first-year students; see Richardson and Tate (2013) for discussion of the concept of 'extended induction').

In practical terms, existing undergraduate students thought that it was most appropriate to express their voices during this extended induction period in two ways. First, peer mentors adopted a clearly defined role supporting one first-year tutor group each. To facilitate this, mentors received ethics training from the university and led the last 20 minutes of each weekly tutorial. For this to work effectively, and avoid any awkwardness, each group's tutor was primed in advance to leave the room. Sometimes mentors used their time with the group to reinforce the key message of the session; sometimes they empathised with the new undergraduates over how different learning at university was compared to at a school; sometimes they answered general questions from the group. Here student mentors acted as a helping hand, a sounding board to listen to questions and concerns from the new students, while also offering reassurance.

In addition, as part of this new extended induction programme, student mentors developed *The A–Z Geography Student Handbook*, as another way for existing students to pass practical advice, hints, and tips about making the transition to university onto the new intake of geography undergraduates (see Richardson and Tate (2012) for discussion). The creation of the handbook was again student-led with the emphasis being to encourage student mentors to reflect upon all aspects of their geography degree and to produce a document for the next generation of first-year students. A copy was given to each new undergraduate by their mentor in the first week of term in the hope that this written expression of the student voice would both increase the effectiveness of the mentor meetings and would also be a useful addition to the usual staff perspective which has tended to dominate previous, shorter induction periods. In the intervening years, various Facebook, WhatsApp, Instagram, and Twitter groups have also developed.

While for most tutor groups, the peer mentoring role and handbook became redundant somewhere between Christmas and Easter, in line with the literature, the presence of peer-mentors in that first term enhanced retention as 'it is only students who feel connected to the university who persist in their studies' (Scanlon, Rowling and Weber, 2007, p. 226; see also: Ozga and Sukhnandan, 1998; Smith and Naylor, 2001; Brooks, 2002; Thomas, 2002; Christie, Munro and Fisher, 2004; Bidgood, Saebi and May, 2006). This is just one example of how student perspectives do not just highlight problems; instead, by empowering students to speak, this example illustrates how their voices can provide insights into the solutions as well.

From this project it also became clear that our original project in 2009 and 2010, asking students to focus on improving their transition to university by adapting syllabuses, was too narrowly focussed. Taking this idea of extended induction one stage further, what the students were also highlighting is that they experience their academic transition to university as an elongated process, rather than as an event, and that we need to think carefully about how we design our university programmes (and specific modules) to better reflect this. While extending the induction process by weeks is a useful start, as indicated in a report we wrote for the Higher Education Academy in the UK (Tate and Hopkins, 2013), it is better to conceptualise the academic transition as being both *to*, and also *through*, university. In other words, the challenge for us as geographical educators is to move beyond the provision of the typical first-year 'skills module' and think about how we can extend our support beyond this to help students develop and transition successfully throughout their degree.

STUDENT PERSPECTIVES ON THE SOCIAL TRANSITION TO STUDYING UNIVERSITY GEOGRAPHY

Imagine it is early October. We are giving our first lecture of the year to our new first-year geography students. We look out at a sea of expectant-looking students – they are mostly around the same age, mostly wearing similar fashions, and (with similar entrance grades) we assume they are of similar academic ability. Now imagine it is early December and we are giving one of our last lectures of the term to the same first-year students. There are also meetings to attend that day, marking to complete and Christmas shopping to do. By this point, it is hard to do anything except to look out at the class and, instead of seeing individual faces, just see a crowd! Why is this important? It matters because in either scenario it is possible for us, as academic educators, to fall into the trap of assuming that all of our students are the same (or at least similar enough) to be experiencing the transition to and through university in the same (or a very similar) way. One reason for this is that our instinct as academics tends to be to prioritise thinking about students' *academic* transitions. At its worst, this leads to the stigmatisation by university educators of some students as 'lazy', 'AWOL' or as 'out partying too much' when in fact there may be other factors in play. While such comments are often borne of frustration, could it be that some of the 'problem students' are in fact 'students with problems'?

With this in mind, we now consider the social aspects of transitions to, and through, university study. As noted earlier, our key point in doing this is to draw attention to the significance that broader, non-academic experiences and circumstances can play when it comes to transitions to and through university and to illustrate how, because of these circumstances, even a fairly homogenous looking group of students can be experiencing their transitions to and through university in completely different ways. To help with this task, we turn to debates in youth studies about the transition to adulthood:

> The process of moving from total physical dependence to independence is one of the basic underpinnings of how we understand the transition to adulthood. Learning to crawl then walk, crossing the road, walking to school with friends, learning to drive and travelling alone are widely viewed as stages in a story of social development. (Henderson et al., 2007, p. 101; see also, for example, Wyn and Woodman, 2007)

Although the transition to adulthood was once conceptualised as a simple step between specific stages – such as moving from part-time temporary work to gaining full-time secure employment – increasing attention is now being given to the contested nature of youth transitions and the elongation of the 'youth' phase. These debates are international in flavour with a strong tradition of youth transitions work being found in Australia, Scandinavia and the UK (for example Holdsworth and Morgan, 2005; Woodman and Wyn, 2015). Attentive to the multiple transitions which young people negotiate, researchers have become increasingly aware of the significance of a range of 'critical moments' in young people's biographies, and what these moments mean and feel like for young people (Thomson et al., 2002). A critical moment is 'an event described in an interview that either the researcher or the interviewee sees as having important consequences for their lives and identities' (Thomson et al., 2002, p. 339). Critical moments may be relatively minor and not particularly significant for some students but for others they may have a major influence over their sense of self, and ability to focus on their studies. Some examples of critical moments are provided in Box 2.1 below. Scholars have applied these to youth transitions in diverse contexts, such as youth exclusion in North East England (Shildrick and MacDonald, 2008), and rural youth in Malawi and Lesotho (Ansell et al., 2011), pointing to their broad appeal.

BOX 2.1   CRITICAL MOMENTS

FAMILY
Being kicked out of home
Parents splitting up
Disclosing abuse
Father remarrying
Falling out with step parents
Parental unemployment
Disowned by mother
DEATH AND ILLNESS
Death of a parent
Aunt committing suicide
Loss of a baby
Diagnosis of dyslexia
Diagnosis of chronic illness
Death of grandparents
Depression
EDUCATION
Sitting GSCE exams
Choosing GSCEs
Failing GSCE exams
Dropping out of school/college
Excluded from school
Bullying at school
Changing/leaving school
Starting college
Careers Advice
Conflict with teacher
RITES OF PASSAGE
18th birthday

Passing driving test
'Coming out'
Religious conversion
TROUBLE
Getting caught taking drugs ('busted')
Getting arrested
Getting pregnant
Father going to jail
Getting into drugs
LEISURE AND CONSUMPTION
Becoming involved in gay community
Joining amateur dramatic society
Starting to go to the pub
Going clubbing
Getting a mobile phone
Getting a car
MOVING
Moving town
Moving house
Moving country
RELATIONSHIPS
New boyfriend
Falling out with best friend
Making new friends
Being excluded from friendship group
Changing friendship group
Breaking up with girlfriend
Girlfriend going to university
Sexual experience

Source: Thomson et al. (2002, p. 341)

As Box 2.1 indicates, there are a whole host of critical moments that students may negotiate, some of which are relatively minor and insignificant and others that are potentially life-changing or very risky. Some happen in isolation whereas others happen in combination or in succession, and therefore their impact can be exponential. Indeed, some of the critical moments negotiated by students might appear to be very unimportant, yet may have substantial consequences for the individual who is facing them. The same too can be said for those that are seen to be crucial, such as the transition to university. For some students, this is a major change in their everyday lives; others negotiate this transition without much thought. Also, some critical moments are literally 'moments' that pass by without much notice, but others can be more significant and present longer-term consequences for the individual. We contend that it is useful for our practice as university educators to be aware of, and sensitive to, the diversity of critical moments our students may experience so that we are better placed to support them in their academic and social transitions to and through university.

As you will have gathered by now, we both strongly believe that when it comes to transitions to and through university, one of the best ways to understand the issues is by listening to students talk about their own experiences and allowing their voices to be heard. In this vein, we now consider some of the social aspects of the transitions to and through university with reference to the experiences of two students, interviewed as part of a project we ran between 2009 and 2011. For the project, we spoke to a group of students three times during their studies. They all completed a 'transitions map' at the culmination of their degree, reflecting back on their negotiation of university life. By no means unique or extreme examples amongst the students involved in the project, we chose two students – who we have given the pseudonyms George and Rachel – in order both to shed light on the complexity of some students' lives at the same time as they are negotiating their academic transition to and through university, while also pointing to the complex relationship between these social and academic transitions.

First, we turn to George, a student who grew up only a few miles away from the university at which he ended up studying geography. A critical moment during George's university studies was his parents splitting up at roughly the same time as he started university:

> *Practically the day I began university, my parents broke up. For many months I did not see either my Dad or my Nana, which was quite difficult. I assume this had a major effect on my experiences during my first year of university, which I didn't enjoy very much, and which subsequently affected my entire time at university.*

When deciding to apply to university, George was not expecting this and he wondered whether or not he would have made a different decision about going to university and about where to study had he been able to predict his parents splitting up. With his family situation in turmoil, George reflected back to his first year at university, noting:

> *As a direct result of my family problems when I began university, I was unable to get involved in freshers' week as much as I'd have liked, and this left me on the back foot in terms of making friends. During first year I had virtually no friends from outside of the people I knew from school.*

Arguably interconnected with George's early experiences of university, he also felt that '*my lack of confidence was holding me back a lot, and I resolved to get help to try and conquer my shyness, so I went to see a doctor*'. He contends that his confidence did improve and his experiences in second year were more positive; he made more friends at university, partly due to moving into a student house and taking part in social activities with other students. His participation in a compulsory international geography fieldtrip as part of his degree helped too, so we can see clear evidence of social and academic factors working in collaboration for George. For financial reasons, George decided to move back home in the third year of his degree:

> *In third year I felt I grew out of touch somewhat with many of the friends I had made in the previous year, which is perhaps understandable. I also made fewer new friends, presumably partly because I was living at home and thus somewhat separated from things, because there were fewer opportunities to go on university trips, and also because I spent so much more time working! Also, by the end of third year I had lost contact with many of the people I knew from school as well.*

Here then, we see a set of critical moments that undoubtedly had a significant impact on George's transitions to and through university. His parents splitting up and his inability to participate in fresher's week were key moments that shaped his early experiences of university life. Although his situation improved in second year, as he made more friends and lived away from home, George felt that the extent of these early critical moments had already had a lasting negative impact. Moving home for his third year meant that he was less able to make more friends at university; furthermore, he found he had also lost contact with friends from 'home'. Although staff were aware of some of the challenges George experienced while a student, most attention was focused on his academic transitions with less focus being given to the issues he had been experiencing socially; had George's personal tutor given more attention to this, perhaps he could have been provided with additional support in order to assist with both his academic and social transitions together rather than attention only being focused on the former.

For our second example, we turn to Rachel, another student who grew up close to the university where she studied Geography. Like George, as part of our project, Rachel participated in an interview during each year of her degree. As part of the research process, we also invited all participating students to complete a 'transitions map' to consider how key domains of their life changed as they arrived at university and progressed through their studies. Rachel's transitions map in relation to housing, family and friendship is included below.

Rachel's transition map demonstrates the complex social issues that Rachel faced as she negotiated her transitions to and through university. A difficult home situation meant she decided to move into university accommodation; when her flatmates left, she ended up living between halls, her parents' house and her boyfriend's home. Then, in her final year, she bought a house and moved in permanently with her boyfriend. Some of these moves were motivated by the challenging relationships Rachel had with her family. These residential transitions represent very significant moments in many people's lives; Rachel found herself having to negotiate a number of these critical moments during her period at university.

While it would be a mistake to assume that correlation equates with causation, it is worth noting the link between George's account of his relationship with his parents and his grades. In his first-year George's average was 55 and his third-year average was 54. In the second year of his degree, when George reported feeling at his happiest, his average rose to 60. Within these yearly averages, George had module marks spanning 70s to 50s. This is an unusual profile of marks for any student and raises questions as to whether George was a working class (widening participation) student struggling to make the academic transition to university or a very capable student who was struggling to cope with a series of critical moments occurring at the time he was transitioning to university. As staff were unaware of George's family circumstances, at the time they assumed the former. By the end of his degree they had concluded that it could well have been the latter and the Board of Examiners used their discretion to award George a 2.1 degree. In contrast, Rachel's grades remained fairly static throughout her degree, with an end of year average of 62 in first year, 67 in second year and 64 in third year. Needless to say, she graduated with a comfortable 2.1 degree. To staff, Rachel looked like a student who had made an easy transition into university and should have been stretching and challenging herself in second year to attain a first-class degree. Some staff commented that they were disappointed she had not quite 'fulfilled her true potential'. Of course, it is clear from Rachel's transitions map that her marks mask a myriad of critical moments that she was dealing

Table 2.1 Rachel's transitions map through university

Year, Semester	Housing	Family relations	Friendship groups
Y1, S1	I lived in student accommodation as getting away from a difficult family situation was the major reason I changed my mind and decided to go to university. The awful living situation in halls meant both my female flatmates left.	When I first moved away I saw and heard little from my family, while others spoke to their parents most days. Family circumstances resulted in me being self-sufficient and independent from an earlier age. From 16 to 19 I was in a relationship which allowed me support and space from my mother. The breakdown of this and boredom with my job resulted in my university application (which my brother mainly completed).	When I first moved to university, I was very close with my female flatmate. We went out together, shopped, cooked, watched DVDs etc. even though we had next to nothing in common. I continued making efforts to see my friends from home; it was on one such night out at home I met my boyfriend. For several weeks after this, I remained up in Newcastle most of the weekends but it became harder.
Y1, S2	After my friend dropped out, I spent an increased amount of time away from halls. During term I lived out of a bag between my boyfriend's parents, halls and my parents.	My brother was very supportive of my degree and disappointed at my disintegrating life away from home. I have always been very close to my brothers; I tried to spend some time at home which overlapped with them.	Both my female flatmates had left and I felt lonely in halls. I had friends at university but tended to avoid seeing them apart from on days with lectures. My friends from home remained close, though it was an effort between university, commuting, their jobs/kids/partners/courses and seeing my boyfriend.
Summer	I moved out of halls and back home but spent 3 nights a week at my boyfriends'.	My friends all lived with partners/husbands/kids so I felt I had no choice but staying at home.	I got to see a lot more of my friends; they are not one big group but individuals from all different times in my life. As such we do lots of different things together from going out and going on holiday to playing with their kids.
Y2, S1	I made the decision to commute to university from Durham, continuing the living arrangements of the previous summer.	Given the choice between letting me stay and me dropping out my dad let me live at home (paying rent).	I remained close to the same people throughout university but we did become a lot closer as a group particularly after the New York field trip.

Table 2.1 (*continued*)

Year, Semester	Housing	Family relations	Friendship groups
Y2, S2	Although time consuming and difficult I found commuting preferable to living in halls.		We would go for meals, shopping etc. together although I have tended to make excuses to avoid parties, going out etc. Commuting makes it difficult, and even though I feel guilty about it I don't feel the need to make the same effort as I would with older friends.
Summer	I generally felt my life experiences, interests, values and aspirations fit a lot better with people from home. I feel that life transitions are made much earlier here and as such other students can come across as immature.		Get to see more of my friends from home.
Y3, S1	I bought a house with my boyfriend and moved away from my parent's home permanently. The house is in County Durham, so I can remain close to my friends and brothers.	Living at home became increasingly difficult/distressing so I felt I had to leave.	I still feel better understood and more comfortable with my friends from home. They just seem to understand where I'm coming from.
Y3, S2	I feel a lot happier and more secure, although I think living away from university especially in non-typical arrangements has made the local/student divide greater.	I continue to make every effort to see my brothers. I get on better with my dad now and having somewhere of my own makes my relationship with my mam easier. I do however make most of the effort to stay in touch.	I have made a couple of friends I won't forget from university. I think I and to an extent they sought out other people from 'normal' school with regional accents who seemed approachable and less intimidating.

26

with at the same time as making the academic transition to and through university and that Rachel's 'full potential' at the time was to find a way to cope with these and achieve a 2.1 degree. More broadly, how can we account for the differences between George and Rachel in terms of their academic transition to and through university, when faced with a similar set of critical moments? In part, these differences could be accounted for by the different resilience levels of George and Rachel to the critical moments they faced. In part, they could be due to the fact that running through Rachel's transition map is the theme of 'taking back control', by buying a house with her boyfriend, and rebuilding her relationship with her father. In contrast, George's account is marred with a feeling of loss and hopelessness at his situation.

CONCLUSION

As we come to the end of this chapter, hopefully we have achieved our main aim of planting some seeds that will allow you to think about transitions from school to degree-level geography in different ways. Maybe those seeds will even grow into different practical steps and initiatives to improve the social and academic transition to and through university for your students. For us, there are three key points we will take away and discuss further in our department. First, is the need to continue to engage with students about their perspectives on the academic and social transition to university. If our students are to achieve their full academic potential, we contend that we need to find ways to give them the time and space as individuals to express their critical moments to us in their own terms.

Second, rather than only focusing on the nuances of academic transitions to and through university, we will be careful to also pay attention to the challenges students face in relation to social transitions. Although both George and Rachel revealed to pastoral staff relatively late in their degree the social issues they had been negotiating throughout their studies, these cases illustrate the importance of university educators paying attention to both academic and social transitions to and through university, as well as the relationships between these different transitions. They also speak to the importance of supportive pastoral tutors who are trained to listen to students' voices and to support students through the critical moments they may be negotiating as they transition to and through their degree. Importantly, this does not mean that pastoral tutors should feel obliged to provide 'solutions' to the 'problems' their students face; although this chapter does also serve to reinforce the importance of resolving the much-reported crisis in many university counselling services (see, for example, Weale, 2016). Instead, as we can see from the cases of George and Rachel, when faced with similar critical moments, the reactions of the two students (and the impact of the events upon their marks) was very different.

This connects to our third main point, the need to focus not only on transitions to university but also transitions through university and how these are negotiated by students. Understanding students' transitions through and out of university are areas in need of further research. For example, we can see that during their degree both George and Rachel blurred the boundaries between students who live at home and those who live way from home – but we only have glimpses of the extra levels of complications and benefits that this fluid status added to their lives and how it shaped their student identity (see Holdsworth, 2006, 2009a. 2009b). We also know that Rachel went on to complete an MA with distinction, while at the end of his degree George went travelling for several years, which resonates with the elongation of youth transitions. However, the impact of their transition to and through university on their transition out of university remains unexplored. While much of the literature focuses on the transition to university, and we have argued here for a focus on the transition to and through university, it could be that what is really needed is a holistic understanding of students' social and academic transitions to, through and out of university (Barnes et al., 2011; Tate and Hopkins, 2013).

USEFUL RESOURCES

- Christie, H. (2007) 'Higher education and spatial (im)mobility: nontraditional students and living at home', *Environment and Planning A*, 39(10), pp. 2445–2463.
- Holdsworth, C. (2006) 'Don't you think you're missing out, living at home? Student experiences and residential transitions', *Sociological Review*, 54(3), pp. 495–519.
- Hopkins, P. (2006) 'Youth transitions and going to university: the perceptions of students attending a geography summer school access programme', *Area*, 38(3), pp. 240–247.
- Richardson, M.J. and Tate, S. (2013) 'Improving the transition to university: introducing student voices into the formal induction process for new geography undergraduates', *Journal of Geography in Higher Education*, 37(4), pp. 611–618.
- Tate, S. and Hopkins, P. (2013) *Re-thinking Undergraduate Students' Transitions To, Through and Out of University: A Report for the HEA*. York: HEA.
- Tate, S. and Swords, J. (2013) 'Please mind the gap: students' perspectives of the transition in academic skills between A-level and degree-level geography', *Journal of Geography in Higher Education*, 37(2), pp. 230–240.

REFERENCES

Ansell, N. van Blerk, L. Hajdu, F. and Robson, E. (2011) 'Spaces, times, and critical moments: a relational space-time analysis of the impact of AIDS on rural youth in Malawi and Lesotho', *Environment and Planning A*, 43(3), 525–544.
Barnes, L., Buckley, A., Hopkins P. and Tate, S. (2011) 'The transition to and through university for non-traditional local students: some observations for teachers', *Teaching Geography*, Summer 2011, pp. 70–71.
Bidgood, P., Saebi, N. and May, S. (2006) 'Influences on student withdrawal from further education: a case study', *Journal of Vocational Education & Training*, 58(2), pp. 223–236.
Birnie, J. (1999) 'Physical geography and the transition to higher education: the effect of prior learning', *Journal of Geography in Higher Education*, 23(1), pp. 49–62.
Bonnett, A. (2008) *What is Geography?* London: Sage.
Brooks, R. (2002) 'Transitional friends? Young people's strategies to manage and maintain friendships during period of repositioning', *Journal of Youth Studies*, 5, pp. 449–467.
Bryson C. (2013) 'Creating space for student autonomy and engagement through partnership and letting go', in Bilham, T. (ed.), *For the Love of Learning: Innovations from Outstanding University Teachers*. Basingstoke: Palgrave Macmillan, pp. 180–185.
Bryson, J.R. (1997) 'Breaking through the A level effect: a first-year tutorial in student self-reflection', *Journal of Geography in Higher Education*, 21(2), pp. 163–169.
Castree, N., Fuller, D. and Lambert, D. (2007) 'Geography without borders', *Transactions of the Institute of British Geographers*, 32, pp. 129–132.

Christie, H., Munro, M. and Fisher, T. (2004) 'Leaving university early: exploring the differences between continuing and non-continuing students', *Studies in Higher Education*, 29(5), pp. 617–636.

Ferreira, J. (2018) 'Facilitating the transition: doing more than bridging the gap between school and university geography', *Journal of Geography in Higher Education*, 42(3), pp. 372–383.

Haigh, M.J. and Kilmartin, M.P. (1999) 'Student perceptions of the development of personal transferable skills', *Journal of Geography in Higher Education*, 23(2), pp. 195–206.

Henderson, S., Holland, J., McGrellis, S., Thomson, R. and Sharpe, S. (2007) *Inventing Adulthoods: A Biographical Approach to Youth Transitions*. London: Sage.

Hirsch, E.D. (2007) *The Knowledge Deficit*. Orlando, FL: Houghton Mifflin.

Holdsworth, C. (2006) 'Don't you think you're missing out, living at home? Student experiences and residential transitions', *Sociological Review*, 54(3), pp. 495–519.

Holdsworth, C. (2009a) 'Between two worlds: local students in higher education and "Scouse"/student identities', *Population, Space and Place*, 15(3), pp. 225–237.

Holdsworth, C. (2009b) 'Going away to uni: mobility, modernity, and independence of English higher education students', *Environment and Planning A*, 41(8), pp. 1849–1864.

Holdsworth, C. and Morgan, D. (2005) *Transitions in Context*. Buckingham: Open University Press.

Hopkins, P. (2006) 'Youth transitions and going to university: the perceptions of students attending a geography summer school access programme', *Area*, 38(3), pp. 240–247.

Huckle, J. (2002) 'Reconstructing nature: towards a geographical education for sustainable development', *Geography*, 87, pp. 64–72.

Imrie, R. and Cowling, D. (2006) 'Forging partnerships with institutions of higher education', *Teaching Geography*, 311, pp. 23–25.

Jeffrey, C. (2003) 'Bridging the gulf between secondary school and university-level geography teachers: reflections on organising a UK teachers' conference', *Journal of Geography in Higher Education*, 27(2), pp. 201–215.

Lambert, D. (2011) 'Reviewing the case for geography, and the "knowledge turn" in the English National Curriculum', *The Curriculum Journal*, 22(2), pp. 243–264.

Maguire, S., Evans, S.E. and Dyas, L. (2001) 'Approaches to learning: a study of first-year geography undergraduates', *Journal of Geography in Higher Education*, 25(1), pp. 95–107.

Marriott, A. (2007) 'The transition from A level to degree geography', *Teaching Geography*, 321, pp. 49–50.

Morgan, J. (2002) 'Constructing school geographies', in Smith, M. (ed.), *Teaching Geography in Secondary Schools*. London: Routledge, pp. 40–59.

Ozga, J. and Sukhnandan, L. (1998) 'Undergraduate non-completion: developing an explanatory model', *Higher Education Quarterly*, 52(3), pp. 316–333.

Pain, R. (2004) 'Social geography: participatory research', *Progress in Human Geography*, 28, pp. 652–653.

Prykett, J. and Smith, M. (2009) 'Rediscovering school geographies: connecting the distant worlds of school and academic geography', *Teaching Geography*, 341, pp. 35–38.

Richardson, M.J. and Tate, S. (2012) 'University is not as easy as A, B, C. . .: How an extended induction can improve the transition to university for new undergraduates', *Emerge*, 4, pp. 11–25.

Richardson M.J. and Tate, S. (2013) 'Improving the transition to university: introducing student voices into the formal induction process for new geography undergraduates', *Journal of Geography in Higher Education*, 37(4), pp. 611–618.

Scanlon, L., Rowling, L. and Weber, Z. (2007) '"You don't have like an identity. . . you are just lost in a crowd": forming student identity in the first-year transition to university', *Journal of Youth Studies*, 10(2), pp. 223–241.

Shildrick, T. and MacDonald, R. (2008) 'Understanding youth exclusion: critical moments, social networks and social capital', *Youth and Policy*, 99, 46–64.

Smith, J.P. and Naylor, R.A. (2001) 'Dropping out of university: a statistical analysis of the probability of withdrawal for UK university students', *Journal of the Royal Statistical Society; Series A (Statistics in Society)*, 164(2), pp. 389–405.

Stannard, K. (2003) 'Earth to academia: on the need to reconnect university and school geography', *Area*, 35, pp. 316–332.

Standish, A. (2008) *Global Perspectives in the Geography Curriculum: Reviewing the Moral Case for Geography*. London: Routledge.

Tate, S. and Swords, J. (2013) 'Please mind the gap: students' perspectives of the transition in academic skills between A-level and degree-level geography', *Journal of Geography in Higher Education*, 37(2), pp. 230–240.

Tate, S. and Hopkins, P. (2013) *Re-thinking Undergraduate Students' Transitions to, Through and Out of University: A Report for the HEA*. York: HEA.

Thomas, L. (2002) 'Student retention in higher education: the role of institutional habitus', *Journal of Educational Policy*, 17(4), pp. 423–442.

Thomson, R., Bell, R., Holland, J., Henderson, S., McGrellis, S. and Sharpe, S. (2002) 'Critical moments: choice, chance and opportunity in young people's narratives of transition', *Sociology*, 36(2), pp. 335–354.

Weale, S. (2016) 'Bristol student deaths highlight campus crisis in mental health', *The Guardian*, 26th November https://www.theguardian.com/education/2016/nov/26/bristol-student-deaths-highlight-campus-crisis-in-mental-health (accessed 16th September 2018).

Woodman, D. and Wyn, J. (2015) *Youth and Generation*. London: Sage.

Wyn, J. and Woodman, D. (2007) 'Researching youth in a context of social change: a reply to Roberts', *Journal of Youth Studies*, 10(3), pp. 373–381.

3. Bridging the divide between school and university geography – 'mind the gap!'
Graham Butt

INTRODUCTION

Across academic subjects, and in different countries, there is a growing appreciation of the importance of understanding how students cope with transition from school to university in terms of adaptation to university life, developing self-identity as university students, gaining greater emotional intelligence with respect to expectations of academic achievement and coping with new approaches to pedagogy in the academy (Bryson, 1997; Marriott, 2007; Baer, 2008; Tate and Swords, 2013; see Chapter 2 in this volume by Tate and Hopkins). Understanding the processes involved in making a successful transition between the two sectors must include gaining an appreciation of the nature of the gap, or divide, between the geographical content taught, the skills required of students and the pedagogy evident in both. Research suggests that students starting their undergraduate geography courses are less concerned about a content gap and more with the range of skills required to study successfully at degree level (Tate and Swords 2013; see Chapter 12 in this volume by Waller, Miller and Schutz).

This chapter begins by considering the persistent nature of the gap between school and university geography. It argues that educators from each sector have both pragmatic and important disciplinary reasons for attending to the gap. The second section in the chapter examines what global reviews of geography education have to teach us. It advises caution about over reading such reviews but identifies common challenges experienced in different national contexts. The chapter ends with suggestions about how to overcome transition problems and minimise the impact of the 'gap' between school and university geography education. Whilst being mindful of discussions about different jurisdictions, a case study of England is worked through this section. It highlights the embedded nature of the gap and suggests valuable avenues for all to explore, which will ensure that the impact of the known 'gap' is minimised.

THE 'GAP'

It is now over a quarter of a century since Andrew Goudie, then President of the Geographical Association in England, expressed his view that with respect to geography and geography education 'a chasm has developed between those who teach at school and those who teach in universities' (Goudie, 1993, p. 338). There is little to suggest that this gap has narrowed significantly in recent years. Gap and transition issues are persistent, well documented (Clifford, 2002; Thrift, 2002; Bonnett, 2003), and possibly cyclical (Morgan, 2002). Despite claims regarding the popularity and positive experiences of students studying geography in schools and universities (Butt, 2008, 2011) there is a noticeable disjuncture between geographical themes, content and skills across the two sectors. Over a number of years, and across a range of jurisdictions, similar gap issues and student transfer difficulties have been reported (see Hill, 1992; Biddle 1999; Stannard, 2003; Winter, 2009; DaSilva and Kvasnak, 2011; Basu et al., 2014; Sharpe and Huynh, 2015; Knight and Robinson, 2017), but the persistence of the gaps experienced nationally, internationally and indeed globally should perhaps not surprise us. Differences between the sectors may be regarded as both expected and predictable, given the contrasting aims and expectations of geography education in schools and universities in most countries (Butt 2008; Castree, 2011). As asserted by Butt and Collins (2018, p. 263), it would be astonishing if geography in the sectors were more closely aligned, because '(t)hey are different, with different priorities and different purposes. We should perhaps expect a "gap"?'

The gap has impacts for both schools and universities. A decline in the number of students studying geography in schools, a lack of qualified geography teachers, or a minimal involvement of academic geographers in developing school geography, has a direct effect on the number and quality of applicants to geography degree courses in universities. For the continuing health of the subject there should always be conceptual and disciplinary connections between the two – not just borne from mutual needs, but reflective of the imperative to 'think geographically' (Morgan, 2018) and to recognise the contested and changing nature of geography. Essentially, these connections are neither to create uniformity, nor an overly regimented continuity and progression of geographical themes, but to achieve a mutual, coherent and agreed understanding of the subject, recognisable by both sectors (Butt and Collins, 2018, p. 271). Self-evidently, the school and university sectors – almost regardless of national context – will have their own particular concerns and difficulties.

When considering the gap between the two we must attempt to isolate and understand the particular issues that intersect and connect. Bonnett (2003) recognises that achieving an accurate appreciation of this gap can be problematic given the nature of the disjuncture between school and university geography. Academic geography, and geographers, tend to be rather insular, having a somewhat problematic relationship with 'the world outside'. The foundations for this assertion, according to Bonnett, are evidenced within university curricula, research agendas and the profile of academics beyond the academy. Importantly, Bonnett considers that learners' perceptions of the subject – and where these perceptions come from – are rarely acknowledged and that the solutions to gap and transition issues tend to be discussed only within universities, with little reference to schools, even though their successful resolution are linked. Knight and Robinson (2017) hint at this in their review of the perceptions of geography among first year undergraduates in South Africa:

> To develop an understanding of the contemporary context(s) and purpose(s) of Geography in South Africa is to consider the understanding of the discipline from the perspective of first year undergraduates. This is because their viewpoints may be strongly influenced by previous school experiences, their families/communities, and the media; and as such their viewpoints may reflect elements of the wider national discourse of the context and purpose of Geography and cognate disciplines. (Knight and Robinson, 2017, p. 231)

When school geography is discussed in the academy the focus is usually on the implications of trends in school geography – syllabus changes, uptake of courses, student performance – which will affect future undergraduate recruitment. However, academics should resist being instrumentally, and narrowly, interested in school geography simply because this is where their next cohort of undergraduates will come from. Arguably, there also needs to be a greater recognition in academia that the increasing fragmentation of academic geography – often towards greater inter-disciplinary work – can result in the production of new geographical content that is not even recognised as 'geography' in schools. This chimes with Marriott's (2001) related observation that school geography 'has become dated and out of touch with the innovative and exciting research being undertaken in university departments' (p. 36).

In conclusion, it is concerning that many academic geography departments 'would rather their new students had no previous "geography" and consider that school geography is a hindrance rather than a help' (Stannard, 2003, p. 319). With regards to the continuing health and viability of the subject, there is clearly a need for greater numbers of academic geographers not only to involve themselves in public engagement and the media, but also to work with schools and examination boards in setting, marking and monitoring public examinations. We need to return to a situation, as previously described by Winter (2009) in the English context, when:

> during the 1960s and 70s lecturers in research-led universities played prominent roles in promoting school Geography, leading in-service courses for teachers, acting as Chief Examiners, presenting their research at Geographical Association local branches, annual conferences and in publications. (p. 672)

GLOBAL REVIEWS OF GEOGRAPHY EDUCATION

Global reviews of the state of geography education in schools and universities tend to be infrequent and piecemeal. They are complicated and expensive to conduct, require prior agreement about the criteria to be assessed and often result in rather subjective, inaccurate or idiosyncratic findings. These reviews present a comparative perspective across different countries, although they neither follow any consistent structure, nor pursue common themes. As such, the outcomes of such reviews need to be handled with caution. Geography, as a school subject, is expressed in a wide variety of ways – state and private education sectors often differ in how they teach the subject, while national and regional organisational structures for curricula vary (from national curricula, national standards, or state programmes, to more liberal approaches to the curriculum and its development). In short, the political, cultural, social and philosophical traditions of different countries – and of their education systems – affect how they value and represent geography as a subject in their schools and how easily students can make the transition to learning geography in universities. This all makes comparisons across jurisdictions 'hazardous' (Butt and Lambert, 2014, p. 1). Unfortunately, the more easily completed descriptions of 'who teaches what' in different national settings only get our analysis so far; what is arguably more useful is to attempt to identify some universal 'truths' about geography education in schools and universities. We should, perhaps, also be more concerned with identifying commonalities, rather than differences.

Many of the reviews that claim to be global in their reach are neither comprehensive, nor complete. Indeed, many global reviews are in fact composites of research conducted for diverse purposes, initially undertaken at the national scale by commissioned researchers and then amalgamated into overviews at the international scale. Often having been carried out over different time periods and with different foci, these reviews tend not to compare 'like with like'. Some reviews attempt to make comparisons between pupil and/ or undergraduate performance in other jurisdictions, using this as a proxy for evaluating the overall health of geography education in particular countries – however, the lack of directly comparable national data on examination performance in geography makes this problematic. As a consequence, even less reliable media-driven surveys or national polls have been used to highlight a supposedly alarming lacuna in geographical learning (usually with reference to poor public recall of (say) capital cities, or rivers, or mountain ranges), or to challenge commonplace notions of geographical learning in the discipline. These 'reviews' serve to highlight aspects of difference in global education in geography, but there is a danger of superficiality and an inability to clearly identify common problems. DaSilva and Kvasnak (2011), for example, attempt to review national school systems to show 'how geography is taught around the world' (p. 17) but their analysis results are an oddly focused overview of nine countries – USA, UK, Australia, Canada, Switzerland, Turkey, Iran, Nigeria and Argentina – within which two national reviews require only seven lines of text, with each merely citing one reference apiece.

What is clear, though, is that the most complete and objective global reviews of geography education indicate that the common challenges faced by schools and universities have remained remarkably persistent across different national settings for a number of years. They observe:

- That geography occupies an uncertain place in the school curriculum, especially within primary education.
- An erosion of the connections between school and university geography.
- Shifts in initial teacher education, creating decline in specialist (and specialist trained) geography teachers and reduction in the quality of teacher preparation.
- Assessment and performance-led systems impact on curriculum development.
- A need to ensure technological developments are represented in geography curricula.
- Poor public image/perception of the subject, including lack of recognition of the subject's potential (among policy makers, employers, parents, students) (after Butt and Lambert 2014).

For many countries one could also add to this list: an apparent lack of appropriate preservice training for geography teachers (especially those preparing to enter the primary sector); poor teacher preparation in geographical knowledge; the domination of history, rather than geography, as a discrete subject taught in schools (or within integrated courses in the social sciences); the dominance of human rather than physical geography in schools; a lack of standardized testing in geography (with a concomitant diminution of the subject's status); and wide variation with respect to how much geography is taught (DaSilva and Kvasnak, 2011). With respect to initial teacher education (ITE), Biddulph (2016) recognises that making the transition from geography graduate to geography teacher is also frequently problematic, involving 'a compromise between their identity as a geographer and their emerging identity as a geography teacher' (p. 8). Given the commonality of these core concerns across jurisdictions they might serve as a framework for suggestions to improve practice in geography education in schools, universities and initial teacher education.

Global reviews have sometimes been conducted before major international geography and geography education conferences – such as the International Geographical Union conferences, or the more frequent regional conferences of their Geography Education Commission. These reviews have occasionally included consideration of concerns about student transition from school to university in different countries (see Rawling, 2004; Lidstone and Williams, 2006; Butt and Lambert, 2014). Basu et al. (2014), for example, report on a workshop at the 2012 American Association of Geographers–Center for Global Geography Education (AAG CGGE) conference in Bangalore which considered how to facilitate the connection of high school and university teachers of geography in national and international contexts. Here, secondary geography teachers and university academics from the USA, India and New Zealand not only looked at creating strategies and resources (including online modules, see Solem, 2002) for teaching geography from a global perspective, but also at the ways in which the two sectors could collaborate successfully in attempting to bridge the gap between them. Concerns about the *nature* of collaboration quickly came to the fore: teachers mentioned issues of 'respect and trust' and voiced that they should not be seen as passive recipients of geographical content handed down from universities, an issue recognised elsewhere (Hill and Jones 2010). As such, teachers wanted to be acknowledged as: 'capable of contributing to the development of educational materials rather than [being viewed as] purveyors of already developed course materials' (Basu et al., 2014, p. 44). Such workshops not only rehearse the nature of the social and economic forces underpinning the globalisation of education, the importance of 'robust collaboration' between the different institutions involved in geography education across the sectors, and the varying national and international perspectives on education, but also serve to highlight the differing educational practices between sectors (with representatives from some jurisdictions reporting existing collaboration, complementarity, and synergy, whilst others describe situations of dissonance or even conflict).

STRATEGIES FOR BRIDGING THE GAP

We may recognise that striving to bridge the persistent gap between geography education in schools and universities – sometimes described as a 'chasm', 'border' or 'discontinuity' (see Bradford, 1996; Machon and Ranger, 1996; Marsden, 1997; Bonnett, 2003; Butt, 2008; Hill and Jones, 2010) – is desirable, but not necessarily achievable, given the conflicting aims of the two sectors. Nonetheless, we must recognise that there are mutual advantages in attempting to do so. This section illustrates key themes with examples from England from which readers can make their own judgements about what action might be taken based on the unique set of circumstances within their own jurisdiction. Although some might find this approach parochial, the aim is to suggest ways forward to help solve transitional issues that are commonly faced in many countries. Table 3.1 indicates ways in which academic geographers, initial teacher educators, professional associations,

Table 3.1   Bridging the divide

Activity	Agents
Professional development conferences and events	Professional associations (e.g. Geographical Association (GA) and GA branches, Royal Geographical Society with Institute of British Geographers (RGS-IBG) and GA conferences)
Academic conferences and events	Academic geographers and initial teacher educators (with some geography teachers) (e.g. Council of British Geographers (COBRIG), Association of American Geographers (AAG) Conference, International Geographical Union (IGU), Economic and Social Research Council (ESRC) 'Engaging Geographies' seminar series, RGS-IBG and GA conferences)
Producing textbooks/ journal articles for school students/ geography teachers	Geography teachers, academic geographers and/or initial teacher educators (in schools and universities) (e.g. *Teaching Geography*, *Geography Review*, *Geography*)
Producing scholarly/ research texts	Academic geographers and/or initial teacher educators (in schools and universities) e.g. Geography Education Research Collective (GEReCo) Rawling and Daugherty (1996), Kent (2000), Butt (2011)
Research projects	Geography teachers in association with academic geographers and/ or initial teacher educators (in schools and universities) (e.g. Young People's Geographies Project)
Curriculum development projects	Notably subject associations (e.g. see under 'projects' on geography. org.uk)
'Mediation'	'Mediators' and 'ambassadors' working in/with geographers in schools (e.g. GA Chief Executive/Professor of Geography Education; RGS-IBG subject officers; key geography academics; initial teacher educators in geography; geography undergraduates in schools; A level geography students attending day 'outreach/widening participation' courses in university geography departments)
Special interest groups	As represented in professional associations (IGU, GA, RGS-IBG, etc.)
Political lobbying for government funded initiatives	Professional associations (GA, RGS-IBG) (e.g. Action Plan for Geography); 'mediators'
Award-bearing courses/ CPD (Masters, Ed D, PhD geography education)	University Schools of Education
Initial Teacher Education	New geography teachers, with geography educators (e.g. Post Graduate Certificate of Education (PGCE) and Post Graduate Diploma of Education (PGDipED) courses)
Development and review of examination specifications	Awarding bodies in association with academic geographers, teacher educators and geography teachers. A Level Content Advisory Board (ALCAB) (after Butt and Collins, 2018).

Notes: A Level Content Advisory Board (ALCAB) – an organisation established by the UK government to provide advice to its Office of Qualifications and Examinations Regulation (Ofqual) on the content required in new A levels in subjects identified by leading universities as particularly important.

Table 3.1   (continued)

Council of British Geographers (COBRIG) – established in 1988 to coordinate the promotion of Geography in the UK. COBRIG also acts on matters concerning the status of the discipline in education, research and public policy, where geographers' views need to be made known.

Economic and Social Research Council (ESRC) – the UK's largest organisation for funding research on economic and social issues, supporting independent high-quality research which has an impact on business, the public sector and civil society. ESRC is a key member of UK Research and Innovation, which brings together the UK's seven research councils, Innovate UK and Research England to maximise the contribution of each council and create the best environment for research and innovation to flourish.

Geographical Association (GA) – an independent charity with a core objective to further geographical knowledge and understanding through education. It is one of the leading subject associations for teachers of geography, providing a specialist community of practice for teachers to share ideas with one another, supporting teachers' professional needs through its journals, publications, conferences, resources and local and national networking activities.

Geography Education Research Collective (GEReCo) – a group of geography educationists dedicated to the promotion of high-quality research and scholarship in geography education who seek to disseminate widely findings in geography education research. Their aim is to add value and impact to the research activities of the international geography education community.

Postgraduate Certificate of Education (PGCE) – a one- or two-year academic qualification achieved during teacher training. As part of a university or school-led postgraduate programme of teacher training, the PGCE is an additional qualification gained alongside Qualified Teacher Status (QTS) – the status required to teach in state schools in England. The PGCE carries Masters level credits (usually 60) which can be used towards gaining a full Masters accreditation.

Post Graduate Diploma of Education (PGDipEd) – similar to the PGCE in that it is a teacher training programme leading to QTS, but with greater accreditation at Masters level (usually 120).

Royal Geographical Society with Institute of British Geographers (RGS-IBG) – a learned society and professional body based in the UK which supports geography and geographers across the world. It has a range of publications, research groups and lectures.

Young People's Geographies Project – a project led by the GA aimed at making school geography more exciting and relevant to students by involving them in curriculum making and focussing on their lived geographies. The project aimed to explicitly connect, through 'conversations', academic geographers, teacher trainers, school teachers and students.

---

awarding bodies and geography teachers might reduce the gap between school and university geography (see also Ferreira, 2018). There are overlaps between many of the suggested 'activities' and 'agents' – the key to success lies in establishing stronger, more frequent and clearer lines of communication between the sectors. This is often mediated by the actions of particular 'ambassadors' interested in the development of geography content and pedagogy. Maintaining a dialogue between school teachers and university academics is mutually beneficial, but this should avoid being either paternalistic, or one-sided.

Reformation of Curriculum Content

Recent reforms of public examinations in England have affected geography education in schools and higher education. From 2014, the A Level Content Advisory Board (ALCAB) – which included academic geographers and representatives both from the Geographical Association (GA) and Royal Geographical Society with Institute of British Geographers (RGS-IBG) – helped revise the geography content of A and AS Level school syllabuses. This has led to a partial reconnection – following years of decline of university influence on school examination syllabuses and curriculum design (Unwin 1996) – between the content of geography studied in A levels and that which is studied in undergraduate geography courses (Evans, 2015). A greater involvement of university academics in examination preparation and the curriculum development process in English schools is certainly welcomed.

Interestingly, and almost certainly as a result of the greater involvement of academic geographers in the revision of A levels, some of the content areas reported by first year undergraduate students as 'previously lacking' in their school geography education have now been introduced into the new A level syllabuses. This should make transitions easier with respect to continuity and progression. Unfortunately, even with a clearly defined 'core content' in the new geography A levels, it is still difficult to predict exactly where the 'pinch points' might be for new undergraduates. There still exists a range of A level geography syllabuses that schools can choose from and within these there are numerous options for study – therefore no two university applicants are exactly the same with respect to their coverage of geography content at the point of university entrance. Just as previously, some students will find their experience of the first year of university work familiar (or indeed, in some cases, repetitive), whereas others will be 'breaking new ground' intellectually from week one. Finn (2017) notes that many geography A levels now adopt the use of a 'systems' approach in their presentation of physical and human geography themes – this will aid student transition to some university geography courses, but not all, depending on the extent to which such an approach is adopted in their first-year studies.

Changes in school geography curricula should definitely include *some* of the changes from the academic frontiers of the subject. In the past this process has often been mediated by teacher educators in university education departments (for example, through the Schools Council geography curriculum development projects of the 1970s and 80s). Although curriculum development projects often encourage a heightened focus on academic geography, they also tend to incorporate (and value highly) the application of innovative curriculum and pedagogical theory. Shifts in university-based geography have often proved confusing for school-based geographers, with (some) recent ideas eventually working their ways into (some) schools, but with much new geographical content being deemed inappropriate, even for advanced level teaching. Teachers tend to be conservative about changing syllabuses, mindful of their own professional accountability which is primarily determined by their students' performance in high stakes, public examinations. Combined with harsh inspection regimes, the publication of examination performance 'league tables', the prioritising of assessment data, and career progression being based largely on results, no wonder teachers tend to be risk averse with respect to making curriculum change.

In another example, this time from the United States, borne perhaps from a traditional lack of geography education in schools, the Advanced Placement Human Geography (APHG) programme has served to introduce secondary/high school students to take up the equivalent of introductory modules at undergraduate level and to be assessed and gain credit for these (Basu et al., 2014). This is a concrete example of links being built between schools and universities in geography education (College Board 2003). Although APHG might be criticised for promoting somewhat narrow notions of geography – specifically human geography – it has attempted to bridge the gap by advancing popular, topical and contemporary themes in geography through compiling modules on climate change, migration, national identity and global economies. In addition, national forums for geography education operating across the school and university sectors, such as the GA in England and other networks of alliances for geography education (including the National

Council for Geographic Education and International Network for Learning and Teaching Geography in Higher Education), have similarly worked to bring school and university geography closer together. Indeed, Biddle (1999), in the Australian context, claims evidence of 'university geographers working with geographic societies and geography teacher associations (to provide) the impetus, or political pressure, to retain geography in the school curricula' (p. 89).

Attend to the Experiences of Transition

The experiences of students making transitions from schools to universities is reasonably well researched and evidenced. Here, the impacts on students of shifts in subject content in England, typically from A level to undergraduate studies, may not be as significant as previously thought; for example, Tate and Swords (2013) report that concerns about content change mainly link to areas of subject content that students had limited or no previous experience of in schools (such as cultural geography, radical geography and social geography). Greater impact was felt with regard to the introduction of new skill-sets and pedagogy – such as the ability to engage in deeper and more critical thinking, to write well in an extended form and to carry out certain practical, independent fieldwork tasks. However, as Finn (2017) points out, these changes will have only 'limited value if school teachers, examiners and university lecturers all mean different things' when referring to the skills of evaluation and constructing arguments.

It is thought-provoking to consider how 'gap avoidance' or 'gap transition' might be made easier. As we have seen, the solutions are not as straightforward as simply 'filtering down' selected content, themes and skills from first-year geography undergraduate courses to A level syllabuses. Undergraduate students do not necessarily see content shifts as presenting significant problems – they don't expect the transition from A level to degree level to be seamless and have a realistic appreciation of the continuity and progression of content. The greater disparity, and potential upset, appears to be in relation to skills, not content – what Marriott (2007) refers to as a 'sharp discontinuity' (p. 49) between school and university-level study. Undergraduate students, according to Tate and Swords (2013), often identify a perceived gap in their own practical, cognitive and critical thinking skills. These skills may relate to fieldwork, IT (particularly GIS) and laboratory work, as well as to their criticality, argumentation and evaluation skills. In essence, many undergraduates describe a dawning realisation that they are now expected to show greater originality and independence of thought than was required of them at A level. Simply accepting a set of (so-called) 'facts' – or adopting an uncomplicated 'map' of geography, as conveniently provided by a single text book (Bryson, 1997) – is soon recognised as unacceptable. The need to engage with a *range* of sources, often contradictory in nature, including journal articles, research reports, papers and books is a revelation to some students. In the words of Morrison and Collins (1996), undergraduate students need to develop greater 'epistemic fluency' – to be aware of the different ways in which they are learning and to nurture the ability to think through perspectives other than their own. The very nature of disciplinary geography in higher education – research driven and contested, as opposed to teaching focused and defined – shifts students from a previously comfortable, modernist 'take' on their subject into more challenging, postmodern and increasingly inter-disciplinary approaches.

Focus on Geographical Knowledge in Schools

With respect to the gap in content between schools and universities in England, Lambert (2011) and Mitchell and Lambert (2015) have argued for teachers to re-focus their attention on geographical knowledge. This has parallels in other places – Biddle's (1999) review of geography teaching in five jurisdictions (England and Wales, Finland, USA, Japan and Hong Kong) at the start of this century forced him to conclude that he was witnessing 'a move back to the disciplines in school curricula to counteract the anti-intellectualism of populist integrated courses of the progressive education movement' (Biddle, 1999, p. 88).

However, he also found evidence of an increase in enquiry and thinking skills, environmental geography and citizenship (see also Chapter 19 in this volume by Robinson). From Table 3.1, activities that would increase or promote geographical knowledge mainly include: professional development conferences and events, academic conferences and events, producing textbooks/journal articles for school students/geography teachers, producing scholarly/research texts, research projects, curriculum development projects, 'mediation', special interest groups, award-bearing courses and initial teacher education. We must be mindful of the scale and reach of such activities (an award-bearing programme such as an education doctorate (EdD) will have a comparatively narrow reach, directly affecting a modest number, while initial teacher education programmes will impact on all those training to become geography teachers in schools) and whether the activities are designed to create new knowledge (such as research projects) or disseminate existing knowledge (such as continuing professional development events, or 'mediation' activities).

The erosion of geographical knowledge in schools has occurred as a result of a previous overemphasis on pedagogy, on the rise of so called 'moral' and 'ethical' geography (Standish, 2009), on 'therapeutic education' (Ecclestone and Hayes, 2009) and on the use of geography as a vehicle to deliver aspects of numeracy, literacy, transferable skills and citizenship. The extent to which concerns about pedagogy have come to dominate knowledge has now been recognised and partly reversed. As Peter Jackson (2006) asserts, we must stress that 'thinking geographically' – allowing one to apply geographical knowledge and conceptual understanding to different settings – is a uniquely powerful way for students to understand the world. To think geographically one must first have geographical knowledge. This has resonance in recent work conducted internationally by geography educators on geocapabilities, where exhortations to 'think like a geographer' may help particular students make the transition from school to university geography (Solem, Lambert and Tani, 2013a, 2013b; Ulenwinkel et al., 2016).

Teacher Preparation

The traditional importance of initial teacher education (ITE) and teacher preparation in helping to 'bridge the gap' is also significant. From Table 3.1, these mainly include professional development conferences and events, textbooks/journal articles for school students/geography teachers, scholarly/research texts, curriculum development projects, 'mediation', award-bearing courses and initial teacher education in its myriad forms. ITE has itself experienced accelerating, radical shifts in form, structure, content and location (both physically and intellectually) since the mid-1990s. University-led teacher education has largely been replaced by school-based training both in England and increasingly in other jurisdictions, affecting the quality of teacher preparation and the development of geography curricula (Butt, 2015). The role of the specialist geography educator in higher education institutions (HEIs) is disappearing, leading to narrower forms of teacher preparation, the loss of subject specialisms and a reduction in the quality of geographical knowledge experienced by students in schools (Tapsfield, Roberts and Kinder, 2015; Butt and Collins, 2018). Each trainee teacher, regardless of their subject, must make their own bridge between university and school knowledge-sets. Each must strive to translate or transform their knowledge, understanding and skills from the lecture theatre to the classroom. Essentially ITE students acts as conduits, bringing aspects of recently acquired geography content from their university courses into schools – a process mediated by specialist, university-based, teacher educators and school mentors.

University Training Schools

An innovative approach to 'bridging the gap' between schools and universities comes in the form of University Training Schools (UTSs) in England. From Table 3.1, the activities linked to UTSs are: professional development conferences and events, academic conferences and events, producing textbooks/journal articles for school students/geography teachers, producing scholarly/research texts, research projects, curriculum development projects and 'mediation'. UTSs are particularly involved in the research associated with initial teacher education and contain teachers who are expected to gain additional qualifications (for example, all Heads of Department in such schools may be expected to already possess, or be willing to study for, a Masters degree in education). Currently only two UTSs exist, both of which opened in 2015 following substantial investment from central government and their university sponsors – the University of Cambridge (which sponsors a primary school) and the University of Birmingham (a secondary school). The University of Birmingham School – an entirely new school, housed in purpose-built accommodation – has worked closely with the parent university's academic departments and subject specialists from their School of Education to recruit staff who are already considered to be 'research active' and 'research informed'. All staff are expected to maintain close links with university academics. The aims of the UTS include enabling teachers to engage with, and undertake, their own educational research, to foster projects with academics and their subject departments and to make knowledge creation a focus for ITE. Once established, both UTSs in England were inundated with requests to help facilitate research projects from a variety of organisations (including national and local governments, higher education institutions, research councils, etc.). At present the majority of these projects are directly linked to their host universities and although there are no immediate government plans to extend this initiative there will be interest in the first cohort of GCSE results from the University of Birmingham School (in 2018), as there has already been in the previous two cohorts of A level results. If such results are deemed exceptional when compared to national trends (for the particular socio-economic mix of students and for the costs involved) it is likely that the UTS model may be extended elsewhere.

CONCLUSIONS

A quarter of a century ago David A. Hill (1992), writing about geography education and initial teacher education in the USA, encapsulated many of the problems experienced across the school and university sectors as follows:

> Despite impressive in-service teacher training by the geographic alliances and a growing amount of new instructional material, there are woefully inadequate supplies of well- trained geography teachers and of good instructional materials. The system of higher education support for geographic education is also inadequate: academic geographers pay little attention to the special needs of students preparing to become precollegiate teachers; there are too few graduate students being trained in geographic education; and there is too little research being done in geographic education. (Hill, 1992)

Across many jurisdictions these issues have not gone away, indeed many have got worse. The gap between geography in the school and university sectors is increasingly multi-faceted; it is not simply one of differences in geographic content but also – perhaps more importantly from the students' perspective – one of shifts in the necessary skills required at university level. As such, bridging this divide does not simply involve negotiating a shift in content, but also responding to changes in pedagogy, academic expectations and life course. Traditionally it has been an expectation of the initial teacher education sector (in England and often elsewhere) to help bridge this divide; however, with the advent of UTSs – which model how university academics in tandem with teachers and teacher educators can support students in making the transition to university education – this situation may be changing. With academics in university geography departments becoming mindful of the need to actively sustain numbers on undergraduate-degree courses and with the decline of university-based ITE, it is perhaps timely for the former to become more directly involved in the work of schools. The forums and activities in which academics can become engaged are highlighted in Table 3.1.

The variation between the aims, rationale and endeavours of school and academic geography educators is readily apparent, particularly with regard to the priorities they afford to teaching and research. University geography moves forward in innovative, experimental, tentative and uncertain ways – this is 'part and parcel' of the manner in which academic research advances the very boundaries of disciplinary thinking. Research is inherently messy; a 'backwards and forwards' process that is uncertain, time consuming, expensive and tentative. Teaching in schools is a very different endeavour. It would be impossible for schools to function in the ways in which universities function; the aims of schools closely align with the teaching and learning of their curricular subjects, not with the advancement of disciplinary research.

Hence the geography taught in schools is *informed* by knowledge gains achieved by academic geographers, but it rarely contributes to this process and its subject content must be more stable, enduring and certain than that of the parent academic discipline. School geography cannot, and should not, seek to replicate disciplinary content that has recently been culled from the frontiers of academic research. This is not to say that the two sectors should therefore be allowed to drift apart – they must regularly debate their relationship, whilst acknowledging that the expectations of both are inherently different. Where appropriate, it may soon be realised by universities that developing geographic resources for undergraduate geographers alone represents something of a missed opportunity. Wider dissemination of selected and differentiated geographic content to school students, to professional development courses for geography teachers and for the creation of educational resources that span across both sectors (possibly with the greater use of information technology) may prove fruitful in helping to bridge the divide.

In essence the key ways to 'bridge the gap' between school and university geography, both in England and elsewhere, appear to be those which involve academic geographers in universities, initial teacher educators (particularly those geography specialists who are still to be found in university schools of education), teachers and students as genuine partners. The long-term and sustainable solutions must directly involve teachers and academics taking responsibility for understanding the gap and then actively facilitating transition for the students who will progress to university education in geography. The mediators may be various, supported by professional associations and research organisations (see Table 3.1).

USEFUL RESOURCES

- Butt, G. and Collins, G. (2018) 'Understanding the gap between schools and universities' in Lambert, D. and Jones, M. (eds.) *Debates in Geography Education* (Second Edition). London: Routledge. pp. 263–274.
- Hill, J. and Jones, M. (2010) 'Joined-up geography: Connecting school-level and university-level geographies', *Geography*, 95(1), pp. 22–32.
- Stannard, K. (2003) 'Earth to academia: on the need to reconnect university and school geography', *Area*, 35(3), pp. 316–322.
- Tate, S. and Swords, J. (2013) 'Please mind the gap: students' perspectives of the transition in academic skills between A-level and degree-level geography', *Journal of Geography in Higher Education*, 37(2), pp. 230–240.

REFERENCES

Baer, L. (2008) 'Misunderstandings about student transitions to university: a slow-motion dialogue between staff and students', *Journal of Geography in Higher Education*, 32(2), pp. 303–320.

Basu, P., Pawson, E., Akhter, M., Palmer, D. and Mervine, V. (2014) 'Connecting high school and university teachers in national and international contexts: perspectives from the 2012 Bangalore workshop of the AAG-CGGE', *Journal of Geography in Higher Education*, 38(1), pp. 40–48.

Biddle, D. (1999) 'Geography in schools', *Australian Geographer*, 30(1), pp. 75–92.

Biddulph, M. (2016) 'What does it mean to be a teacher of geography? Investigating the teacher's relationship with the curriculum'. Unpublished PhD thesis. University of Nottingham.

Bonnett, A. (2003) 'Geography as the world discipline: connecting popular and academic geographical imaginations', *Area*, 35(1), pp. 56–63.

Bradford, M. (1996) 'Geography at the secondary/higher education interface: change through diversity', in Rawling, E. and Daugherty, R. (eds), *Geography into the Twenty-First Century*, Chichester: Wiley, pp.277–288.

Bryson, J. (1997) 'Breaking through the A level effect: a first-year tutorial in student self-reflection', *Journal of Geography in Higher Education*, 21(2), pp. 163–169.

Butt, G. (2008) 'Is the future secure for geography education?', *Geography*, 93(3), pp. 158–165.

Butt, G. (ed.) (2011) *Geography, Education and the Future*. London: Continuum.

Butt, G. (2015) *What Impact will Changes in Teacher Education have on the Geography Curriculum in Schools?* Presentation at RGS-IBG Annual International Conference, University of Exeter, 3 September 2015.

Butt, G. and Collins, G. (2018) 'Understanding the gap between schools and universities', in Lambert, D. and Jones, M. (eds), *Debates in Geography Education* (Second Edition). London: Routledge, pp. 263–274.

Butt, G. and Lambert, D. (2014) 'International perspectives on the future of geography education and the role of national standards', *International Research in Geographical and Environmental Education*, 23(1), pp. 1–12.

Castree, N. (2011) 'The future of geography in English universities', *The Geographical Journal*, 136(4), pp. 512–519.

Clifford, N. (2002) 'The future of geography: when the whole is less than the sum of its parts', *Geoforum*, 33, pp. 431–436.

College Board (2003) 'A brief history of the advanced placement program'. Available at: http://www.college board.com/prod_downloads/about/news_info/ap/ap_history_ english.pdf (downloaded: 22 February 2019).

DaSilva, E and Kvasnak, R. (2011) 'Taking stock in geography education around the world: an international perspective on the teaching of geography', *The Geography Teacher*, 8(1), pp. 16–23.

Ecclestone, K. and Hayes, D. (2009) *The Dangerous Rise of Therapeutic Education.* Abingdon: Routledge.

Evans, M. (2015) *Reconsidering Geography at the Schools–HE Boundary: The ALCAB Experience.* Presentation at RGS-IBG annual International Conference, University of Exeter, 3 September 2015.

Ferreira, J. (2018) 'Facilitating the transition: doing more than bridging the gap between school and university geography'. *Journal of Geography in Higher Education*, 42(3), pp. 372–383.

Finn, M. (2017) 'Transitions to university. From the "new" geography A level to the 1st year of a geography degree'. Draft paper. Unpublished.

Goudie, A. (1993) 'Schools and universities – the great divide', *Geography*, 78(4), pp. 338–339.

Hill, D. (1992) 'Geography and education: North America', *Progress in Human Geography*, 16(2), pp. 232–242.

Hill, J. and Jones, M. (2010) 'Joined-up geography: connecting school-level and university-level geographies', *Geography*, 95(1), pp. 22–32.

Jackson, P. (2006) 'Thinking geographically', *Geography*, 91(3), pp. 199–204.

Kent, A. (2000) *Reflective Practice in Geography Teaching.* London: Philip Chapman Publishing.

Knight, J. and Robinson, K. (2017) 'What is geography? Perceptions of first year undergraduates in South Africa', *Journal of Geography in Higher Education*, 41(2), pp. 230–245.

Lambert, D. (2011) 'Reviewing the case for geography, and the "knowledge turn" in the English National Curriculum', *The Curriculum Journal*, 22(2), pp. 243–64.

Lidstone, J and Williams, M. (eds) (2006) *Geographical Education in a Changing World: Past Experience, Current Trends and Future Challenges.* Dordrecht: Springer.

Machon, P. and Ranger, G. (1996) 'Change in school geography', in Bailey, P. and Fox, P. (eds), *Geography Teacher's Handbook.* Sheffield: Geographical Association.

Marriott, A. (2001) 'A seamless geography from 5 to 22?', *Teaching Geography*, 26, pp. 36–37.

Marriott, A. (2007) 'The transition from A level to degree geography', *Teaching Geography*, 32, pp. 49–50.

Marsden, B. (1997) 'On taking the geography out of geographical education – some historical pointers on geography', *Geography*, 82(3), pp. 241–252.

Mitchell, D. and Lambert, D. (2015) 'Subject knowledge and teacher preparation in English secondary schools: the case of geography', *Teacher Development*, 19(3), pp. 365–380.

Morgan, J. (2002) 'Constructing School Geographies' in Smith, M. (ed.), *Teaching Geography in Secondary Schools.* London: Routledge, pp. 40–59.

Morgan, J. (2018) 'Are we thinking geographically?' in Jones, M. and Lambert, D. (eds), *Debates in Geography Education* (Second Edition). London: Routledge, pp. 287–297.

Morrison, D. and Collins, A. (1996) 'Epistemic fluency and constructivist learning environments', in Wilson, B. (ed.), *Constructivist Learning Environments: Case Studies in Instructional Design.* Englewood Cliffs, NJ: Educational Technology Publications, pp. 107–119.

QAA (2014). *Subject Benchmark Statement: Geography.* Available at: http://www.qaa.ac.uk/en/Publications/Do cuments/SBS-geography-14.pdf (downloaded: 22 April 2019).

Rawling, E. (2004) 'Introduction: school geography around the world', in Kent, A., Rawling, E. and Robinson, A. (eds), *Geographical Education: Expanding Horizons in a Shrinking World.* Glasgow: SAGT with CGE, pp. 167–169.

Rawling, E. and Daugherty, R. (eds) (1996) *Geography into the Twenty-First Century.* Chichester: Wiley.

Sharpe, B. and Huynh, N. (2015) 'A review of geospatial thinking assessment in high schools', in Muniz Solari, O., Demirci, A. and van der Schee, J.A. (eds.) *Geospatial Technologies and Geography Education in a Changing World, Advances in Geographical and Environmental Sciences.* Japan: Springer, pp. 169–180.

Solem, M. (2002) 'The online center for global geography education', *International Research in Geographical and Environmental Education*, 11, pp. 295–298.

Solem, M., Lambert, D. and Tani, S. (2013a) 'Geocapabilities: toward an international framework for researching the purposes and values of geography education', *Review of International Geographical Education Online*, 3(3). Available from: https://dergipark.org.tr/download/article-file/115300 (accessed: 22 April 2018).

Solem, M., Lambert, D. and Tani, S. (2013b) *GeoCapabilities: A Transatlantic Approach to Researching and*

Improving Teacher Preparation and Leadership in Geography. AAG. Available at: http://www.aag.org/galleries/education-files/geocap1_year1report_final.pdf (downloaded: 22 April 2019).

Standish, A. (2009) *Global Perspectives in the Geography Curriculum: Reviewing the Moral Case for Geography*. London: Routledge.

Stannard, K. (2003) 'Earth to academia: on the need to reconnect university and school geography', *Area*, 35(3), pp. 316–322.

Tapsfield, A., Roberts, M. and Kinder, A. (2015) *Geography Initial Teacher Education and Teacher Supply in England*. Sheffield: Geographical Association.

Tate, S. and Swords, J. (2013) 'Please mind the gap: students' perspectives of the transition in academic skills between A-level and degree-level geography', *Journal of Geography in Higher Education*, 37(2), pp. 230–240.

Thrift, N. (2002) 'The future of geography', *Geoforum*, 33, pp. 291–298.

Unwin, T. (1996) 'Academic geography: the key questions for discussion', in Rawling, E. and Daugherty, R. (eds), *Geography into the 21st Century*. Chichester: Wiley, pp. 19–36.

Winter, C. (2009) 'Geography and education I: the state of health of geography in schools', *Progress in Human Geography*, 33(5), pp. 667–676.

4. Embodied teaching and learning through a large lecture: strategies for place-based pedagogies
Matt Finn and Carrie Mott

INTRODUCTION

This chapter is the result of several months of dialogue between the authors regarding the challenges of geography lectures of 200 or more undergraduate students and the practical strategies we employ in our respective classrooms. Throughout, we discuss our personal positionalities and contexts, and how our decisions and strategies for teaching large lectures have emerged. In addition to our differently gendered identities, we also write from two distinct national contexts (the United Kingdom and the United States), something which we discovered has a powerful impact on the ways we approach teaching. Our dialogue was informed not only by our differences, but also through a similar background in education with children. Matt taught in a secondary school in the UK prior to pursuing his studies in Geography, and Carrie worked in elementary education in both public and Montessori charter contexts in the US before completing a PhD in Geography. We both feel that our teaching backgrounds outside of higher education have provided us with pedagogical skills that have been assets to the large lecture classroom. Further, we have found that teaching young adults is not necessarily so different from teaching children and embrace 'the idea that learning at university can be fun and creative' (Bovil, 2018, p. 2). It is not without challenges, however, and, as Jenkins et al. (1993) note, runs alongside the question how to teach a large lecture in geography, specifically, and to develop strategies that speak to core disciplinary concepts (see also Tasch and Tasch (2016) on the implications of large lectures for teaching physical geography).

We have constructed this chapter by reflecting on dialogue that occurred through video chats and email exchanges and illuminate some of the successes, frustrations, and practical strategies that have been a part of large lecture teaching for both of us. Further, our conversation offers insights into the often significant differences in how we teach that are related to our respective contexts and positionalities, including gender, but also job security, levels of institutional support, and national political climate. For example, Matt has experienced much higher levels of institutional support for teaching, as well as more oversight where subject matter and class organization are concerned. In contrast, Carrie has experienced significantly less institutional support for teaching, but enjoys a high degree of creative freedom in course design. Our relative institutional contexts certainly contribute to different experiences. In Carrie's case, most students enrolled in order to fulfill a university general education requirement, and were not geography majors. However, students in Matt's classes are typically pursuing a degree in geography, and so his students are more likely to view the classes as connected to their longer-term ambitions.

The dialogue that follows is organized around three core themes, each a common thread which appeared consistently throughout the conversations. The first, 'The

Emotional and Embodied Experience of Teaching a Large Lecture' provides an introduction in which we talk through the challenges, frustrations, and successes of the large lecture, and how the educator's experience carries over into one's ability to educate effectively. The second, 'The Role of Context in Teaching a Large Lecture' includes our reflections on aspects of our teaching that we found to be similar or different due to our respective positionalities and overall contexts. Through the third and final theme, 'Strategies for Enhancing Teaching a Large Lecture', we discuss the practicalities of student engagement in large lectures and specific ways we each work to provide students with an individual learning experience, despite the anonymity that is created by large numbers in the room.

1. THE EMOTIONAL AND EMBODIED EXPERIENCE OF TEACHING A LARGE LECTURE

The question of emotion and embodiment is an important one, because it speaks directly to the mental and physical well-being of the teacher in the performance of a large lecture. This can be a challenge, especially for early-career academics and graduate students, who may find themselves teaching for the first time without much preparation, unless they have sought it out themselves (Grasgreen, 2010). This section also offers some reflection into how the classroom can be a space of either 'possibilities or despair for students and teachers, and our aims to maintain sensitivity to students' experience' (Reza-Lopéz et al., 2014, p. 109). However, we also see the classroom as a critical site for 'political conscious-ness raising' (Inwood, 2017, p. 454), and understand that discomfort can be an important pedagogical tool when we strategically mobilize 'controversy capital' in the classroom – the amount of emotionally charged or controversial subject matter that an educator can realistically handle (LaLiberté et al., 2017, also Dowler, 2002; see also Chapter 18 in this volume on teaching challenging material by Maddrell and Wigley). Here we talk through how we manage our own emotion and energy in teaching a large lecture, as well as our approach to politically sensitive topics, and offer some advice for how one should prepare oneself to teach a big lecture, particularly for those who may have very little experience teaching.

CM: How do you balance the challenge of the energy required to teach big classes? On days when I teach more than one class, I find that I can be really wiped out by the end of the day.

MF: I did a lecture on day two of the term and felt like it must be nearly the end of term given how tired I felt! Considering what one needs afterwards (quiet, food, and rehydration for example) and making sure that, where you can, you give yourself time to recover is important.

CM: After my first lecture in my 260 student class, I couldn't believe how drained I was. In part this had to do with the hectic pace of the beginning of a term. But it was also from having to fill this enormous room with my voice. There is a real physiological thing that happens when you lecture like that.

MF: It's a kind of self-projection, through your voice and persona, in occupying the space which can be very draining. If the term/semester is a marathon of sprints it's about working out how to pace yourself within that. There is an emotional labour to working in education, and I find this is often heightened when dealing with difficult topics. We may discuss a range of contentious issues in lectures. It is important, I think, that they know they can disagree, although a lecture may not be the best venue to voice or explore that disagreement. Offering 'balanced' views or attempting neutrality can be important for some issues whilst in others the lecturer can make it clear that they are making an argument (and modelling a way of doing this) and so are going to be partisan. Either way, this can be emotionally charged work. How does this work out for you?

CM: I don't want to avoid challenging topics in a large class, but it does require caution. I try to control the conversation when sensitive topics come up, often in a large class I deliberately do not ask for questions or comments, I will just speak on the topic and move on. In the bigger lectures, it is difficult to gauge where your students are at. I definitely agree with the strategy of presenting different sides of the issue to portray it in as neutral a way as I can. People are more receptive to difficult topics when they don't feel attacked, or as if they are to blame.

MF: I've noticed that some students distance themselves from some of the topics that are controversial as being 'out there', so trying to create a space to supportively work through and engage personally challenging issues is important here, but can be very hard to achieve.

CM: After the November 2016 US presidential election I was very nervous to talk about any of the things that were happening because I didn't trust my own emotions about it all – I knew I could not act as if I was neutral on the topic. It was just too volatile. In general, I do work to incorporate recent current events. My approach is rooted in case studies which I use to illustrate the theoretical themes I'm working with. I've been thinking more about how to talk about things like nationalism and the nation, place, inequality, and so on in relation to the Trump administration. I will still move cautiously, but I don't want to ignore or talk around it either.

MF: I agree, as hard as it can be engaging with our contemporary moment, it seems crucial for those of us who consider ourselves as educators and not just 'instructors'. To facilitate or lead discussion can pose risks for us and some, or all, of our students, and so there is a need for wisdom, courage, and humility. I think we should also recognize how little we know about our students and their lives, and be cautious about imputing motives to what we see of their behaviours in class. I do think we need courage to persist, in community and with support, in the process of education that can be as demoralizing as it is rewarding. Without training, practice and encouragement it can be very challenging to project confidence or 'hold a room' with a sense of authority. What advice would you give colleagues who ask you about this?

CM: There can be a steep learning curve and it is often very challenging for someone who does not have much experience or training as a teacher. Particularly for those of us who come from institutions and departments that emphasize research over teaching – someone may do amazing grant-funded research, but that doesn't mean we know how to teach. You have to perform as if you embody those things and project yourself accordingly. Something you said, Matt, in one of our conversations was that teaching the big lecture is actually a lot like performing stand-up comedy and I think this is so true!

MF: To be clear: I don't think of myself as a comedian! Certainly, students don't laugh at my attempts at jokes (they humour me perhaps!), but I do think that there are not many other forms of public speaking where people sit and listen, in person, for extended periods. The two other places I can think of are speeches made at political rallies and religious sermons. I have done a bit of preaching in a church and was given some training on this, which was useful on how one clarifies key messages, thinks about audiences, and develops an authentic and effective presenting style. Although it's not something I typically talk about I think this has informed my experience too. There may be things to learn from streaming services too concerning maintaining attention or in how media engagement has become more social. For example, some lecturers use Twitter and messaging services to enable dialogue and questions during lectures.

CM: There is a lot of power in the 'fake it 'til you make it' strategy – I have used this myself many times. This means that even if you don't feel knowledgeable, students don't know this.

MF: Yes, and even with some training, lecture hall experience can be a good, if cruel, teacher! One frustration is that some lecturers I've observed start with an apology for the session for one reason or another. I want to say to them: don't undercut yourself at the beginning – you are effectively saying, 'I give you permission not to listen or engage with this, I don't have confidence in the material or myself'. The students are looking to the lecturer to set a tone or atmosphere even though it is, in the end, co-produced. They expect you to set them at ease and to foster a sense of a positive and safe space for learning.

CM: Ultimately, it's one of those things that you have to dive into and learn through doing. We are both people with professional backgrounds in education and well as other public speaking experience – but knowing how to lecture effectively to 200+ people (and guard your own emotions and energy at the same time) is something you have to develop through experience.

2. THE ROLE OF CONTEXT IN TEACHING A LARGE LECTURE

In this section we reflect on the ways in which the lecture space is embedded in, and not sealed off from, the wider society and local milieu in which we educate. Paying attention to these contexts informs our work as educators in general but also some of the approaches we may take to large lecture teaching in particular. Students educate us about the way they see the world, the university, and themselves, in a range of verbal and non-verbal ways as we lecture, as well as through interactions in hallways, meetings and assessments. In this way, the large lecture is emphatically not as some would have it a monologue or '*one-way technology*' (Twigg, 1994, p. 14 in Jones, 2007, p. 200). Context varies across a range of aspects of the educational experience from the institutional setting to the composition of the student body and the identity of the educator. All of these are refracted through experiences of the increasingly neoliberalized academy (SIGJ2 Writing Collective, 2012) – or at least its financialization (Barnett, 2018). Many academics, and indeed students, face a precarious and indebted present and uncertain futures and this too shapes the conditions of possibility for education.

MF: In our conversations we've talked about how we are not only learners of what we teach but also of our students, our campuses, our wider geographies, and our times (Freire, 1970; Mrs Kinpaisby, 2008; Giroux, 2010). We noticed that we bring something of our sensibility and training as geographers to making sense of the different spaces of education we inhabit. How do you pay attention to context as a geography educator?

CM: Context is very important. At Rutgers[1] I've been able to teach much differently than I could at my previous university. In part, this has to do with where students are when they come in (skills and readiness of the average freshmen), but it also has a lot to do with a much more diverse student body. When I teach about racialized injustice, for example, many of my Rutgers students are already familiar with these ideas. They may not have the same language or theoretical framing that I offer them, but they are not new to the concept, which is a much different experience than working with people who are unfamiliar with concepts such as social privilege, or systemic injustice.

MF: As a contrast then, the two contexts I am most familiar with have been white-majority universities where a greater than average percentage of students come from socio-economically advantaged backgrounds. I am conscious of how issues of inequality and injustice can be understood as learning about 'others', 'out there' and how this can affect the students in the class for whom the topics being talked about resonate much more with their own experiences.

CM: Whatever the diversity of the student body, I try never to assume that my students already know these things – rather, I use a lot of scaffolding when I teach (Vygotsky, 1962; Roberts, 2011). This means that I offer different levels of information, ranging from very basic to more theoretical and complex. In this way I feel like I've been able to serve the diverse student body which I work with here. I'm always aiming to engage and challenge people from different backgrounds simultaneously, including those who hold different political ideologies. I think my own identity is helpful in this regard, I'm from a socially and politically conservative area that is predominantly white – so I am very familiar with those points of view. I'm typically teaching against hegemonic social norms that support those views, in keeping with bell hooks' (1994) concept of 'teaching to transgress', but I try to do so with patience and empathy for students who hold more conservative views. How do you think your identity shapes your approach to teaching large classes?

MF: I think I come across as warm and joyful but also sometimes as quite intense and having high expectations. Part of my role involves handling cases of suspected plagiarism and so being known for this means that some students say they think I'm scary, but students also say I'm a very approachable member of staff. I am a younger academic, and in a teaching-focused post (though I don't know how many students know this or differentiate between staff on different types of contract). With my prior education experience I think I'm am quite 'teacherly' in terms of owning the room (a colleague said I was very 'authoritative', which I didn't quite know how to take, but said I had presence and was persuasive) but also perhaps willing to be a little bit more 'goofy' when the occasion calls for it than some lecturers who have a more consistently earnest demeanor. How about you?

CM: I think I come across as kind and nurturing, the typical feminine stereotypes. But I don't mind it really. I want my students to feel safe with me, and to feel that I care about them. I do think this comes back to bite me a bit at times though, for example at the end of a semester, when people are scrambling for grades, trying to convince me to give them a higher grade than they earned, etc. I tend to be very strict about that sort of thing unless it's someone I've been working with all semester long. When someone comes out of nowhere at the end of the semester, I don't tend to bend where grades are concerned. I think this is probably an unpleasant surprise for students who think 'she's nice' and that I will accommodate whatever it is that they want me to do. I've found that I have to be very firm about boundaries around this sort of thing with certain students and use rather strong language, especially since it is known that students often expect a lot more out of female faculty in terms of granting exceptions and that sort of thing (Flaherty, 2018).

MF: I'm aware that some students are much more 'pushy' with younger female colleagues than I think they would be with me. Some students effectively ask for some of their work to be done for them – '*can you give me a reading list*', '*what should my approach/structure be for this essay*'? I do get asked this but it seems to be accepted when I turn things back to them – what do you think? Where could you go to find out? When one female colleague did this she endured some verbal harassment. Beyond gender, the difference in female staff evaluations and for academics of colour are well documented (Kishimoto and Mwangi, 2009; Gutiérrez y Muhs et al., 2012; Hsing-Chen, 2012; Mengel et al., 2018). Does this resonate with your experience?

CM: Gender absolutely factors into how I am perceived, in the classroom as well as with colleagues. In the classroom, I feel like the perception of my gender is both something beneficial as well as a challenge. I see that I am a role model for young women and I take this very seriously. I know that students see me as someone who genuinely cares about them and wants to help them be successful. However, I do often wonder if the young men in the class would be so comfortable talking in the back of the room if I were male. I also know that there is a culture of competitive aggression that is used to signify intelligence. I don't buy into this at all personally, and work to resist it in my day-to-day life, but I also observe how that dynamic of competition and aggression is often perceived as intelligence when it comes from men.

3.   STRATEGIES FOR ENHANCING LARGE LECTURE TEACHING

In this section we consider practical strategies, borne out of experience, and explored in literature on large lecture teaching. Where pedagogic literature suggests effective strategies, the large lecture poses particular challenges so that these cannot be merely 'applied' but have to be worked through in relation to the context of the education space, as we have discussed above. The large lecture can be understood as a 'contact zone' (Askins and Pain, 2011) in which people, objects and ideas can be brought into uneasy but transformative interaction. However, this potential for transformative interaction is not automatic (as Askins and Pain (2011) discuss) but flourishes under particular conditions of possibility and engagement. Naturally, we strive to make our lectures 'unmissable' (Revell and Wainwright, 2009) and emphasize that engaged attendance correlates with stronger grades (Clark et al., 2011), but the scale and anonymity of a large lecture can make this difficult. We explore this further in our discussion below on the practical strategies we have adopted in our large lecture teaching.

MF: In our conversations we have discussed the repertoire of practices that we draw on in large classes and how we use our sense of our context to tailor strategies from this repertoire to the places, people and times in which we teach. Before we get into that could you say a bit about how your repertoire draws on experiences of teaching outside of Higher Education?

CM: Really, in many ways – teaching at university level is not that different from working with children! You have to think about a lot of the same kinds of things – scaffolding your lectures and assignments, for example. This means that you are always building different levels of understanding into everything you do so that it will be interesting and engaging for students who bring different skills to the table. Scaffolding also means that you aren't penalizing those students who may be inexperienced with the topic in an introductory class, but you are still keeping it interesting for those who are already familiar with the material (Cantiello, 2013).

MF: I think there's a lot that I learnt there about communication, breaking tasks down, thinking about the progression of tasks or a set of material and also 'classroom management', as you put it. In a recent geographies of education lecture I discussed how this is a technique of 'schooling' through trying to maintain a student's attention (Gallagher, 2004). I think of myself as designing moments for learning and resources for teaching that try to work at the level of 'experiences'.

CM: I have seen where my previous experiences working with children have given me a heightened awareness to some of these fundamentals of teaching/learning. For example, how to very clearly write out assignment expectations and formulate concrete steps for students to take. Or, how to map out the arc of a semester in terms of the types of assignments I will offer and things we will do in relation to my own time and capacity for grading and staying on top of my responsibilities along the way. One assignment I give in my introductory lecture course asks students to respond in a short essay to a section in their textbook on, for example, Fordism and Post-Fordism, showing that they are engaging with core concepts in economic geography, and relate it back to material presented in lecture. They are required to address a set of questions through their response and focus on particular parts of the chapter. Ultimately though, I am not looking for a standard answer, I just want to see engagement with these basic economic geography concepts at whatever level works for the student. For some who are new to the subject, their responses may be very basic while still fulfilling the parameters of the assignment, whereas others will have advanced knowledge of the material and provide a much more developed essay.

MF: The strategies we use can complement these other ways in which we think about progression, the goals of learning and assessment. What would be an example then of something you do in the lecture?

CM: I do a lot of 'in-class exercises', which are typically 5–10 minutes in the middle or near the end of class where I ask students to take out a piece of paper and engage with a prompt of some kind, or talk with their neighbor in response to a few questions (Gonzales, 2015). These are not graded for content – it is a quick attendance check and, at the end of the semester, gives me some idea of the percentage of classes a student attended overall. I try to keep these in-class exercises creative and fun; usually I am asking them to think of something that relates to the topic at hand. I find that it is much easier to get people to engage after I have given some time for them to gather their thoughts on a topic. For example, I have a section of my intro to human geography class that looks at the concepts of utopia and dystopia, and how those ideas were mobilized through European colonialism. The prompt I will throw out to students is, '*What is one example you can think of from a film, television show, or book that shows a dystopian view of the future?*' Then I give 3–5 minutes for them to jot down some ideas. This one is fun, because people think of very interesting examples (often things I am not familiar with!), and I will have students explain the basic plot to the rest of the class. It's a light-hearted way to get into the topic and have them think about ideas that we are dealing with in class which show up a lot in popular culture.

MF: I do the same thing with in-class exercises. I might ask them to respond or join in with some conversations and then I report back to the group. I've also sometimes set prompts which I ask students to respond to outside of class. I bring what they say (anonymized) into class time and use them to stage a dialogue. I've also tried live web-based comment boards like padlet[2] (Padlet, 2018) and electronic quiz options but I think you have to be quite confident about using these to give it a go and they operate on a spectrum of more to less structured. It is important to mediate the risk of students using this inappropriately. With padlet I would set out my expectations at the beginning of a session about what I think professional conduct would be and make it clear that I will not use this platform if I am concerned it is being used inappropriately. Some approaches like structured roleplays, the goldfish bowl[3] (GP training net, 2018), or 'staged seminar approach' can be effective, which draw on different forms of staging or drama-work.

CM: Another strategy is to wander the room while students are working through the exercise and talk to some people individually – this way you can also hear from people who don't normally speak in class and tell them that you'd like to call on them when you bring the large group together so that they are prepared. The anxiety factor for students is certainly a concern – but this also has to be mediated with the fact that speaking in front of a large group is a skill that they will be developing throughout their university education, it is beneficial to have a little experience with it.

MF: I have also been thinking about what it looks like to do a lecture well, rather than trying to make it something it can't be. A common pitfall that I've observed is trying to run multiple smaller seminars or workshops within the lecture hall – the lecturer wants the experience to be dialogue-based but is fighting the size of the lecture. There are productive versions of this (for example as above) but to 'monologue' well is a skill in itself and something which can be honed as an effective pedagogy. I'm also not persuaded that a monologue is ever a voice on its own in any case; what we say is shaped and formed in conversation with literature, our context and at its best, with our students. Do you find you tend to adopt a more monologic approach in a large lecture?

CM: While I work hard to shift the dynamics of power and authority around in small classes, with my current class of 260 this would be significantly more challenging. I do think that the tradition of 'lecture as monologue' is rooted in patriarchal and authoritarian norms (Friere, 1970; Dowler, 2002) which discipline students to assume that they have little to offer coming into a class and should be there to listen and learn from an implicitly male teacher. However, it is really difficult to overturn the normative expectation of a monologue because most students have been successfully disciplined to embody a passive role in lecture. I suppose this is one of the more difficult things about the large lecture – trying to upset this dynamic and the way that students and educators have been trained to behave. The physical layout of a lecture hall presents additional challenges to a dialogic approach – seats are fixed in place; inability to move freely around a tightly packed, terraced room; and so on. As a geographer I am constantly thinking about these spatial challenges to teaching, which stem from how the classroom itself was designed and engineered.

MF: Yes! The room makes a real difference and we can read the philosophies of knowledge built into the design. However, the paper by Hill et al. (2016) challenges a risk of determinism in arguing that the space does not have to define the type of teaching that is possible. They argue that while there are dominant assumptions about learning embedded in the architecture of spaces, it is possible to use these affordances creatively. I try to make something of this in one of my lectures in quite a simple way. I start the lecture sitting down in the middle of where the students sit and narrate from there something about how to read this space and how it might be hard – but that it is possible – to overcome some of the disciplining you talk about. I remember too, that you talked about how to make space for students to get to know each other in lectures. Could you say a bit about that?

CM: Yes, this is a really important aspect of teaching the large lecture that is often overlooked. For the most part, unless you are at a fairly small school, your students don't know each other when they begin the class. Especially if you are going to attempt to do in-class exercises where they are paired or grouped together, you have to give them opportunities to get to know each other. In my course evaluations for my big lecture, I have had multiple students write that they appreciate that they were able to get to know other students in the room, because this often doesn't happen in big classes. There are simple ways to do this – on the first day of class, for example, I asked them to take a piece of paper and a pen and to find out from three of the people sitting near them their name, major (or intended major), and hometown.

CONCLUSIONS

In this dialogue we have drawn attention to three key themes from conversations had over several months. Namely: the emotional and embodied experiences of teaching a large lecture; the role of context; and strategies for enhancing teaching a large lecture (see Chapter 5 in this volume by Rink for strategies for assessment of large cohorts). Teaching in these contexts necessitates a particular performance of the self in space: of skills; experience; and flexibility according to the needs of our students. We have considered this as a form of place-based pedagogy where responding to the conditions of the room, our institutional and national milieu, our students, and their lifeworlds, means we cannot simply apply 'good practice' or 'what works' aspatially and impersonally, but with attentiveness to our contexts. We advocate here for a recognition of the challenges and successes brought to the embodied and placed performances of teaching that values the creativity required to meaningfully co-produce knowledge with our students.

In particular, we highlight themes from this chapter and next steps which follow from recognizing the labour of this work and some potential implications for those taking large lectures (Table 4.1).

One need not be uncritically committed to the merits of large lectures to recognize their continued value and contribution to learning in a higher education setting, despite relevant critiques of neoliberalization of the academy. Indeed, as we think this dialogue makes clear, it is precisely by engaging with the challenges of the lecture, by attending to the contexts in which we work, and by opening up dialogue with our students that we can ensure some of the possibilities of the large lecture are realized.

USEFUL RESOURCES

- Anmpalagan, R. and Smith, R. (2018) *Large Class Teaching Challenges and Possible Responses.* Available at https://warwick.ac.uk/fac/soc/al/research/groups/llta/resources/telc/strategies/ (Accessed: 26 April 2019).
- Lang, J.M. (2016) *Small Changes in Teaching.* Available at: https://www.chronicle.com/specialreport/Small-Changes-in-Teaching/44 (Accessed: 23 February 2018).
- Wilsman, A. (2016) *Teaching Large Classes.* Available at https://cft.vanderbilt.edu/guides-sub-pages/teaching-large-classes/ (Accessed: 26 April 2019).

Table 4.1   Forms of academic labour and their implications

Forms of academic labour	Implications
A recognition that large lecture teaching is physically tiring and emotionally draining (just as it can also be fun and exhilarating). It requires a set of bodily and cognitive performances to project your voice, to create ties of engagement with students across the large spaces, to hold attention and communicate meaningfully, such that the large lecture becomes a space for learning.	Consider how you build up to, and rest from, delivering large lectures and what you schedule before, and following, them. What aspects of self-care could you engage in to protect your voice and physical and emotional wellbeing? What support or training could you access from your institution or union? Consider if there are trusted colleagues you could ask to give you peer feedback on this aspect of your lecturing, and discuss with other colleagues their strategies as a form of peer learning.
A recognition that sitting in large lectures is often tiring for students, who are asked to concentrate for extended periods of time to engage with difficult and often new ideas, in environments that may be unfamiliar and alienate and in which other students may act as learning partners and distractions.	Consider how you could change the dynamic of the space to allow for different modes of interaction and encounter. Consider how you could change the dynamic of the experience of time (and pacing) of the large lecture to work with concentration spans and re-engage attention at different points.
A recognition that controversy has a place in the large lecture but that 'doing controversy well' places additional burdens on the lecturer and the students as well as being empowering of voices and positions that may otherwise not have felt heard in other spaces on campus.	Consider what some of the areas of controversy are in your subject area. This may vary and be more or less emotionally affecting for students. Consider your own sense of confidence about hosting conversations like these. How does that affect what you might or might not do?
A recognition that our students are diverse and lead lives which are at least as complex, and sometimes more so, than their lecturers. Their learning and experience of university extends far beyond that which we may be able to 'read' from demeanour and conduct in large lectures.	What assumptions might you be making about your students based on what you see in the large lectures? How can you engage students outside of classes to break down these assumptions? One practice is to convene a voluntary student focus group which meets periodically through the course to provide feedback and ask questions which then inform your teaching.
A recognition that the wider context of higher education and geographical variability and differing inequalities shape the conditions of possibility for large lecture teaching. Good practice cannot simply be 'applied' but the educator implements approaches, techniques, or strategies in embodied and spatially-specific ways.	What are the challenges and opportunities your students face in the context of your institution and regional and national setting. Are they (and colleagues) facing financial hardship, discrimination, or mental health difficulties? Discuss with colleagues how they consider and respond to these issues.
A recognition that typical lecture spaces, and the form of a lecture, bears the inheritances of particular politics of knowledge that enhance the cultural status of the lecturer through the invalidation of the knowledge of students. A variety of alternative approaches allow for the large lecture space to be one of shared meaning-making, which values the distinctive contributions of participants.	What do you consider your role to be as a lecturer? If knowledge is more distributed and not invested solely in the academic how does this affect your teaching practice? Which approaches do you use already, and which would you consider trying? What conditions would enable you to consider other strategies or approaches? What one 'small change' (Lang, 2016) could you incorporate in your next large lecture?

NOTES

1. Carrie was an Instructor with the Department of Geography at Rutgers, The State University of New Jersey from 2016 to 2018.
2. https://padlet.com/
3. http://www.gp-training.net/training/vts/group/goldfish.htm

REFERENCES

Askins, K. and R. Pain (2011) 'Contact zones: Participation, materiality, and the messiness of interaction', *Environment and Planning D*, 29(5), pp. 803–821.

Barnett, C. (2018) *The Means and Ends of Higher Education*. Available at: http://www.journalofculturaleconomy.org/the-means-and-ends-of-higher-education/ (accessed: 28 March 2018).

Bovil, C. (2018) 'Lectures and Legoland: Recapturing the excitement of learning', *Dansk Universitetspaedagogisk Tidsskrift*, 13(24), pp. 1–4.

Cantiello, J. (2013) *Fourth Grade Lessons*. Available at: https://www.insidehighered.com/advice/2013/08/16/essay-job-search-move-elementary-school-college (accessed: 23 February 2018).

Clark, G., Gill, N., Walker, M. and R. Whittle (2011) 'Attendance and performance: Correlations and motives in lecture-based modules', *Journal of Geography in Higher Education*, 35(2), pp. 199–215.

Dowler, L. (2002), 'The uncomfortable classroom: Incorporating feminist pedagogy and political practice into world regional geography', *Journal of Geography*, 101(2), pp. 68–72.

Flaherty, C. (2018) *Dancing Backwards in High Heels*. Available at: https://www.insidehighered.com/news/2018/01/10/study-finds-female-professors-experience-more-work-demands-and-special-favor (accessed: 23 February 2018).

Freire, P. (1970), *Pedagogy of the Oppressed*, New York: Continuum.

Gallagher, M. (2004) *Producing the Schooled Subject: Techniques of Power in a Primary School*, PhD Thesis, The University of Edinburgh.

Giroux, H. (2010) *Lessons to be Learned from Paulo Freire as Education is Being Taken Over by the Mega Rich*. Available at: http://www.truth-out.org/archive/component/k2/item/93016:lessons-to-be-learned-from-paulo-freire-as-education-is-being-taken-over-by-the-mega-rich (accessed: 23 February 2018).

Gonzales, J. (2015) *The Big List of Class Discussion Strategies*. Available at: https://www.cultofpedagogy.com/speaking-listening-techniques/ (accessed: 23 February 2018).

GP training net (2018) *Goldfish Bowl Technique*. Available at: http://www.gp-training.net/training/vts/group/goldfish.htm (accessed: 23 February 2018).

Grasgreen, A. (2010) *Preparing Professors to Teach*. Available at: https://www.insidehighered.com/news/2010/10/15/mit (accessed: 23 February 2018).

Gutiérrez y Muhs, G., Flores Niemann, Y., González, C.G. and A.P. Harris (2012) *Presumed Incompetent*. Logan, UT: Utah State University Press, Project MUSE.

Hill, J., Thomas, G., Diaz, A. and D. Simm (2016) 'Borderland spaces for learning partnership: Opportunities, benefits and challenges', *Journal of Geography in Higher Education*, 40(3), pp. 375–393.

hooks, b. (1994) *Teaching to Transgress*. New York: Routledge.

Hsing-Chen, Y. (2012) 'Feminist teaching practice in masculine higher education institutions in Taiwan', *Asian Journal of Women's Studies*, 18(3), pp. 7–37.

Inwood, J. (2017) 'Critical pedagogy and the fierce urgency of now: Opening up space for critical reflections on the U.S. civil rights movement', *Social and Cultural Geography*, 18(4), pp. 451–465.

Jenkins, A., Daniel, P., Healy, M., Hindle, B., Keene, P., Mills, C., McEwen, L., Robinson, G., Rodaway, P., Slowe, P. and D. Rolls (1993) 'Teaching large classes in geography: Some practical suggestions', *Journal of Geography in Higher Education*, 17(2), pp. 149–162.

Jones, S.E. (2007) 'Reflections on the lecture: Outmoded medium or instrument of inspiration?', *Journal of Further and Higher Education*, 31(4), pp. 397–406.

Kishimoto, K. and M. Mwangi (2009) 'Critiquing the rhetoric of "safety" in feminist pedagogy: Women of color offering an account of ourselves', *Feminist Teacher*, 19(2), pp. 87–102.

Laliberté, N., Bain, A., Lankenau, G. and M. Bolduc (2017) 'The controversy capital of stealth feminism in higher education', *Acme*, 16(1), pp. 34–58.

Lang, J.M. (2016) *Small Changes in Teaching*. Available at: https://www.chronicle.com/specialreport/Small-Changes-in-Teaching/44 (accessed: 23 February 2018).

Mengel, F., Sauermann, J. and U. Zölitz (2018) 'Gender Bias in Teaching Evaluations', *Journal of the European Economic Association*. doi: 10.1093/jeea/jvx057.

Mrs Kinpaisby (2008) 'Taking stock of participatory geographies: Envisioning the communiversity', *Transactions of the Institute of British Geographers*, 33(3), pp. 292–299.

Padlet (2018) *Padlet*, Available at: https://padlet.com/ (accessed: 23 February 2018).

Revell, A. and E. Wainwright (2009) 'What makes lectures "unmissable"? Insights into teaching excellence and active learning', *Journal of Geography in Higher Education*, 33(2), pp. 209–223.

Reza-Lopez, E., Charles L.H. and L. Reyes (2014) 'Nepantlera pedagaogy: An axiological posture for preparing critically conscious teachers in the borderlands', *Journal of Latinos and Education*, 13(2), pp. 107–119.

Roberts, M. (2011) *What Makes a Geography Lesson Good?*. Available at: https://www.geography.org.uk/download/ga_prmghwhatmakesageographylessongood.pdf (accessed: 23 February 2018).

SIGJ2 Writing Collective (2012) 'What can we do? The challenge of being new academics in neoliberal universities', *Antipode*, 44, pp. 1055–1058.

Tasch, J. and W. Tasch (2016) 'Redesigning Physical Geography 101: Bringing students into the discussion', *Journal of Geography in Higher Education*, 40(4), pp. 565–584.

Vygotsky, L. (1962) *Thought and Language*, Cambridge, MA: Massachusetts Institute of Technology Press.

5. Measuring learning for the masses: assessment strategies for large classes
Bradley Rink

INTRODUCTION

In this chapter, I reflect on teaching and learning practices in two undergraduate human geography modules at the University of the Western Cape (UWC) in Cape Town, South Africa with the aim of illustrating the challenges and opportunities inherent in assessment of learning in large classes. I ground my discussion of assessment for large classes in the precursor to assessment: the proposed learning outcomes that the lecturer will assess for diagnostic and formative purposes. This chapter is contextualised both in the local environment of my undergraduate teaching in an historically Black university (HBU) in Southern Africa, as well as more broadly in the contemporary global climate of higher education. Both are complicated by growth through massification of the higher education sector, fiscal belt-tightening in the wake of global financial crises, and growing competition from private education providers and the increasing presence of massive online open courses (MOOCs), which some have seen as an irreversible 'detonator' of change in universities as we know them (García Peñalvo, 2017). While MOOCs and other forms of online learning have undoubtedly influenced the sector, increasingly larger classes taught through a traditional lecture format (discussed in Chapter 4 in this volume by Finn and Mott) are not the exception, but rather the norm.

I begin by discussing the large classroom environment, and by reviewing recent literature on the related concept of large class pedagogy (LCP) as a means of framing my case study of assessment. As I consider the negative impacts of large class sizes on the student experience and the role and demands on the lecturer, this chapter also demonstrates the opportunities for engagement with current and emerging technologies that may be applied to the large classroom environment. While the delivery of content and course resources is often the most tangible engagement with e-learning for many lecturers, it is in the assessment of student learning in large classes where state-of-the-art teaching practices together with the use of technology may successfully address student learning goals, while at the same time addressing the challenges of low-resourced teaching environments. I demonstrate through my own teaching and learning practices in large classes that effective student learning and successful outcomes need not be incompatible with large class size. In doing so, I discuss strategies for assessment tasks ranging from tests, essays, reflective journals, tutorial and practical work through assessment strategies such as peer evaluation, scaffolding, and both diagnostic and formative assessment using online learning platforms such as Sakai and Google Forms. With limited resources and learning goals which focus on understanding the complex relationships between people, the natural environment, and the non-human world, the undergraduate curriculum requires students to demonstrate their learning through a variety of assessment tasks ranging from tests, essays, reflective journals, tutorial and practical work.

THE LARGE CLASSROOM ENVIRONMENT

For the first-time lecturer, preparing to deliver content and assess learning for a large number of students in a cavernous lecture theatre may seem daunting. Along with a sense of disengagement from the students given the size of the class or the space of the lecture theatre, the management and delivery of course material and assessment tasks to such large classes can pose significant challenges even to the most seasoned lecturer. Complicating this situation is the need to assess learning across a cohort of hundreds of students with limited resources for invigilating and marking such assessment tasks. As I discuss below, a large class in my case numbers around 400 students. But is that large? Hornsby and Osman (2014) and Hornsby, Osman and De Matos-Ala (2013a) refrain from defining what constitutes a large class through a numerical threshold. Rather, they consider 'large' class environments as those where the quality of student learning may be impacted, negatively, by the number of students in the class (Hornsby, Osman and De Matos-Ala, 2013a, p. 8). Therefore, the measure of what is 'large' varies depending on the discipline and nature of the course. Given the nature of the discipline of geography – both human and physical – many courses require the engagement of students in practical settings, tutorials, GIS labs, or in the field supervised by tutors and/or lecturers. Therefore, what constitutes a large class in geography may differ greatly from disciplines whose learning activities do not require hands-on, laboratory- or small-group-based engagement. In the second-year human geography module with 200 students that I discuss below, the class may be considered large when measured against the learning goals of the tutorial groups which focus on small-group interaction, discussion and debate. While my second-year module is 'large' in the context of its learning activities and goals, 'large' classrooms in an era of global massification of higher education may exceed 1000 students (Exeter et al., 2010; Arvanitakis, 2014). Irrespective of size, large classes have impacts on both students and lecturers. In the current climate of higher education, large classes are increasingly the norm. Therefore, addressing the challenges and making use of the opportunities may be the best way forward.

Impacts on Students

Whatever the measure, large classes may impact on the learning environment and the experience and success of students themselves (Ehrenberg et al., 2001). Student experience, in this case, is closely aligned with the degree of student engagement, defined by Exeter et al. (2010) as the time, energy and resources that students spend on activities designed to enhance learning. The experience of large classes for many students is one characterised by feelings of anonymity and isolation (Biggs, 1999; Mulryan-Kyne, 2010) that lead to low levels of participation and disengagement from learning activities. In spite of the negative aspects of large classes, as Hornsby, Osman and Matos-Ala (2013a) contend, class size on its own does not mediate student performance. Rather, they argue that '*class size matters in relation to education goals and the quality of the educational experience'* (2013a, p. 8). The learning experience that I set out for my students is one of deeply-engaged learning and higher-order cognitive skills within the framework of human geography. Such skills are critical to the social- and economic-development role of higher education for the future of South Africa as elsewhere. As Hornsby, Osman and De Matos-Ala (2013b) argue, 'large classes challenge the motivation, engagement and fostering of higher order cognitive skills: that is, they tend to discourage the acquisition of the very skills that are integral to economic development' (p. 173). With a deliberate connection between massification and economic development in many emerging economies, pressure on lecturers to achieve positive results from a growing student body is greater than ever.

The View from the Lectern

From the perspective of lecturers, similar negative feelings about large classes are prevalent. In their study of lecturers from large classes, Albertyn, Machika and Troskie-De Bruin (2016) found that lecturers themselves struggled to attend to the needs of students in large classes, particularly those in large first-year modules where students need additional support during the transition to university. Like the example of GES111 that I teach, in many higher education settings it is often in first-year classes where enrolments are the highest (Foley and Masingila, 2014). In high-enrolment, low-resourced environments such as mine in South Africa, and in consideration of the social justice dimension of broader access to higher education, lecturers are faced with an unavoidable tension. On the one hand, lecturers are being saddled with the additional burden of the massification model, while on the other they are compelled to provide quality teaching in order to unlock the transformative power of tertiary education (Albertyn, Machika and Troskie-De Bruin, 2016, p. 50).

Foley and Masingila (2014) contend that the challenges of delivering large classes can be confronted, and in many ways diminished, through the use of current and emerging technologies. Their discussion of large class pedagogy (LCP) in the context of institutions in the USA and Kenya concludes that the principle challenges in teaching large classes – including teaching skills, resources, and campus infrastructure – may be offset by opportunities brought on by mobile technology and e-learning platforms such as those that I employ. Critical to success, in their view, is the role of capacity building in LCP through the use of emerging technology, faculty development and support, and enhanced infrastructure (Foley and Masingila, 2014, p. 808). Those same technologies, when applied to diverse student bodies such as that which we experience in South Africa with a variety of language and cultural backgrounds, can assist in the success of first-year students (Snowball, 2014). In the case study that follows, a combination of emerging technology, support, and enhanced infrastructure has made an impact specifically on assessment, and more generally on the learning experience, within large class environments.

NAVIGATING TEACHING AND LEARNING WITH LARGE CLASSES: A CASE STUDY OF UWC

The potential perils in the large class environment are many for both student and lecturer. Yet, as argued by Hornsby and Osman (2014, p. 714) 'by focusing on the structure of the curriculum, the strategies employed for instruction and the way students are assessed, problems associated with large class teaching environments can be addressed and quality education ensured'. In the case study below I demonstrate how content delivery and assessment of student learning make use of mobile technology and e-learning platforms in an effort to achieve learning outcomes for students in a large class environment. For the purpose of this chapter, I focus my discussion on two of the largest undergraduate modules that I teach at UWC, 'Introduction to Human Geography' and 'Space, Place and Mobility in Southern Africa'.

Teaching Context: University of the Western Cape

The context of my undergraduate teaching at UWC is one comprised of courses that for my department and discipline may be considered large, with enrolment of nearly 400 students in the first-year module GES111 'Introduction to Human Geography' and 200 students in the second-year module GES225 'Space, Place and Mobility in Southern Africa'. I teach these modules in a department that combines the related disciplines of geography, environmental studies, and tourism (see Chapter 9 in this volume by Griffin for a discussion of teaching in multidisciplinary contexts). My department has a small lecturing staff of six, each with heavy teaching loads that have increased due to the massification of enrolments in tertiary education within South Africa as elsewhere on the African continent (Mohamedbhai, 2014). High enrolment is also driven by the interdisciplinary nature of geography as a field of study, and its serving as a pre-requisite for modules in cognate disciplines such as tourism and sustainability studies that begin in the second year. Geography is also a teaching subject for primary and secondary educators in South Africa, thus our modules draw students who are pursuing B.Ed degrees.

The growth that we have experienced in our enrolments is complicated by an environment of fiscal austerity in the higher education sector generally and my institution specifically where budgets for hiring additional lecturers and tutors have become increasingly strained in spite of growing enrolment. Such challenges are typical of the higher education institutions where massification is experienced (Hornsby and Osman, 2014). In spite of the limited resources, my colleagues and I continue to strive to achieve learning goals which focus on understanding the complex relationships between people, the natural environment, and the non-human world.

It is within this context that my teaching of GES111 'Introduction to Human Geography' and GES225 'Space, Place and Mobility in Southern Africa' takes place. Within these two human geography modules, learning outcomes focus broadly on human/environment relationships, with specific foci on mobilities and the urban environment. In GES111 we do this by introducing students to the sub-discipline of human geography through an exploration of society, politics and social processes through a spatial lens. In the second-year GES225 we aim to develop students' understanding of the concept of contested spatialities through notions of landscape, mobilities, migration, and diasporas.

Understanding both the challenges of transition to university for first-year students, and the impacts of the large classroom environment, a principal goal of my teaching practices is to engage students in active (Lea, Stephenson and Troy, 2003) and 'authentic learning' (Herrington and Oliver, 2000; Herrington, Reeves and Oliver, 2010; Bozalek et al., 2013) through the illumination of students' lived realities and experiences of mobility in our South African context. By way of harnessing students' lived experiences of mobility, this approach seeks to address the disengaged, anonymous, and isolated feeling that is typical of large classes (Biggs, 1999; Mulryan-Kyne, 2010). By taking a student-centred approach, my teaching practices draw upon students' everyday realities and bring them into conversation with theory. Active learning design works with the assumption that students bring knowledge to the learning environment which must be productively embraced and built upon. In an active learning environment, the transmission of knowledge is not unidirectional from the 'expert' lecturer to the 'passive' student. Such environments help to ensure a student-centred approach to learning that promises the greatest possible impact on learning outcomes and higher retention of knowledge (Lea, Stephenson and Troy, 2003). Related to the student-centred approach, authentic learning situates knowledge within the realm of everyday life (see Chapter 27 in this volume by Hill and Wirth for a discussion of authentic assessment). Authentic learning is a related concept that can be simply defined as 'learning in contexts that promote real-life applications of knowledge' (Rule, 2006, p. 1). Attention to such authentic context 'leads to an intense feeling of engagement with the learning' (Bozalek et al., 2013, p. 2). Within the context of my teaching and learning approaches as above, I turn to examples of assessment strategies used for both diagnostic[1] and formative[2] assessment purposes.

ASSESSMENT STRATEGIES

No matter the size of the class, lecturers cannot overlook the fact that students are assessment-focused, and motivated to participate in learning activities for the purpose of getting results (Worth, 2014). The challenge for the lecturer in a large class environment is accurately measuring student learning given constraints on time and other resources available to them. In alignment with the findings of Foley and Masingila (2014), my experience in GES111 and GES225 has demonstrated the critical role of e-learning technologies in the management and delivery of assessment tasks in large classes. The principle challenges in my case of LCP lie not in the delivery of content which is easily scaled-up using e-learning platforms and appropriately-sized lecture venues, but in the marking of assessment tasks and more critically the provision of good quality feedback which Nicol and Macfarlane-Dick (2006) demonstrate as the key element of formative assessment. They describe seven principles of good feedback practice, as feedback which:

1. helps clarify what good performance is (goals, criteria, expected standards);
2. facilitates the development of self-assessment (reflection) in learning;
3. delivers high quality information to students about their learning;
4. encourages teacher and peer dialogue around learning;
5. encourages positive motivational beliefs and self-esteem;
6. provides opportunities to close the gap between current and desired performance;
7. provides information to teachers that can be used to help shape teaching.
(Nicol and Macfarlane-Dick, 2006, p. 205)

The challenge in large classroom environments lies in providing high quality feedback to a student cohort numbering in the hundreds or thousands. Below I will reflect on examples of diagnostic and formative assessment from my experience in GES111 and GES225 in

order to illustrate how assessment in large class environments many be applied successfully in the context of the discipline of geography.

Class Polls and Surveys for Diagnostic Assessment

As its title implies, GES111 provides an introduction to human geography. The module
aims to introduce students to key concepts in the discipline, and to explore the complex
relationships between society and space (see Chapter 6 in this volume by Fouberg, for a
discussion of threshold concepts and curriculum design). As social science and humanities
scholars, the human geographers including myself who teach the module want students to
understand society, politics, and social processes. One of the principle learning objectives
of the module is to help students to understand everyday events and processes within a
spatial context. Since 2016 I have included in the GES111 class a learning activity where I
aim to illustrate the relationship that students have with the city and our campus through
their daily mobility. Underlying this aim is the need to assess the degree to which students
understand and express spatial relationships in the city, and to set up a framework for
discussing mobilities that emanates from their own 'authentic' knowledge of everyday
life. The survey is delivered through our Sakai-based e-learning platform (called *iKamva*,
a name which means 'future' in isiXhosa) using Google Forms. Delivery through iKamva
allows me to frame the activity alongside readings and other resources available on the
platform, while the survey itself (designed through Google Forms) provides a platform
that is easily accessible using mobile devices. Most students complete the survey on their
mobile devices, many of them as the activity is being introduced in the lecture. Once the
survey has been completed, the results are shared with students in real-time during one of
our two weekly lectures. A wide disparity in travel times and experiences of mobility are
always a catalyst for intense discussion between students during lecture. Such a learning
activity may be considered authentic, following Herrington, Reeves and Oliver (2010).
The authenticity of learning in this context was echoed by the degree to which students
began to make linkages between theory and practice. In a class of nearly 400 students, the
lecture theatre came alive with conversations between students and hands raised in the
air to share stories. This excitement was carried through to the practical sessions offered
in the same week, and reflected upon at the conclusion of the semester when one 2017
student noted in the module evaluation that two of the most impactful learning activities
included '*[t]he survey we did as a class on mobility . . . [and] Online pracs (they are super
convenient and easier to complete)*' (GES111 student, 2017).

As an authentic learning activity (Herrington and Oliver, 2000; Herrington, Reeves
and Oliver, 2010), the diagnostic assessment provided by the survey satisfies a number
of attributes of such environments. Firstly, the activity may be seen as authentic because
the learning has real-world relevance. The vast majority of my students have had similar
experiences or can at least relate to what this student has reflected upon. Accordingly,
the context of the course represents the kind of setting where the appropriate skills and
knowledge will be applied – in the context of moving through the city. Second, the task
mirrors a realistic application of knowledge, as students use such embedded knowledge-
systems to make mobility decisions every day. They relate to the lived experience of
mobility not only through the survey, but through their daily application of knowledge.
Thirdly, the environment – both online and in the lecture theatre – provides multiple roles

and perspectives for learning. Students are able to explore other perspectives of mobility from others' experiences, consider them, and allow them to enhance their learning. They do this by seeing other responses both online and in the real-time display of responses in the lecture theatre. Fourth, this activity helps to promote reflection which was evident in the cacophony of discussions that arose from sharing the survey results. Finally, the activity helps to promote articulation, through a growing understanding of concepts that is evidenced in comments from students in module evaluation results. With the inclusion of surveys, live polling using clickers or text-based services such as www.polleverywhere. com as discussed by Foley and Masingila (2014), large class lectures can be interactive and used for important diagnostic assessment of learning. This example of diagnostic assessment in the context of a large class allows me to gauge student learning in the process of delivery of teaching content. By examining the degree to which students make links between their own experience of mobility (their practice) and course content (theory), I am able to assess the degree to which they understand and express spatial relationships in the city. In that way, I have a better understanding of my students' learning, and I am thus able to better shape teaching and learning activities of an engaged student body.

Formative Assessment Using Online Multiple Choice Questions

Driven initially by the constraint of finding an adequate testing venue that could accommodate all GES111 students and limited resources for marking assessments in the required time period, I re-designed the term test for my section of the module as an online multiple choice question (MCQ) based test using our Sakai-based e-learning platform. Following a successful testing in the first year of my teaching the module, I extended the use of online assessments using MCQs into practical tasks as well. Although the roughly 400 students are divided into four equally-sized groups for their weekly practical sessions, those groups of roughly 80 to 100 students may be considered large given the highly interactive and collaborative goals that we set out for the activities. While the online test for GES111 assesses a range of knowledge and cognitive skills, the practical task focuses specifically on the spatial dimensions of inequality in Cape Town, requiring students to interpret maps, respond to questions about selections of text, and compare statistics on human development and inequality.

In this exploration of e-assessment, Nicol (2007) argues that using MCQs via e-learning platforms can be an effective means of assessing student learning. However, he also notes that MCQ tests are often criticised for offering limited opportunities for feedback that is critical in articulating students learning. Nevertheless, in the context of a first-year geography course, Rød, Eiksund and Fjær (2010) found that marks from MCQ tests did not differ significantly from other forms of assessment, although their use of MCQs constituted a small percentage of students' overall course marks. Authors agree that quality feedback remains vital when using MCQs in assessment tasks (Nicol, 2007; Rød, Eiksund, and Fjær, 2010). Through the use of e-learning platforms such as Sakai, it is possible to provide detailed feedback. An example of one such MCQ and the related feedback is below (Box 5.1).

The final practical task (Practical Eight) in GES111 has learning objectives that focus on the spatial dimensions of inequality in the South African context. Amongst the objectives for this practical are to: 1) Have an appreciation of the various social and economic

---

BOX 5.1   AN EXAMPLE MULTIPLE CHOICE QUESTION WITH FEEDBACK

Compare the area marked 'B' in the maps above. Which of the following statements best describes the area indicated?

A. The area marked 'B' is densely populated and predominantly low-income
B. The area marked 'B' is a low-density settlement and is in the lowest income group
C. The area marked 'B' is densely populated and has a middle-income population
D. The area marked 'B' a low-density settlement and has a high HDI

Answer Key: A

Incorrect Feedback: The number of dots grouped closely together on the map demonstrates the density of the population, while the colour of the dots (according to the map key) shows that the area is predominantly in the lower income categories. Thus, the area marked 'B' is both densely populated and predominantly low-income.

---

indicators of inequality; 2) be able to recognise and analyse inequality at various levels (for example local, provincial, national, regional); and 3) have a basic appreciation of at least two measures of inequality. The practical readings and other resources such as maps are provided online through our GES111 iKamva site. Students were provided access to the task over five days, with no pre-determined time limit other than the access window for the task. After a student submits their responses, and within a pre-determined timeframe, student marks and correct/incorrect responses are made available to students for revision. The most critical aspect of this part of the assessment is not the marks themselves, but the feedback provided for incorrect answers. In the example below, students are shown two maps: In the first map, annual household income across Cape Town from the 2011 South African census is indicated with each dot representing 25 households; the second map provides a visual and spatial representation of predominant race groups across the city and its suburbs. Each dot represents 100 people. The density of dots therefore represents greater population density of a particular income and/or race group. Along with the maps are a series of MCQs, one of which is provided below in Box 5.1.

The question text and answer options are seen in Box 5.1, along with feedback that is given to students who return an incorrect response. While the practical assessment task allowed students only one opportunity to complete, GES111 students have the opportunity to engage in a practice test that they may take as many times as they wish in preparation for the actual class test. The practice test, like the example above, provides detailed feedback for students who choose an incorrect answer. At the same time, these examples demonstrate that assessment tasks delivered to hundreds of students from a single lecturer can still provide quality feedback that assists in the formative process of learning. In a traditional (paper-based) MCQ assessment, a student might only know that their response is correct or incorrect, without understanding why. Feedback provided in the example above satisfies a number of Nicol and Macfarlane-Dick's (2006) principles of good feedback practice, in that it: clearly identifies the correct answer (the expected standard); delivers detailed information about the map-reading skills required; and helps to close the gap between current performance in the case of an incorrect response and desired performance. This is especially the case in the practice tests that allow students to continue to close the gap through multiple testing opportunities. An examination of a subset of the 2018 cohort is illustrative of the potential that online formative assessment may have for student learning. Although the majority of GES111 students took the practice test only once, a small number of students took the test more than once. An even smaller number were what I would consider 'super-users', taking the test three or more times. There were five super-users in the 2018 class. In all cases, student scores increased dramatically from the first to the last testing opportunity. While the mean result of all students on the 2018 practice test was 58, all super-users concluded their multiple test runs with scores of 100. Furthermore, the final results on the actual test for this small group of super-users exceeded the class average by as much as 13 marks. These statistics are made readily available through the Sakai platform, which not only provides detail on overall class performance, but also useful statistics on student performance (by question) that aids in identifying shared gaps in knowledge that emerge through assessment tasks.

Assessment of student learning using MCQ tests on our Sakai-based e-learning platform provides other benefits as well. While the online tests are available for students to take at their convenience within a limited timeframe, I am able to reduce the likelihood of student misconduct during testing by using question pools in Sakai to ensure that no two students write the same test. In this way, MCQs are randomly drawn from a pool of available questions and answer options. Although the same answer options are provided in each instance, the options are randomised in their order of appearance. Being able to access the test in their own time and away from direct invigilation means that the test is an open-book variety. In this way the assessment task facilitates self-assessment and reflection in learning (Nicol and Macfarlane, 2006; Nicol, 2007) thus allowing students to self-correct during the testing session.

Peer and Online Assessment of Student Writing

Like the first-year module, an authentic learning approach continues in the large second-year module GES225 'Space, Place and Mobility in Southern Africa'. This second-year human geography module builds upon content and skills from GES111 and is tied together by the concept of socio-spatial contestation, the dynamics of trans-local relationships, and the resulting changes in human/environmental relationships. Incorporating concepts such as mobilities, migration, urbanisation, and landscape, the module explores the ways that space and place are shaped and understood in the context of Southern Africa. The principal assessment task of my section of GES225 is a creative essay that uses autoethnography of the students' everyday mobility. Rather than base their assessment solely on the final outcome, the assessment task takes a scaffolded approach (Herrington, Reeves and Oliver, 2010) that begins with a free-form reflection on mobility through student reflective journals in the first two tutorials and ends with a peer review and assessment of the final draft of the full autoethnographic essay before submission. The assessment is built up gradually over a series of learning activities, some which are formally assessed, and others which are not. In this way the formative assessment task of the essay is scaffolded in stages. In shaping the assessment task this way, students are provided with multiple opportunities for feedback from myself and their peers. The result of the assessment process is not simply a mark, but more critically that students build skills in writing, reflection, referencing and appropriate theory throughout the four-week process.

When it comes to my own assessment of student submissions, I use the online submission and plagiarism detection platform Turnitin®. By allowing students several opportunities to upload drafts of their autoethnographic essays, they have the chance to review and correct any evidence of plagiarism that may be found in their work. If I were to have used a traditional paper-based submission, I would not have been able to provide intermediate feedback, nor would students have an opportunity to improve their work. In their draft submissions, therefore, it is Turnitin that provides feedback automatically. Then, with their final submission, I use a marking form that I designed with Turnitin's Feedback Studio that addresses Nicol and Macfarlane-Dick's (2006) first characteristic of good feedback practice in that the marking form helps clarify goals, criteria, and expected standards as aligned with the assessment brief provided to students at the start of the course. Marking against these pre-established standards enables more accurate assessment across the large cohort of students. The customisable 'grademarks' – detailed feedback notations that are placed into the student's electronic text – in *Feedback Studio* also allow me to provide high quality feedback quickly for each submission in the class of several hundred. Rather than a series of red ticks and hand-scrolled comments in the margin, the online feedback platform allows me to help improve student writing and to contribute to formative assessment in every sense of the word.

The tendency in large classroom environments is to limit assessment tasks to those that may be easily marked. In the more advanced pedagogical and theoretical setting of the second-year module, the proposed learning outcomes required that students be assessed on their writing skills. Through the use of an online assessment tool, I was thus able to provide quality feedback in a timely manner for more than 200 students. With the combination of a traditional assessment task and a powerful e-learning platform, I was able to effectively address formative assessment goals of the scaffolded task. Results from this formative assessment not only satisfy the learning goals of the module, they also give students a deeper engagement with learning beyond simply achieving a mark. As one GES225 commented in their evaluation of the module:

> *I valued the in-depth approach we took to analyse mobility. With the help of the readings, I discovered that mobility is more than just the movement from A to B, it involves the complexities of why you're moving the way you're moving and what is the force behind that movement. Mobility is a complex process and this section brought new light to mobility for me.* (Anonymous GES225 student, 2017 Course Evaluation)

CONCLUSION

Assessment of student learning in large classes provides a variety of challenges at the same time that it opens opportunities for new teaching and learning practices. Using a case study of my teaching at UWC in two human geography courses, I have attempted to demonstrate that through careful consideration and setting of learning goals, adoption of student-centred and authentic learning approaches, and articulation of knowledge both online and in class-based learning activities, feelings of anonymity and isolation that often characterise the large class experience for students can be addressed.

These serve as precursors to both diagnostic and formative assessment activities in large class environments in that students may become more engaged in assessment as something more than simply getting results in the form of a mark. Through an acknowledgement of student inputs to the learning process and articulation of that knowledge, students feel more invested in both the content and the outcomes of their learning. While I embrace mobile and e-learning technologies in my teaching and learning practices, I recognise that in spite of the asynchronous learning opportunities provided via e-learning platforms, face-to-face contact and articulation of knowledge remains a critical element in the development of student learning and in preparation for assessment tasks.

USEFUL RESOURCES

- Higher Education Learning & Teaching Association of Southern Africa (HELTASA): http://heltasa.org.za/
- *Journal of Authentic Learning*: https://dspace.sunyconnect.suny.edu/handle/1951/384
- Sakai Community: https://www.sakailms.org/sakai-lms-community

NOTES

1. I use the term diagnostic assessment with reference to assessment that is focused on evaluating current knowledge of concepts and ideas that relate to course content. This form of assessment is useful to determine what knowledge students bring to the classroom.
2. Formative assessment is designed to provide constructive feedback for improvement of student learning within a course or module. This differs from summative assessment that is applied at the conclusion of a course or module, usually in the form of a final exam.

REFERENCES

Albertyn, R., Machika, P. and Troskie-de Bruin, C. (2016), 'Towards responsible massification: Some pointers for supporting lecturers', *Africa Education Review*, 13(3–4), pp. 49–64.

Arvanitakis, J. (2014), 'Massification and the large lecture theatre: From panic to excitement', *Higher Education*, 67(6), pp. 735–745.

Biggs, J. (1999), 'What the student does: Teaching for enhanced learning', *Higher Education Research and Development*, 18(1), pp. 57–75.

Bozalek, V., Gachago, D., Alexander, L., Watters, K., Wood, D., Ivala, E. and Herrington, J. (2013), 'The use of emerging technologies for authentic learning: A South African study in higher education', *British Journal of Educational Technology*, 44(4), pp. 629–638.

Ehrenberg, R.G., Brewer, D.J., Gamoran, A. and Willms, J.D. (2001), 'Class size and student achievement', *Psychological Science in the Public Interest*, 2(1), pp. 1–30.

Exeter, D., Ameratunga, S., Ratima, M., Morton, S., Dickson, M., Hsu, D. and Jackson, R. (2010), 'Student engagement in very large classes: The teachers' perspective', *Studies in Higher Education*, 35(7), pp. 761–775.

Foley, A. and Masingila, J. (2014) 'Building capacity: Challenges and opportunities in large class pedagogy (LCP) in Sub-Saharan Africa', *Higher Education*, 67(6), pp. 797–808.

García Peñalvo, F.J. (2017), 'Are universities aware of the changes that are occurring in higher education?', *Education in the Knowledge Society*, 17(4), pp. 7–13.

Herrington, J. and Oliver, R. (2000), 'An instructional design framework for authentic learning environments', *Educational Technology Research and Development*, 48(3), pp. 23–48.

Herrington, J., Reeves, T.C. and Oliver, R. (2010), *A Guide to Authentic e-Learning*. London: Routledge.

Hornsby, D.J. and Osman, R. (2014), 'Massification in higher education: Large classes and student learning', *Higher Education*, 67(6), pp. 711–719.

Hornsby D.J., Osman, R. and De Matos-Ala, J. (2013a), 'Teaching large classes', in Hornsby, D.J., Osman, R. and De Matos-Ala, J. (eds), *Large-Class Pedagogy*. Stellenbosch: SUN Press, pp. 7–20.

Hornsby, D.J., Osman, R. and De Matos-Ala, J. (2013b), 'Large classes, student learning and quality education', in Hornsby, D.J., Osman, R. and De Matos-Ala, J. (eds), *Large-Class Pedagogy*. Stellenbosch: SUN Press, pp. 173–178.

Lea, S., Stephenson, D. and Troy, J. (2003), 'Higher education students' attitudes to student-centred learning: Beyond educational bulimia?', *Studies in Higher Education*, 28(3), pp. 321–334.

Mohamedbhai, G. (2014), 'Massification in higher education institutions in Africa: Causes, consequences and responses', *International Journal of African Higher Education*, 1(1), pp. 59–83.

Mulryan-Kyne, C. (2010), 'Teaching large classes at college and university level: Challenges and opportunities', *Teaching in Higher Education*, 15(2), pp. 175–185.

Nicol, D. (2007), 'E-assessment by design: Using multiple-choice tests to good effect', *Journal of Further and Higher Education*, 31(1), pp. 53–64.

Nicol, D.J. and Macfarlane-Dick, D. (2006), 'Formative assessment and self-regulated learning: A model and seven principles of good feedback practice', *Studies in Higher Education*, 31(2), pp. 198–218.

Rød, J.K., Eiksund, S. and Fjær, O. (2010), 'Assessment based on exercise work and multiple-choice tests', *Journal of Geography in Higher Education*, 34(1), pp. 141–153.

Rule, A. (2006) 'The components of authentic learning', *Journal of Authentic Learning*, 3(1), pp. 1–10.

Snowball, J.D. (2014), 'Using interactive content and online activities to accommodate diversity in large first year class', *Higher Education*, 67(6), pp. 823–838.

Worth, N. (2014), 'Student-focused assessment criteria: Thinking through best practice', *Journal of Geography in Higher Education*, 38(3), pp. 361–372.

6. Finding your way in liminal space: threshold concepts and curriculum design in geography
Erin H. Fouberg

INTRODUCTION

> *Not only do I find myself look[ing] at the world with a new understanding but I am constantly connecting new pieces of the puzzle while adding new[ly] discovered pieces. I find myself doing research above and beyond the need for school just so I can understand more and answer the questions that I write in my notebook margin during class. I know that my thinking has deepened as I reflect more often about the world and geography.* (Student reflective essay, fall 2017)

The reflection of a first-year student in a 'world regional geography' class during their first semester of college describes almost perfectly how concept-learning (Jo and Bednarz, 2011) and learning cycles (Hay, 2007; Hay, Wells and Kinchin, 2008) can combine to deepen student learning. Students structure prior knowledge in their schemata, which are 'systems of organization or scaffolds of information learners carry in their minds' (Fouberg, 2013, p. 66). Scaffolds come together like pieces in a puzzle, and with active and recursive building of scaffolds, students can assess how to connect new knowledge, concepts, and thoughts – new pieces of the puzzle. Learning, applying, personalizing, and integrating concepts help students refine their scaffolds and prepare for deeper learning.

In the transition to university, general education courses in the United States including 'world regional geography', seek to put students in the driver's seat of their education, and ideally are designed to help students make connections between concepts and across disciplines. This chapter contends that designing a curriculum which integrates threshold concepts and incorporates writing for learning assignments and formative assessment gives students the opportunities and space needed to self-author their education (see also Chapter 23 in this volume by Moore-Cherry). The path to self-authorship is ambiguous and sinuous because learning to think critically is not a clearly designed, step-wise progression.

Through qualitative analysis of student assignments and surveys in a 'world regional geography' course, this chapter establishes that students can actively break down, build, and refine their schemata when the curriculum integrates: 1) threshold concepts; 2) a learning space that encourages uncertainty and liminality; and, 3) formative feedback and assessment.

Jan Meyer and Ray Land (2003), the architects of the threshold concept movement in education, contend that each discipline has threshold concepts that, once learned, enable students to see the world differently and to think like practitioners in a discipline. 'A threshold concept can be considered as akin to a portal, opening up a new and previously inaccessible way of thinking about something' (Meyer and Land, 2003, p. 1). Threshold concepts are not simply core concepts in a discipline; a core concept, according to Meyer and Land (2003), is a building block that 'progresses understanding of the subject' (p. 1), but the distinction between core concepts and threshold concepts is that when a student understands a core concept 'it does not necessarily lead to a qualitatively different view of the subject matter' (ibid.). Conversely, threshold concepts shift a student's way of seeing the world, and may transform a student's 'internal view of subject matter, subject landscape, or even world view' (ibid.).

Learning to think in a discipline requires not a clearly defined path, but a learning space where students can actively engage with, apply, and make connections among threshold concepts and core concepts (Renshaw and Wood, 2011). Hill et al. (2016) define learning spaces as 'places of engagement' (p. 376) where students make connections among ideas and shift their perceptions and understanding. When learning spaces encourage self-authorship and disruptive creativity, they are defined by Hill et al. (2016) as 'borderlands'. A partnership between teacher and learner forms in a borderland, and the 'division between teaching and learning becomes blurred' (p. 379). Not all learning spaces are borderlands – *how* the learning space is used determines *whether* the learning space becomes a borderland (Hill et al., 2016). Recognizing the value of distinguishing between learning spaces and borderlands, this chapter contends that it is the feedback and assessment which instructors give, and the willingness of students to enter (and stay) in liminal space that determine whether learning is deep or rote (see also Chapter 27 in this volume by Hill and Worth). Recognizing the implicit value of liminal space, this chapter draws from the well-established literature in writing for learning and formative assessment to make a case for how curricula can be designed to inspire students to enter liminal space, become comfortable with uncertainty, and actively engage in their own learning.

Disruptive creativity and student self-authorship require students to become comfortable with uncertainty (Land et al., 2014), with what Meyer and Land (2006) call 'liminal space', a state of knowing and unknowing, of mimicry and uncertainty. Liminal space requires practice that is free from judgement, but receives consistent and authentic feedback. Instructors should not rush students through liminal space, a state of uncertainty – of knowing and unknowing. Rather, liminal space should be seen as a sign the learner is in a borderland, using a learning space for deep learning.

Education researchers from Blumenfeld (1992) to Hay (2007) recognize assignments must be authentic, and research in formative assessment (Wiggins and McTighe, 1998) can be tapped to help educators give authentic feedback. Writing for learning assignments (Fulwiler, 1987; Fouberg, 2000), such as the thinking assignments in the 'world regional geography' course studied for this project, are inherently formative and should be assessed formatively (Wiggins, 2011). Coupling writing for learning assignments with formative assessment puts students into a liminal space, and in charge of their own learning; it centres students in the middle of the learning cycle and asks them to take the reins. Integrating thinking assignments that use formative assessment encourages students into liminal space where they can express prior knowledge, engage with course concepts in meaningful ways, and forge a partnership in learning between learner and teacher.

Transformative learning, deep learning, comes in the struggle. It comes in knowing a question does not have a single right answer and in being okay with that. The present research contends the goal of educators should not be to push undergraduate students through liminality to being an expert in a discipline. Rather, the goals of those of us educating undergraduates should be to help students to apply and personalize concepts, to think deeply and recursively, and to be comfortable in liminal space. To accomplish these goals, educators must write meaningful assignments that integrate threshold concepts, give constant and consistent feedback through formative assessment, and model how to think in our disciplines through class lectures and discussions. If an educator wants to encourage students into liminal space, give them meaningful assignments, and understand students' prior knowledge, formative assessment is critical. Through formative assessment, educators encourage students to be okay with being unsure.

THRESHOLD CONCEPTS

The concept-learning literature broadly accepts that students best learn concepts by personalizing them, and by applying concepts in authentic assignments. A discipline can have hundreds of concepts. Determining which concepts are transformative within a discipline, and which concepts fundamentally shift the way students see the world, is the focus of the threshold concept literature. The premise is that each discipline has its own set of threshold concepts that, once learned, help students think as practitioners in the discipline. Meyer and Land (2003) describe threshold concepts as 'akin to a portal, opening up a new and previously inaccessible way of thinking about something' (p. 1). While Meyer and Land did not specify threshold concepts for every discipline, several geographers have worked to establish threshold concepts within geography (for example Slinger, 2011; Fouberg, 2013).

In enumerating threshold concepts, researchers examine five characteristics outlined by Meyer and Land (2003): transformative, irreversible, integrative, bounded, and counter-intuitive. Threshold concepts are *transformative* in that once they are learned, they shift perceptions. For example, in geography, students who understand core and peripheral processes will continue to see that wealth is generated not by *what* goods are made, but by *how* goods are made (Fouberg, 2013). Threshold concepts are *irreversible*, in that once a student can see the world in terms of a threshold concept, they cannot unsee it. In geography, for example, once a student learns to read cultural landscapes, it is a practice they conduct frequently, if not daily. Threshold concepts are *integrative*, in that one concept helps deepen a student's understanding of another concept. A student who understands commodity chains can use that knowledge to gain deeper understanding of unequal exchange. Fourth, threshold concepts are *bounded*, in that a given concept should be at the crux of a given discipline. Place is perhaps the most bounded concept in geography, though the idea of the uniqueness of a location is borrowed by architects and landscape architects. Finally, threshold concepts are generally *troublesome* and often counter-intuitive, and in that vein, they should challenge a student's assumptions. The concepts of authenticity and commodification of local culture in the study of tourism is often jarring for students because it fundamentally shifts their assumptions about tourism as an innocuous form of economic activity.

LEARNING CYCLE AND LEARNING SPACE

Piaget's cognitive development theory (1936) inspired educators to see children as moving through stages of development where they learn concepts in age-appropriate and increasingly complex ways. Education researchers drew from Piaget to create learning cycle theories. Using the learning cycle, instructors design activities to build student understanding of abstract concepts in a step-wise approach (Szabo et al., 1985). The focus has been on teaching students to apply concepts in ways similar to professionals in a discipline. Ideally, instructors craft authentic assignments that ask students to apply concepts and problem solve 'in a manner similar to the way in which individuals in the field under study generate and use knowledge' (Blumenfeld, 1992, p. 277).

Piaget's cognitive development theory continues to influence education theorists, including Novak (1998) and Jarvis (1992), who have fleshed out specific traits of the learning cycle. Learning cycle theories examine learner's prior knowledge, student engagement with abstract concepts, application and personalization of concepts, deep versus rote learning, and change in student thinking. Novak's (1998) learning cycle theory contends that meaningful learning has three traits. First, the learner's prior knowledge is relevant to new learning. Second, what is to be learned needs to be presented in meaningful ways. Finally, 'the learner must choose to learn meaningfully' (Hay, 2007, p. 41). In Novak's learning cycle, the learner chooses whether to engage with meaningful learning or rote learning. The teacher also plays a central role in requiring meaningful learning by assigning meaningful material and assessing students' relevant prior knowledge (Novak, 1998).

In Jarvis's (1992) learning cycle theory, learning is rooted in a student's experiences in and out of the classroom. To learn, students must reflect, evaluate, and experiment with concepts (Hay, 2007). In Jarvis's learning cycle theory, the learner is at the centre, learning is not necessarily sequential, and the learner must choose to learn. Learning happens when personal change occurs, which generally happens when learning is reflective. Jarvis's learning cycle theory recognizes non-learning is a possibility (Hay, 2007); because the student must choose to learn, even the best-designed curriculum can result in non-learning.

Simply constructing a curriculum that integrates threshold concepts is not enough to ensure student learning. Both Novak and Jarvis recognize that non-learning is an option and that students must choose to learn – must choose to self-author their education. Self-authorship occurs when students recognize what they know, reflect on and critically analyze their understanding, ask their own questions, integrate concepts and make connections across disciplines, and see the world from multiple perspectives (Hill et al., 2016). It is the role of the instructor to design curricula and feedback which encourage students to choose to learn, to drive the learning cycle, and to take steps toward self-authorship. Instructors cannot control whether students learn, as students must choose to learn. However, instructors can control how thoughtfully they construct learning spaces, feedback, and assessment in their curricula.

LIMINAL SPACE AND FORMATIVE ASSESSMENT IN WORLD REGIONAL GEOGRAPHY

To cross the threshold into thinking in geography, a student will need to unpack their way of seeing the world and build up a new way of seeing around threshold concepts. Crossing the threshold requires students to spend time in liminal space (Meyer and Land, 2006). Meyer and Land (2003) first identified liminal space as a space of knowing and unknowing where a student is in a suspended 'state in which understanding approximates to a kind of mimicry or lack of authenticity' (p. 10). Their 2003 study did little beyond identifying liminality. Cousin (2006) used the idea of mimicry to again identify the state of liminality as when 'learning is the product of ritualized performances rather than integrated understandings' (p. 5). Cousin sees mimicry as akin to rote learning because the student only superficially grasps concepts, but does not understand concepts deeply. In liminal space, the learner oscillates between knowing, and not knowing; understanding, and not understanding.

Cousin (2006) astutely asks: 'How can teachers design a curriculum which invites students to enter liminal space?' (p. 5), and offers four insights for curriculum design 'associated with threshold concept mastery' (p. 5). First, threshold concepts can be used 'as jewels in the curriculum' or teachable moments where the class must pause and students must master the concept before teaching continues. Second, Cousin (2006) asks educators to listen to students to 'hear what the student's misunderstandings and uncertainties are in order to sympathetically engage with them' (p. 5). Third, Cousin suggests teachers must 'demonstrate they can tolerate learner confusion and can "hold" their students through liminal states'. The teacher can tell students early on that a concept is difficult and can devise activities that uncover student confusion. Fourth, Cousin suggests that to help students through liminal spaces, curricula must be designed to be recursive: 'In short, there is no simple passage of learning from "easy" to "difficult"; mastery of a threshold concept often involves messy journeys back, forth and across the relevant literature' (2006, p. 5).

'World regional geography' is a course taught in many American universities at first-year level, typically with high enrolments because the course meets general education requirements. K-12 geography education in the United States is limited and is often focused on 'facts' to be memorized. The knowledge is disembodied and the student is not asked to struggle through the knowledge, but just to know it. Transformation comes in the struggle. Integrating concepts, transforming thinking, and understanding troublesome threshold concepts require that students 1) know there is no one right answer and 2) are okay with that. To teach students to think geographically and critically in higher education in the United States, instructors should integrate threshold concepts into curriculum, create assignments with formative assessment, and encourage students into liminal space where they can ask questions, reflect, and think deeply about threshold concepts.

METHODS

The fundamental questions in the present research are: 1) How can curricula be designed to integrate threshold concepts into the learning cycle? 2) What does it mean to think geographically?; and 3) What is the value for students of being in liminal space? To answer these questions, this study analyzes student reflective essays in an introductory college course in 'world regional geography' taught at a small, public, regional university in the Midwest United States.

The course curriculum, including the textbook *Understanding World Regional Geography* (Fouberg and Moseley, 2015), is organized around threshold concepts in geography. Students are assigned a series of 13 thinking assignments over the course of the semester. Each assignment requires students to apply one or more threshold concepts to case studies, including: cultural landscape on campus; agriculture in Uzbekistan;

identity in Russia; migration in Mexico; unequal exchange in the world-economy; commodity chains in the production of t-shirts; place, language, and colonization in Kenya; tourism and authenticity in Bali; and, formal economy and informal economy in Papua New Guinea. The thirteenth thinking assignment is a reflective essay, analyzed later in this chapter. The reflective essay is a metacognition assignment which requires students to analyze their own learning over the course of the semester. Students are told in the syllabus and in class that the purpose of all 13 of the thinking assignments is for them to learn to think, and to think geographically by applying geographic concepts. Students are also told the thinking assignments will be graded based on: completion; whether they did their own thinking; whether they pushed themselves to think; and, whether they applied geographic concepts and class readings.

Students in 'world regional geography' voluntarily completed a mid-semester and end-of-semester survey designed for the present research in fall 2017. Forty-four students (out of 64 students who completed the course) took the mid-semester survey, and 22 students completed both the mid-semester and end-of-semester surveys. Survey data for the 44 respondents along with the full text of their reflective essays were entered into Nvivo for content analysis. Reflective essays of the 22 students who completed both the mid-semester and end-of-semester surveys were coded for geographic concepts, threshold concept traits, and personalization of concepts. The reflective essays of the 44 students who completed either survey were analyzed qualitatively and word trees for frequently occurring words referring to liminal space were generated using Nvivo.

THINKING GEOGRAPHICALLY IN LIMINAL SPACE

Discussion of liminality in the threshold concept literature focuses on moving forward and backward through liminal space, mimicking practitioners to find one's way into liminal space, and crossing through the threshold of liminal space to thinking as a practitioner in a discipline (Meyer and Land, 2006). Rather than considering liminal space as something to get through, the present research suggests liminal space is something to be embraced. Teaching students to be okay with being unsure and to having a space where they can experiment with concepts and receive formative assessment is valuable to teaching and learning in geography.

Change from beginning to the end of the semester was a common theme in students' reflective essays, and often students credited the whole course, or the sum of the thinking assignments, with being transformative, rather than one threshold concept. For example, one student commented: '*This class is going to leave an imprint on me and I will forever have a little geographical way of thinking in me.*' Students also saw specific assignments as probably irreversible. One student, referring to the thinking assignment on commodity chains for t-shirts, explained, '*I had honestly never thought of where or how my clothes were made and now at least once a week when I put my clothes on I think of the girl from Bangladesh.*'

Threshold concepts are valuable, but simply integrating threshold concepts into the course curriculum is not likely enough to get students into liminal space or across a threshold to thinking as a practitioner. Instead of focusing on getting across a threshold, introductory geography courses should focus on getting students into liminal space and helping them become comfortable with being unsure. To transform thinking, and to get students to think geographically, faculty have to offer a space in the curriculum where students can be unsure about concepts, play with applying and connecting threshold concepts across multiple case studies, and personalize geographic concepts through their own curiosity and discovery.

When students become comfortable in liminal space, they become the driving force in the learning cycle. Students take responsibility for their own learning, ask their own questions, and seek their own answers. Students also recognize the limitations of their pre-existing knowledge:

> *I think a turning point for my thinking was during the assignment 'Inside Putin's Russia'. I didn't know anything about Russia before this course. I knew the name 'Putin' but no information on the government or culture. I had never thought about the term 'Identity'. While watching the video I can remember in my mind just thinking 'what in the world . . . how did I not know all of this already?' Russia's use of propaganda and Identity was foreign to me. I remember having the same feeling while we watched the video on North Korea. When I thought of Korea I always put it into a group with China and Japan. The difference between the North and the South was completely unknown to me.*

Creating a learning space where students freely describe and assess their pre-existing knowledge and how they grappled with it over the semester helps forge an instructor–student partnership and enables instructors to meet the next semester's students where they are by recognizing holes in college preparation in their region of the country.

Integrating threshold concepts into learning space is the first step in teaching students to think in a discipline. The next step is to persuade students, through well-constructed writing for learning assignments and formative assessment, that they can enter the uncertainty of liminal space and think for themselves. It is the work students do with threshold concepts which transforms their thinking, not simply the concepts themselves:

> *So, these thinking assignments have been kind of fun. I mean yeah, horribly depressing, but I feel like I have learned a lot. I would go as far as I would say that these thinking assignments have radically changed the way that I look at the world around me . . . I think the biggest effect that my one semester of college has had on me is this: I have started to learn how to process information and use it to come up with my own opinion.*

Students are invigorated when they are asked to drive the learning cycle for themselves. The instructor can encourage students into liminal space – a place where they can think for themselves – by using formative assessment. At the end of the semester survey, students nearly universally strongly agreed (mean 4.85 on a scale of 1 to 5) that they read the written feedback on the thinking assignments from the professor. Students also strongly agreed (mean 4.52) that the written feedback on their thinking assignments 'made them want to try harder'. Feedback on early assignments frequently asks students to focus less on being right or wrong and to play around with the concepts and see where it takes them. Formative assessment looks for patterns of student thinking on the first thinking assignment, where students are asked to pick something in the cultural landscape of campus and explain what its significance is, and why it is where it is. An example of formative assessment on the cultural landscape thinking assignment is this feedback given to a student:

> *What sources did you use for this? I'm glad you picked Cecil [a statue on the campus green] – did you go talk with people or ask questions? Did you go to the library? I'm glad you are thinking – push*

yourself to ask questions and seek answers. Why is the statue there – specifically where it is and how it fits into the larger picture of campus? I think you're too worried about being right and not enough about letting yourself think and wonder and be curious. Remember, the point of these assignments is your thinking and improving your thinking. Need to push yourself out of your comfort zone of thinking – ask questions, talk to people, seek answers.

The student received 5 out of 6 points for the assignment. To encourage students to think more in future assignments, rarely are full points awarded on the first thinking assignment. My feedback urges students to use the thinking assignments as a space to think for themselves. In her reflective essay, the student who received this feedback explained how difficult it was for her to simply think and not try to be perfect:

I remember the first think assignment, NSU Cultural Landscape. This assignment probably took me the longest to complete, and looking back now it was honestly one of the simplest. I remember my exact thought process of that assignment because now my thought process is totally different. I looked at the syllabus and thought I need to show Fouberg that I am the best student she has. I wanted it to be perfect. The perfect format, perfect sentence structure, perfect everything and in return I got my worst grade on that assignment. Why? I was too focused on being perfect that I forgot to actually think about what I was doing and the point of the assignment. During that assignment, I was so stressed to show how good I was and wanted to give you what you wanted . . . growing up in school this is what you learn. You learn to produce thoughtless papers and assignments or I guess I shouldn't say that. More appropriately I could say papers that were filled with thoughts and processes that pleased others. This process does not push anyone rather put a drag on writing. I do agree papers need to be formatted correctly and all that good stuff but what is better a perfect paper or a thoughtful paper? After I got my first feedback on my so thought perfect assignment I was beyond stressed out. All I wanted to do was please you and get a good grade. So, when it came time to the next assignment, Uzbekistan Agriculture I knew I had to change it up and think more freely. This was harder than you would think . . . I had to keep telling myself not to worry as much about how things were coming out and just type exactly what I was thinking. You can still see in that assignment my use of clear structure with transitions and thesis statements. These things aren't bad but they hinder the free feeling you get when you write everything that comes to your mind.

The student implicitly recognized the difference between formal writing and writing for learning and between summative assessment and formative assessment. She recognized that formal writing and summative assessment are not bad, but they 'hinder the free feeling' of writing for learning.

Students in liminal space have their 'wheels spinning' and are more likely to ask their own questions, make connections to other case studies, apply and connect geographic concepts, and think in an introspective and reflective way. One student explained in his reflective essay:

Throughout the semester, the journal [thinking] assignments we did greatly developed my ability of thinking geographically. Each assignment had me thinking deeply and trying to establish connections between other events in history. Perhaps my favorite journal entry was 'Decolonizing the Mind'. It was very striking to me how the author explained the cultural changes that were imposed by their colonizers, and how these changes effected the people fundamentally. Cultural domination is a truly ugly thing, and seeing how adversely it affected the people really got my wheels spinning. Immediately I began thinking of other examples of these cultural change practices. The first example that came to mind was when the United States expanded west, and in turn tried to quell and pacify the Native Americans they encountered. Prior instruction had implied to me that colonization was more of a physical presence, but through this particular journal assignment I learned that often it was physical, cultural and emotional. This entry got me more interested in the human element of geography, and has made me more curious. *My whole life I always wondered 'why' about anything and everything, and these journal entries satisfied those questions. By understanding the consequences of colonization on Africa and other regions,* I started making the connection of the problems those areas face today. *Now when I think or hear of a country in turmoil or crisis, I automatically rewind to their past, were they colonized? By who? What happened after decolonization? By using these patterns, I can apply them to other regions to see if they had a similar effect.* (emphases added)

The student who wrote this reflection made a connection between British language policies in Kenya, which are highlighted in the segment of 'Decolonizing the Mind' he read, to American policies aimed to 'quell and pacify' American Indians.

CONCEPT LEARNING

Twenty-two students completed the end-of-semester survey where they could assess their learning over the entire semester. The reflective essays of these 22 students were coded for application of geographic concepts to uncover frequency of concept use and to look for agreement with concept use by students five years earlier (Fouberg, 2013). In the present research, students mentioned 22 different geographic concepts in their reflective essays. In 2013, when analyzing 80 reflective essays, 28 different geographic concepts appeared in reflective essays. In 2013, commodity chain, core–periphery, agriculture, cultural landscape, and development paired most frequently with threshold concept traits of: transformative, irreversible, integrative, and counter-intuitive (troublesome). In the present data, cultural landscape, tourism, colonization, language, identity, and religion were the most frequently cited geographic concepts that paired with threshold concept traits of: integrative, transformative, and counter-intuitive (troublesome) (see Table 6.1). The consistency in cultural landscape between 2013 and now is interesting because it pairs so highly with 'thinking geographically' in the present data. This consistency confirms cultural landscape as a threshold concept in geography. The differences between other concepts stressed by students in 2013 and today may be a factor of what concepts the instructor stressed most in class lectures and in thinking assignments, as some assignments changed.

Reflective essays of the 22 students who completed the end-of-semester survey were coded not only for appearance of geographic concepts but also for evidence of threshold concept traits, specifically integrative, transformative, and counter-intuitive (troublesome). Additionally, essays were coded for student self-assessment of 'thinking geographically' and 'thinking expanded'. The threshold concept trait which students expressed most frequently was transformative (38 segments), followed by integrative (25 segments), and troublesome (14 segments). 'Thinking expanded' described more segments (53 segments) than 'thinking geographically' (18 segments). Using cross-tabs in Nvivo, segments coded for threshold concept traits or expanded thinking or thinking geographically were paired with the 22 geographic concepts which students discussed in their reflective essays. Of the 47 segments that demonstrated a threshold concept trait of transformative or integrative and overlapped with a geographic concept, the most frequent segment pairs were colonization being integrative, identity being integrative, cultural landscape being

Table 6.1   Coding results of 22 reflective essays showing when geographic concepts overlapped with traits of threshold concepts (integrative, transformative), deep thinking (thinking expanded, or thinking geographically)

	integrative	transformative	thinking expanded	thinking geographically	total pairs
tourism	2	4	7	1	14
colonization	4	2	3	1	10
cultural landscape	2	5	0	3	10
language	2	3	2	2	9
identity	3	1	1	1	6
region	0	2	2	2	6
religion	1	2	2	1	6
scale	0	2	1	2	5
development	1	1	2	0	4
migration	1	0	3	0	4
authenticity	1	1	1	0	3
environment	2	0	1	0	3
globalization	1	1	0	1	3
core and periphery	0	0	2	0	2
culture	1	1	0	0	2
unequal exchange	1	0	1	0	2
commodity chain	0	0	0	0	0
ethnicity	0	0	0	0	0
global economy	0	0	0	0	0
network	0	0	0	0	0
place	0	0	0	0	0
spatial interaction	0	0	0	0	0
frequency	22	25	28	14	

transformative, language being transformative, and tourism being transformative. Pairing 'thinking expanded' and 'thinking geographically' with geographic concepts finds the most frequent segment pairs with tourism 'expanding thinking', colonization 'expanding thinking', and cultural landscape 'thinking geographically'.

WORD TREES

Word trees allow researchers to take the words students use and analyze them in context to see what words or phrases come immediately before or after a word or concept. Using interaction techniques, software including Nvivo can generate word trees that reveal common contextual patterns associated with a word or phrase, as well as the tree structure embedded in the context, so the viewer can see the branches of thought around a word or phrase (Wattenberg and Viégas, 2008). Word frequency is useful, but adding context through word trees provides 'more nuances' and 'reveals themes' (Wattenberg and Viégas, 2008, p. 1221).

To discern whether students found themselves in liminal space and became comfortable

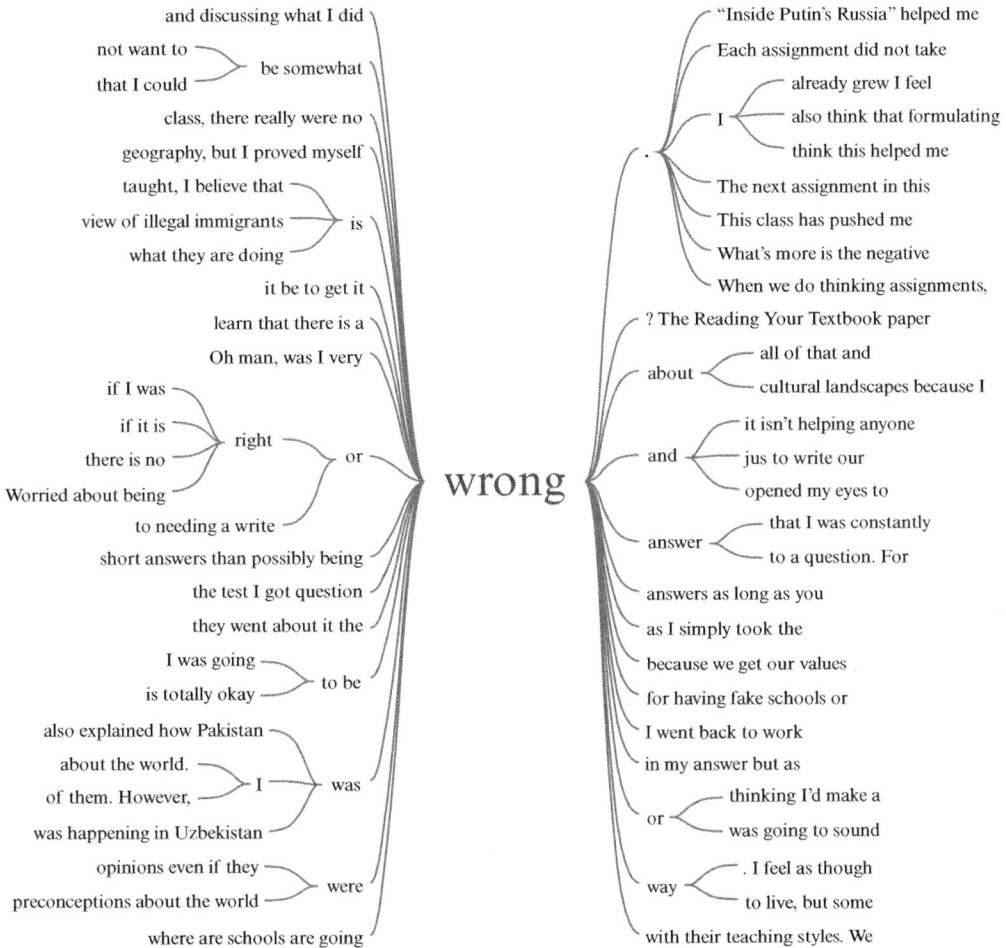

Figure 6.1   Word tree for 'wrong' generated by Nvivo based on reflective essays written by 44 students in a world regional geography course in fall 2017

with uncertainty through the thinking assignments, Nvivo software was used to generate word trees for words from 44 reflective essays submitted by students who completed either the mid-semester or end-of-semester survey. The most frequent words were combed through to find those associated with liminality and uncertainty. The word tree for 'wrong' (see Figure 6.1) reveals connections such as 'it is totally okay to be wrong' and 'if I was right or wrong'. Analyzing the context created by the word tree for 'wrong' reveals students were grappling with whether an answer or thought was right or wrong, as the words frequently appearing before or after 'wrong' included 'I' and 'me'.

Coupling the writing for learning thinking assignments with formative assessment helped students discover the liberating feeling of being okay with being wrong. When students became comfortable with uncertainty, the thinking assignments transformed from a learning space to a borderland (Hill et al., 2016). In their reflective essays, students recognized their own inhibitions to thinking, began to see themselves as integral to and driving the learning cycle, and recognized their own growth over the semester. As one learner explained in her reflective essay, she became more comfortable with the idea of being wrong over the course of the semester, and more confident in her ability to think through the assignments and make connections:

> *The first thinking assignments we were assigned I was clueless how to write them and answer the questions. I was so used to needing a right or wrong answer that I was constantly searching my brain for the correct answer instead of just putting my thoughts about the subject on paper. As I read through the first few assignments I noticed myself struggling to put my thoughts into words, but by the fourth and fifth assignments I could tell I had gotten the hang of it as the papers just flowed more smoothly. The first assignments, such as the cultural landscape, I struggled to connect the information we learned in class to everyday life. I was unsure of how to explain exactly what cultural landscape was and how it was seen on campus, but by T-shirt Travels and Taylor reading assignments I was able to connect the information in the videos and articles to class and to everyday life.*

To help forge a student–teacher partnership, instructors can use qualitative assessment, specifically word trees, in their own reflection on student work to see patterns from the context provided. Drawing from reflection and analysis of word trees, instructors can set expectations the next time they teach the course by voicing and assuaging student concerns about being 'wrong' and encouraging students to challenge themselves and be okay outside their comfort zone.

Word trees for terms associated with the learning cycle, deep thinking, and thinking geographically show connections to specific geographic concepts and thinking assignments. A word tree for 'made me think' (Figure 6.2) revealed linkages to thinking assignments on India, Kenya, Bali, Papua New Guinea, Uzbekistan, China in Africa, Mexican migration, Putin in Russia, and the Taylor reading, and to geographic concepts including: commodity chains, globalization, tourism, migration, and identity. When students expressed that a thinking assignment or geographic concept 'made me think', it typically overlapped with personalizing the assignment or geographic concept, as one student described:

> *I never realized how big the commodity chain for a simple shirt is. This whole class in general has taught me things I never knew went on in this world. It's often difficult to realize that just one person has an impact on the global economy; we have to learn to be careful of what we are providing for the economy. I try to connect what I learn from these assignments to something in my own life to help me retain the information.*

Students who were made 'to think' through the thinking assignments took a significant step toward self-authorship and also found opportunity to integrate concepts and ideas. In this segment of her reflective essay, the student recognized the complexity of a commodity chain, realized her personal impact on the global economy, and saw the value in connecting her assignments to her own life.

LIMITATIONS AND FUTURE RESEARCH

Not all courses or coursework lead to learning. As Hay (2007) contends, drawing from Jarvis (1992), education researchers must allow for non-learning as a possible outcome. In

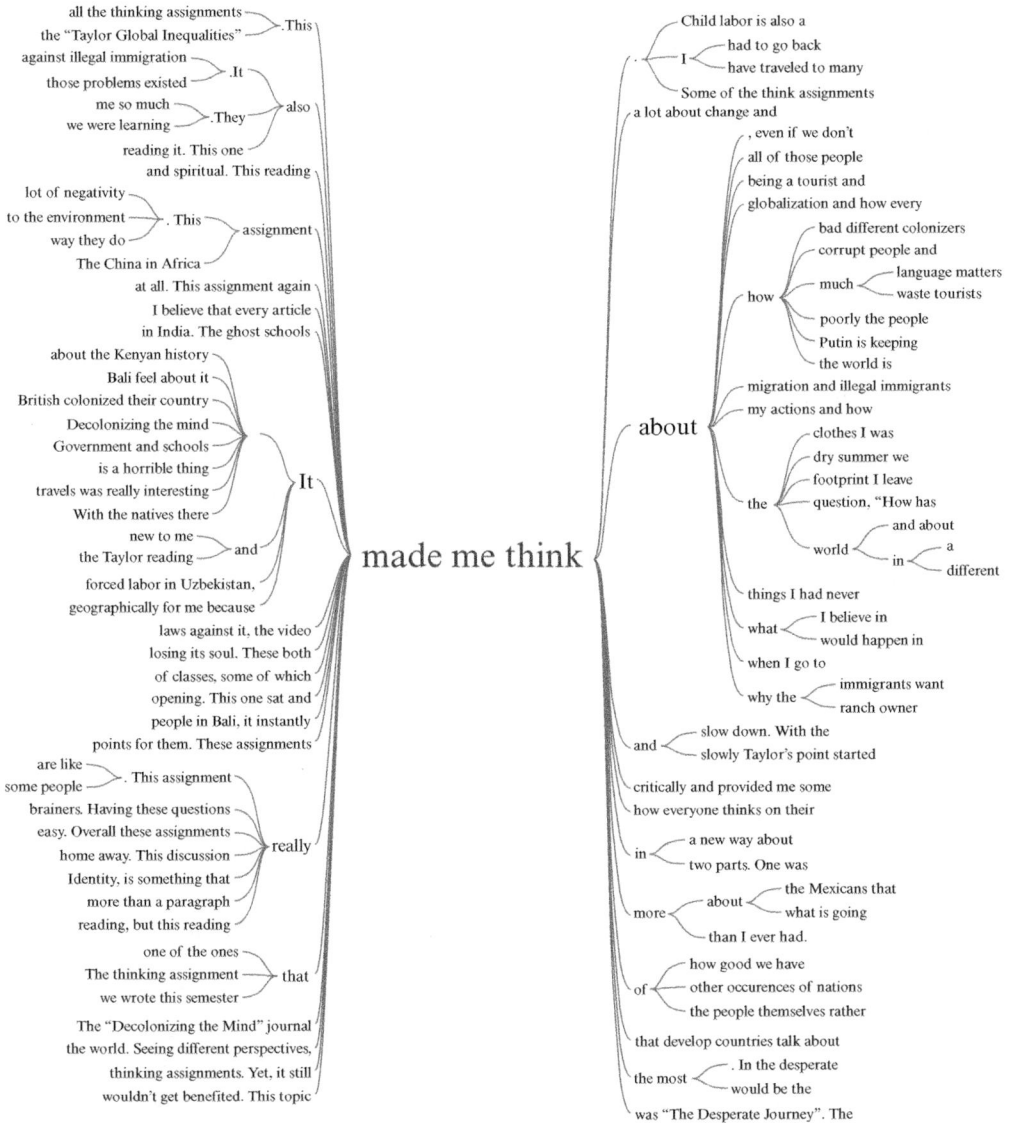

Figure 6.2   Word tree for 'made me think' generated by Nvivo based on reflective essays written by 44 students in a world regional geography course in fall 2017

the present research, it is safe to assume that some of the non-responses to the survey were students who experienced non-learning in the course or through the thinking assignments in the coursework. The response rate for the mid-semester survey was twice the response rate for those who completed both the mid-semester and end-of-semester surveys, which may be a result of survey fatigue. The limitations of the mid-semester data are that not all thinking assignments were complete at that point and several questions were not included.

For future research, an end-of-semester survey, coupled with content analysis of reflective essays, would provide a stronger response rate.

Another path of research for geography education uncovered by the present project is whether there is a hierarchy of threshold concepts, and whether threshold concepts should be taught in a certain order based on student experience and prior knowledge. In the present case (a Midwestern university in a rural state), 77.27 per cent of students who responded to the survey reported the thinking assignment on agriculture in Uzbekistan made them 'think the most'. One survey question asked students to say which thinking assignment had the biggest impact on how they think about an issue or place, and to explain the impact the assignment made, and why. Of the students who listed Uzbekistan agriculture as having the biggest impact, responses referenced a student's agricultural background helping them have an insight into what was wrong with the cotton industry in Uzbekistan: '*I am from an agricultural family so I could relate to what I was reading. It made me really think about what is happening in the world, and why it's happening.*'

Another student noted the Uzbekistan agriculture assignment helped him to see differences and similarities between two seemingly disparate places:

> *I think that completing the thinking assignment on Uzbekistan agriculture has affected my thinking because I come from a farming background. Even if we don't produce cotton, it has really brought insight of how farming around the world can affect the region if the crop being produced isn't usually fit to live in that environment. Also it helped me to realize all the different technology we have back home in order to get crops in, and it's not as labor intensive, yet it is still hard work in both places.*

Another student recognized that reading and thinking about agriculture in Uzbekistan made her '*realize there is more than just the world inside my little bubble, a world outside of myself and what I know in the United States*'. Going beyond one's bubble also helped yet another student appreciate the impact one person or one policy can have, both spatially and temporally:

> *By doing this thinking assignment [on Uzbekistan agriculture] it made me realize how much harm one person can do in the world and how it can affect so many people for such a long time. When I'm looking at a place I now look at the different aspects of the area to see what it is like there and what the issues are in the region instead of just looking at one specific spot.*

Whether the same assignment would create the same reaction among students in an urban school or in a classroom where the instructor does not integrate world-systems theory and core and periphery concepts into the curriculum remains to be seen.

This research focuses primarily on the role of students and meaningful assignments and feedback in the learning cycle, but we have much to discover regarding the role of instructors in terms of integrating lecture, class discussion, prioritization, and recursive approach to teaching threshold concepts, and curriculum design. All of these factors work together to affect student learning. Future research could integrate reflective essays by both instructors and students to unpack the many moving parts in the learning cycle so that best practices can be established.

Teaching and learning threshold concepts does not automatically create students who can think in a discipline. Designing curricula based on learning cycle theory; writing meaningful assignments that require students to personalize and apply threshold concepts; formatively assessing student assignments with a conscious eye to understanding students' prior knowledge; and modeling thinking in the discipline during class lecture and discussion will help students find a comfortable home in liminal space. In liminal space, students can freely be unsure, engage, and play around with applying and connecting concepts, and take control of their own learning. The findings from this research suggests that we should reconsider the purpose of liminal space. Instead of seeing liminal space as something to 'get through', we should embrace liminal space as a sign student and instructor have successfully transformed learning space into a borderland where deep learning and self-authorship can occur.

USEFUL RESOURCES

- Cousin, G. (2006) *An Introduction to Threshold Concepts.* Available at: https://www. ee.ucl.ac.uk/~mflanaga/Cousin%20Planet%2017.pdf.
- Flanagan, M. (no date) *Threshold Concepts: Undergraduate Teaching, Postgraduate Training, Professional Development and Social Education. A Short Introduction and a Bibliography.* Available at: https://www.ee.ucl.ac.uk/~mflanaga/thresholds.html.
- Reis, R. (no date) Stanford University Teaching Commons. *Before and After Students 'Get It': Threshold Concepts.* Available at: https://teachingcommons.stanford.edu/ teaching-talk/and-after-students-get-it-threshold-concepts.
- Wiggins, G. (no date) *Formative vs Summative Assessment – and Unthinking Policy About Them.* Available at: https://grantwiggins.wordpress.com/2011/08/25/for mative-vs-summative-assessment-and-unthinking-policy-about-them/.

REFERENCES

Blumenfeld, P.C. (1992) 'Classroom learning and motivation: Clarifying and expanding goal theory', *Journal of Educational Psychology*, 84(3), pp. 272–281.
Cousin, G. (2006) 'An introduction to threshold concepts', *Planet*, 17, pp. 4–5.
Fouberg, E.H. (2000) 'Concept learning through writing for learning: Using journals in an introductory geography course', *Journal of Geography*, 99(5), pp. 196–206.
Fouberg, E.H. (2013) 'The world is no longer flat to me: Student perceptions of threshold concepts in world regional geography', *Journal of Geography in Higher Education*, 3(1), pp. 65–75.
Fouberg, E.H. and Moseley, W.G. (2015) *Understanding World Regional Geography.* New York: Wiley.
Fulwiler, T. (ed.) (1987) *The Journal Book.* Portsmouth, NJ: Heinemann.
Hay, D. (2007) 'Using concept maps to measure deep, surface and non-learning outcomes', *Studies in Higher Education,* 32(1), pp. 39–57.
Hay, D., Wells, H. and Kinchin, I. (2008) 'Quantitative and qualitative measures of student learning at university level', *Higher Education*, 56, pp. 221–239.
Hill, J., Thomas, G., Diaz, A. and Simm, D. (2016) 'Borderland spaces for learning partnership: Opportunities, benefits and challenges', *Journal of Geography in Higher Education*, 40(3), pp. 375–393.
Jarvis, P. (1992) *Paradoxes of Learning.* San Francisco, CA: Josey-Bass.
Jo, I. and Bednarz, S.W. (2011) 'Textbook questions to support spatial thinking: Differences in spatiality by question location', *Journal of Geography*, 110(2), pp. 70–80.
Land, R., Rattray, J. and Vivian, P. (2014) 'Learning in the liminal space: A semiotic approach to threshold concepts', *Higher Education*, 67(2), pp. 199–217.
Meyer, J. and Land, R. (2003) *Threshold Concepts and Troublesome Knowledge: Linkages to Ways of Thinking and Practicing Within Disciplines. Enhancing Teaching–Learning Environments in Undergraduate Courses,* Occasional Report 4, Edinburgh: ETL Project, University of Edinburgh.

Meyer, J. and Land, R. (2006) 'Threshold concepts and troublesome knowledge: Issues of liminality', in J. Meyer and Land, R. (eds), *Overcoming Barriers to Student Understanding: Threshold Concepts and Troublesome Knowledge.* New York: Routledge, pp. 19–32.

Novak, J. (1998) *Learning, Creating and Using Knowledge: Concept Maps as Facilitative Tools in Schools and Corporations.* Mahwah, NJ: Lawrence Erlbaum.

Piaget, J. ([1936] 1963) *The Origins of Intelligence in Children.* London: Routledge. Reprint, New York: Norton.

Renshaw, S. and Wood, P. (2011) 'Holistic understanding in geography education (HUGE) – an alternative approach to curriculum development and learning at Key Stage 3', *The Curriculum Journal*, 22(3), pp. 365–379.

Slinger, J. (2011) 'Threshold concepts in secondary geography education', Paper presented at the Geographical Association Annual Conference. Available at: https://www.geography.org.uk/download/ga_conf11slinger.pdf (downloaded: 12 April 2019).

Szabo, S.E., Atkinson, M.P. and Spooner, W.E. (1985) 'Teaching abstract concepts in sociology', *Teaching Sociology*, 13(1), pp. 95–106.

Wattenberg, M. and Viégas, F.B. (2008) 'The word tree, an interactive visual concordance', *IEEE Transactions on Visualization and Computer Graphics*, 14(6), pp. 1221–1228.

Wiggins, G. and McTighe, J. (1998) *Understanding by Design.* Alexandria, VA: Association for Supervision and Curriculum Development.

Wiggins, G. (2011) *Formative vs Summative Assessment – and Unthinking Policy About Them.* Available at: https://grantwiggins.wordpress.com/2011/08/25/formative-vs-summative-assessment-and-unthinking-policy-about-them/ (accessed: 1 July 2018).

7. Fieldwork as transition pedagogy for non-specialist students in geography: promoting collaborative learning amidst uncertainty
Kamalini Ramdas

INTRODUCTION

Transition remains a key concern in higher education where it can pertain to a variety of issues, from learning to cope with a new learning environment (for example high school to university), to learning to live away from home, to transforming oneself into an active autonomous learner, less dependent on more directed learning usually associated with the high school setting (Hussey and Smith, 2010; see also Chapter 2 in this volume by Tate and Hopkinson, for a discussion of academic and social transitions). At university, students have to cope with a modular system, where they do not have a fixed 'home' class. They also have greater flexibility and control over module choice and how much time to invest in learning. For example, at university, lecturers are less likely to take attendance in a large lecture hall. This can make for a more comfortable experience for some students, while for others who are used to the more structured approach of high school, greater flexibility can be a source of stress as they navigate their first year.

In recent years the increasing pressure for universities to demonstrate their ability to produce socially and economically relevant human capital for the workplace, and their commitment to watching over the social, emotional, and academic well-being of students, has brought transition pedagogy into the limelight. Transition pedagogy has evolved from the study of the longitudinal process of schemes to understand college dropout (Tinto, 1987) to the study of strategies and processes that occur at the 'nexus of institutional, lecturer and student concerns and expectations' (Sheridan and Dunne, 2012, p. 238). These strategies are varied and have evolved from those that treat curricular and co-curricular strategies as separate (termed first- and second-generation transition) to more integrated approaches that bring together curricular, co-curricular, and external or community involvement in the transition process (Nelson and Kift, 2005; Mytton and Rumbold, 2011).

The key aim of this chapter is to discuss how transition pedagogy can be a form of collaborative learning that empowers students who are more attuned to exam-oriented learning outcomes. The chapter focuses on my experience teaching a general education module for non-majors in geography. The module, 'Changing Landscapes of Singapore', is one of the pillars of general education that students must fulfil before graduation at the National University of Singapore. Departments throughout the university provide different modules that fall under this category. The module is offered by the Department of Geography and aims to broaden students' knowledge and understanding of Singapore's critical geographies by studying how its landscapes have changed since independence (Ho, Woon and Ramdas, 2013). Drawing from student feedback on the module, I analyse the qualitative comments students provided about the value of field trips to learning. While there were no specific questions asked about field trips, students volunteered this information under the question they were asked about what they liked about the module. Under this question heading I draw upon student comments that pertain specifically to their experience of field trips and analyse these comments over ten years (2006–2017).

Specifically, I analyse how fieldwork allows these students to become immersed in an experiential learning environment where they interact first-hand with the landscapes of Singapore that they learn about in the module. The purposes of this chapter are two-fold: first, to share strategies for how fieldwork may be deployed as a transition pedagogy to promote a spirit of discovery, networking and peer learning, as well as to acquire soft skills that students can take with them as they progress to higher level modules and beyond the university; and second, to compare the outcomes of different fieldwork exercises students have had to engage with over the years. In particular, I compare lecturer-guided 'look and see' fieldwork, and self-guided fieldwork. The rest of the chapter is divided into five sections. The first section provides a brief overview of the changing context of higher education in Singapore. This is followed by a review of the extant literature relevant to transition and fieldwork as transition pedagogy. Following this I demonstrate how I made use of different types of fieldwork-based activities in a transition pedagogy for the module. This is followed by a brief analysis and critique of the outcomes for these strategies. The chapter concludes with a summary of the key findings, challenges, and suggestions for areas of further research.

NUS GEOGRAPHY AND THE CHANGING CONTEXT OF SINGAPORE'S HIGHER EDUCATION

The National University of Singapore (NUS) is the only university in Singapore offering a full undergraduate and graduate academic program in geography. Since the establishment of the department in 1928, geographical education at NUS has evolved to reflect the development, modernisation, and nation-building goals of the state (Savage, 2003). More recently, alongside the broader push within the university to become a key player in the global knowledge-based industry, the department has also become more internationalised in terms of faculty, students, teaching texts, and research (Huang and Ramdas, 2019; see also Chapter 20 in this volume by Parton and Haigh, for a discussion of internationalisation).

General Education (GE) was devised to instil all graduates with a 'broad range of knowledge, abilities, predispositions and attitudes' such that their disciplinary perspectives are supplemented with 'the skills needed for lifelong learning beyond the university' (National University of Singapore, 2018, no page). The Singapore Studies pillar of the GE programme is critical in providing students with an understanding of key historical and geographical developments in Singapore since independence. 'Changing Landscapes of Singapore' aims to provide students with the skills to read critically Singapore's landscapes as text, thus allowing for more in-depth and critical interpretations of state ideology and policies as well as non-state actors who contest and resist the hegemony of the state through landscapes (Ramdas, Woon and Ho, 2018). As the university and the department take on the mandate to become global players in higher education, there has been greater impetus to produce lifelong learners (see Chapter 27 in this volume by Hill and Worth and Chapter 29 in this volume by Shepherd) who are both ready for the global economy, and a possible life after graduation beyond Singapore's borders, while at the same time maintaining their ties to the nation.

Students who take the modules are typically in their first year at the university and come from diverse disciplinary backgrounds with very little prior knowledge of geography as a subject. For many of the students the last time they engaged with the subject would have been at lower secondary school level and their engagement with it would have been structured along the lines of human versus physical geography. Furthermore, there would also have been limited discussion of landscape studies or the cultural turn in human geography and its impact on landscape studies. These are students who struggle with understanding landscape as a concept, and also with writing longer argument-driven essays as part of their continuous assessment and final exam for the module. For example, negative feedback from students about the module over the years included comments such as: 'too dry'; 'too much content'; and 'too much focus on essay writing and language'. The majority of the students who take the module are majors in the physical sciences (for example School of Computing, Faculty of Science, Pharmacy or Engineering). They find the module challenging because it is not in a discipline about which they have prior knowledge, and also requires skills such as essay writing and a good command of language; skills traditionally associated with 'Arts' students.

Teaching the module is, therefore, very challenging as transitioning for first years at the university means having to cope with new subject content such as university geography, in addition to being in a new learning environment where they have more freedom as well as responsibility to choose what subjects they would like to learn in their first year. Many of the students choose to take the module because it is about Singapore, a place they have some knowledge about. There is some knowledge of geography as a subject they would have taken in secondary school but this is quite different from what they have studied before in secondary or high school. With greater pressure to increase student enrolment in modules offered by the department and within the Arts and Social Sciences, faculty who have taught the module have thus had to develop interesting and engaging lecture material, and assignments to fuel student interest and enhance their learning. One such strategy has been the use of fieldwork to promote experiential learning.

LITERATURE REVIEW: FIELDWORK AND TRANSITION PEDAGOGY

The majority of the existing literature on transition pedagogy emerges from the UK and Australia. Here, the focus has been on how to promote transition and the kind of strategies to deploy. These have evolved from first- and second-generation strategies that focus on curricular or co-curricular reform to third and fourth-generation strategies that adopt a 'whole of institution approach' (Nelson et al., 2014) and support from outside the university (Donnison et al., 2017). Where curricular reform is concerned, researchers have focused on how to promote constructivist or student-centred learning where students are seen as constructing rather than merely acquiring knowledge (Nelson and Kift, 2005). Other studies have also focused on how to promote student interest in learning by fostering perceptions of universities as research-rich environments (Vereijken et al., 2016; Kahu et al., 2017; see also Chapter 15 in this volume by Hodgkins and Bullard). With regard to co-curricular reform, research includes efforts to improve the transition process through the use of peer-led workshops that promote sharing and learning about life in the university between senior and junior students (Mytton and Rumbold, 2011), and notes the relevance of student societies and friends in promoting a better transition for international postgraduate students (Menzies and Baron, 2014). The whole-of-institution and outside-institution approaches each reflect how transition research has evolved to acknowledge the involvement of multiple stakeholders beyond just students and lecturers. In other words, there is greater awareness

> that the learning and success of students in transition must be a shared responsibility of all areas of the university – academic and professional, student services and environmental support – and, while much can be achieved by faculties formally and informally through the curriculum, embedded institutional change is dependent on the creation of organisational structures (Swing, 2003). (Nelson and Kift, 2005, p. 232)

In geography, much of the literature on transition has addressed the issue of coping with the differences between high school and secondary school geography and what is taught at the university level (Tate and Swords, 2013; Ferreira, 2018). Several strategies have been put forth in the literature to cope with the gap between the two. These include research that focuses on students' perspectives of the differences in subject content of the discipline (Tate and Swords, 2013) to the use of induction programmes (Richardson and Tate, 2013), improving collaboration between high school educators and university lecturers (Imrie and Cowling, 2006), and improvements to curriculum and more specialised skills training for better transition to the job market (Piróg, 2014). Within the transition literature in geography, there is little about fieldwork as a transition pedagogy in spite of the fact that fieldwork is deemed to be a key component of education in geography (Sauer 1956; Haigh and Gold, 1993; Kent et al., 1997; Hovorka and Wolf, 2009). A large part of the focus in the literature on fieldwork has been on the pedagogical effectiveness of fieldwork-based learning (Lonergan and Andresen, 1988; Fuller et al., 2006; Boyle et al., 2007; Hope, 2009) and also how different strategies for fieldwork (from the virtual to the 'real') can be crafted to manage the challenges to providing a field-based learning experience as classroom enrolment becomes larger and budgets smaller (Jenkins 1994; McEwen, 1996; Friess et al., 2016). However, given the literature on fieldwork iterates fieldwork's ability to 'serve as a model for constructivist instructional design through their direct establishment of a learning environment' (Jonassen, 1994, p. 35), fieldwork would seem 'conducive to fulfilling the need of today's students for active learning through discovery, challenge and autonomy' (Hovorka and Wolf, 2009, p. 91). In the next section I explain how fieldwork has been deployed in the Changing Landscapes of Singapore module over the years. Later I analyse the outcomes of these strategies and show how they have helped with transition.

FIELDWORK AND FIELD TRIPS IN SINGAPORE GEOGRAPHY – CHANGING LANDSCAPES AND BEYOND

Fieldwork or going on field trips is seen as a core practice in geographical education (McEwen, 1996; Fuller et al., 2006; Boyle et al., 2007). As Fuller et al. (2006, p. 90) argue, fieldwork 'not only is considered essential . . . it is considered by both academics and students to be an extremely effective and enjoyable learning and teaching method'. In Singapore, the use of fieldwork in geographical education begins in secondary school and is called Geographical Investigations (GI) (Curriculum Planning and Development Division, 2014). Students are taken on field trips with their teachers to conduct fieldwork on topics such as coasts, climate, tourism, and food sustainability (see for example: Seow and Chang, 2016). This practice continues into high school or junior college level, and is testament to the fact that in addition to gaining subject specific knowledge and skills, fieldwork in Geographical Education is also seen as a means by which 21st-century core competencies may be acquired by citizen-learners in Singapore (for example confident, self-directed learner, active contributor, and concerned citizen) (Ministry of Education, 2009).

In line with this strong focus on fieldwork in geography, the department at NUS also prioritises fieldwork or field-based learning. These range from standalone field studies modules, to day-trips to various parts of Singapore. Residential fieldwork courses are offered as modules that students can take to fulfil their modular credit requirements for graduation. Over the years, fieldwork modules have taken students and lecturers to field sites in Thailand, Kenya, Malaysia and Fiji for anywhere between two to six weeks. Many other modules offer fieldwork as part of the course component and these range from two-week long residential fieldwork to day trips where students head to the field to collect data or go on traditional 'look and see' field trips with their lecturer. However, for the purpose of this chapter I focus on the use of fieldwork in the teaching of the general education module, Changing Landscapes of Singapore.

Over the years the Changing Landscapes of Singapore module has offered fieldwork and field visits as part of its curriculum. These have ranged from visits to places of heritage or tourism value, to visits to the planning and public housing authority where students are able to meet with planners to learn about key topics covered in the module, namely urban and public housing planning in Singapore. The module was first offered as a general education module in 2001 and even in the early days field trips were an integral part of the learning experience. From 2003, when I first joined the teaching team for the module, there were compulsory field trips which all students were expected to attend. Students were taken on hired coaches to various sites and spent three to four hours with the lecturer and graduate student tutors, during which they would be taken around sites such as Chinatown, Little India, and the Malay precinct, Kampong Glam. At these sites they were taught about heritage, conservation, and the battle between 'authentic' conservation and the development of these sites as tourist attractions. However, such in-depth and lengthy field trips are few and far between today due to cutbacks in funding. The cost of coach hire and entry fees for some places of interest can no longer be borne by the department. The time taken to plan the field trips also made them less attractive as classes became larger (at its height, module enrolment for the Changing Landscapes reached 450 students!). Furthermore, faculty members were experiencing greater pressure to publish

Table 7.1   Changing Landscapes: time line of field trips

Year	Type	Site	Description
2003–2007	Compulsory, look and see	Chinatown, Little India, Kampong Glam, War Commemoration Sites, Changi Boardwalk	Coach hire, all students had to attend, travelled to field sites that were less accessible, multiple sessions required to complete exercise for enrolment of 450 students (about 4 times)
2008–2013	Optional, look and see	Chinatown, Little India, Kampong Glam, Tiong Bahru Housing Estate	Interested students would take public transport and met lecturers there, travelled in smaller groups, and fewer sessions required (1–2 times only)
2014–2017	Self-guided	Little India, Joo Chiat Housing Estate	Students went in groups on their own. Completed field trip report for grading. Lecturers not required to accompany
2017 onwards	Self-guided	Students select site themselves as it is tied to their group project work	Students travel on their own to a site of their choice, they present preliminary data about the site and its links to their graded group project assignment

research papers in addition to teaching as part of promotion and tenure requirements. As a result, offering compulsory 'look and see' field trips for the module became less sustainable. From 2008 onwards the field trips were no longer compulsory. Lecturers took a smaller group of students on a first-come, first-served basis and students took public transportation to the field site where they met the lecturers. From 2014 onwards the teaching team put in place self-guided field trips where students go to the various field sites with the use of detailed descriptions about each site, prompting questions to guide students on the field trip, and the use of Google Maps. Students later submitted a field-work report or completed a worksheet about the self-guided visit. From 2017 onwards students were required to go on field trips to collect data for a graded group assignment that they submitted at the end of the semester. The choice of site was up to them, and they were then required to return to class and present some of their findings to their tutorial classmates (refer to Table 7.1 for time line).

While fieldwork and field trips have remained an integral part of the Changing Landscapes of Singapore module, their intensity in terms of lecturer presence has waned within the curriculum in that we now rely more on self-guided field trips and traditional 'look and see' field trips where the lecturer and teaching team accompany the students on the field trip.

In the next section of the chapter I analyse student feedback for the module to show why fieldwork for non-specialist students who are new to the university learning environment can be effective for transition. The feedback is taken from a university-wide evaluation exercise carried out at the end of each semester. Students can choose whether or not to take part; however, in the case of the Changing Landscapes the response rate has generally been 50–75 per cent of the class. I have studied student responses between 2006 and 2017 as these are the years for which I was able to access the feedback data. As part of the feedback exercise students are asked to provide scores to a fixed set of questions regarding how the module has enhanced critical thinking, whether they received timely feedback and how well they thought they would do for the module. They are also asked for qualitative feedback on what they liked or did not like about the module. While fieldwork and field trips are not listed in the feedback exercise, it is in the qualitative feedback that the students talk about fieldwork and field trips, and these are the responses I focused on.

FIELDWORK AS TRANSITION PEDAGOGY: WHY IT WORKS

There are three main reasons why fieldwork is a useful strategy for easing transition through the Changing Landscapes of Singapore module: first, the link between theory and seeing something in practice; second, the opportunity to meet other students; and third, the acquisition of essential practical skills that will enable them to transition to higher-level modules at the university, and later on, to their workplace. The first, similar to what McEwen (1996, p. 382) argues, is that fieldwork is 'a good learning environment for reinforcing and developing areas taught in formal lectures or practical sessions'. This is especially significant for first-year students who are new to geography and new to the university's educational landscape. The Changing Landscapes of Singapore module has always included the fieldwork experience since its early years for precisely this reason. In fact, while the type of fieldwork offered to the students has changed from 'look and see' to self-guided (see Table 7.1 above), students have continued to say that what they liked best about the module was the possibility of going on field trips. Comments from students in the feedback exercise included over the years for 'look and see' field trips with the lecturers included, '*Fieldwork was excellent. It improved understanding of concepts on a practical basis*' (2008/2009) and '*The field trip that was conducted is very effective in helping me to understand the module even better*' (2011/2012). Students found the first-hand interaction with their lecturers and the landscape exciting and it helped them to more easily make sense of complex concepts (Fuller et al., 2006; Hovorka and Wolf, 2009, p. 92) such as place, heritage, inclusion and exclusion as they visited field sites such as Chinatown, Little India, and Tiong Bahru: '*[The] field trip to Tiong Bahru was very interesting as it allowed us to see first-hand the things we have learnt in lectures are actually happening in our everyday landscapes. It has increased my critical thinking skill[s]*' (2013/2014).

Students were also given time to explore the field sites on their own during the 'look and see' field trips. This helped to promote a spirit of self-discovery. The self-guided field trips also helped to promote a spirit of self-discovery, as one student shared how going on a self-guided field trip to Joo Chiat was interesting and taught her '*a new perspective about landscapes in Singapore. The fieldtrips that I've been through were eye-opening (Joo Chiat and Skate Park for my group project), made me better appreciate and understand landscapes from a geographer's point of view*' (2014/2015). For many of the students this 'geographer's point of view' can be challenging as they are newcomers to university geography. The fact that students learn how to apply a geographical lens of analysis while on their self-guided field trip is indeed promising given the challenges faced by the teaching team when taking students in a large module for 'look and see' field trips.

Whether guided by the lecturer or self-guided, the first-hand experience with the landscape outside the lecture hall or classroom setting (Day and Spronken-Smith, 2017) is something the students found very enjoyable and it helped to break the monotony of classroom learning which was quite challenging for many who were new to the style of learning at the Faculty of Arts and Social Sciences. Some students struggled with the volume of reading and this was very different for many who were more used to laboratory settings, or more practical case studies-based approaches to learning. Field trips thus help to connect what students perceived as 'dry' and theoretical' to a 'real world'. It helped to build confidence as many continued to worry about their grades and felt they were ill-equipped to score well for a geography module. Given that the general education module is usually taken by non-specialist students (that is, non-geographers or non-Arts students), students often felt they were out of their depth. As one student said, '*Non-Arts students find it a struggle to understand what the lecturers and tutors want in terms of good work*' (2006/2007) and another said, '*I feel that the module content is heavy and the module has overwhelming readings*' (2011/2012). For many students going on the field visit with the lecturer was a more manageable way to learn how to read landscapes as text, even as they struggled with readings that described and analysed this process. As one student said, '*It is a breath of fresh air from my core modules, [the] fieldtrip was interesting as well as the project work*' (2017/2018). First-year students who are new to geography thus find the field experience unique and useful for completing their final group project. This is primarily because the teaching team has tried to make clearer the connection between fieldwork and the final group project that the students must submit as part of the continual assessment requirements. Between 2014 and 2017 the self-guided field trip was not linked to the group project. However, for the past two semesters since the start of the academic year 2017/2018, we have allowed the students to choose their own field trip site which is relevant to their group project. Students return to the classroom after they have completed their fieldwork and discuss their findings and observations in class. In this way we are not limited to a fixed type of landscape and students benefit from peer-learning when groups present each of their different field experiences in different field sites in Singapore. Students are given guiding questions on what to observe in the field in relation to the aims that have been set for their projects by the teaching team. When they return from the field they are guided by the teaching team on how to interpret their observations and improve on their analysis for their final project.

A second reason why fieldwork can help with transition is the opportunity it provides for students to socialise and work in groups (see also Chapter 8 in this volume by Conradson, for a discussion of fieldwork as a supportive learning environment). This is significant as students entering university after junior college or high school might be less familiar with the modular system where they are not tied to a fixed 'home class'. Through fieldwork they get to develop identity by socialising with new friends while on field trips and while conducting fieldwork for their projects. For example, Sheridane and Dunne (2012) explain that the transition process for students can be a challenging one where group work is involved as they are often working with new people and experience the emotional stress of developing interpersonal relationships with individuals they do not already have friendships with. The massification of higher education means that in modules like Changing Landscapes the lecture hall and even the tutorial classroom can become quite impersonal spaces where students find it challenging to form personal relationships and a sense of place with the move from one class to the next. Working in groups and going on field trips as part of their smaller group allows students to socialise and have fun while in the field. They are also responsible for choosing their field site and their project work site. For many, the exploring together was quite enjoyable and helped to provide a more social context in which to make friends in a large module setting:

The group work was really fun. I enjoyed it a lot. It was fun to do ethnography. My first time doing such a thing. Furthermore, studying humans, culture, the expression of values was intriguing to experience in reality. (AY 2017/2018)

The field trip is helpful, however, I think there should be more interactions between tutor and students. (AY 2009/2010)

The two quotes above from the feedback reports show that students enjoyed the fun aspects of working in a group and learning to do ethnography together. However, they also wanted more interactions with their tutors. The feedback also seems to indicate that while students enjoy going on their own self-directed field trips and doing fieldwork for their projects on their own, they also want more interactions with faculty and graduate tutors in the field similar to those experienced by students who went on 'look and see' field trips with the lecturers in the earlier years. The challenge, therefore, is in balancing independent learning with opportunities for tutors and students to interact and assist students to develop their projects.

Over the years we have tried to make the connection between self-guided fieldwork and lecturer consultation and classroom feedback sessions. As mentioned earlier, once students return from the field they can either meet with the lecturer to discuss some of the outcomes and plans for their group projects or, in more recent semesters, we have asked students to give presentations during tutorials to share with the class and their tutors what the group has discovered during fieldwork. Greater interaction occurred between the group members while on fieldwork, and after the fieldwork the class and the tutor were able to interact both inside and outside the classroom, improving their skills and gaining confidence as they can now check in with the lecturer/tutor. According to Hussey and Smith (2010) transition can be quite complex in scenarios such as Changing Landscapes where there is a diverse student body, some students are able to cope with the uncertainty of being in a new academic environment while others need more guidance.

Finally, the skills learnt while doing fieldwork including: learning through inquiry, collecting and analysing data, observing, describing, analysing, and theorising, can be useful for first-year students as these are necessary skills for higher level modules in geography as well as skills that can be put to use in the workplace. For example, these are essential and practical skills that students need to be equipped with for critical thinking and to achieve the high-order learning outcomes the university wants undergraduates to master by the time they graduate. Moreover, as noted by Day and Spronken-Smith (2017, pp. 6–7), 'undergraduate research equips students with transferable skills better preparing them for future postgraduate study and/or the workplace'. In the field students learn to cope with the uncertainties of the field, including how to network with contacts and people outside the university or classroom context to gain access to data or interviewees, and these are important skills to develop. As McEwen and Harris argue, 'the goal posts have shifted so that expected learning outcomes from fieldwork now embrace much more than purely academic objectives' (McEwen and Harris, 1996, p. 412). These useful 'soft skills' can thus be used to serve non-academic objectives and may also help students better prepare for transition from higher education to the workplace (see also Boyle et al., 2007). By starting early in the first year with self-guided field trips we have been able to instil this spirit of inquiry and critical thinking that is crucial to successful transitioning.

CHALLENGES AND AREAS FOR FUTURE RESEARCH

In spite of the positive effects of fieldwork on students' transition experience, there are challenges. For example, students in Singapore tend to be focused on grades and tend to take a pragmatic approach to learning. For those who take general education modules like Changing Landscapes of Singapore, the module, while fulfilling a university level requirement, is seen as distracting and taking attention away from time which could otherwise be spent on their primary discipline or major modules. Even when students find the module and the fieldwork interesting and fun, they are more concerned about issues such as 'free riders' and the volume of content being covered in the module. So, while fieldwork may serve to allay some of these fears by creating an out of classroom context in which students can interact and socialise with their peers and the lecturers and tutors, it cannot completely address some of the transition concerns students have. For example, one student said, '*Field trips were time consuming and students might not know what to look out for if they went by themselves*' (2014/2015). One strategy to address this complaint would be for lecturers and tutors to take students on these field trips to show them how to do the fieldwork before sending the students off on their own. However, the issue of time is also a challenge for lecturers who find it difficult to run field trips for so many students during the work day and make sure that everyone returns back to the university in time for the next class they need to attend.

There is clearly a need for more research to show the true impact of fieldwork on transition. This study makes use of data from a general feedback exercise by students. This is not data that was obtained as part of a project whose aims were specifically about fieldwork or field trips and transitioning. More research needs to be done on this in the context of geography in Singapore comparing, for example, the transition experience between students who participated in fieldwork-based learning as part of module requirements versus those who did not participate in fieldwork.

As geographers, we know and believe that field trips are a unique learning environment outside the traditional classroom. The trick is in being able to provide field-based learning even as classroom enrolment become larger and as lecturers face cost-cutting measures and the pressures on their time. For Changing Landscapes of Singapore, the solution came in the form of self-guided field trips where students were provided the opportunity to experience field-based learning on their own before returning to the classroom for more in-depth discussions about what they had observed. While the first-year students who took the module had to cope with the uncertainty of being in a new learning environment and grasping a new subject (geography), the self-guided field trip was a way to incrementally encourage independent learning through fieldwork with the added support of in-depth discussion in a more traditional classroom setting when they returned from fieldwork. The experience for Changing Landscapes of Singapore has shown that fieldwork remains a viable strategy for first-years transitioning from high school to university because it allows for more social, interesting, and independent learning.

USEFUL RESOURCES

- Nelson, K. et al. (2014), *Transition Pedagogy Handbook: A Good Practice Guide for Policy and Practice in the First Year Experience in QUT*, Australia: Queensland University of Technology. Available from: https://eprints.qut.edu.au/76333/.

REFERENCES

Boyle, A. et al. (2007) 'Fieldwork is good: the student perception and the affective domain', *Journal of Geography in Higher Education*, 31(2), pp. 299–317.

Curriculum Planning and Development Division (2014) *Lower Secondary Geography Teaching Syllabus*, Singapore: Ministry of Education.

Day, T. and Spronken-Smith, R. (2017) 'Geography education: fieldwork and contemporary pedagogy, *The International Encyclopaedia of Geography*. Available at https://onlinelibrary.wiley.com/doi/10.1002/978111878 6352.wbieg0523/figures (accessed: 22 March 2019).

Donnison, S., Penn-Edwards, S., Greenaway, R. and Horn, R. (2017) 'Trialling a 4th generation approach to the first year experience: the CommUniTI', *Student Success*, 8(1), pp. 63–72.

Ferreira, J. (2018) 'Facilitating the transition: doing more than bridging the gap between school and university geography', *Journal of Geography in Higher Education*, 42(3), pp. 372–383.

Friess, Dan. A., Oliver, Grahame J.H., Quak, Michelle S.Y. and Lau, Annie Y.A. (2016) 'Incorporating "virtual" and "real world" field trips into introductory geography modules', *Journal of Geography in Higher Education*, 40(4), pp. 546–564.

Fuller, I. et al. (2006) 'International perspectives on the effectiveness of geography fieldwork for learning', *Journal of Geography in Higher Education*, 30(1), pp. 89–101.

Haigh, M. and Gold, J.R. (1993) 'The problems with fieldwork: a group-based approach towards integrating fieldwork into the undergraduate geography curriculum', *Journal of Geography in Higher Education*, 17(1), pp. 21–32.

Ho, E.L.E., Woon, C.Y. and Ramdas, K. (2013) *Changing Landscapes of Singapore: Old Tensions, New Discoveries*. Singapore: NUS Press.

Hope, M. (2009) 'The importance of direct experience: a philosophical defence of fieldwork in Human Geography', *Journal of Geography in Higher Education*, 33(2), pp. 169–182.

Hovorka, A.J. and Wolf, P.A. (2009) 'Activating the classroom: geographical fieldwork as pedagogical practice', *Journal of Geography in Higher Education*, 33(1), pp. 89–102.

Huang, S. and Ramdas, K. (2019) 'Generative spaces of gender and feminist geography in Singapore: entanglements of the personal and political', *Gender, Place and Culture*, 26(7–9), pp. 1233–1242.

Hussey, T. and Smith, P. (2010) 'Transitions in higher education', *Innovations in Education and Teaching International*, 47, pp. 155–164.

Imrie, R. and Cowling, D. (2006) 'Forging partnerships with institutions of higher education', *Teaching Geography*, 31(1), pp. 23–25.

Jenkins, A. (1994) 'Thirteen ways of doing fieldwork with large classes/more students', *Journal of Geography in Higher Education*, 18(2), pp. 143–154.

Jonassen, D.H. (1994) 'Thinking technology: toward a constructivist design model', *Educational Technology*, 34(3), pp. 34–37.

Kahu, E., Nelson, K. and Picton, C. (2017) 'Student interest as a key driver of engagement for first year students', *Student Success*, 8(2), pp. 55–66.

Kent, M., Gilbertson, D.D. and Hunt, C.O. (1997) 'Fieldwork in geography teaching: A critical review of the literature and approaches', *Journal of Geography in Higher Education*, 21(3), pp. 313–332.

Lonergan, N. and Andresen, L. (1988) 'Field based education: some theoretical considerations?', *Higher Education Research and Development*, 7, pp. 63–77.

McEwen, L. (1996) 'Fieldwork in the undergraduate geography programme: challenges and changes', *Journal of Geography in Higher Education*, 20(3), pp. 379–384.

McEwen, L. and Harris, F. (1996) 'The undergraduate geography fieldwork: challenges and changes', *Journal of Geography in Higher Education*, 20(3), pp. 411–421.

Menzies, J.L. and Baron, R. (2014) 'International postgraduate student transition experiences: the importance of student societies and friends', *Innovations in Education and Teaching International*, 51(1), pp. 84–94.

Ministry of Education (2009) *The Desired Outcomes of Education*. Singapore. Published online 1 December 2009. https://www.moe.gov.sg/education/education-system/desired-outcomes-of-education.

Mytton, G. and Rumbold, P. (2011) 'Enhancing the transition from a foundation degree to the third year of an undergraduate degree', *Innovations in Education and Teaching International*, 48(3), pp. 251–261.

National University of Singapore (2018) Undergraduate Curriculum Structure. Available at http://www.nus.edu.sg/registrar/education-at-nus/undergraduate-education/curriculum-structure.html (accessed 9 March 2018).

Nelson, K. and Kift, S. (2005) 'Beyond curriculum reform: embedding the transition practice experience', in Brew, A. and Asmar, C. (eds), *Proceedings HERDSA 2005*, 28, pp. 225–235, The University of Sydney, Sydney Australia. Available at: http://eprints.qut.edu.au/archive/00003944 (assessed: 9 March 2018).

Nelson, K., Creagh, T., Kift, S.M. and Clarke, J.A. (2014) *Transition Pedagogy Handbook: A Good Practice Guide for Policy and Practice in the First Year Experience in QUT*, Australia: Queensland University of Technology. (Unpublished). Available at: https://eprints.qut.edu.au/76333/ (accessed: 22 March 2019).

Piróg, D. (2014) 'Do geography degree programmes facilitate a smooth transition to the job market? Reflections of working and job-seeking graduates in Poland', *Journal of Geography in Higher Education*, 38(2), pp. 155–174.

Ramdas, K., Woon, C.Y. and Ho, E.L.E. (2018) 'Changing landscapes as text: geography and national education in Singapore', *Area*, 50(1), pp. 50–54.

Richardson, M.J. and Tate, S. (2013) 'Improving transition to university: introducing student voices into formal induction process for new geography undergraduates', *Journal of Geography in Higher Education*, 37(4), pp. 611–618.

Savage, V. (2003) 'Changing geographies and the geography of change: some reflections,' *Singapore Journal of Tropical Geography*, 24, pp. 61–85.

Sauer, C. (1956) 'The education of a geographer', *Annals of the Association of American Geographers*, 46(3), pp. 287–299.

Seow, T. and Chang, J. (2016), 'Whose place is this space? Exploring place perceptions and the cultural politics of place through a field-based lesson', *Social Education*, 80(5), pp. 296–303.

Sheridan, V. and Dunne, S. (2012) 'The bigger picture: undergraduate voices reflecting on academic transition in an Irish university', *Innovations in Education and Teaching International*, 49(3), pp. 237–247.

Tate, S. and Swords, J. (2013) 'Please mind the gap! School to higher education: still bridging the gap', *Journal of Geography in Higher Education*, 37(2), pp. 2302–2340.

Tinto, V. (1987), *Leaving College*. Chicago: University of Chicago Press.

Vereijken, M.W.C. et al. (2016) 'Fostering first-year student learning through research integration into teaching: student perceptions, beliefs about the value of research and student achievement', *Innovations in Education and Teaching International*, 55(4), pp. 425–432.

8. Supportive learning environments and the transition to university
David Conradson

INTRODUCTION

Beginning a programme of study at university often involves transition of several different kinds. Students typically have to navigate unfamiliar settings and institutional processes, to meet new people, to exercise greater control of their finances, and to be (or become) independent and self-directed learners. The transition to university may at times be exciting and even somewhat liberating (perhaps especially if it involves leaving home, or an opportunity for greater independence), but it can also be difficult. There is a lot to adjust to, and being away from one's usual surroundings and the associated support networks can make the transition to higher education challenging (Christie et al., 2004; Christie, 2009; see also Chapter 2 in this volume by Tate and Hopkins).

Mindful of these challenges, this chapter explores the significance of supportive learning environments for students beginning university. The discussion has three main sections. First, and by way of context, a number of observations are made about the transition to university in Anglophone countries such as Australia, Canada, New Zealand, South Africa, the United Kingdom (UK) and the United States (US). The discussion is focused around a particular kind of student, the recent school leaver, who is arguably representative of the majority of undergraduates in these countries. That said, many of the points made are also relevant to other kinds of students, including those attending university after a period of employment or later in life (for example as part of a mid-life career change). Second, the characteristics of supportive learning environments are considered, with particular attention given to the significance of welcome, interpersonal recognition and attunement, which are viewed as elements of relational hospitality. A third section then looks at three specific pedagogical practices that can be used to foster supportive learning environments for undergraduate geography students, namely residential fieldtrips, group work and alternative modes of assessment. Some of the obstacles that may be encountered are considered, and a short conclusion follows.

TRANSITIONING TO UNIVERSITY: THE STUDENT EXPERIENCE

When beginning university, a student is typically confronted by a range of unfamiliar environments and institutional processes (Chow and Healey, 2008; Holton, 2015). The extent to which a student is able to come to terms with this novelty – to find his or her place and to begin to 'feel at home' – can be a significant influence upon academic progress and well-being (Weiner-Levy, 2008; Christie, 2009). It is therefore noteworthy that many studies indicate that the transition from school (or work) to university can be a significant challenge, with non-completion and dropping out as all too common outcomes. In Australia, for example, a major research study found that between 2008 and 2010, 27 per cent of students 'seriously considered departing an Australian university before graduation' (ACER 2011, p. 1). Previous research in the United States has indicated that among students enrolled in four-year degree programmes, some 37 per cent never complete their degree, with the equivalent figure approaching almost 60 per cent for community college students (Tinto, 2012, p. 2). Although these figures obscure a range of institutional variation, it is evident that a significant proportion of students find the transition to university difficult, and that this difficulty can have quite striking implications for the completion of their studies.

For those struggling with the transition to university, a range of factors may be at work. First, and particularly for new students, universities can be experienced as confusing or even hostile bureaucracies, with an array of unfamiliar terms and potentially bewildering processes (for example faculties, moderation, pro-vice chancellors, vivas and aegrotats). For those who have spent significant time working within university systems (and who may therefore have become somewhat accustomed to them), it is easy to forget just how hierarchical and idiosyncratic the contemporary university can be. Although it varies by institution, the legacies of patriarchal and privilege-based approaches to learning are also often still evident, in ways that work against inclusivity and diversity (see, in this volume, Chapter 13 by Hughes and McDuff; Chapter 17 by Esson and Last).

A second factor is that a significant proportion of contemporary university students experience mental health problems, including anxiety, depression, eating disorders and suicidal thoughts (Gotlib 1984; Eisenberg et al., 2007; Garlow et al., 2008; Zivin et al., 2009). Although some research indicates that these problems are no more common among university students than the wider population (for example Blanco et al., 2008), other studies have found that levels of mental distress among university students are in fact higher than their non-college counterparts (Stallman, 2010). In any case, a growing proportion of university students report themselves as experiencing mental health issues, in ways that negatively affect their ability to learn and complete their programmes of study. Many university counselling services and related mental health support systems report growing demand, with increasing numbers of students presenting with complex and, in some cases, quite severe mental health problems (Gallagher et al., 2000; Benton et al., 2003; Cook 2007; Kitzrow 2009).

Although mental health is shaped by genetic and familial factors, the contemporary university does appear to present some specific challenges for student mental well-being. The competitive ethos and performance orientation in some programmes of study can induce or exacerbate anxiety, for example, in ways that may negatively impact academic performance (Andrews and Wilding, 2010). Such experiences are by no means confined to students in professional programmes, such as medicine, law, dentistry and engineering, but are also evident in the humanities, social sciences and sciences, and among students of geography. Financial pressures, including the expense of tuition fees, are another common source of stress (McMillan, 2013), and attending a university away from home may reduce access to established forms of social support, potentially contributing to a sense of dislocation and homesickness (Finn, 2017). There is also the discrimination, overt or otherwise, that some students experience at university on the basis of their race, gender, sexual orientation, disability, or other form of difference. Any of these factors can make the university a challenging place for student mental well-being.

A third consideration is that, in comparison to secondary schools, most universities operate larger class sizes and offer less personalised attention from educators. Although there is undoubtedly variation between institutions and countries in this regard, most degree programmes in publicly funded universities are still delivered through large lecture courses, accompanied where possible by small group learning (for example tutorials, seminars and laboratory classes). (See, in this volume, Chapter 4 by Finn and Mott and Chapter 5 by Rink, for discussion of large cohort teaching.) For the average school leaver, the transition to university thus involves a shift from a situation in which they are known to some degree personally by a teacher (or teachers), to being one of several dozen (or even several hundred) young people in relatively anonymous and large lectures (albeit with some more personal interaction available through tutorials, seminars and the like). In such circumstances, it is quite possible that a student may become socially disconnected and even isolated. In addition, the reduction in personalised academic attention at most universities presumes that first-year students have (or are quickly able to develop) the capacity to operate as independent learners. Although some university entrants undoubtedly possess such capacities, many do not.

THE GENERAL CHARACTERISTICS OF SUPPORTIVE LEARNING ENVIRONMENTS

Given that the transition to university involves these inherent challenges, and that many students struggle as a result, what might be done? One solution might be to offer the kinds of small class sizes, advising and personalised support characteristic of Ivy League colleges in the US and a select few European institutions. This would likely help at least some students to feel more known and supported. For most publicly funded institutions, however, staffing and funding levels are insufficient to offer these kinds of learning environments. If we accept that most public universities in western countries are unlikely to receive significant per student increases in financial resources in the coming decades, it seems likely that large university classes will continue to exist (whether in person or online formats). Within these resource constrained systems, a key issue is therefore how we might nevertheless create learning environments that (i) support the learning of a diverse range of students, and which (ii) assist these students to develop a sense of ease and belonging at their particular university. Educational settings with these characteristics can be thought of as *supportive learning environments*.

As articulated within scholarship on the relational dimensions of education (for example Rogers 1983; Nemiroff 1992), a supportive learning environment is an educational setting in which a student is known by her peers and teachers; in which she feels welcomed, recognised, and valued; and in which her aspirations to learn are encouraged and facilitated. In a supportive learning environment, education is understood as a relational achievement, rooted in engagement and interaction. From this perspective, the social and emotional dynamics of the setting (be it a lecture, seminar, laboratory, or field class) become important rather than ancillary matters. It is understood that the experiences, histories and capabilities of students extend beyond what they share or reveal in the classroom. It is also recognised that, for most students, life will include periods of difficulty, illness and bereavement, with challenges that may relate to issues such as money, employment and relationships. Within a supportive learning environment, educators will recognise that such difficulties do occur and they will be willing, within the scope of what is possible and reasonable, to offer assistance and accommodations to those students affected by them. Attention will also be given to helping students develop connections with their peers, as this can help to offset the sense of anonymity and disconnectedness that some experience at university (McMillan, 2013). From the perspective of interpersonal neurobiology (Siegel, 2012), a supportive learning environment affords a degree of psychological safety, such that a student is able to feel sufficiently at ease to engage with and be open to new information, and to make positive connections with other learners.[1]

Before looking at particular pedagogical practices that can be employed to foster supportive learning environments, I would like to consider three more general relational characteristics of these environments: welcome, interpersonal recognition and attunement. Each of these characteristics can be understood as one element in a more general practice of relational hospitality (Gill, 2018; Kallio and Riding, 2018). In broad terms, relational hospitality is understood here as the practice of creating and holding space for another person, their life and well-being. In the university setting, relational hospitality might thus be construed as a practice of interacting with students in ways that create and hold space for their learning, growth and development. This is a significant aspiration, of course, and it will likely only be realised intermittently. As educators, however, we may be able to cultivate our own capacity for relational hospitality by recalling that new students often experience themselves as outsiders, at least initially, and that this experience of outsideness can be materially and emotionally difficult. In some instances, it may even be distressing and disorienting. But if we are willing to engage imaginatively with the experience of a new student – to place ourselves in her shoes, so to speak, and to contemplate (or even remember) what it might be like to leave home, move to an unfamiliar place, and to then encounter a host of new expectations, environments and people – then we may be more able to offer relational hospitality.

As one element of relational hospitality, *welcome* is about the kind of reception a student experiences when first arriving at a university, ready to begin a course of study. It is about how she is greeted and related to by academic staff and other students in the lecture theatres, labs and seminar rooms that constitute her degree programme. From the perspective of the educator, the practice of welcome is therefore about engaging students in a warm and friendly manner, showing interest in their experiences, and being willing to offer academic support, where possible, if needed or requested. Being welcoming may include offering practical assistance (for example giving a student directions to help them navigate a university campus), offering advice regarding administrative and bureaucratic processes (for example how to apply for an extension to an assignment deadline), or simply listening. Welcome is about the initial reception a student experiences as she begins and then seeks to continue a course of study.

Interpersonal recognition is closely related to welcome, but it denotes more specifically the experience of being related to as an individual with a particular biography and history, as a person with a specific set of capabilities, knowledge and learning needs. Recognition is about being seen for who one is. Unfortunately, as many of us know, the experience of interpersonal recognition is by no means assured when interacting with large organisations and systems. Standardised and bureaucratic processes seldom cater well to individual needs or personal preferences (Sennett, 2004). Relational practices that contribute to a sense of interpersonal recognition can therefore be of particular significance in a university environment, assisting it to become a place in which a student perceives that she is both noticed and known personally. Where appropriate, even the simple gesture of learning and using a student's first name can be meaningful in this regard. Because tutorials and other small group teaching settings often allow for a reasonable degree of interpersonal interaction, they generally have the most potential to become places in which students experience interpersonal recognition. Another aspect of recognition is the need for a university to acknowledge and, as appropriate, to take account of identity differences. Differences in terms of (dis)abilities, ethnic and cultural identity, sexual and gender identity are all important in this regard; and the presence of clubs, safe spaces and administrative processes which recognise these forms of difference can all help a student to feel that his/her/their identity and way of being in the world is not only acknowledged but also valued.

The notion of *attunement* is used here to describe the degree to which a university's interactions with its students are calibrated to their experiences and actual learning needs. The notion of attunement has come into the social sciences most directly through considerations of infant–caregiver attachments. Attunement in this context describes the process by which a caregiver is able to recognise an infant's needs and to adjust her/his response in accordance to those needs (Stern, 1985). When a caregiver's responses are related and appropriate to the infant's needs, then they can be considered to be attuned. When an infant experiences significant periods of attuned relating from their caregiver(s), this helps to foster emotional security, the emergence of a stable sense of self, and a belief in the validity of one's own experience (Stern, 1985, 2004; Stolorow and Atwood, 2002).

In a university setting, attunement might thus be understood in terms of the degree to which the educational content and experiences offered are well related to students' learning needs. There will be a greater chance of good educational attunement if (i) an educator has the ability to deliver the material in a variety of ways, and (ii) the content is configured so that students are able to engage with it in a variety of ways (for example because it includes learning tasks of varying difficulties, or because it caters for different learning styles, such as kinesthetic as well as visual or verbal). The possibility of educational attunement is also present in the ways in which academics respond to students' questions, and the degree to which these responses are aligned with what a student asks or expresses (as well as what they do not ask or express). In short, the possibility of attunement is present in each and every relational interaction within the university system.

As elements of relational hospitality, the educational significance of welcome, interpersonal recognition and attunement is supported by a range of research. A number of studies, for example, have demonstrated that emotional warmth, encouragement and actions that support social connectedness and student self-esteem have positive effects on both academic progress and student mental well-being (Azmitia et al., 2013; Carr et al., 2013; Finn, 2017). Such findings make sense if we consider that the ability to learn, think clearly and engage in higher order cognitive tasks (for example integrating knowledge from across disparate domains) is easier when we are: (i) emotionally calm (a state that is dependent in part upon being able to self-regulate emotionally); (ii) have a sense of self-efficacy (our perceived ability to set goals and take constructive action towards them);

and (iii) are able to persevere through the difficulty that is often inherent in learning, including periods of feeling that one is 'not getting it' or 'not making progress'. Although the transition to university has the potential to disrupt a student's sense of emotional calm and self-efficacy – and thus to impair temporarily his/her/their academic progress – practices of relational hospitality can have an ameliorating effect. Feeling welcomed, recognised and attuned to generally increases a student's capacity to settle, to engage with new material and to learn.

The educational significance of welcome, interpersonal recognition and attunement is further supported by insights from emotional geographies and relational psychotherapy (Stolorow and Atwood, 2002; Davidson et al., 2005; Smith et al., 2009; Stern, 1985, 2004). A foundational insight in both these fields is that a person's context influences how they think, feel and behave in any given moment, as well as the forms of selfhood they exhibit over longer periods of time. As a person dwells within and moves between the various environments that characterise his/her/their life course, so the material and relational dimensions of these settings inevitably has a bearing on the development and form of subjectivity and personhood (Conradson, 2003, 2005). This perspective on the spacing of subjectivity and selfhood is relevant not only to the domain of psychotherapy but also to educational institutions, including those settings where students and academics come together for the purpose of learning.

FOSTERING SUPPORTIVE LEARNING ENVIRONMENTS WITHIN GEOGRAPHY PROGRAMMES

Alongside the more general practices of welcome, interpersonal recognition and attunement, there are discipline-specific opportunities to cultivate supportive learning environments for students of geography. Here I discuss three pedagogical practices in particular. Our traditions of residential fieldtrips and group work offer important opportunities, as each has the potential to foster social connectedness and to help students feel they are part of a cohort. There is also the possibility of organising our assessment practices in ways that minimise anxiety. Each of these possibilities for fostering supportive learning environments for students of geography – residential fieldtrips, group work and assessment approaches – can be discussed in turn.

For academics working in the field of geography, residential fieldtrips can be a useful setting in which to foster connections among students, and to engage with them in ways that build confidence and cultivate their willingness to engage with new ideas (see Chapter 7 in this volume by Ramdas, for a discussion of fieldwork as a transition pedagogy). Living together for a period of time provides an opportunity for students to develop collegial relationships with their peers, as well as with faculty and staff members (Kent et al., 1997; Hope 2009). Although residential fieldtrips are typically expensive in terms of academic time and financial resources – and have consequently come under pressure, in view of budgetary constraints and health and safety considerations – their educational value continues to be recognised (Fuller and France 2015). In their research on the effects of residential fieldwork, Walsh et al. (2014, p. 379) noted 'the increased connectedness of our field trip group' and that 'students had begun to feel part of a community of learners'; in short, their investigation demonstrated the 'pedagogical and pastoral value of residential fieldwork' (p. 380). Through the tasks undertaken and the social interaction that occurs, residential fieldtrips enable students to connect with their peers in ways that can help them navigate the complexities and unfamiliarity of a university setting. Even when not undertaken in a residential form, Boyle et al. (2007) found that fieldwork tended to increase students' positive feeling towards and engagement with their studies.

As a form of collaborative learning (Healey et al., 1996), group work also has the potential to help students as they transition to university. In group work, students must learn how to communicate effectively, to negotiate differences, to deal with conflict, and to draw upon their collective expertise in a coordinated fashion, so as to complete a shared task. These skills are academically and professionally valuable, but their development also requires students to employ or develop a measure of interest in and attunement to each other. The connections which result can help to offset the relative anonymity of some forms of undergraduate education, particularly when it orients around large group lectures.

In their review of the advantages of group work in geography, Healey et al. (1996) identified a number of academic benefits – including the ability to tackle larger and more complex problems, and to facilitate active learning – but also noted that group work offered students 'a sense of belonging and a source of mutual support' (p. 169). Although conflict and tension can occur in group work (Tuckman 1965), the group environment typically enables students to share knowledge and resources in a manner that can compensate for individual differences in capacity and capability. The group environment may also increase student awareness of the challenges their peers experience at university, including issues such as balancing their studies with part-time employment, experiences of disability, and family caring roles. The group can thus assist students to develop a deeper understanding of the personal and structural factors that shape learning, as well as enabling them to meet others who may be grappling with challenges similar to their own.

Another way in which to foster supportive learning environments for geography students is through the thoughtful design of assessment tasks. Most contemporary universities employ a range of formal assessment tasks as a means to evaluate students' learning within a given course (or unit, or module, depending on the local terminology). These assessments are used to determine students' academic performance relative to their peers and in relation to external criteria. At the same time, there are often pressures to make assessment processes more 'efficient', by reducing the time and effort involved in evaluating student work. Such pressures typically lead towards standardised assessments, such as online quizzes and multichoice tests, which tend not to generate rich feedback. In addition, in large first-year classes there is often limited opportunity for students to engage in developmental conversations with academic staff regarding their work, if only because of the numbers of students relative to staff. For these and other reasons, it is no great surprise that many students feel anxious about assessment tasks, in ways that have the potential to disrupt their academic performance and even their progression through a degree programme.

There are a number of approaches to assessment that can help to mitigate such anxiety, including formative and self-assessment (see, in this volume, Chapter 6 by Fouberg and Chapter 27 by Hill and Worth, for further discussion). Formative assessment can be used to give students the opportunity to deepen their understanding and competence through a sequence of linked assignments. Constructive feedback can be given on each assignment, in a manner that combines an appreciation of its strengths and an indication of how it might be developed further. The educational intention (and hope) here is that the student will use the feedback to develop and improve their subsequent items of work. Rather than submitting a research dissertation or undergraduate senior project as a single completed item, for example, a formative assessment approach might allow a student to submit versions of the core elements (for example a literature review, methodology section, findings section(s), an introduction and conclusion) in a sequential fashion, spaced out over time. Specific feedback would be given on each element submitted, so as to help the student understand its strengths and weaknesses, and how to develop and improve it (if necessary). By submitting draft versions of the key project elements in this way, a student could be supported to learn as they proceed, rather than only discovering the merits and limitations of their work after final submission (at which point it is too late to adjust one's practice, except in future assessment tasks). Spacing out the component parts of an assignment across time can also help students to develop a more consistent rhythm to their academic work, as opposed to one characterised by periods of great intensity immediately prior to deadlines.

Self-assessment is another approach which can be employed to allay assessment-related anxiety. It can help to reduce the mysteriousness of the assessment process (as the student has to become familiar with the characteristics of unsatisfactory, satisfactory, good and excellent work, and use a short template to evaluate their own work prior to submission). Self-assessment can help to reduce a student's sense that their grade is a matter of an academic delivering a final and unyielding judgement on their work, in a manner which may feel discouraging and/or mystifying, especially if the outcome is not particularly positive. The capacity of self-assessment to rebalance the power relationship between the student and their assessor can be increased if the student's self-assessment will determine a non-trivial proportion of their final grade (for example 15 per cent), as long as the self-assessment includes a coherent justification relative to a set of agreed criteria.

Each of these three pedagogical activities – residential fieldtrips, group work, and formative and self-assessment approaches – has the potential to foster the kinds of social connectedness and belonging that can support students as they transition from school or employment to the university environment. And each can be supported by practices of welcome, interpersonal recognition and attunement. For both students and educators, however, the contemporary university can be a busy and demanding place, and in such circumstances it is all too easy for interpersonal interactions to become relatively transactional ('how can I obtain A from person B so that I can undertake task C?') and less 'relational'. In addition, the spread of commercialism within universities in Australia, Canada, New Zealand, the United Kingdom and the United States tends to nudge academic staff and students towards the roles of content provider and customer respectively, and this too can work against more relational forms of education. So while there is a need for learning environments that support students as they transition to university, the creation of such environments – both as a matter of daily practice and as part of institutional efforts over longer time scales – is not always straightforward. It is important, however, and in my view is therefore deserving of effort and attention.

CONCLUSION

Seeking to create supportive learning environments is one way in which educators can help students navigate the sometimes challenging transition to university. As noted, supportive learning environments can be fostered through particular pedagogical practices (for example residential fieldtrips, group work and alternative assessment approaches) and by the expression of relational hospitality (of which welcome, interpersonal recognition and attunement are significant elements). There are of course other activities which can contribute to supportive learning environments that have not been discussed here, including student geographical associations, peer mentoring schemes, service-based learning opportunities, and internships (particularly where the host organisation is committed to providing a positive and developmental working experience). Within academic departments and programmes, the creation of supportive learning environments can be considered complementary to the academic skills workshops and support services provided centrally at most universities nowadays.

In any given academic department or programme, there will be opportunities to employ existing pedagogical activities in ways that not only promote academic development but which also foster a supportive learning community. In the discussion here, I considered two commonly used pedagogical practices in geography – residential fieldtrips and group work – that can be used to facilitate social connectedness and a sense of support among students. I also looked at formative and self-assessment approaches, as these can be useful for increasing student engagement and reducing anxiety. The most effective and relevant suite of pedagogical practices will of course vary for any given department, but I would suggest that fostering a supportive learning environment is best handled as a collaborative process, in which representatives from both academic staff and undergraduate students come together to share their insights and experience. When academics and students convene in this way, it has the potential to create new forms of social connection and collaboration within a programme of study.

Although no simple panacea, supportive learning environments can help students as they negotiate the transition to university. When students feel welcomed, recognised and attuned to, they will typically be more at ease and better able to learn. In turn, this will increase the likelihood that they will both complete their studies and be well positioned to move forward in their lives and work. Given the current challenges with student progression and retention in many universities, this would be a very positive development.

USEFUL RESOURCES

- Christie, H. (2009) 'Emotional journeys: Young people and transitions to university', *British Journal of Sociology of Education*, 30(2), pp. 123–136.
- Tinto, V. (2012) *Completing College: Rethinking Institutional Action*. Chicago: University of Chicago Press.

ACKNOWLEDGEMENTS

I am grateful to Sarah Dyer for her helpful editorial comments on a previous version of this chapter.

NOTE

1. The underlying observation here is that our nervous systems are constantly examining the environments in which we find ourselves, assessing them for both safety and potential danger. The relational dynamics and associations of particular learning spaces can thus exert a significant influence upon a student's nervous system, and in both subtle and more obvious ways this can impact a student's capacity to engage in the higher order cognitive tasks typical of a university education.

REFERENCES

Andrews, B. and J.M. Wilding (2004) 'The relation of depression and anxiety to life-stress and achievement in students', *British Journal of Psychology*, 95, pp. 509–521.
Australian Council for Educational Research (ACER) (2011) 'Dropout DNA, and the genetics of effective support', *Australasian Survey of Student Engagement Research Briefing*, 11. Available at: https://www.acer.org/files/AUSSE_Research_Briefing_Vol11.pdf (accessed: 15 July 2018).
Azmitia, M., M. Syed and K. Radmacher (2013) 'Finding your niche: Identity and emotional support in emerging adults' adjustment to the transition to college', *Journal of Research on Adolescence*, 23(4), pp. 744–761.
Benton, S.A., J.M. Robertson, W.-C. Tseng, F.B. Newton and S.L. Benton (2003) 'Changes in counseling center client problems across 13 years', *Professional Psychology: Research and Practice*, 34(1), pp. 66–72.
Blanco, C., M. Okuda, C. Wright, D.S. Hasin, B.F. Grant, S.-M. Liu and M. Olfson (2008) 'Mental health of college students and their non-college-attending peers: Results from the National Epidemiologic Study on Alcohol and Related Conditions', *Archives of General Psychiatry*, 65(12), pp. 1429–1437.
Boyle, A., S. Maguire, A. Martin, C. Milson, R. Nash, S. Rawlinson, A. Turner, S. Wurthmann and S. Conchie (2007) 'Fieldwork is good: The student perception and the affective domain', *Journal of Geography in Higher Education*, 31(2), pp. 299–317.
Carr, S., K. Colthurst, M. Coyle and D. Elliott (2013) 'Attachment dimensions as predictors of mental health and psychosocial well-being in the transition to university', *European Journal of Psychology of Education*, 28(2), pp. 157–172.
Chow, K. and M. Healey (2008) 'Place attachment and place identity: First-year undergraduates making the transition from home to university', *Journal of Environmental Psychology*, 28(4), pp. 362–372.
Christie, H. (2009) 'Emotional journeys: Young people and transitions to university', *British Journal of Sociology of Education*, 30(2), pp. 123–136.
Christie, H., M. Munro and T. Fisher (2004) 'Leaving university early: Exploring the differences between continuing and non-continuing students', *Studies in Higher Education*, 29, pp. 617–636.
Conradson, D. (2003) 'Spaces of care in the city: The place of a community drop-in centre', *Social and Cultural Geography*, 4(4), pp. 507–525.
Conradson, D. (2005) 'Landscape, care and the relational self: Therapeutic encounters in southern England', *Health and Place*, 11(4), pp. 337–348.
Cook, L.J. (2007) 'Striving to help college students with mental health issues', *Journal of Psychosocial Nursing and Mental Health Services*, 45(4), pp. 40–44.
Davidson, J., L. Bondi and M. Smith (eds) (2005) *Emotional Geographies*. Burlington, VT, USA and Aldershot, UK: Ashgate.
Eisenberg, D., S.E. Gollust, E. Golberstein, and J.L. Hefner (2007) 'Prevalence and correlates of depression, anxiety, and suicidality among university students', *American Journal of Orthopsychiatry*, 77(4), pp. 534–542.
Finn, K. (2017) 'Multiple, relational and emotional mobilities: Understanding student mobilities in higher education as more than "staying local" and "going away"', *British Educational Research Journal*, 43(4), pp. 743–758.
Fuller, I.C. and D. France (2015) 'Securing field learning using a twenty-first century Cook's Tour', *Journal of Geography in Higher Education*, 39(1), pp. 58–172.

Gallagher, R., A. Gill and H. Sysko (2000) *National Survey of Counseling Center Directors*. Alexandria, VA: International Association of Counseling Services.

Garlow, S., J. Rosenberg, J. Moore, A. Hass, B. Koestner, H. Hendin and C. Nemeroff (2008) 'Depression, desperation, and suicidal ideation in college students: Results from the American Foundation for Suicide Prevention College Screening Project at Emory University', *Depression and Anxiety*, 25(6), pp. 482–488.

Gill, N. (2018) 'The suppression of welcome', *Fennia – International Journal of Geography*, 196(1), pp. 88–98.

Gotlib, I.H. (1984) 'Depression and general psychopathology in university students', *Journal of Abnormal Psychology*, 93(1), pp. 19–30.

Healey, M., H. Matthews, I. Livingstone and I. Foster (1996) 'Learning in small groups in university geography courses: Designing a core module around group projects', *Journal of Geography in Higher Education*, 20(2), pp. 167–180.

Holton, M. (2015) 'Adapting relationships with place: Investigating the evolving place attachment and "sense of place" of UK higher education students during a period of intense transition', *Geoforum*, 59(1), pp. 21–29.

Hope, M. (2009) 'The importance of direct experience: A philosophical defence of fieldwork in human geography', *Journal of Geography in Higher Education*, 33(2), pp. 169–182.

Kallio, K. and J. Riding (2018) 'Geographies of welcome', *Fennia – International Journal of Geography*, 196(2), pp. 131–136.

Kent, M., D. Gilbertson and C. Hunt (1997) 'Fieldwork in geography teaching: A critical review of the literature and approaches', *Journal of Geography in Higher Education*, 21(3), pp. 313–332.

Kitzrow, M.A. (2009) 'The mental health needs of today's college students: Challenges and recommendations', *NASPA Journal*, 46(4), pp. 646–660.

McMillan, W. (2013) 'Transition to university: The role played by emotion', *European Journal of Dental Education*, 17(3), pp. 169–176.

Nemiroff, G. (1992) *Reconstructing Education: Toward a Pedagogy of Critical Humanism*, New York: Bergin & Garvey.

Rogers, C. (1983) *Freedom to Learn for the 80s*, London: C.E. Merrill Publishing Company.

Sennett, R. (2004) *Respect in a World of Inequality*, New York: Norton.

Siegel, D. (2012), *The Developing Mind: How Relationships and the Brain Interact to Shape Who We Are*, New York: Guilford Press.

Smith, M., J. Davidson, L. Cameron and L. Bondi (2009) *Emotion, Place and Culture*, Aldershot: Ashgate.

Stallman, H.M. (2010) 'Psychological distress in university students: A comparison with general population data', *Australian Psychologist*, 45(4), pp. 249–257.

Stern, D. (1985) *The Interpersonal World of the Infant*, New York: Basic Books.

Stern, D. (2004) *The Present Moment in Psychotherapy and Everyday Life*, New York: W.W. Norton and Company.

Stolorow, R.D. and G.E. Atwood (2002) *Contexts of Being: The Intersubjective Foundations of Psychological Life*, London: Routledge.

Tinto, V. (2012) *Completing College: Rethinking Institutional Action*, Chicago, IL: University of Chicago Press.

Tuckman, B.W. (1965) 'Developmental sequence in small groups', *Psychological Bulletin*, 63(6), pp. 384–399.

Walsh, C., L. Larsen and D. Parry (2014) 'Building a community of learning through early residential fieldwork', *Journal of Geography in Higher Education*, 38(3), pp. 373–382.

Weiner-Levy, N. (2008) 'Universities as a meeting point with new academic knowledge, society and culture: Cognitive and emotional transitions during higher education', *Cambridge Journal of Education*, 38(4), pp. 497–512.

Zivin, K., D. Eisenberg, S.E. Gollust and E. Golberstein (2009) 'Persistence of mental health problems and needs in a college student population', *Journal of Affective Disorders*, 117(3), pp. 180–185.

9. Teaching in a multi- or interdisciplinary context
Amy L. Griffin

GEOGRAPHY, AN INTERDISCIPLINARY SUBJECT

Many university geography teaching staff are no strangers to multi- and interdisciplinary research teams.[1] Indeed, we are often members of such teams. As a group, geographers have a long history of stepping across disciplinary boundaries. One early president of the American Association of Geographers in fact insisted on the necessity of this practice: 'Progress is ever through the interaction of the sciences one on another; and scientific trespass is one of the profitable modes of interaction' (Gilbert, 1909, p. 122). While problems such as inconsistencies in language and epistemology present challenges, geographers are often well placed to overcome these challenges because of the breadth of perspectives within the discipline and the myriad contexts to which geographical thinking is applied. Furthermore, interactions with other disciplines have profoundly shaped the evolution of geographers' thinking about key geographical concepts, such as space, risk, and landscape (Clifford et al., 2009, p. xv).

As university budgets become more constrained there is ever more pressure on scholars to focus on impactful teaching and research – that which leads to solutions to society's big problems and to producing graduates who can solve these problems in real-world contexts.[2] In a globally interconnected world, many problems are not easily solvable by drawing upon narrow subject-matter expertise. For example, devising solutions to global climate change requires that we understand the physical processes involved (climatological, hydrological, and earth sciences), potential technological 'fixes' such as reducing carbon emissions generated by industrial processes or transportation modes (engineering) and the human behaviours and practices that generate carbon emissions (urban planning, economics, political science, psychology). Thus, it is critical that teachers of geography help their students prepare for collaboration with colleagues who have expertise in different areas. This collaboration may take multiple forms, though in practice multidisciplinary collaboration may be a more common form of teamwork than interdisciplinary collaboration, both inside and outside the academy.

In many countries, geography programmes now sit within either multi- or interdisciplinary administrative structures (Holmes, 2002; Wainwright et al., 2014; Hall et al., 2015).[3] Although such structures might intuitively seem to encourage interdisciplinary collaboration in teaching and learning as well as in research activities, in practice they lead to both opportunities and challenges. Further, we are perhaps less prepared to meet these challenges in the context of our teaching than we are in our research. This circumstance may arise when we have a tacit, rather than explicit, understanding of how geography's disciplinary character shapes our teaching.

This chapter begins by discussing what makes a discipline and how disciplines inform the way we structure learning activities for our students.[4] It then presents a discussion of the skills needed for, and a model of, interdisciplinary collaboration, followed by the pedagogical implications raised by the model. It next identifies some practical pedagogical activities that can be used to develop students' capabilities to participate in interdisciplinary learning. Finally, it concludes with a discussion of the practical challenges involved in multi- and interdisciplinary teaching.

WHAT MAKES A DISCIPLINE AND WHAT IS A DISCIPLINE'S ROLE IN TEACHING AND LEARNING?

The increasing specialization of knowledge that gathered speed beginning in the 1800s led to the development of a strong connection between academic disciplines and undergraduate teaching programmes. At the same time, being able to work effectively in teams became more important – largely because, with the general increase in knowledge, it became less possible for any one individual to acquire all of the knowledge needed to solve a given problem. A fundamental skill required for effective teamwork is understanding one's own role and potential contributions to the programme of work the team aims to accomplish. In the case of multi- or interdisciplinary teams specifically, this requires an understanding of how one's own disciplinary knowledge may be applied to the problem and thereby contribute to the team's capabilities. Thus, in order to be multi- or interdisciplinary we must first be disciplinary, and a critical part of preparing geography students for multi- and interdisciplinary work is helping them to achieve a strong grounding in their own discipline. After all, it is hardly possible to explain a concept or an approach clearly to someone else if one does not understand it oneself. Given this, we might then ask which aspects of disciplinary self-knowledge are most important in this regard, and a short list might include the discipline's epistemology, methods, discourse, and culture.

An epistemology is a theory of how we know something, and different disciplines have different epistemologies. A classic example of this can be found in the legend that has arisen from Huxley and Wilberforce's infamous argument about the origin of species at the British Association in 1860. According to the legend, Huxley argued that humans evolved from other species, basing his argument on inductive reasoning from observations of the natural world, whereas Wilberforce argued that humans were created by God, using the Bible's description of the origins of humankind as the basis for his argument.[5] In other words, biology and theology base their understandings of how we know something (how the human species came to be) on different forms of evidence (observation of the world versus appeals to the authority of a religious text).

In comparison with many other disciplines, geographers tolerate (perhaps even encourage) a wider range of epistemologies including among others, geographical writing, mapping, field observation, laboratory experimentation, and conversation (Withers, 2011).[6] The editors of the volume *Key Concepts in Geography* argue not for *a* geographical tradition, but demonstrate how geographers work within several traditions by commissioning chapters exploring geographers' engagement with each: those of the physical sciences, social sciences and humanities (Clifford et al., 2009). One might, on this basis, describe 'geography's tradition' as one of ontological and epistemological pluralism.

However, the purpose of this chapter is neither to summarize nor debate what constitutes geography's epistemology. I leave that to historians and philosophers of geography. Rather, the salient point for thinking about geography teaching within multi- and interdisciplinary contexts is that different disciplines have different epistemologies, leading to flow-on effects on judgments that teachers make about what constitutes valid knowledge and valid methods of inquiry. In some disciplinary pairings these epistemologies may even be incompatible and irreconcilable, as in the case of the Oxford debate legend, making it a challenge to teach alongside each other. However, geography's diversity is an important resource we can draw upon when teaching in a multi- or interdisciplinary context. Our epistemological pluralism means that there may be substantial overlaps with other disciplinary epistemologies we encounter, which can support geographers when they engage intellectually with other disciplines' students and teaching staff.

A discipline's methods are shaped by its epistemological stance on what constitutes valid ways of understanding the world. Following on with the example of the Huxley/Wilberforce legend, biologists reject interpretation of a theological text as a valid method for and source of information for understanding the origin of species. Because of geography's ontological and epistemological pluralism, the methods geographers employ are both diverse and numerous. An indicator of this is that despite publishing no fewer than 64 different 'Key Concepts In. . .' student reference books for different disciplines (clearly a successful format!), SAGE Publications offers only one 'Key Methods In. . .' volume focused on geography. While the reasons for this may be multiple, the fact that *Key Methods in Geography* is now in its third edition is some indication that poor sales of methods texts is not likely to be the primary driver of this editorial decision. Instead, it may be an indication that the discipline has need of such a volume because of the diverse and numerous methods its practitioners deploy. This methodological diversity provides sites of potential shared understanding in interactions with other disciplines in teaching and scholarship. On the other hand, we might also reasonably ask what geography as a discipline can contribute to engagements with other disciplines. Here we could identify mapping space and place and spatial analytical methods as two unique contributions of the discipline to multi- and interdisciplinary teaching and scholarship.

Working in multi- and interdisciplinary contexts requires effective communication skills. A byproduct of a strong disciplinary grounding is communicative competence within the discipline. In fact, this competence might be a double-edged sword in a multi- and interdisciplinary world without a metacognitive understanding that *different* discursive strategies and use of language may need to be deployed when interacting with 'outsiders' from other disciplines (Taylor, 2018). Hyland (2004) foregrounds the role of disciplinary discourses in *creating* disciplines. In particular, he argues that how academics write is crucial to defining the differences between disciplines. By implication, a student's acceptance into a discipline is at least in part predicated upon their ability to effectively deploy disciplinary discourses. To be persuasive, academic writing must display an awareness of the kinds of framing of claims that the writing's readers will find both credible and convincing. That is, it must demonstrate a so-called insider's understanding of the discipline (Hyland, 2006).

Finally, disciplines have distinct cultures, and these cultures can hinder effective communication when teachers lack awareness of either their own culture or those of others. Becher (1981, 1987) and Becher and Trowler (2001) have written extensively about disciplinary cultures, arguing that disciplinary knowledge structures are a primary determinant shaping academic practices, and are composed of cognitive and social dimensions. Like all cultures, disciplinary cultures are sometimes explicit, sometimes tacit, and largely unexamined by their practitioners. Becher's ideas have been widely critiqued as being epistemologically too essentialist, failing to account for the role of a number of factors in shaping practices, including local organizational context and individual identity (Trowler, 2012). Of particular interest here is the concept of a disciplinary learning culture in which there are commonly implemented pedagogies within a discipline. This concept is linked closely with Shulman's (2005) notion of signature pedagogy – one that is pervasively found within the curriculum in a discipline, and is often associated strongly with a profession (for example doing clinical rounds in medicine). One account of a geographical learning culture that is commonly referenced is Healey and Jenkins' (2000) description of geographical pedagogy as often involving learning-by-doing.

Each of these aspects of disciplinary identity is a key site of reproduction of the discipline. They form the basis through which that identity is developed among students. Because being able to communicate what one's own discipline has to offer is an important skill for multi- and interdisciplinary collaboration (among staff who are teaching and among students who are learning), attention to developing explicit, rather than tacit, knowledge of the discipline can prepare both staff and students for teaching and learning in multi- and interdisciplinary contexts.

TEACHING STUDENTS TO BECOME MULTI- AND INTERDISCIPLINARY THINKERS

When thinking about how to structure and develop activities that will help students learn to become multi- and interdisciplinary thinkers, we can look to the resources geography offers through its own internal diversity. However, we can also look to the work of scholars who study the pedagogy of interdisciplinary learning and that of scholars who study how successful interdisciplinary research teams function.

In their systematic review of pedagogical research about how to support students to become effective interdisciplinary thinkers, Spelt et al. (2009) identified five subskills of interdisciplinary thinking: knowledge of disciplines, knowledge of disciplinary paradigms, knowledge of interdisciplinarity, higher-order cognitive skills (for example the ability to switch between different disciplinary perspectives), and communication skills (for example resolving language differences to develop shared understanding). One would hope that existing geography curricula, even in the absence of an overt effort to develop skills in multi- and interdisciplinary thinking, would provide a strong grounding in the first two of these for the discipline of geography itself. It is perhaps worth emphasizing that developing the latter two capabilities requires foundational knowledge of a discipline. This implies that although it is useful to demonstrate that geographers can contribute successfully to multi- and interdisciplinary work and knowledge creation during the early years of the programme, explicit attention to developing multi- and interdisciplinary collaboration skills is perhaps best placed in later years of the curriculum when students have a sufficiently strong understanding of their own discipline to be able to both understand and communicate what it offers to teams.

Pennington (2016) presents a conceptual model that although built to describe and predict the conditions that lead to successful interdisciplinary research teams, can also be used to provide guidance on the kinds of learning activities that might be used to support students to develop the ability think in multi- and interdisciplinary modes. In applying her model, the distinction between and requirements of multi- and interdisciplinary team-work become important. An understanding of the difference between the two modes of thinking points to the different skills needed for each, and therefore the kinds of learning activities that might develop these skills.

In multidisciplinary modes, each team member focuses on applying his or her disciplinary knowledge to a well-defined shared problem or question, but is not necessarily required to combine that knowledge with other disciplinary expertise or perspectives to generate a new understanding of the problem or question. For example, when an ecologist and a mathematician collaborate to study predator–prey population dynamics, the ecologist contributes an understanding of the biological and environmental requirements of the two species, while the mathematician brings skills in solving Lokta-Volterra equations to the collaboration. Neither scholar needs a deep understanding of the other's domain to work effectively together to build the model: the ecologist describes and parameterizes the domain problem while the mathematician, using those parameters, applies one of her disciplinary tools to solving the equations.

What may be most helpful then, when working in multidisciplinary modes, is a strong grounding in one's own discipline, and an ability to recognize how disciplinary expertise (and that of teammates) maps onto the shared problem or question, in what Pennington calls transactive memory. Note that this does not require a shared understanding (mental model) of the problem or question. An understanding of where one's own expertise fits within one's own understanding of the problem or question is sufficient. Following the example of the population dynamics model, each of the team members needs to know what she or he needs to contribute to solving the problem, and they exchange the knowledge needed for each team member to do their job. The challenges of communication when working in a multidisciplinary mode relate primarily to the coordination of work across team members rather than integrating the knowledge of team members to produce a new conceptual understanding, such as identifying a previously unknown parameter that is needed to describe predator–prey population dynamics. A collaborative, project-based approach, centred around a well-defined problem or question may work well for helping students to develop the communication skills needed for multidisciplinary collaboration.

While it is possible for an individual with a sufficiently deep grounding in multiple disciplines to undertake interdisciplinary thinking on their own (Klein, 2014), it is typical that such thinking is distributed across a team. This creates new challenges in communication, but also generates substantial benefits in a well-functioning team, as the range of potential disciplinary knowledge and perspectives that can be incorporated is greater, and the (substantial) cognitive burden of achieving new insights can be shared across team members. I present one interpretation of the main features of Pennington's model here and then discuss how it might be used to think about appropriate pedagogical strategies and practical techniques for helping students to build the skills needed to engage in interdisciplinary thinking (Figure 9.1).

Pennington's model identifies knowledge exchange activities as a requirement for developing and growing integrated knowledge capital (IKC). IKC is composed of knowledge that is held by more than one member of the team, although the full extent of knowledge may not be equally accessible to all members of the team (Figure 9.1a). Knowledge exchange activities generate individual transformational learning, in other words, growth

Integrated Knowledge Capital (IKC)

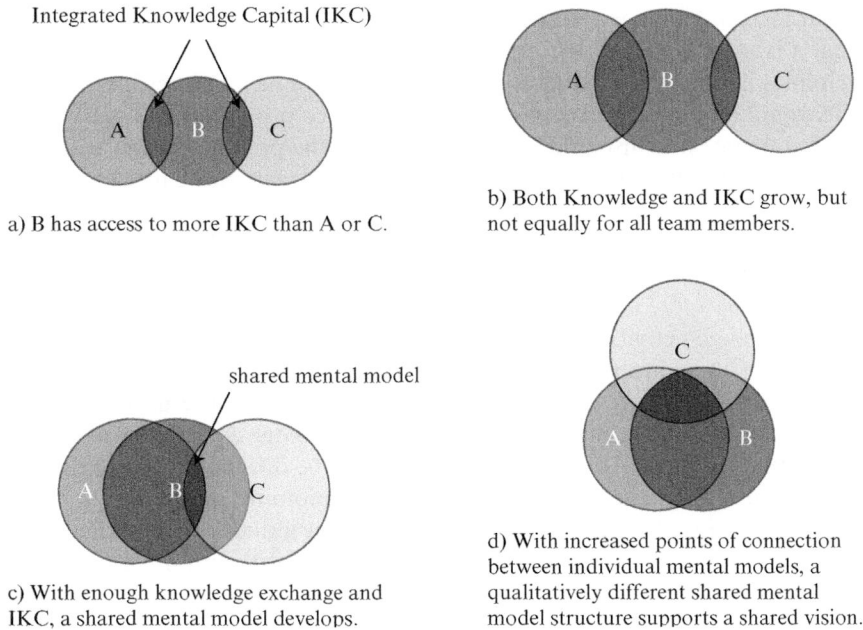

a) B has access to more IKC than A or C.

b) Both Knowledge and IKC grow, but not equally for all team members.

shared mental model

c) With enough knowledge exchange and IKC, a shared mental model develops.

d) With increased points of connection between individual mental models, a qualitatively different shared mental model structure supports a shared vision.

Figure 9.1   An interpretation of how mental models change using Pennington's (2016) model of interdisciplinary research teamwork

of an individual's mental model of a problem or research question to accommodate new perspectives from other disciplines (Figure 9.1b). As team members experience individual transformational learning events, integrated knowledge capital increases, and more points of connection develop between individuals' mental models, creating integrated knowledge capital that *is* held by all team members, improving shared mental models (Figure 9.1c). With enough connection points, individuals restructure their mental models into something that has a qualitatively different structure, forming the basis for truly new ideas and a shared vision of how to solve the problem or answer the research question (Figure 9.1d).

Next, I turn my attention to some implications of Pennington's (2016) model for pedagogical practice.

IMPLICATIONS OF THE MODEL FOR PEDAGOGICAL PRACTICE

Students Need Some Disciplinary Grounding to Engage in Successful Interdisciplinary Thinking

If students have very limited disciplinary knowledge (illustrated in Figure 9.1 by the size of the circles), there will be limited integrated knowledge capital among group members (the total area of overlap between circles will be small). As interdisciplinary practice almost always involves the sharing of disciplinary perspectives on a problem or research question (at least in teams without long experience of working together), Taylor (2018) argues that it is an activity best left until students are at least partially socialized into their own disciplines. Nevertheless, students may benefit from having interdisciplinary thinking and learning modeled in earlier years of the degree programme, especially during a student's first degree in a discipline, perhaps through the presentation of case studies of interdisciplinary thinking, research, and teamwork, to demonstrate its benefits.

Student Teams (or Classroom Cohorts) Should be Composed of Students from Disciplines that have an Intermediate Level of Conceptual Distance: a Goldilocks Pairing

Knowledge exchange activities are needed to increase integrated knowledge capital, and the further apart the conceptual distance between disciplines (represented by distance between the centres of the disciplinary circles in Figure 9.1), the more difficult it will be to bridge gaps in understanding and the more knowledge exchange will be needed to create IKC. Pennington (2016) proposes tradeoffs in the difficulty of successfully working together, but also in the creative potential of combining disciplinary expertise. As the conceptual distance between disciplines increases, it induces greater challenges – but also generates greater creative benefits. This is consistent with empirical studies showing that teams tend to work most effectively when there is a moderate level of difference in collaborators' knowledge (Wenger, 2000), and is also consistent with the well-known Yerkes–Dodson Law (Yerkes and Dodson, 1908), which proposes that performance on a task is best under moderate levels of challenge. When the disciplinary differences are too great, the communication challenges may be sufficiently large so as to impede the development of any shared understanding. When the disciplinary differences are too small, there may be limited potential for the transformation of mental models into a qualitatively different form.

Pennington (2016) further suggests that different levels of conceptual distance may require differently structured interactions between individual team members, with conference-type presentations and informal exchanges sufficing if the conceptual distance is small, while greater effort is required to communicate disciplinary fundamentals and how they relate to the problem of interest if the distance is large. She draws a distinction between verbal expressions of knowledge (speech, writing), and graphic expressions (diagrams), and notes that for large conceptual distances, while verbal modes may be more expressive, they may also overwhelm the other team members with too much detail, whereas the abstraction and simplification required when generating graphics and diagrams may help to bridge a large conceptual gap more effectively.

Problem-Based Learning Approaches May Provide a Fertile Platform for Building the Skills Needed for and Practicing Interdisciplinary Thinking

Problem-based learning (PBL) approaches require students to engage with problem scenarios, identify needed knowledge and skills for solving the problem, acquire the needed knowledge and skills, and then apply them to the problem (Pawson et al., 2006). It is notable that a number of authors have made the connection between interdisciplinary learning and problem-based learning approaches (for example, Nikitina, 2006; Rickles and Ellul, 2015; Brassler and Dettmers, 2017; Persov et al., 2017). Often conducted in teams, PBL exercises typically require student interactions with knowledge, methods, and collaborators from multiple disciplines, because many real-world problems are ill-structured, messy, and fall into the cracks between disciplines. Interdisciplinary learning is by nature problem-focused because it is certainly easier to integrate only the knowledge required for the solution of a single problem than that of entire domains. Thus, there is a level of coherence in the two concepts, even if interdisciplinary learning is not guaranteed to be a product of a problem-based learning approach (Stentoft, 2017). Yet, Pennington (2016) suggests that it is precisely the vague and messy nature of ill-structured problems that provides a productive environment for interdisciplinary learning, and an encouraging basis for exploring the potential of a problem-based learning approach in supporting students to develop interdisciplinary thinking capabilities.

Extended and Repeated Interactions Between Students Within a Cohort May Assist in the Development of Strong Communication Skills that Support Interdisciplinary Thinking

The skills needed for interdisciplinary thinking can be developed (Mansilla, 2005), but as in the development of most skills, repeated practice and iteration are typically required to produce a team that functions well. In a study of existing interdisciplinary teams, Zajac et al. (2014) identified that communication is important at several different stages of the collaboration in order to develop and sustain team performance, with repeated communication episodes (that is, knowledge exchange) strengthening the team's shared mental model because they are iteratively exploring the problem space. Knowledge exchange supports the growth of the team's integrated knowledge capital, and is a fundamental activity in Pennington's (2016) model of interdisciplinary collaboration (Figure 9.1). This suggests that Taylor's (2018) contention that developing effective communication skills should be a key outcome of interdisciplinary courses is well founded.

If knowledge exchange can be spread over repeated interactions over time, such as across a semester or degree programme, the group may be more likely to reach a sufficiently shared understanding of a problem space to allow true interdisciplinary thinking and learning to occur. Two examples of approaches to structuring these repeated interactions are the HERO programme in North America and an interdisciplinary Master's degree programme in Europe. In the HERO programme, undergraduate students engage in a month-long programme of community-based, problem-centred, participatory action research, beginning with an intensive summer research apprenticeship, followed by a senior thesis or independent study programme (Cantor et al., 2015). A key skill developed during the summer apprenticeship is that of communication, both within and outside the team, as students are required to repeatedly present aspects of their research to multiple audiences with different types and levels of expertise, including their peers, graduate students, academic staff, and stakeholders in the broader community and university. In the European interdisciplinary Master's programme, students participate in three interdisciplinary courses across the degree programme (Spelt et al., 2016). In one of these three courses, students worked in groups to share their experiences of applying an interdisciplinary approach that combines expertise from technical (for example engineering) and management disciplines to a semester-long problem of food quality management. Notably, even with an entire semester devoted to solving the set task in interdisciplinary groups, and a demonstrated improvement in their ability to integrate disciplinary perspectives, students expressed that they had insufficient time or difficulties in managing time to interact with their peers to engage in interdisciplinary thinking.

Interdisciplinary Learning is an Inherently Social Process, so Attention Must be Paid not only to Cognitive, but also Affective and Interpersonal Dimensions of Learning

While any sort of learning involves some level of challenge, the individual transformational learning described by Pennington's model (Figure 9.1b), caused by exposure to new concepts from other disciplines, can often result in an individual feeling disoriented and uncomfortable (Pennington et al., 2013). Theorists Mezirow (1991) and Bransford et al. (2006) have described this process as cognitive struggle, and proposed that this struggle is required for truly creative, integrative thinking. Experienced interdisciplinary thinkers are aware that they are likely to encounter this struggle and adopt strategies for coping with the emotions that may arise (Parker and Hackett, 2012). Those learners who are caught unawares may misattribute the cause of the emotion and negatively value the learning experience as a result (Spelt et al., 2016). In addition to communicating to students that they should expect to experience cognitive struggle (and emphasizing the eventual benefits thereof), teachers and learning facilitators should pay attention to affective and interpersonal dimensions of interdisciplinary learning.

Psychological studies have demonstrated that people experiencing positive affective states are more likely to think creatively, make efficient decisions, and engage in conceptually-driven relational thinking (D'Mello and Graesser, 2012). Negative emotions, if felt intensely, can lead to learners walking away from cognitive struggle (see Chapter 8 in this volume by Conradson, for a discussion of supportive learning environments). They can also negatively affect the development of trust between individuals, which is required for successful teamwork (Mansilla et al., 2016). Spelt et al. (2016) suggest that interventions which help students to understand the cause of confusion (for example cognitive struggle) may lead to better interdisciplinary learning outcomes. Bracken and Oughton (2006) suggest that careful attention to the disciplinary composition of the interdisciplinary team may help to mitigate these emotions by providing team members with whom the learner can interact without cognitive struggle. They note that when there is more than one member of a given discipline on the team, they can act as an emotional support to counter frustration. Providing an outlet for learners to discuss their emotions might also lead them to discover they are not the only ones who find the interdisciplinary learning to be challenging.

While pedagogy can and should be informed by theoretical and conceptual models, ultimately, all of us standing in the classroom have to translate these theories into practical strategies. The following list presents a number of practical pedagogical strategies that have been reported in the literature to be helpful in developing skills and capabilities that learners need to develop to successfully practice interdisciplinary thinking.

1.   Create analogies and metaphors to explain key concepts in your discipline.
2.   Summarize and explain key concepts from *your own* discipline that are relevant to the problem under consideration (Spelt et al., 2016).
3.   Summarize and explain key concepts from *another* discipline that are relevant to the problem under consideration (Taylor, 2018).

4. Structure discussions to negotiate shared understanding of key concepts that may be defined differently in different disciplines (for example how is 'health' defined in my discipline?) (Taylor, 2018).
5. Use concepts from your discipline to debate an ethical issue (Taylor, 2018).
6. Externalize mental models via graphical means (Pennington, 2016).
7. Consume different discipline-informed writing styles as a precursor to developing the ability to write for all audiences (that is, accessibly) (Falkenberg and Tubb, 2017; Taylor, 2018).
8. Rewrite the abstract from a paper in another discipline in the style of your own discipline (Taylor, 2018).
9. Provide feedback on a piece of writing for a student from another discipline (Taylor, 2018).
10. Practice active listening.
11. Make repeated presentations to a range of different audiences from different backgrounds, developing an opportunity to practice the skill of explaining concepts to non-expert (in the presenter's discipline) audiences (Cantor et al., 2015; Hill et al., 2018).
12. Use a reflective learning journal to identify affective and interpersonal dimensions of learning (Spelt et al., 2016).

PRACTICAL CHALLENGES ASSOCIATED WITH HELPING STUDENTS TO LEARN HOW TO PRACTICE INTERDISCIPLINARY THINKING

Any discussion of teaching in multi- and interdisciplinary contexts would be incomplete if it failed to identify some of the challenges associated therewith. It should be clear that teaching in multi- and interdisciplinary contexts is cognitively challenging and more complex than monodisciplinary teaching, all the more so when that teaching becomes a multidisciplinary collaboration itself – that is, when undertaken in collaboration with a teacher from another discipline. While coordinating activities with teachers from other disciplines may present efficiencies, especially after long periods of close interaction, building the mutual trust that gets the collaboration to that stage often requires a considerable investment of time (Kawabata et al., 2010). Prior to achieving this trust, multi- and interdisciplinary teaching may instead require increased time and resources to undertake negotiation related to curriculum planning and coordination, in addition to (at least sometimes) copresence in the classroom to model effective multi- and interdisciplinary collaboration (Lyall et al., 2015; Spelt et al., 2016). Not only do learners need to spend the time and mental effort to negotiate disciplinary differences in epistemology, methods, traditions and culture, so do teaching staff; a fact that university managers who may have sought to achieve 'efficiencies' through multi- or interdisciplinary collaboration in teaching may fail to understand (McKendrick, 2001; Holmes, 2002). Additionally, when teaching takes place in multi- rather than interdisciplinary contexts, teachers may need to develop deeper knowledge of where students studying different degrees are coming from (for example what they do or do not already know) in order to create learning opportunities that will support all students. Thus, these efforts may be under-resourced.

CONCLUSIONS

Despite a self-image of interdisciplinary prowess, geographers have devoted comparatively little effort to thinking about the pedagogy of interdisciplinary learning. This is a situation that should change, because of the many benefits to the discipline of developing geography students who excel at interdisciplinary thinking. In addition to producing graduates who are better equipped to deal with many of the significant challenges facing the world today, there is evidence that students who are capable of moving between disciplines and synthesizing information are more likely to adopt deep learning approaches rather than surface learning approaches (Bradbeer, 1999). Ironically, geography students who are able to effectively undertake interdisciplinary work may develop a better-defined professional identity as geographers because interdisciplinary collaboration demands a deeper and more complete understanding of one's own discipline (Raento, 2009).

USEFUL RESOURCES

- Edelbroek, H., Mijnders M. and Post, G. (2018) *Interdisciplinary Learning Activities*, Amsterdam: Amsterdam University Press.
- Goldsmith, A.H., Hamilton, D., Hornsby, K. and Wells, D. (no date) *Interdisciplinary Approaches to Teaching*, Available at: https://serc.carleton.edu/sp/library/interdisci plinary/challenges_faci.html (accessed 1 August 2019).
- Pharo, E., Davison, A., McGregor, H., Warr, K. and Brown, P. (2014) 'Using communities of practice to enhance interdisciplinary teaching: lessons from four Australian institutions', *Higher Education Research and Development*, 33(2), pp. 341–354.

NOTES

1. Multidisciplinary teams are those composed of members who have different forms of expertise, each working independently to apply their expertise to the problem. Interdisciplinary teams are also made up of members with varying forms of expertise, but who work interdependently to develop a shared understanding of and solution to the problem.
2. The reality of these big problems notwithstanding, see Sparke's (2018) critique of how the modern, corporate university has hijacked the concept of interdisciplinarity for instrumental aims.
3. In different countries, these structures may be variously called schools, departments, or faculties, among other names.
4. The discussion here is limited to undergraduate and postgraduate coursework teaching. Geography research degrees, such as the PhD, which are often interdisciplinary in nature, are not considered here due to the different roles that teaching activities play in coursework versus research degrees.
5. In actual fact (rather than legend), Wilberforce's refutation of Huxley's argument appears to have been based on his own scientific assessment of Darwin's hypothesis (Lucas 1979).
6. Epistemological pluralism notwithstanding, in many geography teaching programmes, field observation is put forward as a prototypical way of 'doing geography,' thus underpinning the 'geographical' identity. See for example Tucker and Horton (2018) and Fuller et al. (2006), among others.

REFERENCES

Becher, T. (1981) 'Towards a definition of disciplinary cultures', *Studies in Higher Education*, 6(2), pp. 109–122.

Becher, T. (1987) 'Disciplinary discourse', *Studies in Higher Education*, 12(3), pp. 261–274.

Becher, T. and Trowler, P.R. (2001) *Academic Tribes and Territories*, Second Edition, Buckingham, UK: The Society for Research into Higher Education and Open University Press.

Bracken, L.J. and Oughton, E.A. (2006) '"What do you mean?" The importance of language in developing interdisciplinary research', *Transactions of the Institute of British Geographers*, 31(3), pp. 371–382.

Bradbeer, J. (1999) 'Barriers to interdisciplinarity: Disciplinary discourses and student learning', *Journal of Geography in Higher Education*, 23(3), pp. 381–396.

Bransford, J., Vye, N., Stevens, R., Kuhl, P., Schwartz, D., Bell, P., Meltzoff, A., Barron, B., Pea, R.D. and Reeves, B. (2006) 'Learning theories and education: Toward a decade of synergy', in Alexander, P.A. and Winne, P.H. (eds), *Handbook of Educational Psychology*, Second Edition, Mahwah, NJ: Erlbaum, pp. 209–244.

Brassler, M. and Dettmers, J. (2017) 'How to enhance interdisciplinary competence – Interdisciplinary problem-based learning versus interdisciplinary project-based learning', *Interdisciplinary Journal of Problem-Based Learning*, 11(2), DOI: 10.7771/1541-5015.1686.

Cantor, A., DeLauer, V., Martin, D. and Rogan, J. (2015) 'Training interdisciplinary "wicked problem" solvers: Applying lessons from HERO in community-based research experiences for undergraduates', *Journal of Geography in Higher Education*, 39(3), pp. 407–419.

Clifford, N.J., Holloway, S.L., Rice, S.P. and Valentine, G. (2009) 'Preface', in Clifford, N.J., Holloway, S.L., Rice, S.P. and Valentine, G. (eds), *Key Concepts in Geography*, Second Edition, Thousand Oaks, CA: Sage, pp. xiii–xvi.

D'Mello, S. and Graesser, A. (2012) 'Dynamics of affective states during complex learning', *Learning and Instruction*, 22(2), pp. 145–157.

Falkenberg, L.J. and Tubb, A. (2017) 'Undisciplined thinking facilitates accessible writing: A response to Doubleday and Connell', *Trends in Ecology & Evolution*, 32(12), pp. 894–895.

Fuller, I., Edmondson, S., France, D., Higgitt, D. and Ratinen, I. (2006) 'International perspectives on the effectiveness of Geography fieldwork for learning', *Journal of Geography in Higher Education*, 30(1), pp. 89–101.

Gilbert, G.K. (1909) 'Earthquake forecasts', *Science*, 29(734), pp. 121–138.

Hall, T., Toms, P., McGuinness, M., Parker, C. and Roberts, N. (2015) 'Where's the Geography department? The changing administrative place of Geography in UK higher education', *Area*, 47(1), pp. 56–64.

Healey, M. and Jenkins, A. (2000) 'Kolb's experiential learning theory and its application in geography in higher education', *Journal of Geography*, 99(5), pp. 185–195.

Hill, J., West, H. and Kneale, P. (2018) 'Preparing for multi-disciplinary undergraduate research conferences', *Journal of Geography in Higher Education*, 42(1), pp. 148–156.

Holmes, J.H. (2002) 'Geography's emerging cross-disciplinary links: Process, causes, outcomes and challenges', *Journal of Geography in Higher Education*, 40(1), pp. 2–20.

Hyland, K. (2004) *Disciplinary Discourses: Social Interactions in Academic Writing*, Ann Arbor, MI: University of Michigan Press.

Hyland, K. (2006) 'Disciplinary differences: Language variation in academic discourses', in Hyland, K. and Bondi, M. (eds), *Academic Discourse Across Disciplines*, Bern, Switzerland: Peter Lang, pp. 17–45.

Kawabata, M., Thapa, R.B., Oguchi, T. and Tsou, M.-H. (2010) 'Multidisciplinary collaboration in GIS education: A case study of US colleges and universities', *Journal of Geography in Higher Education*, 34(4), pp. 493–509.

Klein, J.T. (2014) 'Interdisciplinarity and transdisciplinarity: Keyword meanings for collaboration science and translational medicine', *Journal of Translational Medical Epidemiology*, 2(2), pp. 1024–1027.

Lyall, C., Meagher, L., Bandola, J. and Kettle, A. (2015) 'A masterclass in interdisciplinarity: Research into practice in training the next generation of interdisciplinary researchers', *Futures*, 44(6), pp. 608–617.

Lucas, J.R. (1979) 'Wilberforce and Huxley: A legendary encounter', *The Historical Journal*, 22(2), pp. 313–330.

Mansilla, V.B. (2005) 'Assessing student work at disciplinary crossroads', *Change: The Magazine of Higher Learning*, 37(1), pp. 14–21.

Mansilla, V.B., Lamont, M. and Sato, J. (2016) 'Shared cognitive-emotional-interactional platforms: Markers for successful interdisciplinary collaborations', *Science, Technology & Human Values*, 41(4), pp. 571–612.

McKendrick, J.H. (2001) 'What's the big deal? Resource and pedagogical implications of teaching Geography to non-geographers', *Journal of Geography in Higher Education*, 25(2), pp. 219–223.

Mezirow, J. (1991) *Transformative Dimensions of Adult Learning*, San Francisco, CA: Jossey-Bass.

Nikitina, S. (2006) 'Three strategies for interdisciplinary teaching: Contextualizing, conceptualizing, and problem-centring', *Journal of Curriculum Studies*, 38(3), pp. 251–271.

Parker, J.N. and Hackett, E.J. (2012) 'Hot spots and hot moments in scientific collaborations and social movements', *American Sociological Review*, 77(1), pp. 21–44.

Pawson, E., Fournier, E., Haigh, M., Muniz, O., Trafford, J. and Vajoczki, S. (2006) 'Problem-based learning in geography: Towards a critical assessment of its purposes, benefits and risks', *Journal of Geography in Higher Education*, 30(1), pp. 103–116.

Pennington, D. (2016) 'A conceptual model for knowledge integration in interdisciplinary teams: orchestrating individual learning and group processes', *Journal of Environmental Studies Science*, 6(2), pp. 300–312.

Pennington, D., Simpson, G.L., McConnell, M.S., Fair, J.M. and Baker, R.J. (2013) 'Transdisciplinary research, transformative learning, and transformative science', *Bioscience*, 63(7), pp. 564–573.

Persov, E., Yehuda, R., Kantor, R. and Pelman, B. (2017) 'PBL 2.0 Interdisciplinary, multicultural, transformative sustainable education for design students', *The Design Journal*, 20(sup1), pp. S1224–S1240.

Raento, P. (2009) 'Interdisciplinarity', in Kitchin, R. and Thrift, N. (eds), *International Encyclopedia of Human Geography*, Amsterdam: Elsevier Science, pp. 517–522.

Rickles, P., and Ellul, C. (2015) 'A preliminary investigation into the challenges of learning GIS in interdisciplinary research', *Journal of Geography in Higher Education*, 39(2), pp. 226–236.

Shulman, L. (2005) 'Signature pedagogies in the professions', *Daedalus*, 134(3), pp. 52–59.

Sparke, M. (2018) 'Textbooks as opportunities for interdisciplinarity and planetarity', *Area*, 50(1), pp. 59–62.

Spelt, E., Biemans, J., Tobi, H., Luning, P.A. and Mulder, M. (2009) 'Teaching and learning in interdisciplinary higher education: A systematic review', *Educational Psychology Review*, 21(4), pp. 365–378.

Spelt, E., Luning, J., van Boekel, M. and Mulder, M. (2016) 'A multidimensional approach to examine student interdisciplinary learning in science and engineering in higher education', *European Journal of Engineering Education*, 42(6), pp. 761–774.

Stentoft, D. (2017) 'From saying to doing interdisciplinary learning: Is problem-based learning the answer?', *Active Learning in Higher Education*, 18(1), pp. 51–61.

Taylor, S. (2018) 'To understand and be understood: Facilitating interdisciplinary learning through the promotion of communicative competence', *Journal of Geography in Higher Education*, 41(1), pp. 126–142.

Trowler, P. (2012) 'Disciplines and interdisciplinarity, conceptual groundwork', in Trowler, P., Saunders, M. and Bamber, V. (eds), *Tribes and Territories in the 21st Century: Rethinking the Significance of Disciplines in Higher Education*, London: Routledge, pp. 5–29.

Tucker, F. and Horton, J. (2019) '"The show must go on!" Fieldwork, mental health and wellbeing in geography, earth and environmental sciences', *Area*, 51(1), pp. 84–93.

Wainwright, E., Barker, J., Ansell, N., Buckingham, S., Hemming, P. and Smith, F. (2014) 'Geographers out of place: Institutions, (inter)disciplinarity and identity', *Area*, 46(4), pp. 410–417.

Wenger, E. (2000) 'Communities of practice and social learning systems', *Organization*, 7(2), pp. 225–246.

Withers, C.W.J. (2011) 'Geography's narratives and intellectual history', in Agnew, J.A. and Livingstone, D.N. (eds), *The SAGE Handbook of Geographical Knowledge*, London: Sage, pp. 39–50.

Yerkes, R.M. and Dodson, J.D. (1908) 'The relationship of strength of stimulus to rapidity of habit-formation', *Journal of Comparative Neurology and Psychology*, 18(5), pp. 459–482.

Zajac, S., Gregory, M.E., Bedwell, W.L., Kramer, W.S. and Salas, E. (2014) 'The cognitive underpinnings of adaptive team performance in ill-defined task situations: A closer look at team cognition', *Organizational Psychology Review*, 4(1), pp. 49–73.

10. Co-pedagogy: teaching together for successful student learning
Sarah Dyer

Two features common to introductory units (modules/courses) are their size and the number of people involved in teaching them. Whilst other chapters in this part of the volume address the challenge of teaching and assessing large cohorts (see, in this volume, Chapter 4 by Finn and Mott; Chapter 5 by Rink; Chapter 7 by Ramdas), this chapter considers the difficulties and opportunities afforded by teaching with others. As this isn't something geographers have given much attention to in print, I draw on research and reflections from other disciplines. Teaching with others introduces a complexity to teaching which is heightened when we are working with diverse groups of educators. Often, introductory units serve a range of programmes and are taught by geographers from different sub-disciplines, with different epistemic commitments. Units are also, in many contexts, taught by multidisciplinary teams (discussed in Chapter 9 in this volume by Griffin), and/or teams which include graduate teaching assistants (GTAs) or people who have recently joined a department. Add to this the challenge of supporting students from diverse prior learning through transition into higher education, and we can begin to appreciate the complexity of the educational collaborations we are part of. I argue it is crucial that we pay attention to these educational collaborations which shape student learning – and our own working lives as educators – because it enables us to be more effective and efficient teachers. Moreover, it is politically important, as I argue below, to draw attention to these working relationships. It highlights concerns about the configuration of contemporary HE and the working lives of those in universities.

This chapter is written for anyone who is involved in managing, planning, or delivering units which are team-taught (see Box 10.1 for definitions). When a module is taught by a group of people, the way in which those people work together has a huge impact on the students taking that unit. This chapter focuses on pedagogy – what I call here co-pedagogy – and not group dynamics. There is no doubt that how well these teams work is down, in part, to personalities and group dynamics. You can find resources elsewhere that can help you think about aspects such as team roles (for example Belbin), personality types (for example Myers Briggs), and so on. In this chapter, though, we examine the different approaches to *teaching* in teams, identifying potential benefits and challenges. It is important to acknowledge that the courses of action open to you as a member of a team are different depending on the role and context in which you find yourself. For example, you may join a unit team where either there is a culture of not meeting or at a point in the academic year when it is not possible to revise the unit structure. The chapter ends with a discussion of 'absent-imagined' teams for those who find themselves in either situation. Alternatively, you may be a unit convenor or year/programme director in a department which is supportive to reviewing and innovating team-taught modules. Prompt questions,

---

BOX 10.1   DEFINITIONS

Sole Lecturer. A lecturer who has responsibility for delivering a unit (module/course). The lecturer may have varying degrees of autonomy. He/she may have created the unit or 'inherited' it. Equally he/she may or may not have freedom to write her/his own learning outcomes and/or material. However, they take sole responsibility for delivering material.
Guest lecturer. A lecturer who is invited to deliver, usually, one lecture or workshop based on their relevant expertise. Jacob et al. (2002, p.96) describe these as a 'cameo performance' and say you would expect the unit lecturer to be present 'as a matter of courtesy'.
Team teaching: Teaching which involves more than one educator.
Sequential teaching: A type of team teaching where a unit is divided in to discrete units and responsibility for each is taken by different lecturers. There is a unit co-ordinator, who may be one of those teaching. The co-ordinator usually does not attend all lecturers and/or classes.
Co-teaching: A type of team teaching which entails those who are teaching being present in lectures/workshops/online at the same time.
Co-pedagogy: An approach to understanding students' learning which recognises the impact of educators' collaboration on student learning.

Note: Different writers adopt different definitions of the above terms. These are the definitions used in this chapter.

---

given in boxes throughout the chapter, can be used by individuals or teaching teams as points for reflection and discussion in the planning or review of units.

I have written this chapter as someone who has had extensive experience occupying different roles in teams teaching first years. I started teaching as a graduate teaching assistant on a team-taught first year unit nearly two decades ago. Since then I have lectured on such units, convened them, and been the director of programmes which employs them. The chapter draws on published literature, along with these experiences, and a growing sense that this is an aspect of teaching which is neglected at our, and our students', peril. The vignettes used to illustrate themes are composites of examples I have come across in my own educational practice and in discussion with other educators (through roles such as chair of the UK's Royal Geographical Society's Higher Education Research Group).

This chapter begins with a short section which frames the discussion of education collaboration as a political as well as a practical one. The subsequent review of literature examines evidence about educators working together, first as co-teachers and then in a sequential model. The final section makes a case for co-pedagogy, an approach which acknowledges the impact of educators' collaborations on student learning.

TEACHING WITH OTHERS AS HIDDEN LABOUR

Educational collaborations and working relationships remain largely hidden in accounts of academic labour and geography pedagogy. This is despite collaboration emerging as a modern mantra in twenty-first century higher education (Macfarlane, 2017). Of course, what is visible or hidden in accounts of academic labour does not occur naturally nor accidentally but emerges from the politics of particular times and places. As such, being attentive to collaborative education work – work that is 'hidden' and unacknowledged in many contemporary HE settings – is not only a practical concern but also a political one. It should inform wider conversations about the reconfiguration of academic labour in the contemporary university. Changing funding mechanisms and accountability regimes have led to an intensification of academic work (Sidaway and Johnson, 2017) alongside a casualisation of employment (Bauder, 2006). Neither of these are experienced uniformly, with black and minority ethnic and women academics experiencing more precarity and less reward (Fung and Gordon, 2016; Madrell et al., 2016). Macfarlane (2017) reminds us that what is called 'collaboration' can include a range of behaviours and relationships which extend from intellectual generosity to parasitism. However, raising the visibility of hidden labour, through for example autoethnography, and stressing collaboration have both served as techniques for challenging contemporary conditions of academic work (Purcell, 2007; Peters and Turner, 2014). To be clear, to call attention to collaborative work is not to valorise collaboration.

Recognising the need to work with others prompts questions about how to do it well. The discussion of GTA–faculty collaboration, towards the end of the chapter, demonstrates how political and practical concerns can be mutually reinforcing. We must address questions such as what conditions are needed for collaboration, what works in different settings, what support people need and who can and should benefit. These are questions which aren't often discussed within pedagogic and academic development literature. Education collaborations are often incidental in such literature, where they appear at all. The next section reviews published evidence.

WORKING WITH OTHERS

In this section I review different approaches to team teaching. I draw on a literature review to highlight the value and challenges of different approaches to team teaching. This literature includes a variety of types of evidence, including literature reviews (for example Robb and Gerwick, 2013) and empirical research (for example Seymour and Seymour, 2014; Money and Coughlan, 2016; Smith and Winn, 2017). This evidence has been collected in diverse national contexts, including Australia (Jacob, Honey and Jordan, 2002; Crawford and Jenkins, 2018), Belgium (Baeten and Simons, 2014), Canada (Lock et al., 2016), Finland (Myllärniemi et al., 2016), Netherlands (Wagner, Rieger and Voorvelt, 2016; Koeslag-Kreunen et al., 2018), the UK (Money and Coughlan, 2016) and the USA (Robb and Gerwick, 2013; Seymour and Seymour, 2014; Morelock et al., 2017; Smith and Wynn 2017). Even taken collectively these do not offer a 'right' answer of how to undertake education collaboration but pose questions for us to think through in our own contexts. That said, this review does pose real challenges to current practice. Reviewing sequential teaching, arguably the most common type of team teaching, Jacob, Honey and Jordan (2002, p. 98) conclude it is 'particularly damaging for students in introductory courses . . . students will gain little from a sequentially taught class unless they are highly motivated'. They recommend that sequential teaching should not be used in any first-year courses. Such assertions call on those of us teaching on sequentially taught units to review what evidence we have that we are avoiding the dangers we have been alerted to.

Co-teaching

Co-teaching is perhaps the 'purest', and least common, form of team teaching. This is teaching where more than one educator is present in the teaching space – be that a lecture hall, laboratory, or online environment (Morelock et al., 2017). Research into co-teaching in higher education is in its infancy (Seymour and Seymour, 2014; Morelock et al., 2017). Co-teaching, and a research base, is more common in school settings where it has emerged as a means of supporting inclusion of pupils with special educational needs and for professional development of teachers (Smith and Winn, 2017). Morelock et al. (2017, p. 182) identify a number of different rationales for co-teaching in HE. These include mentoring GTAs, more effective applications of particular pedagogies, interdisciplinary teaching, and the subversion of individualised teaching practice.

In geography, co-teaching is likely to already occur during fieldtrips and laboratory teaching given the requirements for staff–student ratios. This provides a resource to draw on if we choose to develop co-teaching. We are likely to have units which are already established and co-taught, where we can experiment, reflect on our practice and develop as co-teachers. These units also provide us with a possible route into creating an evidence base and leverage, where we want to create new co-teaching in our departments. Geography academics are unlikely to be familiar with the published evidence about co-teaching or even the term itself. However, they are likely to be familiar with the practice and its positive effects on student learning.

Co-teaching involves a spectrum of practices of interaction between educators teaching together. At one end of the spectrum, towards sequential teaching, one educator may be a silent observer in a co-teaching space whilst the other takes a role similar to that of a sole lecturer. The roles are then reversed as the other becomes the protagonist. Whilst this approach has commonalities with sequential teaching, it differs as there are advantages for students (and educators). Both educators should have a sound and detailed understanding of all of the material the students are being taught, enabling her/him to plan for the sections each will teach. For students, the educators' presence communicates a coherence

---

BOX 10.2   CO-TEACHING: A VIGNETTE

Two academics planned a new unit as co-convenors. They were planning to sequentially teach it. However, for the first year it ran they decided to go along to each other's lectures and to co-run workshops although they ran seminars, in which the cohort was divided in to smaller groups, separately. This was a pragmatic rather than an ideological decision and they assumed it would help the unit run smoothly. They were right. It was also an intellectually stimulating and enjoyable experience but a couple of issues arose. First, they became aware of a gendered dimension to some students' interactions with them. Students took the male lecturer to be the primary academic and the female senior lecturer to be assisting. Second, they became aware of students 'testing' them, going to see each independently and asking a question, then revealing how the other academic had answered the same questions. Despite these issues the co-teaching model worked so well they decided to continue. In later iterations they were more explicit about the equality of their collaboration. They planned points in the lectures where they could stage a dialogue about the material. They also decided to assign marking by seminar group, so students would have no reason to compare and test their answers to questions.

of the unit. At the other end of the co-teaching spectrum, the teachers actively engage with one another in the teaching space. When this is done well, their interaction provides a stimulating learning environment which benefits their students (Brooks et al., 2009).

The student experience
For students, there are possible benefits and challenges to being co-taught. The challenges may well be heightened because co-teaching is unlikely to be the norm for them and they may take time to understand how best to navigate this learning experience. In this section I discuss the advantages for students of the additional educator 'resources' available to them, the potential benefit of being exposed to difference, and the way co-teaching can be used to model disciplinary or professional ways of being. I end by reviewing the challenges for students.

Co-teaching provides additional educational 'resources' for students to benefit from, most obviously educator time. Their co-presence and the need to collaborate in the design of the module are both important. In the learning environment both educators are available to students, particularly useful in break-out or discussion time (Lock et al., 2017). Students can benefit from the different ways educators will listen to and communicate with students. Co-educators are also likely to bring different strengths to the design of the unit. Their collaboration should result in a unit which is coherent and clearly articulated. In contrast with sequential teaching, co-teaching can support students to achieve higher order learning (Bloom et al., 1956; Myllärniemi et al., 2016) as educators are better able to support students to understand the connections between topics (or areas of knowledge).

A second advantage of co-teaching is its potential for exposing students to the difference inherent in academic disciplines. For this to happen in a productive way, educators must engage in a dialogue in the presence of students which 'reveals' the workings of disciplinary and academic ways of thinking. This observation extends the sense that students can benefit from the different ways in which educators might explain material. Students 'hear diverse voices and opinions . . . in regards to theory (and) interpretation of theoretical constructs' (Brooks et al., 2009, p. 828). Making these disciplinary differences and ways of thinking explicit is a means by which wider groups of students can be supported (Haggis, 2006).

Thirdly, much has been written about the value co-teaching has in providing a means for educators to model professional behaviour and interactions. This is perhaps no surprise, given co-teaching has received most attention from those teaching in the vocational areas of medicine and education. In medicine and allied subjects, graduates must be able to work in multi-disciplinary teams. Co-teachers can demonstrate effective teamwork and professional negotiation of differing perspectives and understandings, which are difficult for students to experience in a classroom with a sole lecturer (Seymour and Seymour, 2014, p. 44). In the field of education, co-teaching can enrich students' understanding of teaching practice.

In geography we have both disciplinary approaches and professional behaviours which we aim to instil in our students. Becoming a geographer or 'thinking like a geographer' entails grasping disciplinary knowledge and skills. We cultivate in our students' attributes which we might think of as geocapabilities (Walkington et al., 2018), through signature pedagogies such as fieldwork. These can also be demonstrated or modelled through educators' in-class dialogues. This is an effective way of making visible the implicit values or

---

BOX 10.3 QUESTIONS TO SUPPORT CO-PEDAGOGY IN PROGRAMME MANAGEMENT

Where does team teaching occur in programmes? Is its place intentional or accidental?
Why are units being taught by teams? (There may be pragmatic and/or pedagogic rationales.)
What are models are being used (co- or sequential-)?
What opportunities are afforded by a model of teaching in any given unit? What are the challenges?
What understandings do teaching teams have of co-pedagogic opportunities and challenges? Do they need additional support to reimagine the opportunities and engage with the challenges?
Are GTAs being used effectively? How could they supported to be education collaborators with faculty?
What understanding do students have of co-pedagogic opportunities and challenges? How are they equipped to learn in this way?
What resources are available (time, professional development, other) to support team teaching?
What relative priorities should be assigned to the answers to the questions above?

'workings' of an argument or approach. Moreover, many geography graduates will work in multi-disciplinary or multi-profession teams. Witnessing as well as being told about how people approach questions/tasks from different perspectives and come to resolution and/or productive disagreement is useful for students. Furthermore, co-teaching can be productively aligned to assessment of students' ability to work as a member of a group. Such approaches expand the ways in which students can be taught about 'disciplinary difference' and working collaboratively.

The nature of the potential benefits of co-teaching indicate too the challenges that co-teaching can pose for students. Co-teaching is a means of supporting higher-order learning: integrating understandings of topics and debates, appreciating the contested nature of disciplinary knowledge and engaging with the underlying values and behaviours of a geographer. Whilst these are important, they are also difficult. Seymour and Seymour's (2014) survey of students who had been co-taught suggests that students don't find it enjoyable. Students reported being confused by different opinions, explanations, and expectations (p. 43) and not being confident about the fairness of grading/marks (p.47). This speaks to the challenges of being co-taught. It is likely to be the exception rather than the norm. Students are likely to be encountering and being expected to engage with higher order learning and (multi-) disciplinary difference. These challenges need to be taken seriously and explored by anyone co-teaching.

In order to maximise the benefits for students of being co-taught, students need to be supported to develop the understanding and competencies for learning in this way; appreciating that they are learning important skills of working with different perspectives. This is likely to be particularly challenging for students when it comes to assessments, where uncertainty can provoke anxiety. However, in geography we do have the advantage that co-teaching is likely to be a part of our degrees where we teach in the field or in laboratories. This offers students and educators alike a point of security from which to begin to think about how to do co-teaching as a practitioner or a learner.

The educator experience

This section considers the educator's experiences of co-teaching. The evidence suggests that co-teaching can be an enjoyable experience and that it is of great value for developing skills. At the same time, co-teaching is challenging because it is, arguably, a more demanding undertaking than sole teaching, requiring that educators are open to learning from and working differently with their colleagues.

A first clear benefit of co-teaching, identified in the literature, is that it is professionally and intellectually enjoyable. In their survey of faculty involved in co-teaching, the majority reported so (Seymour and Seymour, 2014). Smith and Winn (2017) describe the pleasure of their developing relationship as co-teachers and the emerging educational experience for themselves and their students. Characterisations are likely to reflect the commitments of those who choose to undertake and report on co-teaching. The experience of co-teaching is likely to vary, depending on the people involved, the autonomy they can exercise, and the conditions they are working in. Where it works well, the deepened professional relationships are likely to benefit other aspects of departmental life (Robb and Gerwick, 2013; Lock et al., 2017).

Secondly, co-teaching offers substantial benefits in terms of professional development, and while the literature highlights its value for induction of new faculty and novice educators (Liebel, Burden and Heldal, 2017; Crawford and Jenkins, 2018), the benefits clearly extend beyond these groups. Peer dialogue is one of the 'lenses' Brookfield (1998) calls for us to view our practice as educators through. The simple act of observing others teach is a beneficial point of reflection. The conversations involved in the design and planning of co-taught units provide a rich source of knowledge sharing and exploration. This is true for both understandings of pedagogy and content knowledge. It is a practice which has the potential to foster innovation and create new knowledge (Koeslag-Kreunen et al., 2018). Taken together co-teaching offers important potential benefits for educators at all levels of experience. These need to be judged in the context of the challenges it requires.

Co-teaching is demanding for educators. Just as for students, this isn't the way we are used to teaching in HE. For co-teaching to work well educators must create and maintain good working relationships. Smith and Winn (2017) argue that collaborations don't emerge naturally and must be developed. Educators have to be prepared to 'invest' in developing trust in their team. There is a 'need for superior communication and compatibility between teachers, the necessity of planning time outside the regular class period' (Seymour and Seymour, 2014, p. 40), alongside 'the need for administrative support and professional development related to co-teaching, and a concern for the potential inequality among teaching partners' (ibid.). Co-teachers must be willing to take risks in front of each other (Smith and Winn, 2017) if they are to be able to design a robust unit and if they are to be able to engage in productive dialogue in learning spaces. As well as developing skills and relationships, co-teaching may require some educators to think differently about themselves. Smith and Winn (2017, p. 440) describe three characteristics which they identified as successful for their co-teaching: being uninterested in competition, being willing to engage in open dialogue and to trust peers (pp. 443–444). They observe that this commitment to collectivity stands in contrast to the characteristics which are valorised in contemporary universities. This may make it difficult for some.

The final challenge for co-teaching is the time it requires. On the face of it, co-teaching is an inefficient way of delivering a unit. In co-teaching the workload is not halved but (almost) doubled (Morelock et al., 2017; Smith and Winn, 2017). Fieldtrips, as an illustrative example, are a time-intensive approach to teaching. There is the 'inefficiency' of multiple educators being present in learning spaces with students. In addition, educators also spend time with each other debriefing and planning, often at the beginning and end of the day, leading to very long days where a lot gets done. The long fieldwork working day can't be reproduced in a normal working environment and requires time to be allocated in the working day. However, as I argue below, the workload required for good sequential teaching may not be so different from co-teaching (although it may appear to be more efficient in management workload allocation systems). The benefits offered by co-teaching will make it a worthwhile investment of educator time at certain points in a students' degree.

In conclusion, co-teaching creates both the potential benefits and challenges for students and educators. This discussion makes sense of many of our experiences of fieldtrips, as rewarding and 'resource'-intensive, and as supporting deep and transformative learning in students. Outside fieldtrips, co-teaching is an unusual way of teaching in geography programmes. We might conclude that it could productively be used more widely. This section also provides an important framing for the discussion of sequential teaching which follows. Sequential teaching can offer some of the same benefits of co-teaching but poses additional challenges.

Sequential Teaching

Sequential teaching is a common approach to team teaching. In this 'tag team' model, one academic acts as the unit co-ordinator; the unit is divided into discrete sections and different academics deliver the different sections, overseen by the co-ordinator. As with co-teaching, sequential teaching includes a spectrum of practices. Educators are not present in the same space, excluding perhaps an introductory lecture. However, at one end of the continuum, teachers stage a 'dialogue' for the students across their classes and workshops in such a way as to create similar outcomes as co-teaching (Brooks et al., 2009). This contrasts with sequential teaching at the other end of the continuum, in which sections of the unit sit independently from each other, albeit related by topic.

The student experience

Sequential teaching benefits student learning when it is used because of clear and appropriate rationale. Jacob, Honey and Jordan (2002) identify three rationales for sequential teaching: it allows students to be taught by topic expert, it enables students to experience a range of specialisms, and it exposes them to a variety of teaching approaches.

The first two rationales posit the benefits to students of being taught a range of disciplinary 'topics' by specialists. This would seem to be a common assumption that underlines much education practice in universities. Being taught by an expert, often implicitly a researcher, is assumed to be better because they should be more knowledgeable and enthusiastic (Jacob, Honey and Jordan, 2002; Robb and Gerwick, 2013). Whilst this assumption is problematic, we could usefully extend the understanding of expertise to include pedagogic expertise.

The second advantage of sequential teaching that Jacob, Honey and Jordan (2002) identify, is that it can enable students to be exposed to a 'smorgasbord' or sample of approaches or subject areas. This can enable students make decisions about which faculty member they want to work with (for example as a research supervisor) or which areas they want to specialise in. This approach plays to the strengths of sequential teaching in that no 'integration' is sought – though students may need support 'de-coding' the experience. This may be difficult without access to a faculty member who has an overview of the sections that were delivered.

The final advantage that Jacob identifies is that students experience diversity of teaching styles (Jacob, Honey and Jordan, 2002). They include the observation that sequential teaching can lessen the damage of a bad teacher. This observation needs nuancing. Sequential teaching exposes students to a range of approaches to disciplinary knowledge and teaching approaches, which increases the likelihood that they will experience approaches that work better for them and their learning. It is, of course, important to note that it also requires students make sense of these different approaches which requires a sophistication from them.

Jacob, Honey and Jordan (2002) observe that the conditions in which sequentially taught units are advantageous to students are specific and limited to these circumstances. They argue there are many attendant challenges, concluding that it is an approach with a significant cost, 'predominantly borne by the students' (p. 95).

Students experience many challenges in sequentially taught units. Some of these challenges occur from the difficulties inherent in planning sequential teaching. These include: content overlap, conflicting messages about assessment, and team members not taking ownership of their roles and responsibilities (Money and Coughlan, 2016). It is important to note that these problems are often created, or exasperated, by a failure to appreciate the task involved in designing and planning. Sequential teaching is often adopted because it is seen as an efficient way of organising academics' time (Robb and Gerwick, 2013). This understanding obscures the work required to do it well. Whilst students may benefit from the range of materials and approaches to teaching, these also pose a genuine challenge to students. Students can become anxious or confused by exposure to different approaches and this is teaching which works against integration of understanding (Jacob, Honey and Jordan, 2002; Money and Coughlan, 2016). It also is described as damaging the student teacher relationship (Jacob, Honey and Jordan, 2002, p. 98), a further reason why sequential teaching can be difficult to reconcile with supporting students' learning during their transition to university.

The educator experience
Sequential teaching is a common way of teaching introductory units at universities and is likely to feel familiar to educators. Being asked or required to think about how to do things differently may be unwanted, especially in the light of the drive for research (and other) outputs. Sequential teaching is often thought to be an efficient way of organising teaching, which enables academics to teach in their area of expertise (Robb and Gerwick, 2013) and this is appealing. However, the literature – and experience – highlights the work that is required to make sequential teaching effective. Where it is done well though, sequential teaching offers some of the same benefits as co-teaching, including mentoring and professional development and stronger working relationships (Robb and Gerwick, 2013). All of these aspects can lead to a commitment to sequential teaching.

BOX 10.4   QUESTIONS FOR SEQUENTIAL TEACHING TEAMS

What are team members' research and pedagogic expertise?

How are team members accountable to each other?

What are the roles of each member? What are the responsibilities of each member? How will this be communicated to students?

How will the team communicate during the design and delivery of the unit?

Who will present which lesson content and on what rationale (e.g. based on expertise, availability)?

What is the narrative of the unit? How clearly is it communicated to students? In what order will the lesson content be presented?

Which evaluation methods will be used? How will course assignments be graded? (How will those marking come to a shared understanding of the criteria and ensure marking is fair and seen to be fair)?

How will assessment and exam questions be generated?

How will course and student concerns be addressed? How will this work be allocated and how will you make sure 'hidden' work is fairly distributed? How will you ensure you are providing clear and coherent answers and student questions?

Will all instructors be present in the first class (or online equivalent) in order for them to be introduced to students and the unit logic be explained?

There are, though, many challenges to sequential teaching from the educator perspective. Planning and communication in team teaching is very important. If this isn't acknowledged by a workload model or workplace culture it will fall to individual faculty to reconcile the gaps between needs and resources. The risks inherent in sequential team teaching is that teachers fail to take ownership of the module and that students experience a module which is poorly designed, in which academics are disinvested (Jacob, Honey and Jordan, 2002; Money and Coughlan, 2016), in which mixed messages are more common than a coherent narrative. Where this occurs, in particular where it occurs in connection to assessment, educators are likely to have to support both students' wellbeing and their additional needs outside the classroom. Again, this tends to be invisible work which isn't evenly distributed. My experience suggests that female and younger academics tend to be seen as more approachable by students and shoulder the bulk of this work.

Sequential teaching is a widely used model. It is important that educators reflect on the benefits and challenges of the model, given the challenges highlighted. When it is used for pragmatic rather than pedagogic reasons, educators should engage seriously with its potential impact on student learning, and plan to mitigate these impacts.

CO-PEDAGOGY

Given its impact we should not ignore the role of educators' collaboration within a unit. As outlined above, there are different models of team teaching available and their adoption should follow a review of the opportunities and challenges of the unit. The term 'co-pedagogy' is a way of recognising and engaging with this. 'Co-pedagogy' acknowledges and makes visible the interconnected and mutual relationships in team teaching. Making them visible enables us to engage with the appropriate questions and review of evidence.

This will support us to better educate our students when we work under these conditions. It should also be, as I have argued above, a conceptual tool which furthers our understandings of, and struggles for, academic working lives.

Co-pedagogy is connected, but distinct from, other philosophies which place the educator in the context of their peers. Social learning and the idea of 'communities of practice' (Lave and Wenger, 1991) has been influential in understandings of professional learning and development, including in higher education (Nagy and Burch, 2009, p. 236). This understanding is built on by Cox (2004) who proposes 'Faculty Learning Communities', small delineated projects of collaboration, as powerful mechanisms for educators' professional development. Co-pedagogy recognises the value of education collaboration for educators' own professional development, but its real focus is on the impact that these 'naturally occurring' collaborations have on student learning.

Another idea which is closely aligned, possibly complementary, but still distinct, is that of pedagogic frailty. Kinchin et al. (2016) are interested in understanding the contexts and relationships which create 'frailty' – potentially problematic conditions in university learning environments. They argued that pedagogic frailty, like clinical frailty, shows itself in a 'limited repertoire of responses to demands' (p. 4). Although pedagogic frailty is an idea which extends beyond co-pedagogic considerations, we can see how under-resourced team-teaching might be a condition which contributes to pedagogic frailty. A team-taught module that is designed, like the one in Box 10.6, to have people slot in or out without disrupting the module as a whole, might be organisationally robust but creates a pedagogic frailty, and one that increases over time. The module either becomes a collection of misaligned sections or the narrative of the module becomes progressively more vague and less meaningful to students. If this module were either co-taught or mindfully sequentially taught, it may not seem so organisationally efficient but it would be pedagogically effective.

The Value of Co-pedagogy

In this section I use two examples to illustrate the value of co-pedagogy. The first example looks at the role GTAs play. It highlights how a co-pedagogy approach is likely to frame GTAs as collaborators rather than assistants and in doing so connect justice and pedagogical effectiveness. The second example extends the reach of co-pedagogy and examines its possibilities for understanding working with 'absent-imagined' teams. I end this section by highlighting how co-pedagogy enables us to develop skills and approaches which support the wider project of co-producing education.

Co-pedagogy for working as/with temporary staff and GTAs
It is very common for GTAs to work with faculty delivering first year units. As is clearly communicated by the role's title, commonly these roles are seen to act as assistants to someone effectively working as a sole lecturer. Let's call this the assistant model. Such a framing limits the potential learning of students being taught and is implicated in the under-valuing of GTAs' work. In our departments and in the literature, GTAs are calling our attention to the ways in which their contribution is under-recognised and their working conditions are exploitative, both in terms of the types of work they are required to do and the compensation they receive (Park and Ramos, 2002; Dyer et al.,

BOX 10.5   QUESTIONS GTAs WHO WANT TO ACT AS EDUCATION
COLLABORATORS CAN ASK

What pedagogic and disciplinary expertise can I provide to the unit/exercise I am teaching on?
Given the time frame and resources available, what changes/innovations am I interested in contrib-
uting to or driving? (Is this for the current version of the unit or its future iterations)?
Who do I need to convince to let me act as a collaborator?
Who are my allies? Who would also like to see these changes? Who can help?
What are the forums for discussing education in my institution? Can I present my ideas and receive
feedback?
Are there any additional resources I can call on, in terms of time/budget/mentoring?
How will I document and evaluate what I contribute, both to ensure effective practice and for
accreditation/future job applications?

2016; Raaper, 2018). The assistant model is one of the mechanisms that naturalises
these conditions.

Taking a co-pedagogic approach requires we recognise that how faculty and GTAs work
together impacts student learning. It prompts a pedagogic question about how these educators can best work together to most effectively support this learning. The answer to this
question will vary by context but this approach promises advantages to all involved. In an
illustrative example, Hunt and Smillie (2016) describe their experiences of moving from
delivering to designing (and delivering) an undergraduate lab. In the films that accompany
their blog, one of the GTAs characterises the assistant model as difficult, because you are
trying to make something come to life that someone else has written. Having GTAs work
as collaborators actively designing a lab is a recognition of their expertise as educators
and their expertise in the material being taught. They describe transforming a 'slow and
dreary lab' into a real time game. Enabling GTAs to act in education collaborations with
faculty led to the production of engaging learning resources which benefited students and
served as a valuable experience which disrupted the assistant role.

Moreover, students benefit from a co-teaching which models professional and disciplinary relationships. Students understand their university learning environments
according to the racialised and gendered scripts of wider society (Morelock et al., 2017).
Co-pedagogy provides an opportunity to examine both the power relations we actively
constitute and the power relations in wider society which impact how students 'read' our
teaching teams. As with the example in Box 10.2, educators working together in ways
that they see as equal need to work hard to ensure that they communicate that relationship to students. That we encounter that challenge at all can be frustrating. However,
co-teaching offers us the opportunity to model these relationships for students, part of
the 'disciplinary and professional' behaviour discussed above. These examples are likely
to be powerful lessons for our students who are shown professionals respected for their
expertise and contribution (rather than unquestioned hierarchy) working collaboratively
and that 'geographers' (and researchers) are not a particular age, gender nor ethnicity.

Co-pedagogy, acknowledging and making the most of educational collaborations, is a
valuable approach to GTA involvement in teaching. The potential benefits are substantial
for all involved. Whilst students experience richer learning environments, faculty and

---

BOX 10.6   WORKING WITH A LEGACY: A VIGNETTE

In the first year in a new department, a lecturer was given a section of a compulsory introduction to geography module to teach. The module had been designed as a series of themed sections so that members of the teaching team could change year by year without too much change to the overall structure of the module. The module was designed around a key concept in geography taught from both a physical and human geography perspective.

The lecturer felt uncomfortable about what she saw as a disjointed narrative and didn't accept the fundamental underpinnings of the module, including a conceptual symmetry between human and physical geography. She experienced a dissonance between her own understanding and that of the module, which caused some unease when teaching a section of the module and much anxiety when she was asked to become the module convenor.

In conversation with the programme directors and others teaching on the module, the lecturer refocused the module around an exploration of conceptual symmetry in the sub-disciplines. This enabled the lecturer to engage with the content in an authentic way which aligned with her own commitments and do so in a manageable way.

With this as a framework the lecturers on the module were able to stage a debate across the weeks, through a 'conversation', and scaffold an introduction to a central debate in the discipline. (Incidentally, the feedback score for the module also improved.) Engaging with nature and the affordances of sequential teaching proved a fruitful way to engage with the legacy the lecturer encountered.

---

graduate students engage in peer learning. These advantages must be weighed against the time required to make collaboration work. However, as has been argued in the case of sequential teaching, ensuring the assistant model is done well is also time consuming.

Co-pedagogy to develop teaching with absent-imagined teams
In this second example, working with absent-imagined teams, I extend the notion of co-pedagogy to include working with people who are absent. This is a common experience in teaching first year students. When we teach in the first year we often teach on units that pre-exist (and outlive) our involvement with them. We need to collaborate with others through their legacy. It is equally common to find ourselves working as part of a team which doesn't see itself as a team, for example when we teach on a sequentially taught unit in which educators are able to distance themselves from the unit. In a context where we are not able to persuade our collaborators that that is what they are, framing them in our own minds as an imagined team offers a technique to use co-pedagogy to develop our own contributions. We have to work with our colleagues' framing of topics, their epistemological, ethical and pedagogic commitments.

A co-pedagogy approach draws our attention to the ways in which absent others' educational practice creates a structure within which we teach. It highlights how we can choose to ignore this structure, work against it, or enter into dialogue with it. Such an awareness requires us to examine the particularity of the structure and what opportunities and challenges it affords. Again, the answers will be different in each context and for each educator. These issues have received more consideration within a school setting. Writing about teaching in the UK, where curricula are set nationally, Lambert and Biddulph (2015) argue that teachers must see themselves as 'curriculum making', drawing on three areas of expertise – in their subject knowledge, as an educator, and their understanding of their students – to actively construct a meaningful and effective curriculum for these students in the here and now. 'Curriculum making' thus conceived captures the expertise and autonomy of educators working within given structures. How we understand these structures and, importantly, how they will impact on how students' experience our teaching, are questions that are too important to be left unanswered.

Taking a co-pedagogic approach extends our understanding of the scope of pedagogy. It provides a conceptual and a skills bridge to the more widely discussed co-construction of higher education. It is now taken to be self-evidently true that as educators we ought to be working with students, alumni, and other stakeholders as we design higher education. Such practice requires a huge leap for educators used to working as a sole lecturer. Taking a co-pedagogic approach provides a means to practise, to scaffold the skills, and explore the framework of co-production of education.

CONCLUSIONS

Co-pedagogy is an approach to teaching which recognises the impact educator collaborations have on student learning. In geography, it is likely that we employ a range of team teaching from the co-teaching of fieldtrips and laboratories to the sequential teaching of many transition and core units. Co-pedagogy is a sensitising concept which draws our attention to the challenges and opportunities of these different models of collaboration – an attentiveness which prompts us to examine evidence from educational literature and reflect on our own contexts and experiences. This chapter explores evidence about the impact of team teaching, using vignettes and prompt questions to support readers to reflect on their own contexts. It is written for educators (faculty and GTAs) and leadership teams. The hope is that it provides support for insights to emerge and education practice to change.

Co-pedagogy provides a useful framing of education practices which connects practical questions about the efficiency and effectiveness of how we teach with political concerns about the visibility and valuing of academic labour. This chapter uses current concerns about the treatment of GTAs in order to explore this connection. So often 'excellent education' is framed as needing educators to make sacrifices. We are told that the needs of students require the exploitation of educators. Our discussion here counters this, seeing the practical and the political as mutually reinforcing. We see that the interests of students and educators are aligned. More broadly too, co-pedagogy highlights how organisational efficiency is often bought as the expense of both pedagogic effectiveness and academic working lives.

USEFUL RESOURCES

- National College for School Leadership (2012) *Powerful Professional Learning: A School Leader's Guide to Joint Practice Development.* Available at: https://assets. publishing.service.gov.uk/government/uploads/system/uploads/attachment_data/ file/329717/powerful-professional-learning-a-school-leaders-guide-to-joint-practice-development.pdf (downloaded 14 October 2018).

- Perr, A. (2017) *Co-Teaching: How to Make it Work, Cult of Pedagogy Blog.* Available at: https://www.cultofpedagogy.com/co-teaching-push-in/ (downloaded 14 October 2018).

REFERENCES

Baeten, M. and Simons, M. (2014) 'Student teachers' team teaching: models, effects, and conditions for implementation', *Teaching and Teacher Education*, 41, pp. 92–110.

Bauder, H. (2006) 'The segmentation of academic labour: a Canadian example', *ACME*, 4, pp. 228–239.

Bloom, B.S., Engelhart, M.D., Furst, E.J., Hill, W.H. and Krathwohl, D.R. (1956) *Taxonomy of Educational Objectives: The Classification of Educational Goals. Handbook I: Cognitive Domain.* New York: David McKay Company.

Brookfield, S. (1998) 'Critically reflective practice', *Journal of Continuing Education in the Health Professionals*, 18, pp. 197–205.

Brooks, J., Fox, D.P., Okagbue-Reaves, J. and Lukomski, A. (2009) 'Best practices for an interdisciplinary team-taught course', *Educational Gerontology*, 35(9), pp. 818–830.

Cox, M.D. (2004) 'Introduction to faculty learning communities', *New Directions for Teaching and Learning*, 97, pp. 5–23.

Crawford, R. and Jenkins L.E. (2018) 'Making pedagogy tangible: developing skills and knowledge using a team teaching and blended learning approach', *Australian Journal of Teacher Education*, 43 (1), pp. 127–142.

Dyer, S., Williams, R., Walkington, H., Morton, K. and Wyse, S. (2016) 'Shifting landscapes: from coalface to quicksand? Teaching Geography, Earth and Environmental Sciences in higher education', *Area*, 48(3), pp. 308-316.

Fung, D. and Gordon, C. (2016) *Rewarding Educators and Education Leaders in Research-Intensive Universities.* York: Higher Education Academy.

Haggis, T. (2006) 'Pedagogies for diversity: retaining critical challenge amidst fears of "dumbing down"', *Studies in Higher Education*, 31(5), pp. 521–535.

Hunt, R. and Smillie, V. (2016) *Whose Voice Is It Anyway? Delivery and Development, What's the Difference and Why Does It Matter?* UK: THE GEES network blog. https://teachingfocusedgeesnetwork.wordpress.com/category/graduate-teaching-assistant/ (accessed 12/02/19).

Jacob, H., Honey, R. and Jordan, C (2002) 'Getting the most out of sequential teaching', *Teaching and Learning Forum 2002: Focusing on the Student*, pp. 95–102, https://pdfs.semanticscholar.org/0484/a76b794ed27b20ff412844b5d5277fd59e65.pdf (accessed 07/02/19).

Kinchin, I.M., Alpay, E., Curtis, K., Franklin, J., Rivers, C. and Winstone, N.E. (2016) 'Charting the elements of pedagogic frailty', *Educational Research*, 58(1), pp. 1–23.

Koeslag-Kreunen, M.G., Van der Klink, M.R., Van den Bossche, P. and Gijselaers, W. (2018) 'Leadership for team learning', *Higher Education*, 75, pp. 191–207.

Lambert, D. and Biddulph, M. (2015) 'The dialogic space offered by curriculum-making in the process of learning to teach, and the creation of a progressive knowledge-led curriculum', *Asia-Pacific Journal of Teacher Education*, 43(3), pp. 210–224.

Lave, J. and Wenger, E. (1991) *Situated Learning: Legitimate Peripheral Participation.* Cambridge: Cambridge University Press.

Liebel, G., Burden, H. and Heldal, R. (2017) 'For free: continuity and change by team teaching', *Teaching in Higher Education*, 22(1), pp. 62–77.

Lock, J.H., Clancy, T., Lisella, R., Rosenau, P., Ferreira, C. and Rainsbury, J. (2017) 'The lived experiences of instructors co-teaching in higher education', *Brook Education Journal*, 26(1), pp. 22–35.

Macfarlane, B. (2017) 'The paradox of collaboration: a moral continuum', *Higher Education Research and Development*, 36(3), pp. 472–485.

Maddrell, A., Strauss, K., Thomas, N.J. and Wyse, S. (2016) 'Mind the gap: gender disparities still to be addressed in UK higher education geography', *Area*, 48(1), pp. 48–56.

Money, A. and Coughlan, J. (2016) 'Team-taught versus individually taught undergraduate education: a qualitative study of student experiences and preferences', *Higher Education*, 72(6), pp. 797–811.

Morelock, J.R., Lester, M.M., Klopfer, M.D., Jardon, A.M., Mullins, R.D., Nicholas E.L. and Ahmed, A. (2017) 'Power, perceptions, and relationships: a model of co-teaching in higher education', *College Teaching*, 65(4), pp. 182–191

Myllärniemi, J., Helander, N., Hellsten, P. and Ilvonen, I. (2016) 'Co-design, co-teaching and co-learning in technology hands-on university tuition', *AcademicMindtrek'16 Proceedings of the 20th International Academic Mindtrek Conference*, pp. 153–158.

Nagy, J. and Burch, T. (2009) 'Communities of Practice in Academe (CoP-iA): understanding academic work practices to enable knowledge building capacities in corporate universities', *Oxford Review of Education*, 35, pp. 227–247.

Park, C. and Ramos, M. (2002) 'The donkey in the department? Insights into the Graduate Teaching Assistant (GTA) experience in the UK' *Journal of Graduate Education*, 3, pp. 47–53.

Peters, K. and Turner, J. (2014) 'Fixed-term and temporary: teaching fellows, tactics, and the negotiation of contingent labour in the UK higher Education System', *Environment and Planning A: Economy and Space*, 46(10), pp. 2317–2331.

Purcell, M. (2007) '"Skilled, cheap, and desperate": non-tenure-track faculty and the delusion of meritocracy', *Antipode*, 39(1), pp. 121–143.

Raaper, R. (2018) '"Peacekeepers" and "machine factories": tracing Graduate Teaching Assistant subjectivity in a neoliberalised university', *British Journal of Sociology of Education*, 39(4), pp. 421–435.

Robb, M. and Gerwick, M. (2013) 'Team teaching: a resource guide for nurse educators', *Teaching and Learning in Nursing*, 8, pp. 78–82.

Seymour, M.W. and Seymour, D. (2014) 'Are two professors better than one? Student and faculty perceptions of co-teaching', *International Journal of Learning*, 20(1), pp. 39–52.

Sidaway, J.D. and Johnston, R.J. (2007) 'Geography in higher education', *Journal of Geography in Higher Education*, 31, pp. 57–80.

Smith, K.K. and Winn, V.G. (2017) 'Co-teaching in the college classroom', *Teaching Education*, 28(4), pp. 435–448.

Wagner, N., Rieger, M. and Voorvelt, K. (2016) 'Gender, ethnicity and teaching evaluations: evidence from mixed teaching teams', *Economics of Education Review*, 54, pp. 79–94.

Walkington, H., Dyer, S., Solem, M., Haigh, M. and Waddington, S. (2018) 'A capabilities approach to higher education: geocapabilities and implications for geography curricula', *Journal of Geography in Higher Education*, 42(1), pp. 7–24.

11. Pedagogies for developing undergraduate ethical thinking within geography
Ruth L. Healey and Chris Ribchester

INTRODUCTION: GEOGRAPHY AND THE VALUE OF ETHICAL THINKING

Hay and Foley (1998) argued that geography 'educators need to give greater attention to the teaching of . . . ethics as part of our contribution to the education of responsible citizens' (p. 169). Although some progress has been made since, twenty years on we may still question the extent to which our geography graduates are prepared 'for practical and ethical engagement with their scholarly, professional and personal worlds' (Boyd et al., 2008, p. 38).

Geography is rife with ethical issues across the human and physical sub-disciplines both in content and in practice, and it has long been recognized that this makes it an ideal subject for the consideration and discussion of ethics (Smith, 1995). In the UK, Royal Geographical Society accreditation of undergraduate programmes is aligned to the Quality Assurance Agency (QAA) subject benchmark statement which argues that geography 'fosters a range of personal attributes relevant to the world beyond higher education, which promote the ability of geographers to engage in lifelong learning, to consider ethics and values, to contribute to the wider community, and to gain employment' (QAA, 2014, p. 7). Walkington et al. (2017) draw attention to the value of 'ethical subject-hood' as one of five distinctive geocapabilities, and ethical awareness and thinking is seen to be a central component of the 21st-century geographer's toolkit (Whalley et al., 2011). As Hay (2016, p. 30) argues, 'ethical geographers are sensitive to the diversity of moral communities within which they work and are ultimately responsible for the moral significance of their deeds'. Furthermore, 'Ethical, Social and Professional Understanding' has been identified by Barrie (2004) as one of five key graduate attributes that universities promote (see further discussion on graduate attributes in Chapter 31 in this volume by Spronken-Smith). This means that graduates should 'hold personal values and beliefs consistent with their role as responsible members of local, national, international and professional communities' (Barrie, 2004, p. 270).

Ethical issues are an example of 'supercomplexity', whereby 'the very frameworks by which we orientate ourselves to the world are themselves contested' (Barnett, 2000, p. 257). Reflecting on ethical issues develops critical thinking skills for dealing with such 'supercomplexity', as the frameworks used to analyse ethical issues may be challenged and are likely to change over time. Yet, teaching ethics is often marginalized and segregated in the geographical curriculum (Gannon, 2014), with a discussion of ethics sometimes being limited to identifying potential ethical issues and mitigating potential harm in order to receive ethical clearance for a student's independent research proposal. Teaching ethics in this manner leaves students unprepared to respond to the inevitable variable ethical challenges that they will face in their future employment and personal lives. Therefore, it is important to adopt a more holistic and wide-ranging approach to the discussion and development of the 'ethical thinking' of geographers. This approach stands the best chance of success if introduced from an early point in the undergraduate degree. Embedding ethical thinking into the Year 1 curriculum then offers significant opportunities to build on these skills throughout the degree. If left until later in the course, students have to grapple with these new skills at the same time as potentially dealing with more complex geographical issues and ideas. Furthermore, early introduction helps prepare students for independent research when ethical problems may emerge whilst away from the direct tutor support they are likely to have in the classroom.

This chapter initially defines the goals of teaching ethics to geography undergraduates, before outlining what a holistic programme approach might look like. This includes identification of seven different contexts, inside and outside the curriculum, when ethical issues might be encountered by geography students; a list which may act as a useful guide for tutors considering teaching ethics for the first time. Whatever specific approaches to teaching ethics are adopted, the next section emphasizes the value of giving students the opportunity to recognize, review, and respond to topics and experiences. Within this context, the value of pursuing non-didactic teaching approaches, the importance of providing a consistent theoretical framework for reviewing ethical problems, and the likely impact of encouraging ongoing personal reflection are discussed. These pedagogic strategies are illustrated further through a case study detailing engagement with ethical issues within small group tutorial discussions using tutor- and student-authored scenarios.

Ethical Thinking

It is important to stress that, from our perspective, the primary purpose of teaching ethics in geography is to foster the ability to critically reflect upon ethical issues and develop the capacity to apply this 'ethical thinking' to real-world situations. Ethical thinking and learning is closely linked to critical thinking and reasoning: 'Ethical learning is impossible without the development of critical reasoning (Kant, 2003) and, at the same time, critical reasoning is reinforced by the aspiration for justice and the independence sought by ethical learning' (Boni and Lozano, 2007, p. 825).

If we understand critical thinking as: 'the identification and evaluation of evidence to guide decision-making' (Critical Thinking Co., 2011, no page), then ethical thinking is about identifying ethical issues and evaluating these issues from different perspectives to guide how to respond. This form of ethics is distinct from higher levels of conceptual ethics or theory (Boyd et al., 2008). The nature of an ethical issue or problem from this perspective is that there is no clear right or wrong response. It is therefore essential that students learn to think through ethical issues rather than follow a prescribed set of ethical codes or rules. There is a need to encourage recognition that, although being ethical is defined as acting 'in accordance with the principles of conduct that are considered correct' (Hanks, 1979, p. 502), these principles vary both between and within individuals. What a person values relates to their social, religious, or civic beliefs influenced by their formal and informal learning experiences. Individual perspectives may also be context dependent, meaning that under different circumstances, at a different time, when they are feeling a different way, the same individual may make different choices. Therefore, in order to analyse ethical issues and think ethically it is necessary to understand the personal factors that influence your own 'code of behaviour' and how these may vary, alongside recognizing and accepting that the factors that drive other people's codes and decision making may be different.

A non-prescriptive focus enables students to critically consider the issues in their own right, evaluate potential responses, and determine what they consider to be the appropriate course of action on the basis of the relevant factors involved. Ultimately, the goal is to develop in students a greater understanding of the complexity, variability, and contingent nature of ethical issues, as well as greater levels of self-awareness, openness to the perspectives of others, and a willingness to take personal ownership of their decisions. Such challenging goals call for a holistic approach to embedding ethics in the curriculum and early engagement to allow these critical thinking skills to mature over the course of a degree programme.

Holistic Programme Approach

Traditionally the teaching of ethics within geography programmes has focused on research methods courses which act as precursors to students conducting their own research – for example as part of their capstone undergraduate research project (Hill et al., 2011; see also Chapter 28 in this volume by Hovorka and Wolf, on capstone research). By its nature, such teaching focuses upon institutional ethical procedures, and consequently can reduce ethics to a one-off, tick box stage in the research process rather than providing opportunities for a more extended critical engagement with the potential ethical issues that geographical research raises (Boyd et al., 2008). Beyond this, space for ethical reflection generally emerges in relation to specific geographic content where ethical issues are inherently part of the discussion of that topic. It is important and valuable to teach ethics in this way as students' interest and enthusiasm typically emanates from the subject content itself (Pace and Middendorf, 2004; Valentine 2005). Yet, as Healey (2014) has demonstrated, there is a danger that the ethical nature of these issues can be so embedded in the subject content that students are unaware that they are studying ethical issues. As a consequence, students may identify such problems as disciplinary – as opposed to ethical – issues, which can also undermine the transferability of ethical thinking strategies between different contexts.

The lack of an explicit, coherent, and consistent recognition of ethics throughout the curriculum limits the opportunities to develop ethical thinking skills (as defined above). Consequently we advocate a programme-based approach to teaching ethics in geography. This is where ethics is integrated into the whole programme in a coherent, systematic and progressive manner through active, social, and creative learning approaches within geographical disciplinary content, supporting students to learn that ethics is a fundamental part of their discipline (Healey, 2014; Walkington et al., 2017).

Furthermore, we suggest that such a programme approach should embrace a 'holistic' perspective, recognizing that ethics and ethical issues can emerge throughout an individual's university experience, within, but also beyond, the curriculum. For example, powerful learning experiences can occur during part-time employment, volunteering, or the extra-curricular activities of our students. A holistic approach not only encourages the take-up of such opportunities, but also provides the chance to explore and discuss ethical challenges that can arise in these different contexts. Indeed, reflecting on ethics within the context of the day-to-day experience of students may sometimes aid the understanding of unfamiliar ethical thinking strategies and help facilitate their subsequent transference to geographical topics. Overall, a holistic programme approach to ethics offers explicit, connected, and relatable opportunities for students to develop intellectually and personally.

In summary, there are at least six, often overlapping, contexts within which ethical issues can emerge for geography students, and a holistic programme-based approach embraces them all as possible opportunities to develop the ethical thinking skills of students (Table 11.1). The first category in the table refers to the discipline-specific opportunities which, as already acknowledged, are diverse across physical and human geography. Secondly, the requirement to devise and apply ethically robust research strategies, whilst longstanding, is being emphasized more than ever before in relation to growing public demands for accountability (Hay, 2016). Fieldwork provides a significant opportunity to bring ethical problems and challenges 'to life' (see Chapter 7 in this volume by Ramdas), actively evaluate the environmental impacts of research data collection, reflect on encounters with other cultures, as well as consider the broader ecological footprint of fieldwork – not least through international travel. Curriculum content can encourage students to explore the ethics of professional practice in their potential future work places as well as provide direct experience of this through work placements. The varied experiences of part-time

Table 11.1   Undergraduate geography students' exposure to ethical issues within and beyond the curriculum throughout the student experience

Ethical Context	Examples
Discipline	● Food insecurity and geographies of food banks (Cloke et al., 2017) ● Geocoding of research data and its potential impacts (van den Bemt et al., 2018) ● Eco-environmental problems of reservoirs (Chen et al., 2018)
Research	● Ensuring meaningful informed consent from research participants (Ruiz-Casares and Thompson, 2016) ● Consideration of sensitive social spaces in physical geography research (Kershaw et al., 2014) ● Ethical use of Google Earth (Sheppard and Cizek, 2009)
Fieldwork	● Analysing the carbon footprint of fieldwork (Ribchester et al., 2009) ● Implications of long-haul fieldwork in undergraduate geography (McGuinness and Simm, 2005) ● Fieldwork with over-researched communities (Pascucci, 2017)
Employment and professional practice	● The role of individuals and professional geographic organizations in ensuring professional research practice (Hay, 1998) ● Trauma and researcher self-care in professional geography (Eriksen, 2017) ● Applied ethical approaches for GIS professionals (Harvey, 2014)
Studentship	● Learning to attribute ideas correctly (Burkill and Abbey, 2004) ● Peer-assessment in group work (Stanier, 1997) ● Use of discriminatory language or images (Vujakovic and Bullard, 2001)
Extra-curricular	● Volunteering in local community organizations (Spalding, 2013) ● Events and activities promoting sustainable development (Lipscombe et al., 2008) ● Initiation practices within university sports teams (Lafferty et al., 2017)

and/or vacation work whilst studying can be included in this fourth category too. The practice of contemporary studentship requires students to frequently traverse the 'ethics minefield' (Vujakovic and Bullard, 2001), for example in relation to academic integrity, plagiarism, and mutual responsibility when undertaking group work. Sixthly, as noted above, a holistic programme approach recognizes that ethical challenges can readily occur within the extra-curricular sphere of university life, for example, when undertaking volunteering activities or participating in sport. Additionally, some programme teams may also be keen to explore a seventh category of engagement with their students, acknowledging the opportunities to reflect on 'everyday' ethical choices and encounters beyond teaching, the curriculum and extra-curricular domains, although not necessarily unconnected to them (for example balancing study and paid work commitments). As Ward (2017) observes 'none of us can avoid enacting moral decisions, we are surrounded by them on a daily basis and they are reflected in our intellectual, structural, organisational and personal lives' (p. 305).

THE THREE 'Rs' OF ETHICAL THINKING

Before considering the strategies that might be employed to embed, deliver and heighten the profile of ethical issues across the geography student experience three principles which 'cut across' these strategies are presented. These might be thought of as the three 'Rs' of ethical thinking: recognize, review, and respond.

Recognize

Recognizing ethical issues, utilizing what might be termed 'ethical awareness' or 'ethical sensitivity' (Clarkeburn, 2002), is the basis of ethical thinking. An ethical problem or issue usually involves a difficult situation when there is no obvious 'right' or 'wrong' course of action. Precise definitions of an ethical issue vary so the process of recognition can be supported by providing a working definition to students. Within the context of our teaching an *ethical problem* is evident when someone's decision/action is predicted to have 1) an *undesirable impact* on something and/or someone else, *and* is 2) causing a *conflict* between two or more of the values and beliefs of the decision maker. This seemingly relatively straightforward definition provides a fertile platform for debate, not least how recognition of an ethical problem can vary widely within a group of individuals as perceptions of what is desirable and undesirable conflict and personal values and priorities differ. What one person views as a straightforward, unproblematic, course of action, another may find to be a complex issue that needs detailed consideration.

Review

Approaches to teaching ethics which progress little beyond the identification of the ethical elements of problems are likely to prove ineffective, and potentially be both discouraging and frustrating to students. A greater degree of success is likely if students are given the freedom and time to review evidence and explore the potential outcomes of different approaches and decisions, without fear of penalty. As discussed further in the next section, providing theoretical frameworks to help scaffold this critical thinking is advantageous, as is the opportunity to compare and contrast perspectives with others. The process of review should enable students to recognize that there are a variety of possible trajectories in any given circumstances depending on the context and the people involved.

Respond

Ethical thinking skills are most likely to be encouraged when students are required to engage actively in an ethical problem by being asked to provide a considered response and hence taking individual responsibility (Ribchester and Healey, 2019). It is one thing to recognize the complexity of factors that underpin an ethical problem; it is something more significant to be asked to decide on an appropriate course of action in a given context. Teaching strategies are likely to be at their most impactful when students are pushed beyond recognition and review towards articulating and justifying a response. Here, the non-prescriptive approach to ethics is critical. Responding to an ethical issue should not be framed as a quest for the 'right answer' or seeking out a particular way of thinking or acting. It is important that students feel they can construct an argument appropriate to their values and beliefs and that where they are being assessed they are judged on the ability to justify their ethical decision, not the decision itself.

Regular opportunities to recognize, review and respond to ethical issues have the potential to develop the ethical thinking skills of geography students as well as increase their confidence when confronted with ethical problems. In some circumstances, thought processes may follow a linear route (perhaps at speed) across these three categories. More typically, they are likely to be experienced as overlapping and interconnected as, for example, review leads to further recognition of the ethical dimensions of a problem or uncertainty about an initial response prompts further review.

PRACTICE OF A HOLISTIC PROGRAMME APPROACH

This section discusses three pedagogic strategies that underpin and reinforce a holistic programme perspective for teaching ethics in geography: 1) adopting a non-didactic approach; 2) providing a consistent theoretical framework; 3) facilitating ongoing reflection. Each of these design and implementation considerations is now discussed in turn.

Strategy 1: Adopting a Non-Didactic Approach

A non-prescriptive ethos to teaching ethics should be aligned with teaching methods which encourage student engagement rather than the passive receipt of accepted knowledge. There is likely to be an emphasis on discussion and debate, occurring (if resources allow) in small group contexts. Indeed the very process of negotiating and refining the 'ground rules' of small group discussions, probably with guidance from a tutor, nicely draws attention to an important facet of the ethics of studentship (Foreman-Peck and McDowell, 2010). Furthermore, the growing interest in compassion focused pedagogies (for example Gilbert, 2017) highlights approaches that might be employed by tutors to encourage their students to contribute to creating an inclusive, supportive learning environment characterized, in part, by respect for the observations of others. Well-facilitated small group discussions also have the potential to create a space within which students are given the time to immerse themselves in the complexity of ethical issues and, crucially, feel safe enough to share their responses and the reasoning behind them (Mummery and Nolton, 2017). Such contexts allow tutors to gain an awareness of students' prior learning and experiences, which becomes all the more important within an increasingly diverse student body, and hence helps them to construct their own meanings and understandings.

Open-ended scenarios, which encourage scrutiny of an appropriate course of action in a given set of circumstances, are a well-established vehicle for ethics teaching (Healey and Ribchester, 2016). They can be used in a wide range of teaching contexts, for example small group tutorials (see case study below, Box 11.1), online discussion forums, large group lectures – where student reactions can be monitored via interactive voting tools (Bruff, 2009), and fieldwork – where the impact of different decisions on people, places and the environment might be readily visualized. Errington (2010) highlights how problem-based scenarios can encourage the integration of practical decision-making and knowledge with theoretical understanding (see next section). To take advantage of situated learning (Lave and Wenger, 1991), scenarios need to be real or realistic. Experience suggests that relevance and the opportunity to explore events unfolding within familiar contexts are motivational for many learners (Kember et al., 2008). Overall, the utilization of scenarios with strong ethical components can facilitate active and collaborative approaches widely recognized to be advantageous to student learning (Gibbs, 2015). A more detailed discussion of approaches to writing effective ethical scenarios is provided in Ribchester and Healey (2019).

Strategy 2: Providing a Consistent Framework

Students' ability to recognize, review and respond to ethical issues is likely to be strengthened by providing and discussing theories which can be applied to problems that they are confronted with. Five well-established theories (Markkula Center for Applied Ethics, 2018) which can be utilized to aid student thinking and decision-making are briefly summarized below:

- Utilitarian: what action results in the most good or least harm?
- Rights: what action respects the rights of those involved?
- Fairness/justice: what action is fair or just in the circumstances?
- Common good: what action contributes to the maintenance of a common good(s)?
- Virtue: what action is consistent with the ideals that are important to you?

Rather than restricting discussions to simply what students might consider to be the 'right' course of action in particular circumstances, the application and evaluation of theory allows for deeper review in a number of ways. Firstly, it allows for an analysis of possible outcomes using different approaches and recognition of how outcomes can vary even within a single approach, depending on the value judgements that are made. Secondly, it encourages an appreciation that individuals and stakeholders can have different perspectives on the same problem, and that these perspectives may be equally carefully considered and thought through. Thirdly, it enables students to identify consistencies (or possibly inconsistencies) in their own past and current decision-making, and to uncover that they are (sometimes unknowingly) closely aligned to particular theoretical perspectives.

Strategy 3: Facilitating Ongoing Reflection

Critical reflection is central to learning and the personal development of students across all disciplines (Moon, 2004). Reflection encourages a realistic appraisal of one's strengths, weaknesses, actions, reasoning, preferences and the changing circumstances within which we live and work. A key dynamic of reflection is one of looking back to move forwards, offering many potential benefits to the practice of studentship, including revising approaches to study, identifying priorities for personal development and refining employment aspirations. Reflection can also have wider confidence-building impacts by allowing students to 'step back' and see how far they have progressed as a learner whilst, at the same time, providing practice in concisely articulating their achievements to others (a valuable employability skill). Furthermore, realistic self-appraisal is critical to the graduate-level workplace (Longcroft, 2017), encouraging flexibility, adaptability and enhancement within the context of uncertain and fluid futures. The more specific reflection on ethical issues and thinking needs to be situated within, and aligned to, this bigger context.

The impact of a holistic programme approach to teaching ethics is likely to be greater if opportunities for reflection are embedded throughout the student experience. Facilitating ongoing reflection in this way serves a number of purposes. Firstly, a key goal of reflection is recognition and articulation of personal values and beliefs, the extent to which these change and, if so, what precipitated such changes. Secondly, reflection encourages metacognitive examination of how approaches to tackling ethical problems and decision-making strategies vary or have changed. Reflection also encourages students to identify particular formative moments or individuals, inside or outside the curriculum, that have precipitated a shift in perspective. These can all be seen as useful opportunities along the journey to 'self-authorship': 'the internal capacity to define one's beliefs, identity and social relations' (Baxter Magolda, 2008, p.269). See Chapter 23 by Moore-Cherry, for further discussion of self-authorship.

Facilitated reflection on ethical thinking skills and personal values is likely to be embedded into sessions which are focusing explicitly on ethical topics. Open, free-writing, or discussion might be encouraged, but a question-based approach is often of value in helping to structure reflections, especially for those relatively new to the exploration of ethical problems. Such prompts may be simply worded, but require carefully considered responses and any discussions may need to be sensitively managed. For example, the Model, Mirror, Mission or '3M' model (Gardner, Csikszentmihalyi and Damon, 2001) is an accessible way into reflection on personal values. '*Model*' requires identification of individuals who you admire, wish to emulate and/or have made a difference to you. '*Mirror*' asks for a realistic self-appraisal of what personal characteristics give you confidence and pride and what you would like to change. '*Mission*' promotes consideration of a very big question: what do you see as your purpose in life? Longstanding models of reflection (for example Gibbs, 1988), which guide students through stages to unpick an experience, can be effective in some circumstances. Reflection on ethics might also be embedded within broader programme structures and processes, for example as part of reflection on personal development within the context of personal tutorials or cross-module reflective assignments. Skills audit-type exercises or discussion of progression towards university-level graduate attributes or programme-specific learning outcomes are other possible vehicles to encourage reflection on the development of ethical thinking skills.

The requirement to complete reflective diaries, journals or logs is common during work-based learning experiences within university programmes (Moon, 2006), sometimes also acting as an assessment component. In some circumstances, these may afford the opportunity to reflect on both the day-to-day and longer-term ethical challenges which we encounter as individuals within the workplace. However, placements also provide a significant opportunity to critically analyse the goals, culture and practice of the host organization, whether large or small, and the internal and external factors which shape these. Much of this reflection can have an ethical component, for example an examination of the environmental impact of an organization's actions or scrutiny of any corporate social responsibility commitments.

The following case study (see Box 11.1) provides an example of how ethics may be embedded into the curriculum. It offers an illustration of the application of the three pedagogic strategies outlined in this section and also provides students the opportunity to practice the three 'Rs' of ethical thinking. It is an approach that could be applied to explore real or hypothetical challenges within any of the contexts identified in Table 11.1

BOX 11.1   CASE STUDY: 'ETHICAL STUDENT' TUTORIALS STRAND

The 'ethical student' strand has been embedded within a second year undergraduate BSc Geography Programme as part of a 'Tutorials' module worth 20 credits (20 hours contact time). Every two weeks, tutorial groups of 6–7 students meet with the same tutor to discuss selected readings and a question brief provided in advance. Two of these tutorials specifically discuss the ethical dimensions arising from eight progressively more detailed scenarios related to experiences they may have during their programme or life at university (see Healey and Ribchester (2016) for a summary of these scenarios). These are gradually released during the module. Students are asked individually to consider and decide on the course of action that they would take in the circumstances described. To help them do this they are introduced to the 'Framework for ethical decision making' (Markkula Center for Applied Ethics, 2018) outlined in Strategy 2 and asked to refer to it when articulating their decision-making. The scenarios are chronological, with the first outlining a problem at the start of the first year at university, finishing with a work placement-based dilemma in the spring of the second year at university. These scenarios articulate not only academic lifecycle problems, but also challenges in the social and professional lives of the students. This ensures that the discussion goes beyond the curriculum to consider the range of factors impacting upon the geography student's experience. Overall, the approach addresses Strategy 3 by providing opportunities for reflection over several weeks, individually as well as with peers and a tutor. Each tutorial is assessed using marking criteria that focus on justification and evidence to support a position rather than the ethical decision itself. This provides students with an opportunity to address the three 'Rs' of ethical thinking by recognizing where they consider an ethical problem to be present; reviewing different ways of addressing that problem; and identifying how they would respond to the scenario. For the final tutorial each student writes a 'ninth' scenario for discussion with their peers (Moore-Cherry et al., 2015). This tends to have the added benefit of highlighting issues that are important for the students at that point in time, for example concerns about the originality of their undergraduate dissertation research proposal.

Source: (Healey and Ribchester, 2016)

but, in this case, the focus is primarily on everyday ethical problems related to the typical experiences of a geography undergraduate.

CONCLUSION

Addressing ethical issues can be intellectually difficult and personally challenging. It is certainly easier, for both tutors and students, to traverse around them and limit engagement with ethics to the territory of formal research procedures and processes. However, such an approach misses out on the huge potential that recognizing, reviewing and responding to ethical problems gives our students to develop their critical thinking skills and their identity as undergraduates and later graduates. Just as importantly, it is likely to leave them less prepared for the challenges that they will encounter as graduates in their professional, civic, and personal futures and less equipped to contribute to tackling pressing interdisciplinary global challenges such as sustainability (see, in this volume, Chapter 19 by Robinson; Chapter 27 by Hill and Worth; Chapter 31 by Spronken-Smith).

Geography is replete with physical and human geographical topics which have an ethical dimension and this chapter advocates the development of critical thinking skills to address these issues as a core attribute of the 21st-century geography graduate. This is most likely to be achieved by pursuing a programme level approach; a spiral curriculum within which engagement with ethics is 'connected up' and progressive through the levels of an undergraduate degree. Within this context, non-didactic teaching methods are favoured, giving students the space to recognize and articulate their own values and beliefs, to develop their ethical thinking skills and, crucially, take ownership of their decision-making. At its most effective, this approach will be holistic by recognizing, and working with, the ethical challenges that emerge in the extra-curricular sphere and in the everyday social and personal worlds of our students. Indeed, learning to recognize ethical challenges in the familiar can serve to develop ethical thinking skills before applying them to geographical subject matter. Furthermore, encouraging frequent reflection on personal experiences and progress is the glue which binds together an holistic programme approach to ethics.

USEFUL RESOURCES

- Boyd, W., Healey, R.L., Hardwick, S.W. and Haigh, M. with Klein, P., Doran, B., Trafford, J. Y. and Bradbeer, J. (2008), '"None of us sets out to hurt people": the ethical geographer and geography curricula in higher education', *Journal of Geography in Higher Education*, 32 (1), pp. 37–50.
- Hay, I. (2016), 'On being ethical in geographical research', in N. Clifford, M. Cope, T. Gillespie and S. French (eds), *Key Methods in Geography*, London: Sage.
- Ribchester, C. and Healey, R.L. (2019), 'Realism, reflection and responsibility: the challenge of writing effective scenarios to support the development of ethical thinking skills', *Journal of Further and Higher Education*, 43 (1), pp. 101–114. DOI: 10.1080/0309877X.2017.1356915
- Vujakovic, P. and Bullard, J. (2001), 'The ethics minefield: issues of responsibility in learning and research', *Journal of Geography in Higher Education*, 25 (2), pp. 275–283.

REFERENCES

Barnett, R. (2000) 'Supercomplexity and the curriculum', *Studies in Higher Education*, 25 (3), pp. 255–265.

Barrie, S. (2004) 'A research-based approach to generic attributes policy', *Higher Education Research and Development*, 23 (3), pp. 261–275.

Baxter Magolda, M. (2008) 'Three elements of self-authorship', *Journal of College Student Development*, 49 (4), pp. 269–284.

Boni, A. and Lozano, J.F. (2007) 'The generic competences: an opportunity for ethical learning in the European convergence in higher education', *Higher Education*, 54 (6), pp. 819–831.

Boyd, W., Healey, R.L., Hardwick, S.W. and Haigh, M. with Klein, P., Doran, B., Trafford, J.Y. and Bradbeer, J. (2008) '"None of us sets out to hurt people": the ethical geographer and geography curricula in higher education', *Journal of Geography in Higher Education*, 32 (1), pp. 37–50.

Bruff, D. (2009) *Teaching with Classroom Response Systems: Creating Active Learning Environments*. San Francisco, CA: Jossey-Bass.

Burkill, S. and Abbey, C. (2004) 'Avoiding plagiarism', *Journal of Geography in Higher Education*, 28 (3), pp. 439–446.

Chen, J., Wang, J., Guo, J., Yu, J., Zeng, Y., Yang, H. and Zhang, R. (2018) 'Eco-environment of reservoirs in China: characteristics and research prospects', *Progress in Physical Geography: Earth and Environment*, 42 (1), pp. 185–201.

Clarkeburn, H. (2002) 'A test for ethical sensitivity in science', *Journal of Moral Education*, 31 (4), pp. 439–453.

Cloke, P., May, J. and Williams, A. (2017) 'The geographies of food banks in the meantime', *Progress in Human Geography*, 41 (6), pp. 703–726.

Critical Thinking Co. (2011) *What is Critical Thinking?* Available at: http://www.criticalthinking.com/company/articles/critical-thinking-definition.jsp (accessed: 14 February 2018).

Eriksen, C. (2017) 'Research ethics, trauma and self-care: reflections on disaster geographies', *Australian Geographer*, 48 (2), pp. 273–278.

Errington, E. (2010) 'Preparing graduates for the professions: achieving employability through the exploration of near-world scenarios', *The International Journal of Interdisciplinary Social Sciences*, 5 (5), pp. 1–10.

Foreman-Peck, L. and McDowell, L. (eds) (2010) *Aims, Ethics and Values in Group Work Assessment*, Occasional Papers No. 5 (Newcastle Upon Tyne: Centre for Excellence in Assessment for Learning, Northumbria University). Available at: https://www.northumbria.ac.uk/static/5007/arpdf/academy/cetloccpaper5.pdf (accessed: 14 February 2018).

Gannon, W.L. (2014) 'Integrating research ethics with graduate education in geography', *Journal of Geography in Higher Education*, 38 (4), pp. 481–499.

Gardner, H., Csikszentmihalyi, M. and Damon, W. (2001) *Good Work: When Excellence and Ethics Meet*. New York: Basic Books.

Gibbs, G. (1988) *Learning by Doing: A Guide to Teaching and Learning Methods*. Oxford: Oxford Polytechnic Further Education Unit.

Gibbs, G. (2015) 'Maximising Student Learning Gain', in H. Fry, S. Ketteridge and S. Marshall (eds), *A Handbook for Teaching and Learning in Higher Education*. 4th Edition. London: Kogan Page, pp. 193–208.

Gilbert, T. (2017) 'When looking is allowed: what compassionate group work looks like in a UK University', in P. Gibbs (ed.), *The Pedagogy of Compassion at the Heart of Higher Education*. Cham, Switzerland: Springer.

Hanks, P. (ed.) (1979) *Collins English Dictionary*. London: Collins.

Harvey, F. (2014) 'Values, choices, responsibilities: thinking beyond the scholarly place of ethics for GIScience and technology profession and GIScience', *Journal of Geography in Higher Education*, 38 (4), pp. 500–510.

Hay, I. (1998) 'Making moral imaginations: research ethics, pedagogy, and professional human geography', *Philosophy & Geography*, 1 (1), pp. 55–75.

Hay, I. (2016) 'On being ethical in geographical research', in N. Clifford, M. Cope, T. Gillespie and S. French (eds.) *Key Methods in Geography*. 3rd Edition. London: Sage, pp. 30–43.

Hay, I. and Foley, P. (1998) 'Ethics, geography and responsible citizenship', *Journal of Geography in Higher Education*, 22 (2), pp. 169–183.

Healey, R.L. (2014) 'How engaged are undergraduate students in ethics and ethical thinking? An analysis of the ethical development of undergraduates by discipline', *Student Engagement and Experience Journal*, 3 (2), pp. 1–21. DOI: http://dx.doi.org/10.7190/seej.v3i2.93.

Healey, R.L. and Ribchester, C. (2016) 'Developing ethical geography students? The impact and effectiveness of a tutorial based approach', *Journal of Geography in Higher Education*, 40 (2), pp. 302–319.

Hill, J., Kneale, P., Nicholson, D., Waddington, S. and Ray, W. (2011) 'Re-framing the geography dissertation: a consideration of alternative, innovative and creative approaches', *Journal of Geography in Higher Education*, 35 (3), pp. 331–349.

Kember, D., Ho, A. and Hong, C. (2008) 'The importance of establishing relevance in motivating student learning', *Active Learning in Higher Education*, 9 (3), pp. 249–263.

Kershaw, G.G.L., Castleden, H. and Laroque, C.P. (2014) 'An argument for ethical physical geography on Indigenous landscapes in Canada', *The Canadian Geographer*, 58 (4), pp. 393–399.

Lafferty, M., Wakefield, C. and Brown, H. (2017) '"We do it for the team": Student-athletes' initiation practices and their impact on group cohesion', *International Journal of Sport and Exercise Psychology*, 15 (4), pp. 438–446.

Lave, J. and Wenger, E. (1991) *Situated Learning*. Cambridge: Cambridge University Press.

Lipscombe, B., Burek, C., Potter, J., Ribchester, C. and Degg, M. (2008), 'An overview of extra-curricular education for sustainable development (ESD) interventions in UK universities', *International Journal of Sustainability in Higher Education*, 9 (3), pp. 222–234.

Longcroft, A. (2017) 'Reflect on the value of reflection and build this capacity with your students – they will need it'. Available at: https://thesedablog.wordpress.com/2017/06/21/15toptips-9/ (accessed: 14 February 2018).

Markkula Center for Applied Ethics (2018) *A Framework for Ethical Decision Making*. Available at: https://www.scu.edu/ethics/ethics-resources/ethical-decision-making/a-framework-for-ethical-decision-making/ (accessed: 16 January 2018).

McGuiness, M. and Simm, D. (2005) 'Going global? Long-haul fieldwork in undergraduate geography', *Journal of Geography in Higher Education*, 29 (2), pp. 241–253.

Moon, J. (2004) *Reflection in Learning and Professional Development: Theory and Practice*. Oxford: Routledge Falmer.

Moon, J. (2006) *Learning Journals: A Handbook for Reflective Practice and Professional Development*. London: Routledge.

Moore-Cherry, N., Healey R.L., Nicholson, D.T. and Andrews, W. (2015) 'Inclusive partnership: enhancing student engagement in geography', *Journal of Geography in Higher Education*, 40 (1), pp. 84–103.

Mummery, J. and Nolton, M. (2017) 'Facilitating the development of integrity and ethical practice via the higher education classroom', *International Higher Education Teaching and Learning Review*, 7, Article 3. Available at: https://www.hetl.org/facilitating-the-development-of-integrity-and-ethical-practice-via-the-higher-education-classroom (accessed: 22 March 2019).

Pace, D. and Middendorf, J. (eds) (2004) *Decoding the Disciplines: Helping Students Learn Disciplinary Ways of Thinking*. San Francisco, CA: Jossey-Bass.

Pascucci, E. (2017) The humanitarian infrastructure and the question of over-research: reflections on fieldwork in the refugee crises in the Middle East and North Africa, *Area*, 49 (2), pp. 249–255.

QAA (2014) *Geography. Subject Benchmark Statement*. Gloucester, UK: Quality Assurance Agency. Available at: https://www.qaa.ac.uk/docs/qaa/subject-benchmark-statements/sbs-geography-14.pdf?sfvrsn=cb9ff781_14 (accessed: 14 February 2018).

Ribchester, C. and Healey, R.L. (2019) 'Realism, reflection and responsibility: the challenge of writing effective scenarios to support the development of ethical thinking skills', *Journal of Further and Higher Education*, 43(1), pp. 101–114.

Ribchester, C., Hunt, T. and Alexander, R. (2009) '"How big's your engine, mate?" Encouraging active participation in ESD by assessing the carbon footprint of field work', *Planet*, 22, pp. 27–33.

Ruiz-Casares, M. and Thompson, J. (2016) 'Obtaining meaningful informed consent: preliminary results of a study to develop visual informed consent forms with children', *Children's Geographies*, 14 (1), pp. 35–45.

Sheppard, S.R.J. and Cizek, P. (2009) 'The ethics of Google Earth: crossing thresholds from spatial data to landscape visualisation', *Journal of Environmental Management*, 90 (6), pp. 2102–2117.

Smith, D. (1995) 'Moral teaching in geography', *Journal of Geography in Higher Education*, 19 (3), pp. 271–283.

Spalding, R. (2013) '"Daring to volunteer": some reflections on geographers, geography students and evolving institutional support for community engagement in higher education', *Journal of Geography in Higher Education*, 37 (1), pp. 59–64.

Stanier, L. (1997) 'Peer assessment and group work as vehicles for student empowerment: a module evaluation', *Journal of Geography in Higher Education*, 21 (1), pp. 95–98.

Valentine, R. (2005) 'Because Hester Prynne was an existentialist, or why using disciplines as frameworks for learning clarifies life', T. Riordan and J. Roth (eds), *Disciplines as Frameworks for Student Learning: Teaching the Practice of Disciplines*. Virginia, USA: Stylus Publishing, pp. 123–134.

van den Bemt, V., Doornbos, J., Meijering, L., Plegt, M. and Theunissen, N. (2018) 'Teaching ethics when working with geocoded data: a novel experiential learning approach', *Journal of Geography in Higher Education*, 42 (2), pp. 293–310.

Vujakovic, P. and Bullard, J. (2001) 'The ethics minefield: issues of responsibility in learning and research', *Journal of Geography in Higher Education*, 25, pp. 275–283.

Walkington, H., Dyer, S., Solem, M., Haigh, M. and Waddington, S. (2017) 'A capabilities approach to higher education: geocapabilities and implications for geography curricula', *Journal of Geography in Higher Education*, 42 (1), pp. 7–24.

Ward, N. (2017) 'Editorial', *Ethics and Social Welfare*, 11 (4), pp. 305–306.

Whalley, W.B., Saunders, A., Lewis, R.A., Buenemann, M. and Sutton, P.C. (2011) 'Curriculum development: producing geographers for the 21st century', *Journal of Geography in Higher Education*, 35 (3), pp. 379–393.

12. Information literacy: benefits, challenges and practical strategies
Richard I. Waller, Gill Miller and David M. Schultz

1. AN INTRODUCTION TO INFORMATION LITERACY

The term *information literacy* was first coined by Paul Zurkowski in the early 1970s in anticipation of the emerging information age and the rapid increase in the amount of information available, and the routes available to access it (Spitzer et al., 1998). In so doing, he identified an urgent need for 'information literates' who had learned the techniques required to make effective use of a range of tools to mould information to their needs, subsequently campaigning for the establishment of a national program to achieve universal information literacy by 1984 (Badke, 2010). As predicted, rapid developments in networked computing technologies led to a proliferation in the availability of digital information in the 1980s and 1990s that was, however, often of uncertain provenance, quality, and reliability. These advances therefore led to the development of an increasingly complex information landscape and of concomitant challenges for society as a whole, with the American Library Association (ALA) cautioning that, 'the sheer abundance of information will not in itself create a more informed citizenry without a complementary cluster of abilities necessary to use information effectively' (ALA, 2018).

This realisation stimulated an acceleration in interest in the information-literacy skills required to successfully navigate this landscape. These skills are central to lifelong learning, are of relevance to all disciplines and levels of education, and enable learners to be more independent and self-directed, allowing them to take greater control of their learning (ALA, 2018). Looking more broadly at their relevance to wider society, the ability of citizens to access and evaluate information is considered central to the continuation of a genuinely participatory democracy (Spitzer et al., 1998).

The concept of *Information Literacy* has subsequently been developed within the pedagogic literature to encapsulate the diverse but related skills required to make effective use of information in order to successfully complete a specific task or to resolve a particular problem. The constituent skills are highlighted within the most commonly cited definition of information literacy as, 'the ability to access, evaluate, and use information from a variety of sources' (Doyle, 1992, cited by Bruce, 2011, p. 326). In recognising the range of competencies required to be information literate, it is important to distinguish the concept of information literacy from the more restricted literature-search skills focusing on the development of information-technology (IT) skills and the use of online search tools simply to locate information of potential relevance. Whilst the definition usefully articulates the diversity of skills, Johnston and Webber (2003) argue that it is rather mechanistic in nature, consequently proposing a broader definition:

> Information literacy is the adoption of appropriate information behaviour to obtain, through whatever channel or medium, information well fitted to information needs, together with

the critical awareness of the importance of wise and ethical use of information in society. (p. 336)

Most recently, the US Association of College and Research Libraries (ACRL) has proposed a new and expanded definition that stresses its key role in knowledge creation, defining information literacy as

the set of integrated abilities encompassing the reflective discovery of information, the under-standing of how information is produced and valued, and the use of information in creating new knowledge and participating ethically in communities of learning. (ACRL, 2015, n.p.)

The limited development of information-literacy skills during pre-university learning can prove problematic for those making the transition into higher-education programmes, preventing students, for example, from engaging with the research literature that is more readily available (for example, Mittermeyer, 2005; Salisbury and Karasmanis, 2011; Hulseberg and Versluis, 2017). In examining the use of sources within undergraduate dissertations in Information Science, Oppenheim and Smith (2001) noted a progressive decline in the use of journal articles and an increase in the use of more easily accessible internet sites. They related this change in behaviour to an emerging skills gap, commenting that 'the real paradox lies in the fact that the more resources are made available, the more students are inclined to confine their search strategies to a few of those resources due to the lack of necessary skills required' (p. 315).

When living in an 'information age', the ability to rapidly locate, evaluate, organise, synthesise and present information is increasingly recognised as an essential graduate employability skill of relevance to a range of careers (Eisenberg, 2008). The central need for such skills within business is illustrated by Cheuk (2008) who explored their value within a large environmental-consulting firm in which 'knowledge management and sharing' is of strategic importance. In spite of these skills being considered to be business critical at board level, their limited development resulted in many employees complaining of 'information overload' and 'knowledge overload'. This in turn resulted in behaviours commonly considered problematic in educational contexts, such as a tendency to use outdated information and to rely solely on Google searches to locate information. The company's subsequent use of an information-literacy framework originally designed for higher education to develop new training programmes and information sharing systems demonstrates the practical applications of these skills (see section 3).

2.   ACADEMIC TRANSITIONS

Successful transitions to higher education require personal changes in attitudes and values, self-awareness, and independence (Hussey and Smith, 2010; see also Tate and Hopkins, 2013 and Chapter 2 in this volume) as well as transformations from passive and dependent, to autonomous and active learning. Of the challenges, information literacy is often considered the least important to sixth-form students, although it is probably one of the most significant to lecturers.

As 'digital natives' (that is those that have been brought up in the era of digital technologies), entrants to higher education in the 21st century have high levels of metaliteracy as they negotiate formal and informal sources of social media platforms (Mackey and Jacobson, 2011). New students often assume that their confident manipulation of blogs, YouTube, Facebook and Wikipedia is sufficient for independent learning (Freeman and Lynd-Balta, 2010). Whilst this can help students to generate valuable skills (Salisbury and Karamanis, 2011), students still have to learn to recognise what is genuine within this 'information fog' (Badke, 2014) in order to make the appropriate and efficient use of information that is critical to lifelong learning. Hughes (2013) found that the associated development of information-literacy skills can be especially challenging for international students. Al-Aufi et al. (2017) note research by Gazali and Lamia (2014) which found that 96 per cent of Algerian students used social media in an academic context. In so doing, they failed to consider the credibility, reliability, and completeness of the information and paid scant attention to its ethical use. Associated concerns regarding the development of information-literacy skills have led to the American Association of College and Research Libraries developing a new framework for higher education (ACRL, 2015) which gives greater emphasis to scholarly communication (see section 3).

There is a growing international consensus in schools that geography is ideally placed to address global issues and challenges of clear relevance to young people and their development as informed global citizens. Although this could also become the Achilles heel of the discipline – where to begin, which challenges to explore, how to balance breadth and depth of study etc. – it also provides an ideal opportunity to promote the information-literacy skills required for independent research that will allow students to take ownership of their learning. See, in this volume, Chapter 11 by Healey and Ribchester, on ethical thinking; and Chapters 14 by Walkington and 28 by Horvorka and Wolf for discussion of research.

Similar demands are made of pre-university students around the world. The Advanced Higher Geography course in Scotland emphasises 'interpretation, evaluation and synthesis of information from a wide range of sources' (p. 5), and the importance of high-level transferable skills (Scottish Qualifications Authority, 2015). Similarly in Queensland, Australia, the new (2019) geography syllabus notes the importance of the '21st century skills of critical thinking, creative thinking, communication and ICT [Information and Communications Technology] (assessing and analysing information)' (Queensland Curriculum and Assessment Authority, 2017, p. 5). These are echoed within the New Zealand Scholarship Geography Performance Standard (New Zealand Qualifications Authority, 2012), with the addition of 'logical development, precision and clarity of ideas' (p. 1). Indeed, New Zealand has a specific information-literacy policy on how to support information management, emphasising its integration throughout the curriculum (Ministry of Education and National Library of New Zealand 2002). A-level Geography in England and Wales has been reformed four times since 1997 with each new specification placing an increased emphasis on active and independent learning. The report of the A-level Content Advisory Board (ALCAB, 2014) emphasised 'engagement with a diverse range of subject matter . . . and a mastery of a broad range of numerical, graphical and reading skills as well as knowledge of the world and global issues' (p. 9). Subsequent Department for Education subject criteria (DfE, 2014) requires geography students to 'engage critically with real world issues; grow as independent thinkers, informed and engaged citizens; develop as critical and reflective learners' (pp. 4–5) going on to highlight the 'interpretation and evaluation of a range of source material' (p. 12) as a key geographical skill.

The developing need for information-literacy skills are therefore explicit within the aims and aspirations of pre-university geography courses. Sadly, several GCE[1] examiner reports in 2017 noted that a lack of extended reading had the potential to reduce student achievement in examinations (Palôt et al., 2018). This reveals the existence of a number of personal and institutional barriers, with the institutional barriers existing within schools and Awarding Organisations (AOs) as well as higher-education institutions. These barriers inhibit the development of information-literacy skills before students begin their undergraduate courses. Kimsey and Cameron (2005), for example, have found that investing time into the development of information-literacy skills encouraged active learning, with librarians being best placed to support their development and to coordinate the purchase of the information resources best suited to assessments. However, with school budgets in the UK being increasingly stretched in the current climate of reducing funding per pupil, few schools have the financial resources and capacity to nurture information-literacy skills in this way. In addition, the pressures associated with school league tables have led to a strong focus on assessment results (see Chapter 3 in this volume by Butt for discussion of the school–university 'gap'). These pressures affect the pattern and style of teaching and learning, which in turn tends to override the aspirations to nurture the active and autonomous learners described within course curricula.

With information literacy not being formally assessed, there is less motivation to spend time on developing good practice within what is already a crowded curriculum. The detrimental impact of this coupled with school bureaucracy has also been recognised in Germany (Botte, 2012). As a consequence of the perceived lack of knowledge and skills required to use digital information sources, the development of information-literacy skills has been delivered instead by librarians. The resultant disconnect between teachers and librarians in combination with the crowded curriculum has led to a marginalisation of these key skills – a problem that has also been recognised within higher education (Johnston and Webber, 2003). Limitations in the information-literacy expertise of teachers, who have themselves often received no training (Hulseberg and Versluis, 2017), therefore constitutes an additional barrier that can negate the benefits associated with the wider availability of information, a situation that can be exacerbated if as 'digital migrants' they feel more insecure than their 'digital native' students. In the UK, the ESRC Teaching and Learning Research programme, for example, found that whilst electronic networks were readily available, teachers did not use them to develop their own professional practice (Wright, 2010).

For some years, the Awarding Organisations (AOs) who run school examinations in the UK have been working in a competitive environment and have promoted their specifications with the support of accompanying texts. This has led to a significant student (and often teacher) dependence on the core text that attempts to cover all the key concepts and knowledge of a specification (Waller et al., 2016). Although this provides a potential opportunity for students to develop the information-literacy skills required to 'read around' the subject, this is in reality hampered by the combination of a crowded curriculum, hard-pressed teachers, and students' utilitarian approach to learning. Core texts are commonly regarded as providing 'all I need to know'; what is *not* in the core text is not needed for examination success. Thus, it seems that whilst high-level curriculum statements are promoting active and independent learning, the challenges faced by teachers and students have resulted in a more pragmatic approach in which the core text has remained the primary source of information. The introduction of non-examination assessments (NEAs) enabled students to submit coursework as part of their examination. These NEAs take the form of an independent, student-led enquiry based on the analysis of primary data collected by the student. NEAs should encourage students to explore a wider range of literature on a chosen topic but their impact on the development of information-literacy skills has yet to be evaluated.

As part of a recent modernisation of A-level geography in the UK, recent attempts have been made to bridge the gap between school and university through the development of a more academically rigorous programme with a more explicit need for independent subject research (DfE, 2014). In taking teachers out of their comfort zone, however, the launch of the new specifications in 2017 has driven many teachers towards increasing dependence on the core text due to a perceived lack of subject expertise. Such insecurity tends to inhibit the ability of teachers to facilitate independent learning, instead reinforcing more carefully scripted and directed teaching. The uncertainty of rapid change is a widely recognised phenomenon of the 21st century and teachers of geography in the UK have faced considerable, simultaneous changes in GCSE and A-level. Consequently, whilst the specifications provide numerous opportunities to make geography a relevant discipline ideally suited to the application of information-literacy skills, this shift in approach has yet to take place.

Resolving this situation and embedding information-literacy skills more firmly into educational curricula poses challenges for both students and those teaching them. Focusing initially on students, although the 'digital native' students of the 21st century may not be familiar with the more scholarly sources of information or the use of referencing, they are certainly not information illiterate. Salisbury and Karasmanis (2011) identified the capability of new entrants to construct the basic search terms required to locate relevant information (see section 3). However, there can be a resultant tendency for students to become complacent and to lack an appreciation of the need for the additional training required to develop the more sophisticated skills required within a higher-education environment. Hulseberg and Versluis (2017) commented that, 'student confidence in their abilities can outpace their actual knowledge'. As a consequence, they tend not to seek assistance, being satisfied with their own skills (Gross et al., 2012). Being time poor, many students also adopt a 'satisfier–sufficiency' model of research, engaging solely with the first few hits on Google without explicitly considering their provenance and reliability.

In order to support student transitions in the specific context of information literacy, teachers in higher education therefore need to explicitly identify and build upon the nascent skills new entrants bring with them (for example Biggs, 1999). Staff are all too frequently unaware of the previous learning environment of their new students, or do not consider it relevant to their own teaching (Baer, 2008). McEwan (2015) is clear that effective transition experiences depend upon a close alignment between student expectations and tutor perceptions. A clear case therefore can be made for academics to be better informed about the nature of the more structured learning programmes in schools and to be clearer about the academic norms and processes that they take for granted (Bonnett, 2003).

3.   CONCEPTUAL MODELS AND PROGRAMME DESIGN

Following on from the pioneering work of Zurkowski and a developing interest in information literacy in the 1980s and 1990s, the USA has continued to lead in the development of a range of information-literacy initiatives that have had national and international impacts (Spitzer et al., 1998). The creation of the Information Literacy Institute in 1998 funded by the American Library Association (ALA) provided staff development programmes for the training of academic librarians. This in turn provided the impetus for the establishment of a series of national information-literacy competency standards for higher education that provide a prerequisite for the learning outcomes, tools, and resources required to embed these information-literacy skills within degree curricula. The first competency standards were developed by a task force set up in 1999 by the Association of College and Research Libraries (ACRL). These were published in the following year comprising five standards, 22 performance indicators, and no less than 88 separate outcomes (ALA, 2018). Focusing on the key standards, these stated that the information-literate student:

1.   Determines the nature and extent of the information needed.
2.   Accesses information needed effectively and efficiently.
3.   Evaluates information and its sources critically and incorporates selected information into his or her knowledge base or system.
4.   Incorporates selected information into one's knowledge base.
5.   Individually or as a member of a group, uses information effectively to accomplish a specific purpose.
6.   Understands many of the economic, legal and social issues surrounding the use of information, and accesses and uses information ethically and legally.

Although these standards identify and emphasise distinctive skills, Johnston and Webber (2003) argue that this type of framework risks fostering a tick-box approach in which a complex set of skills are broken down into a series of discrete units amenable to a recipe-style delivery. In updating this framework in 2015, the ACRL has undertaken a wholesale revision with the new version focusing on a cluster of interconnected 'threshold concepts' rather than a prescriptive suite of skills (see Chapter 6 in this volume by Fouberg for further discussion of threshold concepts). The six concepts incorporate the concept of 'metaliteracy' in which information literacy is viewed as an overarching set of abilities in which students act as consumers and creators of information:

- *Authority is constructed and contextual*: Information resources reflect the creators' expertise and credibility.
- *Information creation as a process*: Information is produced to convey a message and involves varied iterative processes of researching, creating, revising, and disseminating.
- *Information has value*: Information has several dimensions of value that include its value as a commodity and as a means of education.
- *Research as inquiry*: Research is iterative, involving increasingly complex or new questions whose answers in turn develop additional questions or lines of inquiry.

- *Scholarship as convention*: Communities of scholars engage in sustained discourse with new insights emerging over time.
- *Searching as strategic exploration*: Searching for information is often non-linear and iterative, requiring the evaluation of a range of information sources.

An alternative approach to the development of information-literacy skills focusing on the behaviours of the information-literate individual rather than the constituent skills has been developed in Australia. This approach has been driven in part by an interest in the issue at the highest levels in government, with a 1991 report expressing concerns about the future implications of an emerging divide between the information-rich and information-poor (Bruce, 2011). The Australian Council of Australian University Librarians (CAUL) published their own information-literacy standards in 2001 (CAUL, 2001) that built upon those previously published by the ACRL, including two new standards on the information-literate person who:

- recognises that lifelong learning and participative citizenship requires information literacy.
- expands, reframes, or creates new knowledge by integrating prior knowledge and new understandings individually or as a member of the group.

This focus on the developing capabilities of the individual, rather than the skills themselves, reflects the development of what has become a highly influential model developed by Bruce (1997) that identified 'seven faces' of information literacy. In taking a phenomenographic approach, this model attempts to capture the varied experiences of information users progressing from more straightforward experiences focused largely around the use of information technology to more complex experiences relating to the increasingly sophisticated uses of information to develop new insights.

- *First face: The IT experience*: Information literacy is experienced as using information technology for information awareness and communication.
- *Second face: The Info-Sources Experience*: Information literacy is experienced as finding information from appropriate sources.
- *Third face: The Info-Process Experience*: Information literacy is experienced as executing a process (for example, use in problem solving or decision making).
- *Fourth face: The Info-Control Experience*: Information literacy is experienced as controlling information (for example, management of the information retrieved and recognition of material of particular relevance).
- *Fifth face: The Knowledge Construction Experience*: Information literacy is experienced as building up a personal knowledge base in a new area of interest through the application of critical thinking.
- *Sixth face: The Knowledge Extension Experience*: Information literacy is experienced as working with knowledge and personal perspectives adopted in such a way that novel insights are gained.
- *Seventh face: The Wisdom Experience*: Information literacy is experienced as using information wisely for the benefit of others, considering for example the importance of personal values and ethics.

Rather than simply adopting the more advanced faces, the information-literate individual is able to identify and utilise the most appropriate face for the specific situation they encounter. Although it was originally designed for educational environments, this flexibility in combination with the close association of the faces to distinct workplace processes such as horizon scanning, research and development, and professional ethics has resulted in its application within business settings (Bruce, 1999). As mentioned in section 1, this model has, for example, been used to develop training programmes within environmental consultancy that have enabled employees to address the problem of information overload whilst enabling the wider organisation to make more effective use of the diverse range of information available (Cheuk, 2008).

The development of information-literacy skills in the context of higher education in the UK has tended to lag behind the USA, Australia and New Zealand. This in part reflects a lack of high-level recognition and promotion of their value as a key skill set with wider benefits to society at large (in marked contrast to Australia). It also reflects a tendency for information-literacy skills to be subsumed within and overshadowed by a broader focus on information technology (Johnston and Webber, 2003). Nevertheless, a working group of the Society of College, National and University Libraries (SCONUL) was established to develop a UK model of information literacy that was published in revised form in 2011 (SCONUL, 2011). As with the Australian approach, this model focuses on the progressive development of an individual in relation to a series of key skills or competencies and the associated attitudes or understandings displayed by the information-literate individual. The core model designed explicitly for use in higher education employs the metaphor of a circular building in which the practitioner can progress from being a novice to an expert through the construction of seven 'pillars':

1. IDENTIFY: Able to identify a personal need for information.
2. SCOPE: Can assess current knowledge and identify gaps.
3. PLAN: Can construct strategies for locating information and data.
4. GATHER: Can locate and access the information and data they need.
5. EVALUATE: Can review the research process and compare and evaluate information and data.
6. MANAGE: Can organise information professionally and ethically.
7. PRESENT: Can apply the knowledge gained: presenting the results of their research, synthesising new and old information and data to create new knowledge and disseminating it in a variety of ways.

These core descriptors are associated with more detailed descriptions of both the related understandings of the individual and their competencies (SCONUL, 2011). The subsequent development of distinct 'lenses' has in turn been designed to relate the key components of the core model to various specific situations such as graduate employment (SCONUL, 2015).

In considering the ways in which information-literacy skills might be delivered most effectively within the context of a university degree programme, Johnston and Webber (2003) consider their commonplace delivery through a disjointed series of discrete sessions to be inappropriate and ineffective, pointing out that, 'there is more to information literacy than can be learned in a few afternoons in the library' (p. 339). Such an approach fragments the field of knowledge, encourages a tick-box mentality, and promotes a surface learning approach by learners.

Whilst there is widespread recognition of the need for the more effective integration of information literacy into degree-programme curricula (for example Bruce, 2011), there is, however, no agreed consensus as to how this is best achieved in practice. Eisenberg (2008), for example, argues that there is no need to develop new units or modules, suggesting instead that a review of existing curricula should be undertaken to identify ideal opportunities for their inclusion in terms of either appropriate subject coverage or modes of assessment. In contrast, Webber and Johnston (2000) argue that a failure to incorporate information-literacy skills into credit-bearing modules, as is commonly the case when they are delivered by library staff, results in them being marginalised and trivialised by staff and students, echoing the problems encountered within schools (section 2). The authors therefore designed a one-semester, credit-bearing information-literacy module run as a joint venture between the Department of Information Science and the Centre for Academic Practice at the University of Strathclyde. This centrally-run module was then made available as a second- or third-year option module to all students within the university's Business School.

Whatever approach is taken, Bruce (2011) argues that the adoption of the concept of constructive alignment is vital (Biggs, 1999) in order to promote the development of learning activities specifically designed to change the ways in which students learn. In addition, there is increasing recognition of the need for university librarians and academic staff to work more closely and collaboratively to ensure that the skills developed are effectively integrated and therefore validated within any academic programme (for example Johnston and Webber, 2003; Bruce, 2011).

Illustrations of the practical application of this type of academic collaboration within the specific context of geography are provided by Waller et al. (2016) and Hulseberg and Versluis (2017) in relation to year 1 (freshman) and year 2 (sophomore) geographical skills modules, respectively. Waller et al. (2016) describe how a pair of library-skills sessions delivered at different times in the semester where replaced by a more coherent block of four sessions explicitly themed around the development of information-literacy skills. Their delivery at the very outset of the degree programme was deliberately designed to emphasise the important role information literacy can play in facilitating academic transitions (for example, Oppenheim and Smith, 2001). Hulseberg and Versluis (2017) provide a review of the different ways in which information-literacy skills have been integrated into undergraduate programmes and describe the approach they have adopted within a small liberal-arts college in the US (Table 12.1). Following a brief introduction in a first-year seminar, the information-literacy skills are primarily delivered within a 'Research Methods in Geography' course within their sophomore year. The three sessions are aligned to the ACRL Information Literacy Standards for Higher Education (ALA, 2018) and are delivered within the broader context of their personal development as researchers.

With the development of information-literacy skills being explicitly related to lifelong learning, there is a need for those in higher education to identify and build upon the capabilities that new entrants bring with them as well as to identify the skills gaps that need to be bridged. In surveying the information-literacy skills of new entrants to La Trobe University in Australia, Salisbury and Karasmanis (2011) discovered that over three-quarters of new entrants were already capable of generating simple keyword search strategies. However, less than a third displayed a clear awareness of journal citations, peer-reviewed articles, or referencing, highlighting the specific competencies requiring ongoing development.

4.   PRACTICAL APPROACHES

Given the challenges that students face when trying to apply concepts of information literacy to their learning, what can instructors do to help? In this section we present practical examples that could be applied as formative or summative assessments, in lectures or small-group tutorial sessions, or as group or individual work. The goal here is to arm

Table 12.1   Coverage of information-literacy skills within a year 2 research-skills methods course

Session	Topic	Objectives*	Description of activities
1	Using sources in geographical research	• Identify the value and purpose of potential resources. • Recognise the organisation of knowledge into disciplines.	• Students reflect on their own research processes. • Students examine the characteristics of different types of sources. • Students locate, examine and compare a science journalism article with the original publication.
2	Finding sources	• Select appropriate information-retrieval systems (e.g. Google Scholar, Geobase, Web of Science). • Identify different types of information sources. • Broaden the information-seeking process beyond local resources.	• Students discuss the range of available and strategies for identifying them. • Groups create expert guides to a specific resource type. • Students identify and access initial resources on topics.
3	Evaluating sources, tracing scholarly conversations, managing information	• Evaluate information critically. • Access required information effectively and efficiently.	• Students explore methods of organising their research. • Students identify a key article and preliminary list of sources on their topic. • Perform a citation trace to track scholarly conversations.

Note: * Correspond to outcomes from the ACRL Information Literacy Competency Standards for Higher Education (ALA, 2018).

Source: Modified from Hulseberg and Versluis (2017, p. 18).

instructors with tools that can be used to help students develop their information-literacy skills.

Getting students to write is great practice for their dissertations, even as early as their first year. But, throwing them into the deep end without some guidance fails to prepare them for their most ambitious project of their degree. Students therefore need guidance during the transition to university, as well as disciplinary content and perspectives. Reading the scientific literature is daunting, and weaning students off Wikipedia and their textbook in favour of a relevant academic journal can be challenging for any new entrant.

The practical strategies outlined below loosely correspond to the seven pillars of information literacy described in the previous section (SCONUL, 2011). This section shows how to create assignments featuring milestones that follow the seven pillars. The approach is organised as a literature search leading to a report reviewing the literature on a specific research question. Although such literature reviews are a common assignment for university students, the advantage of the approach we outline here is to include milestones for formative or summative assessment along the way. The assignment can be delivered whole or in part to focus on individual information-literacy skills. The milestones serve many purposes, including (1) breaking down a large task into a series of smaller steps that become more easily attainable by goal-oriented students; (2) helping students see the value, and also subtlety, in steps that they might otherwise neglect; (3) ensuring that students learn the techniques and produce satisfactory results at one step before proceeding to the next; and (4) enabling students to become more independent learners.

Two skills precede the assignment: how to use search engines and how to read the literature with a critical eye. As necessary prerequisites for any literature-review assignment, specific exercises that develop these skills are provided below.

How to Use Search Engines

Most students will be familiar with Google or Internet Explorer, which provide a general search tool, but the goal of this exercise is to get them to develop experience with Google Scholar and other commercial search engines for scientific journal articles (for example, Web of Knowledge, Scopus, ScienceDirect) and thereby to build upon their existing skills base (Salisbury and Karasmanis, 2011). Students should be encouraged to reflect on the company ownership of these search engines, their purposes, and the reasons why some articles are hidden behind a paywall. They should also be encouraged to experiment with the use of individual syntax (for example, Boolean operators) and advanced search capabilities available to focus searches more effectively. One exercise that could be given to the students in class is to get them to type search terms of varying specificity (for example, 'climate change', 'hydraulic fracking', 'French geographers') into the different search engines to see the types and numbers of sources revealed. Emphasis should be paid to identifying the origin (for example, journal article, commercial web site, news story, professional society website, personal blog) and the types of source materials (for example, primary, secondary, tertiary). Students should in particular be introduced to scientific journal literature, the peer-review process and its benefits, and how to identify whether or not the sources are peer-reviewed. Students should learn what citations look like, what a reference list looks like, how to find information about source material that comprises a reference or citation, and the different types of referencing and citation formats. Students should also learn how to use the reference list of the source to see what the authors have cited and the cited-by list on the search engine to see which later authors have cited the source.

How to Critically Read the Literature

The present explosion of information available on the internet with extreme political views becoming more mainstream, and #FakeNews has made finding and ascertaining reliable information more challenging. However, it also provides an opportunity to educate students about the approaches required to determine the credibility and reliability of source material. When reading source material, students should take notes on their reading and learn to read the material critically, with an eye toward understanding whether the information is relevant to their explorations, what the author is trying to communicate, whether the material is reliable, and how the information relates to their other reading on the same topic. One way to familiarise students with this type of critical reading is for the instructor to produce a reading guide of questions for the students to answer on an assigned source or sources. Asking a range of questions on the guide – from the basics of reading comprehension ('What was the main point of this paper?'), to synthesis ('How does the method applied by Smith et al. (2008) differ from that by Chen et al. (2013)?'), to critique ('What are the strengths and weaknesses of the approach used by the author?'), to extrapolation ('How has this result held up to further scrutiny?') – can develop the skills referred to in the 'evaluate' pillar. There are many good websites listing questions readers should ask during critical reading, and an exercise for determining the credibility of a source is described by Waller et al. (2016). Having the students bring their reading guides to class can lead to in-class discussions of their answers and potentially stimulating individual perspectives, encouraging the 'knowledge construction experience' described by Bruce (1997).

Research Definition and Literature Search

The 'identify', 'plan', and 'gather' pillars require the ability to identify research questions, articulate current knowledge, and manage time effectively. The scientific literature can be overwhelming, even for experienced researchers. For many students, the vastness of the literature can be used as an excuse to procrastinate by prolonging the search for more literature, rather than being more selective and critically examining fewer, more relevant, sources.

Limitations in the information-literacy skills and experience of new entrants pose real challenges as they learn how best to engage with a varied information landscape. Their initial preference is usually to not delve deep enough (for example, restricting searches to Wikipedia and textbooks) or to read a few journal articles and assume that they represent the field more broadly. Starting an assignment with more specific questions for them to answer can encourage students to delve deeper. Rather than have them write about mid-ocean ridges, have them write about the latest paper to address the factors that affect the geochemistry of lava at mid-ocean ridges.

Set a limit for the amount of time spent searching the literature (Waller and Schultz, 2015). Literature searches should be broken down into two parts. During the first part, the students should read broadly around the subject. Start with introductory textbooks and general-interest websites, but then get more specific with higher-level textbooks and journal articles. This reading should lead to the development of the *problem statement* – what the paper is going to be about. Having the student craft a specific problem statement is an accomplishment; it will be the first sentence they have written for their paper. This sentence may start as 'The purpose of this paper is to. . .'. Reports that fail to contain a problem statement may suffer from a lack of depth, lack of focus, or incoherence.

Having undertaken a more general review of the literature of relevance to the topic, the research can now focus more explicitly on the scientific literature that addresses the problem statement. Once the fixed time for reading and notetaking is over, efforts now proceed to writing the assignment.

Additional Suggestions for Information Literacy

Supplemental lecture material or exercises can also involve students learning to use bibliographic software or websites to manage their reference lists, providing an opportunity to address the 'manage' pillar (SCONUL, 2011). Introducing these tools at the outset of their undergraduate degree programme will encourage students to make use of software of relevance to assignments that occur throughout the programme. There should also be explicit discussion of plagiarism, copyright, and acknowledgements (for example, Creative Commons; using graphics in their presentations, on websites, and blogs).

Finally, students should be provided with opportunities to practice writing reports and giving presentations, thereby gaining valuable formative feedback (Waller and Schultz, 2015). Where possible, engage your students with your research. Many tools and datasets exist online that can be used (for example, Waller and Schultz, 2013). Why not challenge students to write a journal or magazine article, or a blog?

5.   CONCLUSION

The concept of information literacy encapsulates the range of skills and behaviours required to make effective use of information, and has been developed as a response to the increasingly diverse information landscape we now occupy. The limited development of information-literacy skills within pre-18 curricula resulting from a reliance on core texts and resource limitations, for example, can cause challenges to learners making the transition into higher-education programmes. However, new entrants arrive at university with a range of nascent skills that can be built upon, such as the ability to construct search terms. It is incumbent on academics to be more appreciative of these capabilities in addition to the skills gaps. A range of information-literacy frameworks have been developed that can provide the basis for their delivery within degree programmes, although there is as yet no consensus as to how this is best achieved in practice. In their absence, we would encourage higher-education practitioners to experiment with different approaches to their delivery, integration into modules and student activities, and related assessments to find out what works best in their own particular educational circumstances.

USEFUL RESOURCES

- Waller, R. and Schultz, D. M. (2013) *How to Succeed at University in GEES Disciplines: Using Online Data for Independent Research*. Available at: https://www.heacad emy.ac.uk/system/files/resources/gees_9_transitions_resource_wallerandschultz.pdf (downloaded: 22nd April 2019).
- Waller, R. and Schultz, D.M. (2015) *How to Succeed at University in GEES Disciplines: Enhancing your Information Literacy Skills*. Available at: https://www.heacademy. ac.uk/system/files/resources/how_to_succeed_in_gees_0.pdf (downloaded: 22nd April 2019).

NOTE

1. GCE is the General Certificate of Education in England and Wales. It is the most advanced qualification available in schools, and a basic requirement for HE.

REFERENCES

American Library Association (ALA) (2018), *Information Literacy Competency Standards for Higher Education*. Available at: http://www.ala.org/Template.cfm?Section=Home&template=%2FContentManagement%2FCo ntentDisplay.cfm&ContentID=33553 (accessed: 14th February 2018).
Association of College and Research Libraries (ACRL) (2015) *Framework for Information Literacy for Higher Education*. Available at: http://www.ala.org/acrl/standards/ilframework (accessed: 27th February 2018).
A level Content Advisory Board (ALCAB) (2014) *Report of the ALCAB Panel on Geography*. Available at: https:// alevelcontent.files.wordpress.com/2014/07/alcab-report-of-panel-on-geography-july-2014.pdf (accessed: 14th February 2018).
Al-Aufi, A.S., Al-Azri, H.M. and Al-Hadi, N.A. (2017) 'Perceptions of information literacy skills among undergraduate students in the social media environment', *International Information & Library Review*, 49(3), pp. 163–175.
Badke, W. (2010) 'Foundations of information literacy: learning from Paul Zurkowski', *Online*, 34(1), pp. 48–50.
Badke, W. (2014) *Research Strategies: Finding Your Way Through the Information Fog*. Bloomington, USA: iUniverse.
Baer, L.D. (2008) 'Misunderstandings about student transitions to university: a slow-motion dialogue between staff and students', *Journal of Geography in Higher Education*, 32(2), pp. 303–320.
Biggs, J. (1999) *Teaching for Quality Learning at University*. Buckingham, UK: Open University Press.
Bonnett, A. (2003) 'Geography as the world-discipline: connecting popular and academic geographical imagina- tions', *Area*, 35(1), pp. 55–63.
Botte, A. (2012) *Challenges of Educational Reform in Germany and the Potential Role of Information Literacy*. Available at: https://www.pedocs.de/volltexte/2012/6758/pdf/Botte_2012_Challenges_of_Educational_ Reform_in_Germany.pdf (accessed: 14th February 2018).
Bruce, C.S. (1997) *The Seven Faces of Information Literacy*. Adelaide, Australia: Auslib Press.
Bruce, C.S. (1999) 'Workplace experiences of information literacy', *International Journal of Information Management*, 19(1), pp. 33–47.
Bruce, C.S. (2011) 'Information literacy programs and research: an international review', *The Australian Library Journal*, 60(4), pp. 326–333.
CAUL (2001) *Information Literacy Standards*. Available at: http://archive.caul.edu.au/caul-doc/InfoLitStandards 2001.doc (accessed: 22nd February 2018).
Cheuk, B. (2008) 'Delivering business value through information literacy in the workplace', *Libri*, 58(3), pp. 137–143.
DfE (2014) *Geography GCE AS and A level subject content*. Available at: https://www.gov.uk/government/ publications/gce-as-and-a-level-geography (accessed: 14th February 2018).
Eisenberg, M.B. (2008) 'Information literacy: essential skills for the information age', *DESIDOC Journal of Library & Information Technology*, 28(2), pp. 39–47.

Freeman, E. and Lynd-Balta, E. (2010) 'Developing information literacy skills early in an undergraduate curriculum', *College Teaching*, 58(3), pp. 109–115.

Gazalia, M. and Lamia, S. (2014) 'Implications of relying on social media to access scientific knowledge: A field study in light of relying on media theory', *Journal of Theory*, 27, pp. 155–185.

Gross, M., Latham, D. and Armstrong, B. (2012) 'Improving below-proficient information literacy skills: designing an evidence-based educational intervention', *College Teaching*, 60(3), pp. 104–111.

Hughes, H. (2013) 'International students using online information resources to learn: complex experience and learning needs', *Journal of Further and Higher Education*, 37(1), pp. 126–146.

Hulseberg, A. and Versluis, A. (2017) 'Integrating information literacy into an undergraduate geography research methods course', *College & Undergraduate Libraries*, 24(1), pp. 14–28.

Hussey, T. and Smith, P. (2010) 'Transitions in higher education', *Innovations in Education and Teaching International*, 47(2), pp. 155–164.

Johnston, B. and Webber, S. (2003) 'Information literacy in higher education: a review and case study', *Studies in Higher Education*, 23(3), pp. 335–352.

Kimsey, M.B. and Cameron, S.L. (2005) 'Teaching and assessing information literacy in a geography program', *Journal of Geography*, 104(1), pp. 17–23.

Mackey, T.P. and Jacobson, T. (2011) 'Reframing information literacy as a metaliteracy', *College & Research Libraries*, 76(1), pp. 62–78.

McEwan, M. (2015) *Understanding Student Transition to University: The Expectations of Essay Writing for Students and Staff*. Glasgow: Academic Development Unit, University of Glasgow.

Ministry of Education and National Library of New Zealand (2002) *The School Library and Learning in the Information Landscape: Guidelines for New Zealand Schools*. Wellington, New Zealand: Learning Media Ltd. Available at: https://natlib.govt.nz/system/resources/W1siZiIsIjIwMTcvMDMvMDcvZW9xeGtppZDZ oX1RoZV9zY2hvb2xfbGlicmFyeV9hbmRfTGVhcm5pbmdfaW5fdGhlX2luZm9ybWF0aW9uX2xhbm RzY2FwZV9ndWlkZWxpbmVzLnBkZiJdXQ/The-school-library-and-Learning-in-the-information-landsc ape-guidelines.pdf?sha=15a87dc578f23f80 (accessed: 14th February 2018).

Mittermeyer, D. (2005) 'Incoming first year undergraduate students: how information literate are they?', *Education for Information*, 23(4), pp. 203–232.

New Zealand Qualifications Authority (2012) *New Zealand Scholarship Geography Performance Standard*. Available at: http://www.nzqa.govt.nz/qualifications-standards/awards/new-zealand-scholarship/scholarship-subjects/scholarship-geography/ (accessed 15th June 2018).

Oppenheim, C. and Smith, R. (2001) 'Student citation practices in an Information Science department', *Education for Information*, 19(4), pp. 299–323.

Palôt, I., Hore, H., Oakes, S. and Digby, R. (2018) 'How can the AS examiners' reports help improve your students' performance at A level?', *Teaching Geography*, 43(1), pp. 9–10.

Queensland Curriculum and Assessment Authority (2017) *Geography 2019 v1: General Senior Syllabus*. Available at: https://www.qcaa.qld.edu.au/downloads/portal/syllabuses/snr_geography_19_syll.pdf (accessed: 15th June 2018).

Salisbury, F. and Karasmanis, S. (2011) 'Are they ready? Exploring student information literacy skills in the transition from secondary to tertiary education', *Australian Academic & Research Libraries*, 42(1), pp. 43–58.

SCONUL (2011) *The SCONUL Seven Pillars of Information Literacy. Core Model for Higher Education*. Available at: https://www.sconul.ac.uk/page/seven-pillars-of-information-literacy (accessed: 22nd February 2018).

SCONUL (2015) *The Graduate Employability Lens on the SCONUL Seven Pillars of Information Literacy*. Available at: https://www.sconul.ac.uk/sites/default/files/documents/Employability_Lens_only_2015_0.pdf (accessed: 22nd February 2018).

Scottish Qualifications Authority (2015) *Advanced Higher Geography Course Specification*. Available at: www.sqa.org.uk (accessed: 14th February 2018).

Spitzer, K.L., Eisenberg, M.B. and Lowe, C.A. (1998) 'Information literacy: essential skills for the information age'. *Clearinghouse on Information & Technology*. New York: Syracuse University.

Tate, S. and Hopkins, P. (2013) *Re-thinking Undergraduate Students' Transitions to, Through and Out of University.* Available at: https://research.ncl.ac.uk/studenttransitions/researchoutputs/Re-thinking%20undergraduate%20 students%20transitions%20to,%20through%20and%20out%20of%20university.pdf (accessed: 6th June 2019)

Waller, R. and Schultz, D.M. (2013) *How to Succeed at University in GEES Disciplines: Using Online Data for Independent Research.* Available at: https://www.heacademy.ac.uk/system/files/resources/gees_9_transitions_ resource_wallerandschultz.pdf (accessed: 28th February 2018).

Waller, R. and Schultz, D.M. (2015) *How to Succeed at University in GEES Disciplines: Enhancing your Information Literacy Skills.* Available at: https://www.heacademy.ac.uk/system/files/resources/how_to_suc ceed_in_gees_0.pdf (accessed: 28th February 2018).

Waller, R., Adams, C., Miller, G. and Schultz, D.M. (2016) 'Encouraging students to read beyond the core text', *Teaching Geography*, 41, pp. 103–105.

Waller, R.I., Knight, P.G. and Beard, J. (2015) *Developing Information Literacy Skills Within Undergraduate*

Programme. Available at: https://lpdcsolutions.blogspot.co.uk/2015/05/developing-information-literacy-skills.html (accessed: 23rd February 2018).

Webber, S. and Johnston, B. (2000) 'Conceptions of information literacy: new perspectives and implications', *Journal of Information Science*, 26(6), pp. 381–397.

Wright, N. (2010) *e-Learning and Implications for New Zealand Schools: A Literature Review*. Wilf Malcolm Institute of Educational Research, School of Education, The University of Waikato. Available at: https://www.educationcounts.govt.nz/publications/e-Learning/e-learning-and-implications-for-new-zealand-schools-a-literature-review/executive-summary (accessed: 15th June 2018).

PART II

PEDAGOGIES TO FACILITATE MORE AUTONOMOUS LEARNING

13. Inclusive teaching and learning practices in geography
Annie Hughes and Nona McDuff

INTRODUCTION

Universities across much of the developed world, including the UK, have achieved some success in broadening participation in recent years with an increasing number of individuals from a diverse range of backgrounds accessing higher education. Indeed, the current UK government has laid out two targets in this regard – to double the numbers of disadvantaged people progressing to higher education and secondly to increase the numbers from black and minority ethnic backgrounds by a further 20 per cent (Smith and Hubble, 2018). However, the exponential growth in access and participation has not been paralleled by parity in attainment outcomes for a variety of student groups who have arbitrarily been defined as 'non-traditional' (Higher Education Funding Council (Hefce), 2015; Universities UK, 2016). Whilst the category of 'non-traditional' is not entirely helpful given that it combines the experiences of student groups who each have very distinct challenges, it does define a category of students who fall outside 'the (traditional) norm': the (more often than not) white, middle class student attending university straight from college or school and away from home (ECU, 2017). Identifying and addressing these disparate outcomes has been recognised as a key challenge for higher education (Millward, 2018).

In the UK we know that the attainment outcomes for a range of 'non-traditional' student groups are persistently less positive than their 'traditional' counterparts. In the UK, university attainment is measured through a degree classification system with a first-class degree representing the highest attainment and a third class representing the lowest. Generally, a first class or an upper second class are categorised as 'good' degrees. The latest data from the newly formed UK Office for Students (OfS) identifies a ten percentage point difference between students gaining a first or upper second class degree between Participation of Local Areas (POLAR) quintiles one and five. POLAR classifications are a measure used by the OfS of the likelihood that a young person will participate in higher education based on the area in which they live. Areas are assigned to quintiles with 5 representing the highest rates of young people participating in higher education and 1 representing the lowest rates.[1] Differential outcomes based on socio-economic status are also commonplace in the US where, unlike the UK, degree attainment is measured by degree classification. In the US, bachelors' degree attainment by the age of 24 is five times greater in the higher socio-economic quartile, compared to the lowest (Cahalan et al., 2017).

Arguably the most pernicious attainment gap, which has been termed 'the great unspoken shame of higher education' (Ross et al., 2018) is the 'BME (black and minority ethnic) attainment gap' which represents the difference in attainment between UK domiciled minority ethnic students and their white counterparts (Richardson, 2015). The most recent data for 2016–17 graduates exhibits a staggering 22 percentage point difference between the proportions of white graduates gaining a first or upper-second class degree compared with black graduates, and an 11 per cent difference between White and Asian graduates (OfS, 2018).

The awareness of differential outcomes among academics varies dramatically within and between institutions (Mountford-Zimdars et al., 2015). However, thus far academic teachers and their institutional apparatus have relied on a model of student deficit to explain away these attainment gaps, arguing that students from particular backgrounds have additional challenges which prevent them from achieving in higher education. However, statistical analysis looking at the degree outcomes of over 280,000 students graduating in 2013–14, and conducted by the Higher Education Funding Council for England, showed that when a range of factors were controlled for, including: entry qualifications; subject studied; previous school type attended; age; a participation of local areas measure; sex; disability and the type of institution attended, the attainment gap (measured as those students obtaining a first or upper second class degree) between black and minority ethnic students and their white counterparts was only reduced by one percentage point to 15 percentage points (Hefce, 2015).

Robust data exercises and recent qualitative research has challenged the student deficit model and points to the fact that the causes of these long-standing differences are multidimensional and incredibly complex (Mountford-Zimdars et al., 2015). Existing research has told us that students from non-traditional backgrounds feel 'othered' and alienated in many higher education institutions (Reay et al., 2010; Meuleman et al., 2015). These students report a lack of confidence to question and challenge academics and their practices and many do not share the sense of entitlement held by their white, middle class counterparts (Crozier et al., 2008; Southall et al., 2016; Witkowsky et al., 2016). However, there appears to be a greater appetite to explore the 'cultural' aspects of the academy and how institutional cultures and academic practices contribute to the under-attainment of some student groups (Read et al., 2003). The focus has turned to the misalignment between normative academic cultures and the backgrounds, and the behaviours and values of their increasingly diverse student body, with an acknowledgement that academic institutions must embrace institutional change (McDuff et al., 2018).

The notion of creating 'inclusive' learning environments has gained credence in recent years and for many commentators the riposte to the issue of differential attainment centres around the concept of the inclusive curriculum (Berry and Loke, 2011; Singh, 2011; Stevenson, 2012). An inclusive curriculum in higher education is defined as one designed and delivered to engage students in learning that is accessible, relevant and meaningful to them irrespective of their backgrounds (Hockings, 2010). Indeed, recent research has pointed to the importance of the user-friendliness of learning, teaching and assessment practices in students' feelings of belonging and ultimately their success (or failure) (Mountford-Zimdars et al., 2015).

We argue in this chapter that to ensure an equality of opportunity for all students in higher education, teaching staff in all academic disciplines must begin to address this move away from the student deficit model, to one which demands a reflective approach to the accessibility and inclusivity of their own curriculum and the (unwritten) assumptions they bring to their teaching and learning practice (Hughes, 2016). We argue that an 'inclusive' curriculum is crucial in ensuring that all students are connected to their learning and therefore more likely to achieve successful outcomes. However, we begin by exploring the existing narratives of inclusion evident in the geographical literature before we proceed to introduce the principles that we have identified as being imperative to a profoundly inclusive curriculum.

NARRATIVES OF INCLUSIVE LEARNING AND TEACHING IN GEOGRAPHY

Two disparate narratives of inclusive curriculum can be identified in the literature. This first addresses the accommodation of students with disabilities and learning differences and the second centres on debates around the relationship between power, privilege and the construction of academic knowledge. Geography and geographers have, to a greater or lesser extent, embraced both these narratives. For example, there is a significant body of work which addresses the inclusion of students with disabilities into educational practices, particularly around fieldwork. In the late 1990s the Geography Discipline Network conducted some ground-breaking work, in association with the Centre for Active Learning in Geography, Environment and Related Disciplines and the Higher Education Academy's GEES Subject Centre, on how to provide learning support for disabled students undertaking field activities. Their 'Inclusive Curriculum Project' developed case studies documenting disabled students' experiences of teaching, learning and assessment in higher education and the ways in which academic departments supported and guided the learning of students with a variety of physical disabilities (Healey et al. 2001). Indeed, this innovative work also explored how best to provide learning support for students with mental health difficulties undertaking fieldwork, recognising the potential challenges that these students face in unfamiliar and testing situations in which they may feel anxious and unable to cope (Birnie and Grant, 2001).

As a result, the inclusion agenda in the geographical and earth sciences has tended to centre on the accessibility of field learning environments with particular reference to the accommodation of disabled students and the need for HE providers to respond to individual requirements through 'reasonable adjustment'. This focus on learning difference and disability as the key feature of the inclusive education narrative is shared with many other disciplines (May and Felsinger, 2010; Garvey, 2011; Marquis et al., 2016). Arguably, the second narrative of inclusivity identified in the literature has been far less visible in debates in the learning and teaching literature in geography, despite the fact that the epistemological concerns of critical theory focusing on the relationship between knowledge construction, power and privilege, are often robustly addressed in the content of geography curricula. Geographers and geography have drawn extensively on various critical theorists to critique the stalwartly Eurocentric and masculinist nature of academic knowledge; knowledge which has silenced other voices and perspectives (hooks, 1994). However there has been rather less thought given to how our normative pedagogic practices are implicated in maintaining and extending the educational advantage of some groups of our students over others. This is a somewhat anomalous state given the increasingly vocal student body, reflected in several high-profile student-led campaigns which have engaged a global audience such as 'Rhodes must Fall' and the student movement,

'Why is My Curriculum White?' at University College, London, which exposed students' feelings of marginalisation and exclusion.

In the remainder of this chapter, we utilise a framework developed at Kingston University (McDuff and Hughes, 2015) to support the delivery of a more inclusive geography curriculum from concept to review. By curriculum we refer to a student's 'engagement' with their learning experience and not simply the curriculum content (Barnett and Coate, 2005). We argue that the framework helps academic colleagues to translate the principles of an inclusive curriculum into tangible changes to our learning and teaching practices (Grünberg, 2011; Savvidou, 2011; Carey, 2012; McCarthy-Brown, 2014; Marquis et al., 2016). We then present a case study from geography where we examine how adopting the principles of the framework can help to create better outcomes for all students.

AN INCLUSIVE CURRICULUM FRAMEWORK

Our Inclusive Curriculum framework identifies three key principles which together embody inclusive education thereby drawing together the disparate narratives discussed previously. These are i) to create an accessible curriculum, ii) to enable students to see themselves reflected in the curriculum and iii) to equip students with the skills to positively contribute to, and work in, a global and diverse environment (McDuff and Hughes, 2015). We argue that, together, these principles ensure that pedagogical practices value, support and reflect diversity in our student body and demonstrate the strength that this diversity offers to all students.

The multi-dimensional nature of the framework allows for different, often multiple, implementation and intervention points. Indeed, it facilitates the operation of inclusive practices from concept to review, that is that the key principles can be enacted when academic staff are not only designing the concepts and content of their courses/modules and teaching sessions, but also when they are considering their learning and teaching practices, their assessment and feedback/forward strategies, as well as how they evaluate and review their curricula.

AN ACCESSIBLE CURRICULUM

As we have already acknowledged, geography as a discipline has been at the forefront of debates around supporting students with physical and mental disabilities, ensuring that geography in higher education is accessible to students with a range of disabilities and learning differences (Disabled Students' Sector Learning Group, 2017). However, we argue that the principle of accessibility should extend beyond the confines of disability and learning differences to recognise and address how our curricula accommodate a range of differences, including educational background. Indeed, recognising that educational practice is culturally-specific, and therefore not universal, is an important first step in creating an accessible curriculum (Haigh, 2009). Accessibility must be considered in conceptual as well as practical terms, not just limited to the physical accessibility of higher education learning spaces.

Arguably, the accessibility of our learning environments has become even more crucial given the internationalisation of higher education. Learning styles are acknowledged to be culturally-specific and disciplines which have experienced significant international student recruitment have begun to address cross-cultural course design and delivery mechanisms (Felder and Brent, 2005; Song-Turner and Willis, 2011). The challenge is to ensure our curriculum does not give competitive advantage to students with particular local knowledges and as Haigh (2002) suggests, to conceive of all students as 'international'.

Accessibility to institutional norms and cultures are also significant considerations. Whilst recognising the importance of empowering all students to access academic discourse through the development of appropriate skill sets, there is also a responsibility on us as academic teachers to use accessible language and to be cognisant of the racialised and classed assumptions we are making about the 'languages' that our students are using to communicate (McKay and Devlin, 2014). Without intentional strategies to ensure students have both the 'linguistic and socio-cultural knowledge' (Gutierrez, 1995 cited in McKay and Devlin, 2014, p.953) and the skills of generative participation, we contend that students from non-traditional backgrounds, or indeed international students, cannot become fully active members of the UK academic knowledge community (Northedge, 2003). As Mbembe (2016) so eloquently argues 'access' or 'accessibility', is not simply about being in the room, rather 'we are also saying the possibility to inhabit a space to the extent that one can say, "This is my home. I am not a foreigner. I belong here"' (2016, p.30).

Identifying the principle of accessibility as central to an inclusive curriculum also encourages staff to consider their own 'accessibility' in terms of their learning and teaching approach and feedback/forward strategies. For example, 'office hours', the hours that academic staff advertise to students as the times where they are available in their office to be consulted, may not be universally accessible given the differing levels of confidence within cohorts to seek the help that they need. For others who commute to university, alternative forms of communication may be preferable.[2] It is interesting that there are significant differences by ethnicity in the response to the question 'I have sufficient access to academic staff outside class' in the Student Academic Experience Survey[3] with students from black and minority ethnic backgrounds much less likely to agree with this statement (Neves and Hillman, 2017, 2018).

ENSURING THAT STUDENTS SEE THEMSELVES REFLECTED IN THE CURRICULUM

Ensuring that students see themselves and people 'like them' reflected in the curriculum is the second key principle that, we argue, academic educators should consider. The principle operates in two domains. We have already touched on the first domain which relates to the multi-faceted ways in which disciplines address the epistemological challenges to grand Eurocentric narratives which de-legitimate and marginalise indigenous knowledges (Maila, 2010; Tange and Kastberg, 2013). As Gundara and Sharma (2010) argue, a curriculum 'centred on the knowledge of dominant groups does not serve the needs of socially diverse polities' (cited in Daddow et al., 2013, p.480). Whilst in many universities, geography and geographers have robustly challenged issues of decolonisation and embraced postcolonial theoretical perspectives as a mainstream offer in the content of the curriculum, the extent to which we, as academic teachers, consider how our own teaching and learning practices embrace and celebrate the background of our students and how we welcome them into our classrooms, is an issue that we have been far less forthright in addressing (Mbembe, 2016; see also Chapter 17 in this volume by James Esson and Angela Last). It is interesting that black, Asian and Chinese heritage students studying in the UK are much less likely to report that their teaching staff 'worked hard to make their subjects interesting' or 'helped them to explore their own areas of interest' compared to their white counterparts (Neves and Hillman, 2017, 2018). An engagement with the principles and practice of co-creation where students are acknowledged as both holders and producers of knowledge is an important strategy to address differential attainment (Hughes et al., 2017, 2018). Co-creation challenges the traditional model of education 'where staff take on the role of enablers of disempowered students' (Healey et al., 2014, p. 15). As Steele and Ryan (2014) note, some students report feeling like 'untapped resources' in university classrooms, where their diverse backgrounds and experiences are under-utilised as an enriching learning tool. A co-creation approach may not only address some students' feelings of alienation with, and in, the curriculum but will also enrich the curriculum for all (McCulloch, 2009; Bovill, 2010).

It is clear that engagement with, and the utilisation of, the diverse experiences of students by academic teachers must be encouraged and nurtured. This can be achieved in a number of ways, at both a strategic institutional level and in individual classrooms. Clearly moving away from didactic teaching styles which act to 'silence' the audience and adopting more active learning strategies in our University classrooms, is crucial. One could adapt the concept of the 'one-minute paper' to ask students about knowledge that they would like to share in future teaching sessions (Harwood, 1996). Even with large classes, sessions can be planned to ensure that there are 'spaces' for knowledge sharing and assessments can be constructed to encourage students to identify and discuss case studies with which they are familiar.

Using co-creation can also be addressed at a strategic institutional level. Kingston University has a programme called Student Curriculum Consultants. The students are trained in the principles of inclusive curriculum and act as consultants to course teams who wish to rethink their curriculum content, assessment and/or learning and teaching strategies to be more inclusive of their diverse student body. The student consultants who have been attracted to this role have, for the most part, been 'non-traditional' students who have themselves felt alienated or dissatisfied with their own curriculum.

The second domain in which this principle operates is rather more practical and challenges the geographical discipline to ensure that students and staff see 'people-like them' in their everyday higher education experiences as role models, mentors and teachers (Umbach, 2006). As Douglas and Halas (2013) point out 'if individuals do not see anyone who looks like them, to what extent do they feel that they are welcome in the particular program/institution?' (p. 458). Academic teachers must reflect not only what they are teaching, but also who is teaching it. Certainly, in the UK, we know that in terms of gender and ethnic diversity 'human geography has a record as unsatisfactory as most other social sciences' (Economic and Social Research Council, 2013). Men outnumber women (Maddrell et al., 2015) and the lack of ethnic diversity among geography faculty is palpable. Data suggests that only 4 per cent of academic staff are members of ethnic minorities, if non-UK nationals are excluded (Economic and Social Research Council, 2013). Unfortunately, data from current postgraduate programmes suggests that whilst the gender differential may begin to be addressed in the medium term, the same cannot easily be said of ethnic and class minorities. With a predominately white middle class faculty, the potential for alienation of students who do not fit the 'traditional mould' is very real. We need to be cognisant of this and act accordingly. For example, whilst academic teachers are not necessarily responsible for the recruitment of faculty staff, they can ensure that guest speakers represent a diversity that may not be evident in the tenured academic community. Consider how much easier is it to learn and pronounce correctly names from one's own culture compared to those that are alien to us. How much effort do we expend ensuring that we learn all our students' names? In the current climate of the massification of higher education this can be challenging, but we must be aware of the potential for creating a differential experience amongst students. It is interesting that black, Asian and Chinese heritage students are much less likely to report that their teaching staff 'were helpful and supportive' compared to their white counterparts (Neves and Hillman, 2017).

EQUIPPING STUDENTS TO WORK IN A GLOBALISED AND DIVERSE WORLD

The final principle to ensure more inclusive curricula is equipping students to work in a globalised and diverse world. Our starting point with this principle is that if students are exposed to multiple perspectives and life-worlds, learning to respect diversity and difference in the classroom, then they will be better equipped to work collaboratively with others from a variety of cultures, backgrounds and positions in the workplace (Svensson and Wihlbord, 2010). The benefits of engaging students in the classroom extends beyond giving them a sense of legitimacy and belonging in higher education but also enables them to learn from each other. Educational environments are important sites for the development of intercultural knowledge and broader diversity skills. Indeed, cultural differences and divides are often as great between 'home' students themselves as between home and international students (Haigh, 2009). Lee et al. (2012) describe higher education classrooms as hopeful spaces 'where patterns of segregation can be interrupted, and intercultural learning can occur' (2012, p. vii). In this way, they offer significant opportunities for intercultural communication and mixing from which greater integration and social cohesion might emerge and through which inter-cultural competencies can develop. Students, however, must be helped to achieve this (Lee et al., 2012). Intercultural competence is not an inevitable or natural process developed through osmosis simply by being in the company of diverse social identity groups. Social integration is not an automatic by-product of campus diversity (Tienda, 2012). Therefore, university teachers have a central role in enabling the development of inter-cultural competence in their own classrooms by actively facilitating interaction through, for example, prescriptive group formation.

We argue that if academic teachers are mindful of these three principles of curriculum design and student engagement, ensuring that they are addressed in their learning and teaching practices from concept to review, then they will be more able to facilitate students' sense of belonging to, and connection with, their learning, helping them to produce their best work. In the final section of this chapter we provide an example of the change conducted in the teaching of rural geography which, we argue, created an inclusive learning environment by adopting the principles outlined above.

CHALLENGING DISCIPLINARY NORMS: FROM EXCLUSION TO INCLUSION

Geography has been taught at Kingston University for over 50 years. Kingston University is a medium sized public, post-1992 (previously polytechnic) university located in a suburban location in south west London. The demographic of the student body at the university has changed significantly over the past ten years with a growing number of students who commute to university and are therefore London (urban) based. Currently our student body reflects the demographic diversity of Greater London with a much larger proportion of students from ethnic minority backgrounds compared to other UK universities. Aligned with these changes, the students studying for a geography degree at Kingston have diversified significantly during this time.

Rural geography has always been a component part of the geography degree at Kingston University. Rural geography has been taught in variously named modules including Social Change in the British Countryside, Agriculture and the Rural Economy and Restructuring the British Countryside. As the module titles suggest, and in line with the tradition of Anglo-American rural geography which has 'relatively weak ties to the study of rural areas in developing nations' (Woods, 2009, p. 432), the content of these modules focused on rural areas in the developed world at the expense of rural areas internationally. As a result, the module focused on geographies that were quite alien to many of our students.

Whilst ignorant of the existence of the sector-wide attainment gap between white students and those from ethnic minority backgrounds, the module team did have some awareness that students from BME backgrounds were less likely to thrive in the rural geography module and, in many cases, attained less well. Evidence was, however, anecdotal at best and at the time there was no concerted effort to explore differential engagement and attainment based on students' demographic differences. However, contemporaneously, the module team were working on a research project entitled 'Ethnic identities and positioning in the field' which was exploring the differential experiences of our students on rural-based UK field work in their first year at undergraduate level. This research originated from concerns about the links between ethnicity and rurality in the UK, most notably the racialisation of the countryside linked to the absence of ethnic minorities in rural areas and instructive debates about racism in the countryside (Chakraborti and Garland, 2004; Askins, 2009). It highlighted very starkly that our British students from black and minority ethnic backgrounds were much less likely to live in or visit rural areas in the UK compared to their white counterparts. For example, 43 per cent of white British students agreed with the statement that they 'have often travelled to the British countryside for holidays or day trips' compared to only 19 per cent of British students from black and minority ethnic backgrounds. Indeed, our students from BME backgrounds were also more likely to have experienced rural areas outside the UK, often but not exclusively, in the global south (Hughes, 2016). In addition, a growing number of our students from all ethnic backgrounds were urban-based and commuted to the university from various parts of London, and therefore had city-based spatialities.

Armed with this knowledge, it became apparent that our rural geography module did not reflect the experiences and backgrounds of many of our students. In addition, the artificial detachment between the study of rural areas in the global south and global north was inadvertently disadvantaging our students who hailed from increasingly diverse backgrounds. In other words, due to the historical context of the sub-discipline of rural geography, and more specifically, its domination by the interests and experiences of white middle class British (often male) academics, the configured content commonly normalised their experiences, potentially contributing to outcomes that were advantageous to the students whose backgrounds and experiences were reflected in, and by, this curriculum.

The revision of our university's academic framework in 2013 brought an opportunity to restructure our modules. The teaching team agreed to amalgamate the content of two 15 credit modules: Restructuring the British Countryside and a module that focused on Sustainable Futures. Global Rural Geographies was created which explored rural areas in both the global north and the global south. The learning outcomes were to: i) examine and interpret the processes and patterns of contemporary change in the rural areas in both the developing and the developed world; ii) analyse factors conditioning the restructuring of rural land use, and the economic, social and cultural systems in rural areas across the world; and iii) evaluate the contrasting food production systems shaping rural environments in developed and developing countries. Efforts were made to apply theory from 'rural geography' directly to rural areas in the global south, which as McCarthy noted in 2005, are notable 'precisely because they are so rare. "Rurality"... remains at least as much a product of divisions within the academy' (2005, p. 773).

Table 13.1 outlines the key changes that were implemented in the new Global Rural Geographies module. The module was made more accessible through the introduction of the internationalised and globalised curriculum, the assessment strategy was changed to include more choice in the assessment, as well as removing the unseen examination. The module also more effectively enabled students to draw on their experiences and backgrounds, ensuring that their diverse experiences of rural places from across the globe could be brought into the classroom and contribute to the creation of a more comprehensive shared knowledge. The internationalisation of the curriculum also served to facilitate a wider discussion which benefitted all students (from whatever background) providing them with a more robust understanding of a greater variety of rural places (including the UK) equipping them to work in an increasingly globalised and diverse world. Whilst these revisions pre-dated the institutional Inclusive Curriculum Framework, this example has been used extensively to demonstrate how an academic module can be made more inclusive to a diverse student body through the adoption of the three principles of the framework.

Module data which identifies differential attainment based on student demographic has only become available in the last two years. Therefore, we do not have any robust data on the attainment of students from different demographic backgrounds for previous iterations of the rural geography module. However, module attainment gap data for Global Rural Geographies shows that, in the three academic years between 2014/15 and 2016/17, the attainment gap between domiciled white students and domiciled students from black

Table 13.1 *Applying the inclusive curriculum framework to rural geography*

Module example: Rural Geography Teaching	Create an accessible curriculum.	Enable students to see themselves reflected in the curriculum.	Equip students with the skills to positively contribute to and work in a global and diverse environment.
In the concept	Globalised and internationalised.	Students from diverse backgrounds have the opportunity to use their personal experiences and perspectives.	Critical thinking and global awareness.
In the content	Case studies taken from both the global north and the global south.	Reading list included a diverse range of authors – including perspectives from the global south and non-academic perspectives (charities, NGO, and so on).	Understanding globalisation and interlinkages.
In the delivery (learning and teaching)	Engagement strategy. Follow up on non-attendance.	Encourage discussion from personal experience. Using names to encourage discussion and viewpoints.	Seminar classes – discussion based.
In the assessment	Unseen exam was replaced by seen exam.	Formative assessment – debate style with students selecting the position that they wish to defend.	Oral presentations part of the assessment (in addition to written skills).
In the feedback	Detailed feedback – sectionalised by indicative marking criteria. Deadlines and assessment set at start of academic year.	Feedback was individualised and oral and written – oral feedback was in-class.	Students encouraged to reflect on feedback comments, including class-based feedback reflection.
In the module review/ evaluation	Module review evaluated differential attainment of students from different backgrounds.	Involve students in the review and evaluation. – Qualitative discussion.	Reflective practice.

and minority ethnic backgrounds was consistently lower compared to the average attainment gap for the four modules on the human geography programme. Of course, average marks are impacted by a plethora of factors every year, and changes in attainment cannot always be attributed to one alteration but it remains the case that the attainment gap is consistently lower in this module than other human geography modules and indeed in 2014/15 BME British students did better than their white British counterparts by 3.3 per cent which is not a common occurrence over any set of geography modules for which we have data. Whilst we believe that this case study indicates that there is room for muted optimism that longstanding attainment gaps in our universities can be addressed with considered and informed local interventions around the principles of inclusivity, we must continue to be vigilant. Staff in universities are 'agents of change' in addressing differential experiences (Mountford-Zimdars et al., 2015, p. 99) and we must recognise our role in ensuring that we embrace critical approaches to learning and teaching practices in our classrooms, as well as in our research.

CONCLUSION

The purpose of this chapter is to open the debate around differential attainment and the role that our curricula (in its broadest sense) may play in contributing to attainment gaps. We wish to broaden the debate about inclusive learning and teaching practices in the geography discipline beyond a consideration of students with disabilities and learning differences to one which encompasses a whole plethora of diversity in our current student cohorts, based on age, nationality, gender, ethnic background, socio-economic status and also 'new' ways of 'doing' university, such as the growth in students who commute.

We hope that the chapter will encourage academic teachers in geography to reflect on their practice and how it differentially serves our increasingly diverse student body – whether this diversity stems from the widening participation agenda or internationalisation of the higher education sector. It is important to acknowledge here that the pace of change across the sector in terms of widening participation is incredibly varied, with many universities still experiencing very little diversity with respect to their 'home' student cohorts. This may require more robust and positive action to challenge our mono-cultural classrooms and encourage a more diverse student body to select a geography education at University. This may well require us to apply our inclusive curriculum principles to, for example, our course marketing material, which in many cases still presents the geographers' space as a rural one.

The presumption here is that geography is an innately inclusive subject, clearly aligned with the internationalisation agenda. However, we also want to encourage academic teachers of geography to apply the critical theories with which we commonly engage, to their own teaching practice and reflect on how our disciplinary norms and normative cultures may inadvertently advantage some groups of students and conversely disadvantage others. One obvious example would be to challenge the 'place' of alcohol in the cultures of geography field trips (Hughes, 2016). Our Inclusive Curriculum Framework is intended to facilitate these discussions and to encourage individuals to proactively challenge potentially discriminatory practices. The framework is not intended to be a roadmap but rather identifies multiple intervention points where staff can make macro and micro changes to their programmes, modules and teaching sessions to increase their inclusivity and, in the process, address some of our challenges around differential attainment; as well as enhancing learning for all students.

It is important to emphasise that we are not suggesting that we can or should only teach geographies that are familiar to our students. We want to challenge our students to broaden their horizons and to expose them to a myriad of thought-provoking and inspiring issues and topics. We want to create critical thinkers and graduates who can see issues from multiple perspectives. This requires us to challenge our students to leave their comfort zones. However, to ensure an equality of opportunity for all students in higher education, an inclusive curriculum recognises and addresses circumstances where particular curricula content or learning and teaching practices disadvantage a section of our student body. This consideration is particularly important in university curricula, like geography, which commonly deems some content as core, and some as optional. Core elements must be scrutinised to safeguard their inclusivity, and to ensure that they do not centre on the knowledge of dominant groups, leaving the marginal voices as optional (in option modules).

In summary, inclusive curricula are not 'safe or 'anodyne' curricula. On the contrary, they should and do actively encourage practices which challenge students to engage with diversity and difference. Indeed, the impact of engagement with diversity is recognised by Kuh and O'Donnell (2013) as one of only ten learning experiences identified as high-impact with regard to their ability to promote deep learning. Academic institutions must use the increasing diversity in classrooms to enrich the learning for all. As Brink (2009, p. 26) argues 'the university is an educational institution. Our business is about knowledge. That means that we have to learn . . . and we learn more from those people, those ideas, and those phenomena that we do not know, than from those we know only too well'.

FURTHER RESOURCES

- Geography Discipline Network Inclusive Curriculum Project. Available at https://gdn.glos.ac.uk/.
- Kingston University Inclusive Curriculum Framework. Available at: https://www.kingston.ac.uk/aboutkingstonuniversity/equality-diversity-and-inclusion/our-inclusive-curriculum/inclusive-curriculum-framework/.
- Office for Students (2018) *Differences in Student Outcomes*. Available at: https://www.officeforstudents.org.uk/data-and-analysis/differences-in-student-outcomes/.

NOTES

1. POLAR classifications are a measure by the OfS of the likelihood that a young person will participate in higher education based on the area in which they live. Areas are assigned to quintiles with 5 representing the highest rates of young people participating in higher education and 1 representing the lowest rates. Further details can be found on the OfS website: https://www.officeforstudents.org.uk/data-and-analysis/polar-participation-of-local-are
2. Indeed we know that certain demographics are more likely to 'live at home' including mature students, first in family and those form POLAR quintiles 1 and 2 (Neves and Hillman, 2017).

3. The UK Student Academic Experience Survey is conducted by the Higher Education Policy Institute (HEPI) in conjunction with Advance HE and records the views of over 14,000 students.

REFERENCES

Askins, K. (2009) 'Crossing divides: Ethnicity and rurality', *Journal of Rural Studies*, 25, pp. 365–375. doi:10.1016/j. jrurstud.2009.05.009.

Barnett, R. and Coate, K. (2005) *Engaging the Curriculum in Higher Education.* Berkshire: SRHE and OU Press.

Berry, J. and Loke, G. (2011) *Improving the Degree Attainment of Black and Minority Ethnic Students*. York: ECU/HEA.

Birnie, J. and Grant, A. (2001) *Providing Learning Support for Students with Mental Health Difficulties Undertaking Fieldwork and Related Activities.* Geography Discipline Network (GDN). Available at: https://www.researchgate. net/publication/264869313_Providing_Learning_Support_for_Students_with_Mental_Health_Difficulties_ Undertaking_Fieldwork_and_Related_Activities (accessed: 2 April 2018).

Bovill, C. (2010) *Students and Staff Co-creating the Curriculum: Research into Three Case Studies from Scotland, Ireland and the USA*. York: HES. Available at: https://www.heacademy.ac.uk/system/files/university_of_glas gow_co-creating_the_curriculum.pdf (accessed: 8 November 2017).

Brink, C. (2009) '"Standards will drop" and other fears about the equality agenda in higher education', *Higher Education Management and Policy*, 21(1), pp. 11–30. doi: https://doi.org/10.1787/hemp-v21-art2-en.

Cahalan, M., Perna, L.W., Yamashita, M., Ruiz, R. and Franklin, K. (2017) *Indicators of Higher Education Equity in the United States: 2017 Trend Report*. Washington, DC, USA: Pell Institute for the Study of Higher Education, Council for Education Opportunity (COE) and Alliance for Higher Education and Democracy (AHEAD) of the University of Pennsylvania. Available at: http://pellinstitute.org/downloads/publications-Indi cators_of_Higher_Education_Equity_in_the_US_2017_Historical_Trend_Report.pdf (accessed: 8 November 2017).

Carey, P. (2012) 'Exploring variation in nurse educators' perceptions of the inclusive curriculum', *International Journal of Inclusive Education*, 16(7), pp. 741–755. doi: http:dx.doi.org/10.1080/13603116.2010.516773.

Chakraborti, N. and Garland, J. (eds) (2004) *Rural Racism*. Cullompton: Willan.

Crozier, G., Reay, D. and Clayton, J. (2008) 'Different strokes for different folks: diverse students in diverse institutions', *Research Papers in Education*, 23(2), pp. 167–177.

Daddow, A., Moraitis, P. and Carr, A. (2013) 'Non-traditional students in tertiary education: inter-disciplinary collaboration in curriculum and pedagogy in community services education in Australia', *International Journal of Inclusive Education*, 17(5), pp. 480– 489. doi: http://dx.doi.org/10.1080/13603116.2012.685765.

Disabled Students' Sector Leadership Group (2017) *Inclusive Teaching and Learning in Higher Education as a Route to Excellence*, Available at: https://www.gov.uk/government/uploads/system/uploads/attachment_data/ file/587221/Inclusive_Teaching_and_Learning_in_Higher_Education_as_a_route_to-excellence.pdf (accessed 14 March 2018).

Douglas, D. and Halas, J. (2013) 'The wages of whiteness: confronting the nature of ivory tower racism and the implications for physical education', *Sport, Education and Society*, 18(4), pp. 453–474. doi: http://dx.doi.org/ 10.1080/13573322.2011.602395.

Economic and Social Research Council (2013) *International Benchmarking Review of UK Human Geography*. Available at: https://esrc.ukri.org/files/research/research-and-impact-evaluation/international-benchmarking-review-of-uk-human-geography/ (accessed 12 April 2018).

Equality Challenge Unit (ECU) (2017) *ECU Statistical Report 2017*. Available at: http://www.ecu.ac.uk/publica tions/equalityhigher-education-statistical-report-2017/ (accessed: 14 April 2018).

Felder, R. and Brent, R. (2005) 'Understanding student difference', *Journal of Engineering Education*, 94(1), pp. 57–72.

Garvey, M. (2011) 'Inclusion and the student voice: lessons from the Trinity Inclusive Curriculum Strategy', in Thomas, L. and Tight, M. (eds), *Institutional Transformation to Engage a Diverse Student Body*. Bingley: Emerald.

Grünberg, L. (2011) *From Gender Studies to Gender in Studies: Case-Studies on Gender-inclusive Curriculum in Higher Education*. Bucharest: UNESCO-CEPES.

Gundara, J. and N. Sharma (2010) 'Providing access to education: intercultural and knowledge issues in the curriculum', in Mattheou, D. (ed.), *Changing Educational Landscapes*. Dordrecht: Springer, pp. 93–105.

Haigh, M. (2002) 'Internationalisation of the curriculum: designing inclusive education for a small world', *Journal of Geography in Higher Education*, 26(1), pp. 49–66.

Haigh, M. (2009) 'Fostering cross-cultural empathy with non-western curricular structures', *Journal of Studies in International Education*, 13(2), pp. 271–284. doi:10.1177/1028315308329791.

Harwood, W.S. (1996) 'The one- minute paper: a communication tool for large lecture classes', *Journal of Chemical Educations*, 73(3), pp. 229–230.

Healey, M., Jenkins, A., Leach, J. and Roberts, C. (2001) *Issues in Providing Learning Support for Disabled Students Undertaking Fieldwork and Related Activities*, Geography Discipline Network, Available at: http://sid.usal.es/idocs/F8/FDO25268/learning_support__mental_health.pdf.

Healey, M., Flint, A. and Harrington, K. (2014) *Engagement Through Partnership: Students as Partners in Teaching and Learning in Higher Education*. York: The Higher Education Academy. Available at: https://www.heacademy.ac.uk/system/files/resources/engagement_through_partnership.pdf (accessed 12 May 2017).

Higher Education Funding Council (Hefce) (2015) *Differences in Degree Outcomes: The Effect of Subject and Student Characteristics*. Issue paper 2015/21. Bristol. Available at: http://www.hefce.ac.uk/media/HEFCE2014/Content/Pubs/2015/201521/HEFCE2015_21.pdf (accessed 12 May 2017).

Hockings, C. (2010) *Inclusive Learning and Teaching in Higher Education: A Synthesis of Research*. York: The Higher Education Academy. Available at: www.heacademy.ac.uk/assets/York/documents/ourwork/inclusion/wp/inclusive_teaching_and_learning_in_he.doc (accessed 15 January 2017).

hooks, b. (1994) *Teaching to Transgress: Education as the Practice of Freedom*, London: Routledge.

Hughes, A. (2016) 'Exploring Normative Whiteness: Ensuring Inclusive Pedagogic Practice in Undergraduate Fieldwork Teaching and Learning', *Journal of Geography in Higher Education*, 40(3), pp. 1–18. doi: 10.1080/03098265.2016.1155206.

Hughes, A., Potkin, H. and Mohamed, K. (2018) *Curriculum Co-creation: A Transformative Strategy to Address Differential Student Outcomes*, HEA Annual Conference, Birmingham.

Hughes, A., Potkin, H., Mohamed, K. and Michener, C. (2017) *Curriculum Co-creation: A Transformative Strategy to Student Success*, ECU Annual Conference, Birmingham.

Kuh, G.D. and O'Donnell, K. (2013) *Ensuring Quality and Taking High-impact Practices to Scale*. Washington, DC: Association of American Colleges and Universities.

Lee, A., Poch, R., Shaw, M. and Williams, R. (2012) 'Engaging diversity in undergraduate classrooms', *ASHE Higher Education Report*, 38(2). San Francisco, CA: Jossey-Bass.

Maddrell, A., Strauss, K. Thomas, N. and Wyse, S. (2015) 'Mind the gap: gender disparities still to be addressed in UK higher education', *Area*, 48 (1), pp. 48–56. doi: https://doi.org/10.1111/area.12223.

Maila, M. (2010) 'Curriculum as open-ended inquiry in higher education', *Africa Education Review*, 7(2), pp. 263–282. doi: 10.1080/18146627.2010.515385.

Marquis, E., Jung, B., Schormans, A. Lukmanji, S., Wilton, R. and Baptiste, S. (2016) 'Developing inclusive educators: enhancing the accessibility of teaching and learning in higher education', *International Journal for Academic Development*, 21(4), pp. 337–349.

May, H. and Felsinger, A. (2010) *Strategic Approaches to Disabled Student Engagement*, Available at: http://www.heacademy.ac.uk/resources/detail/inclusion/Disability/StrategicApproachesFinalReport (accessed 12 December 2017).

Mbembe, A.J. (2016) 'Decolonizing the university: new directions', *Arts and Humanities in Higher Education*, 15(1), pp. 29–45.

McCarthy, J. (2005) 'Rural geography: multifunctional rural geographies reactionary or radical?', *Progress in Human Geography*, 29(6), pp. 773–782.

McCarthy-Brown, N. (2014) 'Decolonizing dance curriculum in higher education: one credit at a time', *Journal of Dance Education*, 14, pp. 125–129. doi: 10.1080/15290824.2014.887204.

McCulloch, A. (2009) 'The student as co-producer', *Studies in Higher Education*, 34(2), pp. 171–183.

McDuff, A. and Hughes, A. (2015) 'Kingston's Inclusive Curriculum Framework', Available at: http://www.kingston.ac.uk/aboutkingstonuniversity/equality-diversity-and-inclusion/our-inclusive-curriculum/inclusive-curriculum-framework/ (accessed 12 December 2017).

McDuff, N., Tatam, J.C., Beacock, O. and Ross, F.M. (2018) 'Closing the attainment gap for students from black and minority ethnic backgrounds through institutional change', *Journal of Widening Participation and Life Long Learning*, 20(1), pp. 79–101. Available at: https://doi.org/10.5456/WPLL.20.1.79 (accessed 13 April 2018).

McKay, J. and Devlin, M. (2014) '"Uni has a different language . . . to the real world": demystifying academic culture and discourse for students from low socioeconomic backgrounds', *Higher Education Research and Development*, 33(5), pp. 949–961. doi:10.1080/07294360.2014.890570.

Meuleman, A., Garrett, R., Wrench, A. and King, S. (2015) '"Some people might say I'm thriving but. . .": non-traditional students' experiences of university', *International Journal of Inclusive Education International Journal of Inclusive Education*. Available at: http://dx.doi.org/10.1080/13603116.2014.945973 (accessed 14 July 2017).

Millward, C. (2018) Keynote, *Addressing Barriers to Student Success Annual Conference*, London 24th May 2018.

Mountford-Zimdars, A., Sabri, D., Moore, J., Sanders, J., Jones, S. and Higham, L. (2015) 'Causes of differences in student outcomes', Report to HEFCE by King's College London, ARC Network and The University of Manchester. Available at: http://www.hefce.ac.uk/media/HEFCE,2014/Content/Pubs/ Independentresearch/2015/Causes,of,differences,in,student,outcomes/HEFCE2015_diffout.pdf (accessed 12 December 2017).

Neves, J. and Hillman, N. (2017) *The 2017 Student Academic Experience Survey.* UK: Higher Education Academy and Higher Education Policy Institute.

Neves, J. and Hillman, N. (2018) *The 2018 Student Academic Experience Survey.* UK: Higher Education Academy and Higher Education Policy Institute.

Northedge, A. (2003) 'Rethinking teaching in the context of diversity', *Teaching in Higher Education*, 8(1), pp. 17–32. doi: http://dx.doi.org/10.1080/1356251032000052302 (accessed 30 December 2016).

Office for Students (2018) *Differences in Student Outcomes.* Available at: https://www.officeforstudents.org.uk/ data-and-analysis/differences-in-student-outcomes/ (accessed 18 March 2018).

Read, B., Archer, L. and Leathwood, C. (2003) 'Challenging cultures? Student conceptions of "belonging" and "isolation" at a post-1992 university', *Studies in Higher Education*, 28(3), pp. 261–277.

Reay, D., Crozier, G. and Clayton, J. (2010) '"Fitting in" or "standing out": working-class students in UK higher education', *British Educational Research Journal*, 36(1), pp. 107–124.

Richardson, J. (2015) 'The under-attainment of ethnic minority students in UK higher education: what we know and what we don't know', *Journal of Further and Higher Education*, 39(2), pp. 278–291. doi: http://dx.doi.org /10.1080/0309877X.2013.858680.

Ross, F., Tatam, J., Hughes, A., Beacock, O. and McDuff, N. (2018) 'The great unspoken shame of UK higher education: addressing inequalities of attainment', *African Journal of Business Ethics*, 12(1), pp. 104–115.

Savvidou, C. (2011) 'Exploring teachers' narratives of inclusive practice in higher education', *Teacher Development*, 15(1), pp. 53–67. doi:10.1080/13664530.2011.555224.

Singh, G. (2011) *Black and Minority Ethnic (BME) Students Participation in Higher Education: Improving Retention and Success – A Synthesis of Research Evidence.* York: Higher Education Academy.

Smith, A. and Hubble, S. (2018) *Widening Participation Strategy in Higher Education in England*, London: House of Commons Library.

Song-Turner, H. and Willis, M. (2011) 'Re-engineering the course design and delivery of Australian tertiary education programmes: perspectives from Chinese students', *Journal of Higher Education Policy and Management*, 33(5): pp. 537-552. doi: 10.1080/1360080X.2011.605228.

Southall, J., Wason, H. and Avery, B. (2016) 'Non-traditional, commuter students and their transition to higher education – a synthesis of recent literature to enhance understanding of their needs', *Student Engagement*, 5(1), pp. 1–15. doi:10.7190/seej.v4i1.128.

Steele, D. and Ryan, P.A. (2014) 'Students' perceptions of internationalisation in higher education', *SRHE Annual Research Conference*, 10–12 December 2014.

Stevenson. J. (2012) 'Black and minority ethnic student degree retention and attainment'. HEA. Available at: https://www.heacademy.ac.uk/system/files/bme_summit_final_report.pdf (accessed 12 December 2017).

Svensson, L. and Wihlbord, M. (2010) 'Internationalising the content of higher education: the need for a curriculum perspective', *Higher Education*, 60, pp. 595–613. doi: 10.1007/s10734-010-9318-6.

Tange, H. and Kastberg, P. (2013) 'Coming to terms with "double knowing": an inclusive approach to international education', *International Journal of Inclusive Education*, 17(1) pp. 1–14. doi:10.1080/13603116.2011 .580460.

Tienda, M. (2013) 'Diversity ≠ Inclusion: promoting integration in higher education', *Educational Researcher*, 42(9) pp. 467–475.

Umbach, P. (2006) 'The contribution of faculty of color to undergraduate education', *Research in Higher Education*, 47(3), pp. 317–345.

Universities UK (2016) *Working in Partnership: Enabling Social mobility In Higher Education, the Final Report of the Social Mobility Advisory Group.* Available at: http://www.universitiesuk.ac.uk/policy-and-analysis/ reports/Documents/2016/working-in-partnership-final.pdf (accessed: 12 December 2017).

Witkowsky, P., Mendez, S., Ogunbowo, O., Clayton, G. and Hernandez, N. (2016) 'Non-traditional student perceptions of collegiate inclusion', *Journal of Continuing Higher Education*, 64, pp. 30–41. doi:10.1080/073 77363.2016.1130581.

Woods, M. (2009) 'Rural geography', in Kitchin, R. and Thrift, N. (eds), *International Encyclopaedia of Human Geography*, Amsterdam: Elsevier, pp. 429–441.

14. Developing and integrating a student-researcher pedagogy within the geography curriculum
Helen Walkington

INTRODUCTION

The theoretical context for this chapter is founded on the idea that actively engaging in research should be an entitlement for all higher education geography students (Walkington and Jenkins, 2008). Undergraduate research is one of eleven 'high impact' practices (HIPs), educational approaches which result in positive outcomes such as student engagement and retention (Kuh, 2008). However, several other HIPs intersect with a research-based learning pedagogy. 'Capstone projects' are often research-based (such as a final year dissertation), 'collaborative assignments' are frequently project-based, involving teams in research, and in geography 'common intellectual experiences' are often experienced during fieldwork where research skills are practised. Perhaps less obvious are 'writing intensive courses' and 'first year seminars' which have great potential to be research-based and support the scaffolding of a 'student-researcher' pedagogy.

This chapter is grounded in the belief that rather than viewing students as consumers they can become producers or co-producers of knowledge, through engagement with disciplinary research in geography. The work is therefore situated in a partnership learning model based on disciplinary research (Healey et al., 2014). It is also informed by the view that *self-authorship* or the capacity to author one's own beliefs, values, sense of self, and relationships with others (Baxter Magolda, 2009) is a central goal of higher education in the 21st century (Baxter Magolda, 2004).

This chapter outlines a 'student-researcher' or research-based learning curriculum, describing the possibilities of this pedagogic approach, the different contexts in which it can be developed and the levels of student engagement that can be achieved in terms of participation and ownership of the research process. Disseminating research results is an integral part of the research process in which students should be involved, so after consideration of the range of different research dissemination formats and the levels of exposure appropriate for student research in geography, the chapter provides empirical data on the contrasting student learning gains from two case studies. The first is based on writing for a national undergraduate research journal of geography, GEOverse, and it presents the experience of engaging in writing and reviewing processes for undergraduate student authors and postgraduate reviewers. The second explores the student experience of presenting and participating at a variety of student research conferences, from dedicated geography conferences to presenting geographical research at multidisciplinary events. This is the first time that the two research dissemination formats have been compared empirically and differences in student engagement and self-authorship are highlighted. The chapter discusses the relative merits and challenges raised by the case studies and provides suggestions for linking and scaffolding research experiences and dissemination opportunities in a more integrated way through a programme level approach to student research and dissemination. The chapter closes with a discussion of the academic's role in the supervision and mentoring of student research and begins to explore the characteristics of effective research mentors.

A STUDENT-RESEARCHER PEDAGOGY

Research-based learning is an active pedagogy emphasising the process of research and inquiry to develop student knowledge and understanding, and in some cases to contribute to the broader knowledge base of geography as a discipline. A four-fold typology to describe the way in which research can be integrated into the curriculum is based on whether students are treated as *participants in* research or an *audience for* research, and whether there is a focus on the *research content* or research as a *process*. These distinctions are somewhat artificial and in reality much research is carried out at the intersections, however, they provide a useful classification of pedagogic approaches: 'research led' (learning about current research in the discipline); 'research oriented' (developing research skills and techniques); 'research tutored' (engaging in research discussions); and 'research based' (actively undertaking research and inquiry) (Healey et al., 2014).

Kuh and O'Donnell (2013) argue that the deepest engagement in student research happens when students participate in all aspects of the research process, from problem identification to public dissemination, ensuring that reflection is part of the research process. All four approaches are necessary to prepare students for research and allow them to 'complete the research cycle' (Walkington, 2008). The staff–student relationship in developing a 'student-researcher' pedagogy is significant as it shifts the traditional role of teacher as assessor to that of co-inquirer, and students have the potential to become experts in their research area.

Despite undergraduate project work having been a part of higher education learning for two centuries (Council on Undergraduate Research, 2005), the emphasis on research as a pedagogic practice has only relatively recently become an internationally recognised endeavour, with numerous studies demonstrating benefits for student learning (see, for example, van der Rijst and Visser-Wijnveen, 2011 in the Netherlands; Sandover et al., 2012 in Australia and the UK; Alamodi et al., 2014 in the Middle East; Yuhao, 2014 in China; and Padmaja et al., 2015 in India). Particular benefits include the efficacy of undergraduate research in promoting critical thinking and reflection, increasing motivation and confidence, and (for some) the intention to pursue post-graduate study (Hunter et al., 2007; Russell et al., 2007).

Healey (2017) has collated international examples of work to strengthen the research–teaching nexus across a range of disciplines. A meta-analysis of this literature reveals nine international practices that can be implemented across a broad range of contexts (Walkington, 2016). The nine practices are exemplified below with selected examples from the geographical literature.

The first six practices focus on providing opportunites for students to:

1. interview researchers, for example inviting in guest lecturers, students interviewing academic staff about their research in class (Dwyer, 2010), contacting published authors;

2. engage in student-centred active learning, for example problem-based learning (Spronken-Smith, 2005) and simulations which focus on conceptual understanding rather than memorising content;
3. engage in authentic research, for example living labs (Evans et al., 2015), consultancy, live projects (Shah and Treby, 2006);
4. engage with authentic audiences, for example via conferences (Hill and Walkington, 2016), journals (Walkington, 2012), or the creation of other public-facing outputs;
5. engage in reflective assessments of the learning process, for example e-portfolios and research diaries;
6. learn research methods by engaging in guided research.

A further three practices involve academic staff scaffolding:

7. the research design, for example supporting students with the process of framing enquiry (Walkington et al., 2011) and providing constructive feedback on research proposals;
8. the reading process, for example running journal clubs, providing pre-reading for lectures and structuring face-to-face class discussion sessions to check for understanding, including critical reviews of journal articles as individual assignments;
9. the writing process, for example peer review activities (Nicholson, 2011), and linking to dedicated student journals.

The scaffolding process, which allows for experiential learning and reflection, is outlined in more detail in the section on programme-level design below.

Dimensions for Framing the Undergraduate Research Context

Within geographical research there are a variety of contexts within which students can develop as researchers. First, the *people* involved provide the context of supervision, mentorship, or working within a research group involving academics, postgraduates and perhaps peers. Second, the *place* in which the student is working can differ according to the nature of the research, it may be predominantly field-based, in urban or rural environments, distant or local places, in a laboratory, working with collections, archives, and online data. Finally, the *time* frame can differ significantly, for example involvement in ongoing long-term projects, summer schemes, within the curriculum or a taster session.

The range of contexts within which student research takes place can be described in relation to a series of bipolar dimensions (Brew, 2013; Walkington, 2015). Table 14.1 outlines eight prompt questions to consider the dimensions of focus, originality of the research, motivation, inclusivity, setting, collaboration, audience, compensation and staff–student relationship.

The prompts in Table 14.1 are useful for thinking through the design of a new research-based learning project. Three examples below show how the research context can differ significantly in terms of duration of the research experience, involvement in research teams, the autonomy of student research design and relationship to the formal curriculum.

1. *An undergraduate module comprised a weekly lecture followed by a laboratory class.* To learn laboratory techniques, the whole class was provided with samples from the

*Table 14.1   Prompt questions to establish the context for a 'student-researcher'
framework in an assessment, module, programme or department*

1. Focus	What is the focus of the research, is it pedagogic (student learning), the creation of new knowledge for students, or original research findings?
2. Setting	In what setting does the research take place, is it embedded or extra/co-curricular?
3. Inclusivity	How inclusive is the research opportunity, can all students take part or is it selective (for example part of a paid-for expedition, only open to students who achieve a particular grade, only offered at honours level)?
4. Relationship	What is the nature of the staff–student relationship, is it a partnership?
5. Collaboration	Is there a collaborative element to the research, does it take place in a group/team?
6. Motivation	Where does the motivation for the research come from, is it student or staff initiated?
7. Audience	Who is the anticipated audience for the research? A campus, community, public or professional audience?
8. Compensation	If this is an extra-curricular project, are students compensated for their time either through modular credit or in the form of payment?

module leader's field site. Each group was allocated a proportion of the samples. In the laboratory a new technique was taught each week and the students had to complete the laboratory test on the samples, sharing their results across the whole class in an online format provided by the teacher. The final module assessment was an individual write-up of the results and discussion section of a journal article (for which the introduction and methods were provided by the teacher). The students had to synthesise and make sense of all the shared data to complete their assignment.

2. *An institutionally funded summer research opportunity.* The scheme was highly selective and occurred outside the curriculum, over the long vacation. The research was carried out within an existing research group and new knowledge was the long-term target. The research group was formed through an academic collaboration between several disciplines and the research disseminated through a conference on campus, with the potential for publication in the future. The student received a stipend to take part and the staff member acted as a mentor in the research process.

3. *An undergraduate final year fieldtrip to Mexico which formed part of a module.* A group of eight undergraduate students were accompanied by a professor, a post-doctoral student and a Masters' student. The mix of staff and students, in a fieldwork setting, allowed the undergraduates to gain useful insights into how to undertake fieldwork as well as follow up supervision on data analysis and report writing. Each student devised their own project and collected and analysed their own data. The module assessment was a journal article.

The three examples reveal that the design of the curriculum can result in different levels of participation and student engagement in the research process.

Levels of Student Engagement in Research

Students can participate in research to different degrees determined by: ownership of the research question; the level of guidance that students receive; the degree of autonomy that students hold to modify the research as it progresses; and choices made about the dissemination of outcomes. The Research Skill Development Framework of Willison and O'Regan (2007) provides a useful frame of reference (for any discipline and from primary schooling to doctoral level) for showing progressive levels of attainment and autonomy against six facets of the research process from clarifying a question, through to dissemination of results.

Walkington (2015) conceptualised five successive levels which students may participate at over the course of an undergraduate degree programme. Being assigned a research task with a prescribed methodology has been conceptualised as *Level 1*, see example 1 above. At *Level 2* students are consulted about research design or analytical technique. An example might be a summer research opportunity where a staff member is working on an ongoing project and students engage in tutor directed research with the ability to influence the project and contribute to its dissemination, such as in example 2 above. At *Level 3*, while staff frame the enquiry initially, students have a much greater role to play in decision-making with respect to development of methods, reframing, determining courses of action and taking responsibility for the outcomes and dissemination. At *Level 4* students make the decisions but do not consult with university staff. Some students adopt this approach to their dissertation or final project and choose to work unsupervised. This lone worker model may have produced more effective results if the student had received feedback during the process. Initiating a self-directed project with a staff member acting as a mentor is conceptualised as *Level 5*. Here students frame their own enquiry and carry out the research, but in consultation with university staff at a level determined by the student. This allows the student to gain ongoing feedback when they want it and allows them to develop a relationship with an academic research mentor. The undergraduate students in example 3 above could potentially engage at Level 5 (see Walkington 2016c in the Useful Resources section later in this chapter).

PROGRAMME LEVEL CURRICULUM DESIGN

A geography programme should allow students to move from being an *audience* for geographical research to becoming an active *participant* in its creation, a researcher. Over time there will be iterative shifts in emphasis between research *content* and the research *process*. The blend and sequencing of these roles and activities should guide the programme team in designing a well scaffolded and progressive curriculum which supports the transition from guided small-scale team-based research, to autonomous research projects (Spronken-Smith and Walker, 2010) which can then strengthen the links between teaching and research. Walkington et al. (2011) asked 52 international geography academics to identify research skills that are particularly challenging to teach. 'Framing good research questions', and 'developing critical thinking' were deemed most challenging. The authors provided examples of how to scaffold the development of research skills across a geography programme. Initially, students might participate in discrete tasks in the curriculum, for example small-scale data collection or manipulating research data with assignments to simulate research processes. When students are engaged in data analysis, it is important to ensure that they support all their ideas with evidence, so requiring students to make critical judgments (Hinchliffe and Walkington, 2016) about information, arguments, and methods to evaluate the validity and reliability of data is important. As students progress to synthesising and organising material into new, more complex interpretations and relationships, they should learn appropriate presentation styles. Disseminating results is important for promoting reflection and enables students to see the transferable (employability) skills associated with being a researcher as well as developing a sense of belonging to the geographical research community.

An effective way to learn geographical content and methods is through engagement in research, progressively building confidence and autonomy. Ideally, research should be encountered early in the student learning experience (Walkington et al., 2011) so students' understanding is scaffolded. The geography curriculum is challenging to teach because it requires a familiarity with qualitative *and* quantitative research methodologies, reinforcing the need to start earlier. The many specialist subdisciplines have particular methods and techniques in which a student may require training. Careful planning is also required to support students so that 'regardless of the nature of the research, the student's learning requires critical reflection on the potential risks as well as the moral and ethical issues of the research project' (Quality Assurance Agency 2014, p. 13).

DISSEMINATING STUDENT RESEARCH FINDINGS

The Boyer Commission (1998, p. 24) made it clear that sharing the results of research is part of the research process, and students should experience this process in its entirety. This has led to significant interest in dedicated student conferences and undergraduate research journals (Walkington, 2015) as authentic modes of dissemination. However, many other public formats exist including blogs, video-diaries, podcasts, online/virtual conferences, group wikis, published books, trail guides and papers, consultancy reports to clients, exhibitions and shows, and so on. Altering the assessment brief for courses/modules can open students up to the possibility of publishing their work. Replacing dissertations with alternative assessments (Hill et al., 2011) can involve writing for authentic audiences (for example journal articles, briefing papers, web pages) and the development of employer-related transferable skills.

Levels of Exposure and Strategies for Engaging Students in Research Dissemination

There are a range of levels at which student research can be shared beyond the curriculum (Spronken-Smith et al., 2013) from events for just geographers within the university, to sharing geographical research nationally, or in multidisciplinary settings.

A variety of strategies have been reported to embed publication in the student learning experience (Walkington, 2014; Walkington et al., 2013). To engage students with research dissemination it is possible to *build publication into degree programme requirements*. Writing a journal article for a real audience based on final year research is a more transferable skill than writing a 10,000-word thesis for two markers. Explicitly *identifying activities as research* such as literature reviewing, peer review, data synthesis and data presentation makes research accessible to all students. *Using student research findings in the curriculum* also demonstrates the value that staff members put on a 'students as researchers' approach. *Engaging students in the publication process* (for example as editors/ reviewers, sourcing articles, conference/event organisation, marketing and promotion) allows all students to take on a role, even if those students' own research was not suitable for publication. Confidence is one of the biggest barriers to authentic research dissemination, so *scaffolding publication opportunities* is important, for example sharing results in class, then presenting at mini-conferences within a course or module which can in turn build confidence to participate in departmental or institution-wide events. A journal article format for an assignment might develop into a submission for an institutional journal, or co-authorship with a faculty member. Presenting project findings to academic staff in preparation for real client presentations might provide a stepping stone to a national conference. Blogging, before producing final written outputs for a publicly accessible repository, allows for dialogue and feedback with an authentic online community.

CASE STUDIES

The UK's Quality Assurance Agency subject benchmark statement for geography, outlines the expectations of a degree in terms of likely content, skills and experiences. It provides descriptors for threshold, standard and excellent levels of achievement. In terms of research, excellence can be demonstrated by the quality of a student's ability to communicate complex arguments to a variety of audiences (Quality Assurance Agency 2014, p. 18). Yet, there is little empirical work on the student learning gained from participation in research dissemination activities. With only two journals in the world dedicated to sharing research in geography at undergraduate level, GEOview in Australia and GEOverse in the UK, the first case study begins to address this gap by detailing the learning gained from participation in GEOverse, a national e-journal involving undergraduate student authors and postgraduate reviewers. The second case study explores the participation of undergraduate geographers in student research conferences, ranging from discipline specific to multidisciplinary, and at different levels from departmental to national. This is the first time the two dissemination formats have been compared empirically and strategies for maximising the benefits of each format are provided.

Undergraduate Research Journals

GEOverse, a national level journal dedicated to sharing undergraduate research in geography, was launched at the same time as an institutional journal called Geoversity at Oxford Brookes University, UK. The journals adopt a peer review process with postgraduate students carrying out collaborative reviews, in order to ensure that a consistent set of constructive feedback comments are received by the undergraduate author. Postgraduate students therefore carry out the reviews separately, then come together online through a wiki to align their feedback (Walkington, 2012). This rigorous environment of review allows undergraduate research to reach the public domain. Decisions about the journal process, format, focus and values for GEOverse are outlined in Walkington (2008).

Data was collected via questionnaires to three groups: students for whom writing a journal article was a new curriculum-based assignment (27 responded from 87 students), successfully published authors in GEOverse and Geoversity (all published authors responded), and postgraduate reviewers from across multiple institutions in the UK (7 of the 16, that is all of those who had carried out reviews at that time).

For the first two groups the questionnaire focused on the experience of writing a journal article including the benefits and challenges, skills developed, the impact of the review process and the impact of writing for publication on the research process itself (Walkington, 2012) themes from the applied thematic analysis are indicated in italics. Because it was a new format, students reported finding it '*hard to change between writing as a learner to writing as a teacher*'. The students who wrote an article but did not go on to submit it for publication identified three differences to other university assessments: a sense of *ownership* over their research that they had not experienced in previous assignments; a greater *sense of understanding* of the research because of having to justify all aspects in the journal format; and a sense of *creativity* in the writing process, including the ability to leave out material and develop a personal argument. The same group of students shared three further themes with students who submitted their work for publication and successfully became authors: the sense of *achievement* they felt after completing their article; the ability to *apply constructive criticism* (because the journal article process was replicated by the assessment task where students submitted a draft for constructive comments); and gaining the skills of *critical evaluation* of their own work as a result. Themes reported exclusively by the published authors were: *CV material* in terms of a publication; the feeling of *academic recognition* through being published; and a *desire to publish further work* in the future. Finally, they reported a *desire for further dialogue* about their research, partly in frustration at the anonymous review process which only allowed written feedback, whereas students wanted a conversation, and to clarify reviewer comments (ibid.).

For the postgraduate reviewers, the main benefit was being part of a wider geographical community beyond the institution they were based in, as well as developing their reviewing skills as an indirect enhancement to their own writing practice. Interestingly they also struggled giving anonymous written feedback and would have liked a conversation with the authors about the review. The online journals created opportunities for detailed feed-forward and supported iterative processes through writing, reviewing and rewriting. Trusting the written advice of anonymous reviewers was a significant step for authors. Students also reported that their engagement with the literature changed as a result of the journal projects. They stopped reading web and textbook material in favour of journal articles, to immerse themselves in the journal format. As their understanding of the peer review process grew, they understood the importance of clearly justifying their findings in the light of other alternative but peer-reviewed interpretations.

Student Research Conferences

Alongside the international spread of undergraduate research as a pedagogy there has been a growth of multi-disciplinary undergraduate research conferences, culminating in the first World Congress on Undergraduate Research in 2017. This is founded on a strong legacy of annual national conferences in the US with the long running National Conference on Undergraduate Research (NCUR), which inspired the British CUR since 2011 and Australian CUR in 2012. There are also events in Canada, Ireland and the Netherlands as well as a newly established World Congress. However, evidence for the benefits of student participation in these multidisciplinary conferences is limited (Mabrouk, 2009). This case study shows that student research conferences provide an opportunity for students to develop professional capabilities for employment because they promote reflection on learning, the ability to communicate high-level concepts in lay terms to a broad audience, and the ability to make sound judgements 'in the moment'.

Hinchliffe and Walkington (2016) found that geography students presenting in a faculty-wide conference saw it as a space to contest knowledge and made three types of judgement: judgement of the material to include for an audience beyond (but including) their own discipline; judgement of the effectiveness of themselves as a presenter; and judgement of the value of their research. The most capable students could judge the suitability of their knowledge in the conference setting and reframe it to ask questions to students from other disciplines. They could also engage in dialogue about their own research to establish intrapersonally grounded values, a key aspect of self-authorship (Baxter Magolda, 2009). As one physical geography student noted:

> *A conference has two outcomes, I mean it could be seen as informing the people that come to the conference, but it also informs the person presenting at the conference, it is sort of a dual feedback system in other words, it is not just the person coming to the conference who gets information, because by asking questions they're testing the knowledge of the person doing the presentation. That enables me to look more critically at the work I've produced. . . [an anthropologist] had a different perspective, which allowed me to develop my thoughts about the issue.* (Hinchliffe and Walkington, 2016, p. 222)

Walkington et al. (2016) undertook 90 interviews with students from the full range of undergraduate disciplines who presented a poster or paper at the British Conference of Undergraduate Research (BCUR) in three consecutive years (14 per cent of total participants) 2012–2014. They revealed that students ask each other challenging questions, in a liminal environment free from assessment constraints. The language that students need to adopt in this multidisciplinary setting is free from disciplinary jargon. At the highest level, students were empowered to develop their own pedagogy of reciprocal elucidation (a form of bi-directional knowledge exchange). The same data set was also mapped onto the Vitae Researcher Development Framework (Kneale et al., 2016), revealing how the students develop the skills that employers value in their preparation for and participation in the conference. Hill and Walkington (2016) used graduate attributes and self-authorship as concepts to study the learning experiences specific to the Geography, Earth and Environmental Science participants at BCUR. The students identified themselves as researchers as they gained in confidence and moved towards self-authorship through dialogue, by balancing their disciplinary knowledge with goals and values grounded in intra-personal interactions. All students across the data set felt empowered by engaging successfully in an authentic experience which allowed them to escape institutional and disciplinary 'bubbles'. One particularly positive aspect of this for the geography students taking part was the ability to step back and see how other disciplines approach familiar research topics. In so doing, students gained a sense of their GEES perspective and reflected on how their university experience has given them a lens through which to view the world, but also the ability to connect to students from other disciplines. Geography students were generally well prepared for this type of activity because of the synthetic nature of the discipline in which they have to engage with different perspectives, world views, methodologies and ontologies.

Comparing Learning Gains

The two empirical case studies presented have shown that engaging in research dissemination provides different experiences for students depending on the context and format of the dissemination activity. Journals provided students with a requirement to trust and address the written advice of anonymous others, the ability to work with detailed feed-forward (rather than feedback) on their article and they were required to develop critical skills through reflection on their writing. The successful student authors gained recognition as researchers; however, the experience was not dialogic and the lack of a conversation about the research between authors and reviewers was particularly challenging.

In contrast, when presenting at a conference, students had to engage with critical thinking through dialogue. Rather than written comments, they gained instant dialogic feedback from a range of perspectives. They too gained critical skills through reflecting on their conference experience, and were also recognised by others as researchers, which impacted on their identity. However, the timing of most conferences late in the academic year meant that, as a final experience, it was often impossible to take on board the feedback they'd received at the event and turn this into credit within their programme, such as through changes to a capstone project or dissertation. Unlike a journal article, the lack of a discoverable artefact to represent their research meant students found the lack of a 'legacy' disadvantageous in comparison to the journal article format.

In terms of self-authorship both formats engaged students in authoring and justifying their own beliefs, but in different ways. Conferences, due to their multidisciplinary nature, allowed for the 'reciprocal elucidation' of ideas (Walkington et al., 2016) at the event. The unanticipated audience and dialogic format in the conference provided a more liminal fluid, 'borderland' environment (Hill et al., 2019), so identity changes (being an expert/professional) were more frequently reported, and ideas were more open to negotiation than through the journals. The shift in power between staff and students was also more frequently noted in the poster style conference setting as students gained their 'voice' rapidly, and repeatedly experienced recognition as an authority on their topic. In contrast, the reviewers for the journal, being anonymous and offering more critique than praise, retained a more static and non-negotiable power over ideas. Students were more active in their conference experience and a broader range of students, as well as members of the public, could participate. The journal allowed for written engagement between authors and reviewers, but a more passive engagement for readers.

In terms of the learning gained from participating in the publication process through either the journal or conference, students learnt about how to enhance the presentation of their research in an iterative way. By understanding the differences in student learning gains from journal authorship to conference presenter, it is possible to minimise negative aspects. Changing the timing of conferences so that they come early enough for feedback from the event to be incorporated into the work that students go on to submit for credit, or publication as an article, utilises the conference as a formative event part way through the research writing phase. Creating digital artefacts (such as posters online or short presentations to camera saved as video files) for people to access who were not able to attend the event face-to-face can provide a legacy from conferences, without investment in a journal. Such digital artefacts can be linked to online CVs and portfolios. The *Get Published!* student research collection at Oxford Brookes University is part of a dedicated student research repository which includes making posters from the annual institution-wide student conference publicly available.

From an academic's perspective establishing and running a journal is a much more resource intensive activity than the organisation of a poster conference, and institutional conferences yield similar benefits to national events where they are interdisciplinary (Pavlakou and Walkington, 2018). The publication of digital artefacts of a range of types, such as student posters, animated presentations with voice overs, vodcasts of students talking to camera about their research, blog posts and so on, all allow students to share their research at minimal cost, with a wide audience, and to gain the benefits of completing the research cycle. To this end institutional research repositories may provide the infrastructure to display student research across a variety of disciplines, both within and beyond the institution.

MENTORING STUDENT RESEARCH

As research into the benefits of undergraduate research participation across a variety of disciplines has become more extensive (Lopatto, 2009), it is apparent that the quality of academic mentoring is a crucial driver to successful outcomes (Shanahan et al., 2015). Whilst research supervision focusses primarily on the research project and outcomes, research mentoring focusses on the whole student and how the research fits into their learning, sometimes with a longer-term view of developing skills for future careers, and in a way that benefits both the student mentee and the mentor (Koch and Johnson, 2000). A literature review of 20 years of articles on the behaviours adopted when mentoring student researchers reveals ten salient practices characteristic of effective academic research mentors (Shanahan et al., 2015; Walkington et al., 2018b; see Table 14.2). The balance between a research focus and student development focus is clear from the practices.

The socio-cultural and emotional benefits that arise from mentored research, which take place face to face in one-to-one relationships, benefit students from non-traditional backgrounds in particular (Shanahan et al., 2017) with practices such as taking students to discipline conferences and helping them network (see practices 4, 8 and 10 in Table 14.2). Continuing to support students through to the research dissemination phase of the research cycle is therefore central to the widening participation agenda.

Mentoring students is a resource-intensive activity that can provide challenges for academics (Walkington et al., 2018b). In order to maximise participation, mentoring can take place through a variety of models from traditional one-to-one faculty mentor–student mentee relationships, to involving graduate students mentoring teams, and utilising peer mentors in either vertical or horizontal groupings. Academics may also co-mentor students (Ketcham et al., 2018), particularly for mixed methods projects or interdisciplinary research.

Table 14.2   Practices of effective undergraduate research mentors

Effective Practices of Undergraduate Research Mentors
1.   Plan in order to respond to students' varying needs and abilities throughout the research process.
2.   Set clear scaffolded expectations for undergraduate researchers.
3.   Teach the methods and techniques of conducting research in the discipline.
4.   Balance rigorous expectations with emotional support and appropriate personal interest in students.
5.   Develop a community among groups of undergraduate researchers and mentors, including graduate students, and other members of the research team.
6.   Dedicate time to one-to-one, hands-on mentoring.
7.   Increase student ownership of the research over time.
8.   Support students' professional development through networking and explaining the norms of the discipline.
9.   Create opportunities for peers and 'near peers' to learn mentoring skills and to engage more students in research.
10.   Encourage students to share their findings and provide guidance on presenting work in a variety of formats.

Source: Adapted from Walkington, et al. (2018b).

CONCLUSION

Engaging in research is an essential part of asserting the value of geographical thinking and ensuring that graduates develop geocapabilities, in addition to generic graduate attributes (Walkington et al., 2018a). While it is clear that institutional research cultures and strategies *can* be inclusive of students as researchers, and that we *can* personalise and professionalise the curriculum through providing research and dissemination opportunities for students, this requires academics to progressively structure authentic research experiences for students to help build confidence, reflective capabilities and provide liminal environments for the development of self-authorship. This chapter suggests that we should strive to do this early, in dialogic settings, and through carefully scaffolded experiences within and beyond the curriculum. Moreover, to open research experiences to all our students we should adopt embedded research experiences in small teams, with a transition to carefully planned research mentoring, as students take on the identity of producers of knowledge in their own right.

USEFUL RESOURCES

- Walkington, H. (2016a) *Disseminating Student Research*. York: HEA. Accessed from: https://www.heacademy.ac.uk/system/files/resources/walkington-disseminating-student-research.pdf.
- Walkington, H. (2016b) *Engaging Students in Research*. York: HEA. Accessed from: https://www.heacademy.ac.uk/system/files/resources/walkington-engaging-students-in-research.pdf.

- Walkington, H. (2016c) *Levels of Student Participation in Research*. York: HEA. Accessed from: https://www.heacademy.ac.uk/system/files/resources/walkington-levels-of-student-participation-in-research.pdf.
- Walkington, H. (2016d) *Pedagogic Approaches to Developing Students as Researchers Within and Beyond the Curriculum*. York: HEA. Accessed from: https://www.hea cademy.ac.uk/system/files/resources/walkington-pedagogic-approaches.pdf.
- Walkington, H. (2016e) *Students as Researchers*. York: HEA. Accessed from: https://www.heacademy.ac.uk/system/files/resources/walkington-students-as-researchers.pdf.

REFERENCES

Alamodi, A.A., Abu-Zaid, A., Anwer, L.A., Khan, T.A., Shareef, M.A., Shamia, A.A., Nazmi, S.M., Alshammari, A.M., Rahmutallah, H., Alsheikh, A.J., Chamseddin, R.A, Dweik, L.M. and Yaginuddin, A. (2014) 'Undergraduate research: An innovative student-centered committee from the Kingdom of Saudi Arabia', *Medical Teacher*, 36(S1), pp. S36–S42. doi: 10.3109/0142159X.2014.886016.

Baxter Magolda, M.B. (2004) 'Self-authorship as the common goal for 21st century education', in M.B. Baxter Magolda and P.M. King (eds), *Learning Partnerships: Theory and Models of Practice to Educate for Self-authorship*. Sterling, VA: Stylus, pp. 1–36.

Baxter Magolda, M.B. (2009) 'Educating students for self-authorship. Learning partnerships to achieve complex outcomes', in C. Kreber (ed.), *The University and its Disciplines: Teaching and Learning Within and Beyond Disciplinary Boundaries*. London: Routledge, pp. 143–56.

Boyer Commission on Educating Undergraduates in the Research University (1998) *Reinventing Undergraduate Education: A Blueprint for America's Research Universities*. Stony Brook, NY: State University of New York–Stony Brook.

Brew, A. (2013) 'Understanding the scope of undergraduate research: a framework for curricular and pedagogical decision-making', *Higher Education*, 66(5), pp. 603–618.

Council on Undergraduate Research and National Conference for Undergraduate Research (2005) *Joint Statement of Principles in Support of Undergraduate Research, Scholarship, and Creative Activities*. Available at: www.cur.org (accessed: 18 February 2009).

Dwyer, C. (2010) 'Linking research and teaching: a staff–student interview project', *Journal of Geography in Higher Education*, 25(3), pp. 357–366.

Evans, J., Jones, R., Karvonen, A., Millard, L., and Wendler, J. (2015) 'Living labs and co-production: university campuses as platforms for sustainability science', *Current Opinion in Environmental Sustainability*, 16, pp. 1–6.

Healey, M. (2017) *Linking Research and Teaching: A Selected Bibliography*. Available at: www.mickhealey.co.uk/resources (accessed: 15 November 2017).

Healey, M., Flint, A. and Harrington, K. (2014) *Engagement Through Partnership: Students as Partners in Learning and Teaching in Higher Education*. York: Higher Education Academy.

Hill, J.L. and Walkington, H. (2016) 'Developing graduate attributes through participation in undergraduate research conferences', *Journal of Geography in Higher Education*, 40(2), pp. 222–237.

Hill, J., Kneale, P., Nicholson, D., Waddington, S. and Ray, W. (2011) 'Re-framing the geography dissertation: a consideration of alternative, innovative and creative approaches', *Journal of Geography in Higher Education*, 35(3), pp. 331–349.

Hill, J., Walkington, H. and Kneale, P. (2019) 'Borderland spaces: moving towards self-authorship', in T. Bilham, C. Hamshire, M. Hartog and M. Doolan (eds), *Reframing Space for Learning: Empowering Excellence and Innovation in University Teaching and Learning*. London: UCL/IoE Press (forthcoming).

Hinchliffe, G. and Walkington, H. (2016) 'Cultivating the art of judgement in students', in Michael Tomlinson (ed.), *Graduate Employability in Context: Theory, Research and Debate*. Basingstoke: Palgrave Macmillan.

Hunter, A.-B., Laursen, S.L. and Seymour, E. (2007) 'Becoming a scientist: the role of undergraduate research in students' cognitive, personal, and professional development', *Science Education*, 91, pp. 36–74.

Ketcham, C., Hall, E., Fitzgibbon, H. and Walkington, H. (2018) 'Co-mentoring in undergraduate research: a faculty development perspective', in M. Vandermaas Peeler, P. Miller and J. Moore (eds), *Excellence in Mentoring Undergraduate Research*. Washington, DC: Council on Undergraduate Research.

Kneale, P., Edwards-Jones, A., Walkington, H. and Hill, J. (2016) 'Evaluating undergraduate research conferences as vehicles for novice researcher development', *International Journal for Researcher Development*, 7(2), pp. 159–177.

Koch, C. and Johnson, W.B. (2000) 'Documenting the benefits of undergraduate mentoring', *Council on Undergraduate Research Quarterly*, 20(4), pp. 172–175.

Kuh, G.D. (2008) *High-Impact Educational Practices: What They Are, Who Has Access to Them, and Why They Matter.* Washington, DC: American Association of Colleges and Universities, 34 pp.

Kuh, G.D. and O'Donnell, K. (2013) *Ensuring Quality and Taking High-Impact Practices to Scale.* Washington, DC: American Association of Colleges and Universities.

Lopatto, D. (2009) *Science in Solution: The Impact of Undergraduate Research on Student Learning.* Tucson, AZ: Research Corporation for Science Advancement.

Mabrouk, P.A. (2009) 'Survey study investigating the significance of conference participation to undergraduate research students', *Journal of Chemical Education*, 86, pp. 1335–1340.

Nicholson, D.T. (2011) 'Embedding research in a field-based module through peer review and assessment for learning', *Journal of Geography in Higher Education*, 35(4), pp. 529–549.

Padmaja, A., Laxmi Ramana, V.S.V. and Reddy, P.R. (2015) 'Importance of research at undergraduate level', *Proceedings of the International Conference on Transformations in Engineering Education*, pp. 631–632.

Pavlakou, M. and Walkington, H. (2018) 'Multidisciplinary undergraduate conferences – a new pedagogy for student learning?' Guest blog post for Conference Inference [online] accessed from: https://conferenceinference. wordpress.com/2018/05/21/guest-post-by-metaxia-pavlakou-helen-walkington-multidisciplinary-undergraduate-conferences-a-new-pedagogy-for-student-learning (accessed: 21 May 2018).

Quality Assurance Agency (2014) *Subject Benchmark Statement: Geography*. Gloucester: QAA.

Russell, S.H., Hancock, M.P. and McCullough, J. (2007) 'Benefits of undergraduate research experiences', *Science*, 316(5824), pp. 548–549.

Sandover, S., Partridge, L., Dunne, E. and Burkill, S. (2012) 'Undergraduate researchers change learning and teaching: a case study in Australia and the United Kingdom', *CUR Quarterly*, 33(1), pp. 33–39.

Shah, A. and Treby, E. (2006) 'Using a community based project to link teaching and research: the Bourne Stream Partnership', *Journal of Geography in Higher Education*, 30(1), pp. 33–48.

Shanahan, J.O., Ackley-Holbrook, E., Hall, E., Stewart, K. and Walkington, H. (2015) 'Ten salient practices of undergraduate research mentors: a review of the literature', *Mentoring and Tutoring: Partnership in Learning*, 23(5), pp. 359–376.

Shanahan, J.O., Walkington, H., Ackley, E., Hall, E. and Stewart, K. (2017) 'Award winning mentors see democratization as the future of undergraduate research', *Council on Undergraduate Research Quarterly*, 37(4), pp. 4–11.

Spronken-Smith, R. (2005) 'Implementing a problem-based-learning approach for teaching research methods in geography', *Journal of Geography in Higher Education*, 29(2), pp. 203–221.

Spronken-Smith, R. and Walker, R. (2010) 'Can inquiry-based learning strengthen the links between teaching and disciplinary research?' *Studies in Higher Education*, 35, pp. 723–740.

Spronken-Smith, R., Brodeur, J.J., Kajaks, T., Luck, M., Myatt, P., Verburgh, A., Walkington, H. and Wuetherick, B. (2013) 'Completing the research cycle: a framework for promoting dissemination of undergraduate research and inquiry', *Teaching and Learning Inquiry. The ISSOTL Journal*, 1(2), pp. 105–118.

van der Rijst, R.M. and Visser-Wijnveen, G.J. (2011) 'Undergraduate research and inquiry in the Netherlands', *CUR Quarterly*, 32(2), pp. 32–36.

Walkington, H. (2008) 'Geoverse: piloting a national e-journal of undergraduate research in Geography', *PLANET*, 20, pp. 41–46.

Walkington, H. (2012) 'Developing dialogic learning space: the case of online undergraduate research journals', *Journal of Geography in Higher Education*, 36(4), pp. 547–562.

Walkington, H. (2014) 'Quality enhancement of undergraduate research – further strategies to increase student engagement in research dissemination', *Brookes E-journal of Learning and Teaching*, 6 (1). Available at: http://bejlt.brookes.ac.uk/paper/quality-enhancement-of-undergraduate-research-further-strategies-to-increase-student-engagement-in-research-dissemination/ (accessed: 15 September 2017).

Walkington, H. (2015) *Students as Researchers: Supporting Undergraduate Research in the Disciplines in Higher Education.* York: Higher Education Academy. Available at: https://www.heacademy.ac.uk/sites/default/files/resources/Students%20as%20researchers_1.pdf (accessed: 15 September 2017).

Walkington, H. (2016) 'Strategies for engaging students in research and dissemination', Keynote lecture. The Center for Education and Learning 'Innovation Room' Leiden University, The Netherlands 11/11/2017. Available at: http://www.educationandlearning.nl/news/cel-innovation-room-7-investigative-learning (accessed: 20 October 2017).

Walkington, H. and Jenkins, A. (2008) 'Embedding undergraduate research publication in the student learning experience: ten suggested strategies', *Brookes E-journal of Learning and Teaching*, 2 (3). Available at: http://bejlt.brookes.ac.uk/article/embedding_undergraduate_research_publication_ (accessed: 15 November 2017).

Walkington, H., Dyer, S., Solem, M., Haigh, M. and Waddington, S. (2018a) 'A capabilities approach to higher education: geocapabilities and implications for geography curricula', *Journal of Geography in Higher Education*, 42(1), pp. 7–24.

Walkington, H., Edwards-Jones, A. and Gresty, K. (2013) 'Strategies for widening students' engagement with undergraduate research journals', *Council on Undergraduate Research Quarterly*, 34(1), pp. 24–30.

Walkington, H., Griffin, A.L., Keys-Mathews, L., Metoyer, S.K., Miller, W.E., Baker, R. and France, D. (2011) 'Embedding research-based learning early in the undergraduate geography curriculum', *Journal of Geography in Higher Education*, 35(3), pp. 1–16.

Walkington, H., Hall, E., Shanahan, J.O., Ackley, E. and Stewart, K. (2018b) 'Striving for excellence in undergraduate research mentoring: the challenges and approaches to ten salient practices', in M. Vandermaas-Peeler, J. Moore and P.C. Miller (eds), *Excellence in Mentoring Undergraduate Research.* Washington, DC: Council on Undergraduate Research.

Walkington, H., Hill, J. and Kneale, P. (2016) 'Reciprocal elucidation: a student-led pedagogy in multidisciplinary undergraduate research conferences', *Higher Education Research and Development*, 36(2), pp. 416–429.

Willison, J. and O'Regan, K. (2007) 'Commonly known, commonly not known, totally unknown: a framework for students becoming researchers', *Higher Education Research and Development*, 26(4), pp. 393–409.

Yuhao, C. (2014) 'Student development in undergraduate research programs in China: from the perspective of self-authorship', *International Journal of Chinese Education*, (3), pp. 53–73.

15. Who owns the curriculum? Co-production of an evolving research-informed module
Richard Hodgkins and Joanna Bullard

INTRODUCTION

A joke (of sorts) between those teaching environmental change topics in higher education appears on social media every few years, when the Intergovernmental Panel on Climate Change (IPCC) releases new versions of its authoritative assessment reports: 'Now we have to update our lecture slides'. This speaks to the important need to keep our curricula as a whole – and their detailed content – current, but also falls into the familiar trap of regarding teaching as a unidirectional knowledge transfer. However, the reflective practitioner, even the time-pressed one, recognises that knowledge received and potentially remembered is still the poor relation of understanding critically applied (Bloom, 1994).

Therefore, the challenge is to keep curricula and modules/course units up to date, but in a way that allows the teacher to support the development of deep and critical understanding and enables the learner to develop skills other than memorising. Both learner and teacher have specific investments in this challenge: in fast-changing fields, as in a fast-changing society, the ability to update knowledge and understanding, be information literate (see Chapter 12 in this volume by Waller, Miller and Schultz), and the capacity to evaluate, are key skills that students need to develop at least as much as academics; likewise, incorporating the most recent developments in a field into the content of a module strengthens the link between teaching and research, thereby offering greater satisfaction for staff. The challenge of staying current can therefore be productively shared between learner and teacher: rather than being a goal in itself, it can be viewed as an inherent feature of the curriculum, as a process to which both teacher and learner contribute. In other words, rather than being recipients of content delivered, students become collaborators in a current, research-informed curriculum.

In the discipline of geography, maintaining an up-to-date curriculum presents a particular challenge, reflecting its special, integrative nature (Fouberg and Moseley, 2015). As a synthesising discipline (Fenneman, 2009; Heffron and Downs, 2012), geography draws on a wide range of other disciplines from diverse traditions (Blunt, 2009; Johnston, 2009; Richards, 2009), which utilise contrasting methods and approaches, to create new understanding; these traditions may even have different conceptions of knowledge itself, such as generalisable and replicable in the physical sciences, or culturally-contingent and value-laden in the social sciences. The geographer must access, comprehend and evaluate research from across varying subsets of the humanities, social and physical sciences, and unless s/he is a rare polymath, requires a strategy to manage this feat successfully. One approach is that of co-production, in which learners are equipped with an appropriate, unintrusive scaffold and enabled to update the curriculum themselves in directed activities; in the process, valuable skills in the sourcing, assessment and management of information can be attained which will serve students well through both their degree studies and in their lives beyond higher education, in terms of employability and engaged citizenship. This chapter gives an account of such an approach, using a case study from a third-year undergraduate, physical geography module at Loughborough University, in the UK.

PLANNING FOR A RESEARCH-INFORMED MODULE

One of the key changes in higher education learning and teaching over the past couple of decades has been a shift in emphasis, from what the teacher is doing in a session to what the students themselves are doing (Day, 2012), and in the transition away from the lecture as performance towards learning through interactive contact time, for instance in the flipped-classroom approach (Bergmann and Sams, 2012). Although evidence of long-term benefits is still unclear (O'Flaherty and Phillips, 2015), there is a well-developed scholarly basis for this shift in approach. For instance, Noddings (1995) describes teaching as a relationship, to which both teacher and student contribute. Pring (2001) suggests that to teach is to engage consciously in activities which bring about learning, placing the emphasis of the activity on processes and outcomes, rather than on a one-directional transaction from teacher to student. Likewise, Maunder (2015, p. 1) suggests 'co-production emphasizes active engagement, mutual learning and collaborative knowledge creation' and that this leads to a progressive re-evaluation of the often-problematic relationship between research and teaching (Barnett, 1990). Research-informed teaching takes many forms (Healey and Jenkins, 2009):

1.   research-led, in which students are taught research findings in their field of study;
2.   research-oriented, in which students learn research processes and methodologies;
3.   research-tutored, in which students learn through critique and discussion between themselves and staff; and
4.   research-based learning, where students learn as researchers.

Whilst it is tempting to view a close association between teaching and research, with the latter viewed broadly as knowledge production and the advancement of understanding, as axiomatically beneficial for the learner, intended learning outcomes should always guide the actual role which research plays in the curriculum. It is possible to argue that this is above all the case in geography, which draws its strength from its generalist, integrating, synthesising nature, and is highly diverse in terms of content and approaches. Dolan and Collins (2015) have articulated a practical manifesto for active learning, which naturally helps with finding an effective balance for research-informed teaching; it is based on four simple principles which are described in more detail below:

1.   design a module backwards;
2.   aim high;
3.   pose messy problems;
4.   expect students to talk, write and collaborate.

Design a Module Backwards

Planning of curricula and modules seems still too often centred on what content is intended to be covered, with the consequence that teaching is likewise still too often an exercise in fact transfer rather than in the building of critical understanding. A desirable goal might therefore be to de-emphasise content delivery in modules, and instead to conceive teaching sessions in terms of outcomes: what, for example, are the two or three key ideas students should take away at the end of the session? Then, what is the best way to help them acquire that understanding, in terms of activities, and finally, what content is required to facilitate those activities? A more limited amount of content therefore becomes a jumping-off point or a means to exemplify key ideas, rather than something to be memorised and regurgitated. Less content certainly need not mean less learning. This could also extend to assessment, where students might be tasked to find their own content relevant to coursework, for example. In general, this approach also requires fewer PowerPoint slides, making those parts of sessions which remain in a traditional lecture format less of a race against time. The amount of staff overhead in updating content can therefore be significantly reduced, but students, appropriately supported, have more ownership of their learning and understanding, having worked to gain it themselves.

Aim High

Using outcomes as a starting point for designing sessions, and basing those outcomes around key ideas, creates a clear pathway towards a destination: the deep understanding of a subject. Such understanding does not necessarily reliably emerge from content-driven delivery, which depends on fact accumulation and piecemeal comprehension-building. Certain disciplines may justifiably be 'conceived as linear and hierarchical, building up brick by brick towards contemporary knowledge' (Neumann et al., 2002, p. 407), but this is a much less suitable model for geography. A focus on outcomes instead lends itself to big ideas and ambitiousness, which tends to be compatible with the important environmental and societal issues (and their interactions) that are the concern of the geographer. Aiming high, instead of proceeding incrementally, is more accommodating of different learning styles; moreover, it gives students the opportunity to understand and personalise threshold concepts (Fouberg, 2013), to ask geographic questions, and to be creative with the ways they discover, organise and process information to address them (Fouberg and Moseley, 2015). Trading off depth against breadth of understanding in a subject area becomes moot, when the focus is on achieving the most appropriate blend of both required to yield insight into an issue. Furthermore, there are advantages to breaking a linear progression: placing a bold idea front and centre can drive student engagement and give an enhanced sense of purpose to subsequent learning activities, which fill in context and finer levels of detail.

Pose Messy Problems

Researchers are familiar with uncertainty and with gaps in understanding, yet approaches in which the teacher declares s/he 'doesn't have all the answers' don't effectively model the research process and can be frustrating for students who are, understandably, anxious about assessment. However, challenging students with open-ended questions in constrained, scaffolded contexts can be a productive exercise in learning how to accrue understanding. Instead of 'I don't have all the answers' – which is at least as likely to be exasperating as inspiring – 'how are we going to find out?' is a constructive launch pad for a 'messy problem'. In the specific context of higher education, it also helps reinforce the notion that success in assessment depends at least partially on telling the assessor something the learner has not already been told by them. Therefore, messy-problem learning 'is not about sending individual students off into the unknown to fend for themselves intellectually but setting up structured opportunities for investigation that are infused with human interactions [and] peer learning' (Fung, 2017).

Expect Students to Talk, Write and Collaborate

Ceding control of a session can be fraught from the lecturer's perspective, and likewise, can be uncertain from the student's perspective; therefore, it requires careful structuring through a forum with defined actions and specific, accessible outcomes: a classic, SMART approach (Doran, 1981). Research-tutored learning occurs where students are able to develop their understanding of issues, and indeed the place and value of research, through discussion with peers and/or with a tutor (Healey and Jenkins, 2009). However, the expectation for students to talk, write and collaborate in a more structured forum sits naturally with the development of flipped-classroom activities (Lage et al., 2000; O'Flaherty and Phillips, 2015). Classroom-flipping stems from the documented effectiveness of student engagement in learning (Coates, 2006; Barkley, 2010). Bryson and Hand (2007) found that students were more engaged when teachers established inclusive learning environments, expected high results, and challenged students to reach higher levels of Bloom's taxonomy. Hockings et al. (2008) found that disengaged students reverted to superficial learning by copying out notes, focusing on fragmented facts and leaping to conclusions.

Flipped classrooms replace what was previously subject-content delivery with inter-activity designed to achieve the higher-order learning that was previously supposed to accrue through directed, independent study (Lage and Platt, 2000; Pierce and Fox, 2012). Classroom-flipping is therefore a blended approach, combining pre-session, knowledge-acquisition activity outside the classroom, facilitated by technology such as VLEs, followed by a face-to-face session which focuses on the analysis and evaluation of that knowledge, rather than the simple transfer of it (Lage et al., 2000). O'Flaherty and Phillips (2015) point out that the use of technology is important and indeed necessary, since not only are there now a wide range of online options for enhancing student learning, but the current millennial generation of students expects it. Activities utilised within face-to-face, flipped sessions may include; case-study presentations, team-based or panel or expert-led discussions, and quizzes to assess comprehension and provide formative feedback. These may be complemented by micro-lectures to support knowledge and understanding gaps (O'Flaherty and Phillips, 2015).

CASE STUDY

This overall approach can be exemplified by a third-year undergraduate module *Snow, Ice and Society*, originally conceived as a final-year research-led offering reflecting the lecturer's research interests. This module initially concerned studies of ice in its various forms (snow, glaciers, ice sheets, sea ice) and its interactions with the wider environment. While still serving its purpose over a decade later, fast-moving developments in the science of glaciology (especially progress in satellite remote sensing) were dictating frequent and laborious updates of lecture material. Unexpected natural events such as the catastrophic collapse of the Larsen B ice shelf, which was dramatised in the opening sequence of the blockbuster movie *The Day After Tomorrow* and which precipitated what has been described as a paradigm shift in glaciology (Mercer, 1978; Vaughan, 2008) also occurred. At the same time, however, the development of teaching technologies such as Virtual Learning Environments (VLEs; Stewart et al., 2011) and the advent of ubiquitous Wi-Fi and student internet-connected devices provided opportunities to access and process content in fresh ways. Thus, the emphasis of the module was shifted away from a content-driven, 'How do glaciers work? and What happens then?' approach, to a discovery-orientated, 'Why do glaciers matter?' approach, with an embedded concern for human impacts. Dolan and Collins' (2015) framework was mapped onto four main areas of concern in revising this module:

- delivery;
- pathways into literature;
- communication as an outcome;
- citizenship and choices.

Delivery

The original research-led approach tended to promote a rather conventional, unidirectional knowledge transfer. This was to a large extent necessitated by the need to explain fairly complex physical processes and relationships to geography undergraduates who often did not have science backgrounds. Significant time and effort were expended on describing and attempting to secure students' knowledge and understanding of concepts such as stress regimes and hydraulic pressure variation, and too little on discipline-specific understanding and on skills development. Thus, it became clear that it was necessary to find a way to promote active learning within a conventional classroom setting – literally, as the teaching on this module has always taken place within standard, tiered lecture theatres – so Dolan and Collins' (2015) suggestion that students should be expected to 'talk, write and collaborate' was adopted.

The challenge was therefore to provide a clearly-defined and accessible task that could yield a tangible outcome in a short period of time. Adapting a flipped-classroom approach, students are supplied prior to the session, via the university's VLE, with *composite reading bundles* (Box 15.1) covering appropriate aspects of a key issue: these are several packages of content, typically consisting of a peer-reviewed scientific paper, a popular science 'explainer' and a mainstream media article, all with as much rich media content as possible. This approach 'is more feasible than ever before at a time

BOX 15.1   EXAMPLE OF A COMPOSITE READING BUNDLE ON THE TOPIC OF RECENT DEVELOPMENTS IN THE UNDERSTANDING OF WEST ANTARCTIC ICE SHEET STABILITY

Popular media

'Western Antarctic ice sheet collapse has already begun, scientists warn'
https://www.theguardian.com/environment/2014/may/12/western-antarctic-ice-sheet-collapse-has-already-begun-scientists-warn

'This is what a Holy Shit Moment for global warming looks like'
https://www.motherjones.com/environment/2014/05/west-antarctic-ice-sheet-collapse/

Explainers

'Some key questions answered on the news West Antarctic glaciers are collapsing'
https://www.carbonbrief.org/some-key-questions-answered-on-the-news-west-antarctic-glaciers-are-collapsing

'Is the West Antarctic Ice Sheet collapsing?'
http://www.antarcticglaciers.org/2014/05/west-antarctic-ice-sheet-collapsing/

Peer-reviewed research papers

'Marine ice sheet collapse potentially under way for the Thwaites Glacier Basin, West Antarctica.'
Joughin, I. et al. (2014), *Science*, doi:10.1126/science.1249055.

'Widespread, rapid grounding line retreat of Pine Island, Thwaites, Smith, and Kohler glaciers, West Antarctica, from 1992 to 2011.'
Rignot, E. et al. (2014), *Geophysical Research Letters*, doi:10.1002/2014GL060140.

when it is possible for so many to reach into a pocket and pull out a mobile device which connects to 4.66 billion Web pages and rising' (Pappas, 2016). Students are given time within what would previously have been a conventional lecture to respond to and discuss questions raised and/or addressed by the materials in these bundles, and are then asked to contribute entries to a VLE database using a simple template, in order to construct a collective resource which all can access and search once they have made an entry. The approach is therefore an explicitly constructivist one (Jenkins, 2000). The lecturer is free to spend time interacting with students, encouraging active participation, giving formative feedback by answering queries and correcting misconceptions, and by helping to identify and address threshold concepts. The lecturer also reviews the database entries as they come in, drawing the attention of other students to their interest and value, and using them as prompts for discussion: they can be projected on-screen throughout the session, but the author remains anonymous to incentivise participation by less confident students.

Because the students are working with mixed online media, it is easy for them to discover new, hyper-linked material, supporting their development of autonomous, information-retrieval skills. It also makes it much easier for the lecturer to present fully up-to-date material in a fast-changing subject; continually updating lecture slides was time-consuming, but more to the point tended to draw focus too often into specific details rather than big ideas and key messages. As a result, it was easy for lecture material to become fragmented, and for lectures to become exercises in public speed-reading. PowerPoint slides now focus on key ideas and not detailed content, enabling the lecturer to focus on drawing out important messages. If necessary or appropriate, detailed notes can always be inserted into the notes pane of a PowerPoint slide uploaded to the VLE. Without following a bullet-point script, the lecturer is freer to be more discursive, flexible and responsive; in short, to be more natural (maybe even to tell an anecdote or a joke).

Pathways Into Literature

A singular challenge for learning and teaching in geography is how students can be supported to evaluate information from a potentially diverse range of specialisms which may span part or all of the humanities, social sciences and physical sciences, and may employ qualitative and/or quantitative analytical methods. The approach taken here is to introduce reading specific to a particular topic via a hierarchy of sources, of increasing speciality, from a popular media source, through an 'explainer' from a reliable online source, possibly to a peer-reviewed summary paper, but ultimately to a peer-reviewed paper discussing original results relevant to the topic (Box 15.1).

This approach gives students a route into understanding the importance of contemporary research results without becoming bogged down in the specific and potentially intimidating details of complex research methods. Reliable comment and analysis is now available from scholars and scientists in a variety of online sources, offering insights and updates more frequently and more accessibly than research journals. Part of the purpose of this approach is to help students become accustomed to making constructive use of such sources. There is understandable scepticism about online material, and indeed there are pitfalls to using it. However, navigating the online world and discriminating reliable and valuable sources from unreliable and worthless ones are critical skills in contemporary work and life, and very much worth developing in the higher education context. Two examples of very positive online sources are *The Conversation* and *Carbon Brief* (see Useful Resources section). The former describes itself as 'an independent source of news and views, sourced from the academic and research community and delivered direct to the public'. The latter states that it covers 'the latest developments in climate science, climate policy and energy policy. We specialise in clear, data-driven articles and graphics to help improve the understanding of climate change, both in terms of the science and the policy response. We publish a wide range of content, including science explainers, interviews, analysis and factchecks'.

Similarly, the UK Parliamentary Office of Science and Technology (POST) issues 'POST notes', which provide 'balanced and accessible overviews of research from across the biological, physical and social sciences, and engineering and technology . . . based on reviews of the research literature and interviews with stakeholders from across academia, industry, government and the third sector; they are peer reviewed by external experts' (see Useful Resources). Sources of this kind mediate research in a reliable way, with content that is driven by researchers themselves, and underpinned by peer-review, but pitched beyond disciplinary silos. Therefore, they offer pathways into the literature which are up to date and accessible, helping meet some of the key requirements of a current, research-informed curriculum. Moreover, they help foster 'skills of analysis, evaluation, and synthesis [which] will become the hallmarks of a good education, just as absorption of a body of knowledge once was' (Boyer Commission, 1998, p. 20).

Communication as an Outcome

Designing a module backwards forces a greater emphasis on what enduring knowledge, skills and understanding students really need in the context of their geography programme, and on how key skills can be practised in all modules, not simply research-oriented ones. Students need to be able to make sense of a world of rapid environmental and societal change. Moreover, they need to make sense of a world which is intensively explored and where data have become so abundant that the critical task now at hand could be argued to be not generating new data but synthesising and interpreting existing data. This is a key, transferrable skill in geography, and a demonstrable facility that boosts employability (CBI and NUS, 2011). A corollary of unprecedented global change and a world of superabundant information is an imperative to communicate with clarity and effectiveness (Corner et al., 2018), and consequently it is appropriate that this is assessed. Biggs's theory of constructive alignment (Biggs and Tang, 2011) suggests that assessment needs to be more closely associated with learning activities than it is in a traditional lecture and examination process (see Chapter 27 in this volume by Jenny Hill and Nancy Worth), so for *Snow, Ice and Society*, summative coursework reflects the constructivist approach of classroom delivery. Students are asked to discover their own contemporary news story relevant to the module (Box 15.2). This approach is also consistent with the model of a cycle of flipped-classroom learning, which concludes with 'learners [getting] to demonstrate what they learned and apply the material in a way that makes sense to them' through creating personalised projects (Gerstein, 2012). The news story could be a new scientific result, a specific event, or some development in an ongoing situation, as long as it satisfies two common themes: first, that it reflects environmental change affecting and/ or affected by snow and/or ice; second, that there is some kind of material consequence for human society. The students are then requested to represent their chosen story in three different, but supporting, ways (Box 15.2): as a tweet that summarises the story, and should capture its essence in a way that intrigues the reader, includes a relevant URL and uses suitable #hashtags; as a self-contained, one-page 'explainer' suitable for a curious, general layperson; and as a two-page 'deeper analysis' suitable for someone who has a good knowledge and understanding of the climate and environmental change, but is not a snow/ice specialist. This tiered approach diversifies the coursework activity manageably and allows the lecturer to feedback broadly, and therefore with transferable relevance, on the key themes of the module and approaches to communication. While the coursework is summative in this case study, a formative version could equally be introduced to build upon the VLE database class resource.

Citizenship and Choices

Very few students taking the *Snow Ice and Society* module will actually follow careers in glaciology; it has happened, but it is of course exceptional. But whatever occupation they ultimately pursue, these students will still be citizens of the world: a world of warming temperatures and rapidly-diminishing snow and ice. This will, undoubtedly, increasingly

BOX 15.2   COURSEWORK INSTRUCTIONS FOR THE CASE-STUDY MODULE

Case-study coursework

Select a news story relevant to *Snow, Ice and Society*. This could be anything you find interesting – a new scientific result, a specific event, some development in or description of an ongoing situation – as long as it has two common themes:

1.   environmental change affecting and/or affected by snow and/or glaciers/ice sheets;
2.   as a result of (1), some effect on human society: this could be very immediate (for example, drought, floods) or it could be less so, but still significant (for example, sea-level rise).

The only further condition is that your news story must include in some way material from a peer-reviewed scientific paper. This may be the origin of the story, for example, if a group of scientific researchers have made a new discovery which gathers media attention, or it may be used as supporting background to the story, for example, if an event such as a glacier-related flood has occurred and this is subsequently explained with reference to research on glacier change in the area affected.

You have 3 pages to represent your chosen story in 3 different, but supporting, ways:

1. Write a **Tweet** that summarises the story: that's 140 characters or less, including spaces. Use this as the title of your coursework. The Tweet should be short and capture the essence of the story in a way that makes the reader want to find out more. So, it should encapsulate the main result/effect/event (whatever it is you've chosen) in a concise, to-the-point but intriguing way. Include a relevant link (you should use a link-shorterner like bitly.com or tinyurl.com to save characters). Please also use hashtags (#) to emphasise key words. For example:

Williams, A.P., Seager, R., Abatzoglou, J., Cook, B., Smerdon, J., Cook, E. (2015), Contribution of anthropogenic warming to California drought during 2012–2014, *Geophysical Research Letters*, 42, pp. 6819–6828, doi:10.1002/2015GL064924.

describes science results relevant to the Californian drought crisis. A tweet about it could be: *Human-made #globalwarming 'substantially' increases likelihood of extreme #Californian #drought, say scientists* http://tinyurl.com/oafre3c (138 characters).

2. A one-side **Explainer** suitable for a curious general layperson. Include one figure (which can be appended, so it doesn't count in your 1-side limit). This part shouldn't include any references, it should be self-contained.

3. A two-side **Deeper Analysis** suitable for someone who has a good knowledge and understanding of the climate and environmental change, but just happens not to be a snow/ice specialist. Include two figures, one of which should be a map (the figures can also be appended, so they don't count in your 2-side limit). This part should be referenced as normal (references also don't count towards your page limit).

I'm looking for evidence that you can use your skill and judgement to find an interesting snow and ice story with a societal angle, that you can sum it up in an insightful nutshell (the *Tweet-title*), that you're able to communicate the basic essence of it clearly to someone who isn't an expert (the *Explainer*), and that you can show you really understand what's going on at a more detailed level (the *Deeper Analysis*).

Note: The 140-character tweet length was discussed with and preferred by students.

stress water resources and threaten coastlines in both the developed and developing worlds during their lifetimes (IPCC, 2014). The UK Quality Assurance Agency for Higher Education's benchmark statement for geography sets out standards and expectations for the subject and declares that 'geographical knowledge and understanding inform concern about the Earth and its people' (QAA, 2014), which speaks to the broader purpose of learning: 'Education is not a set of technicalities; it embodies an intellectual and ethical position' (Fung, 2017, p. 15). A very important part of the role of the teacher is to help prepare students for participation in a global society, not only as an employee, but as a citizen, by enabling them to develop awareness of the consequences of their actions, and those of others, and the ability to evaluate the consequences of the choices we all make. Ethical subject-hood, with respect to the impacts of geographical processes, has been proposed as a key geocapability: a learning outcome that extends beyond content and skills to foster a distinctively geographical approach to global issues (Walkington et al., 2018). This aligns with the position of the European Forum for Enhanced Collaboration in Teaching (EFFECT): 'The higher education learning experience nurtures and enables the development of learners as active and responsible citizens, critical thinkers, problem solvers, equipped for life-long learning' (EFFECT, 2017, p. 1). Through a curriculum which is research-informed, up to date, focused on societal impacts and implicitly concerned with communication, such development is empowered.

Quantitative student evaluations of this module have hardly changed at all over 12 years (consistently above 4/5). Given the radical transformation that has taken place in higher education during the same time, the evaluations strongly suggest that the changing approach described in this case study has been successful in meeting changing student expectations. Qualitative feedback seems to reflect this interpretation, with comments increasingly focused on specific, perceived benefits of the assessment, the way it is personalised, supported by pathways into the literature, and how it addresses communication; for example:

- *'The coursework allows you to choose and explore own ideas that you are interested in.'*
- *'I was a big fan of the self-made reading list.'*
- *'Shared learning exercises are useful as well, makes it more interactive and interesting.'*
- *'I really enjoyed the coursework aspect of the module because it was different to other pieces of work I have been assigned in the past. It was not merely a task of writing just an essay or report on a specific question but one that involved researching a contemporary . . . topic that impacts on society and then writing about this in more accessible forms.'*
- *'The aims of the coursework were excellent, it tested our abilities which have not been tested before in any coursework so far at university, and I definitely acquired a new skill in the process.'*

CONCLUSION

The challenge of maintaining an up-to-date research-informed curriculum and working more collaboratively with students is an opportunity for active learning and the development of critical skills in the evaluation of varied sources. The injunctions of Dolan and Collins (2015) to 'design a module backwards', 'aim high', 'pose messy problems' and 'expect students to talk, write and collaborate' were mapped on to a major module revision which greatly de-emphasised content delivery, instead using a flipped-classroom approach for students to generate shared learning resources on ambitious and engaging issues. As a synthesising discipline, geography has much to gain from developing students' abilities in finding pathways into specialist literatures (progressing from the general to the specific) and in communicating the complexity found there in an accessible manner to diverse audiences (progressing from the specific to the general). The inherent flexibility of this constructivist approach, navigating into deeper levels of detail from an overview, is very transferable. By guiding students into the role of researchers (through content discovery and communication), teachers can foster co-production in the learning process, they can promote an enhanced sense of ownership of knowledge and understanding among learners, and also encourage greater engagement by tackling big ideas directly. Institutional VLEs can provide tools which facilitate this process, though free and flexible alternatives are widely available online (see Useful Resources section). Assessment may be aligned with this approach and personalised by inviting students, appropriately supported, to pursue ideas they have identified themselves. From the perspective of the teacher, the research-teaching nexus can be strengthened, and there is potential for a greater focus on constructive alignment and pedagogy (Biggs and Tang, 2011), rather than simply on content updating, along with the prospect of more rewarding classroom time spent working at the higher levels of Bloom's taxonomy.

USEFUL RESOURCES

Online Sources with Accessible Introductions to Physical Geography Issues

- Carbon Brief. Accessed from:
  http://www.carbonbrief.org/.
- The Conversation. Accessed from:
  theconversation.com/uk/.
- Parliamentary Office of Science and Technology (POST) notes. Accessed from:
  http://www.parliament.uk/mps-lords-and-offices/offices/bicameral/post/publica
  tions/postnotes/.

Online Collaboration Tools that Provide Alternatives to Institutional VLEs

The suggestions below all offer cross-platform working, with at least basic versions that are free of charge.

- *Pinup.com* (http://pinup.com) offers virtual pinboards to which students with a tutor-allocated URL can contribute and view notes collectively and collaboratively.
- *Padlet* (http://padlet.com/) provides more flexible, template-based virtual pinboards, along with rich multimedia capability, with flexible collaboration and sharing functionality.
- *Evernote* (http://evernote.com/) is a popular note-taking and organising application

that has sharing features in its basic version or full team-working capability in its premium versions.

- *WordPress* (http://wordpress.com/) is primarily a blogging and website creation/ management tool but has team-working and commenting features that enable collaboration and discussion.
- The reference management software *Mendeley* (https://www.mendeley.com/) allows users to create and share searchable reading lists and provides a group facility to discuss them.

REFERENCES

Barkley, E. (2010) *Student Engagement Techniques: A Handbook for College Faculty*. San Francisco, CA: Jossey-Bass.

Barnett, R. (1990) *The Idea of Higher Education*. Buckingham: Open University Press.

Bergmann, J. and Sams, A. (2012) *Flip Your Classroom: Reach Every Student in Every Class Every Day*. Eugene, Oregon; Arlington, Virginia: International Society for Technology in Education.

Biggs, J. and Tang, C. (2011) *Teaching for Quality Learning at University*. Fourth Edition. Buckingham: Open University Press/Society for Research into Higher Education.

Bloom, B.S. (1994), 'Reflections on the development and use of the taxonomy', in Rehage, K., Anderson, L. and Sosniak, L. (eds), *Bloom's Taxonomy: A Forty-Year Retrospective*. Yearbook of the National Society for the Study of Education 93. Chicago: National Society for the Study of Education.

Blunt, A. (2009) 'Geography and the humanities tradition', in Holloway, S., Rice, S. and Valentine, G. (eds), *Key Concepts in Geography*. Second Edition. London: Sage.

Boyer Commission on Educating Undergraduates in the Research University (1998) *Reinventing Undergraduate Education: A Blueprint for America's Research Universities*. Stony Brook, NY: State University of New York–Stony Brook.

Bryson, C. and Hand, L. (2007) 'The role of engagement in inspiring teaching and learning', *Innovations in Education and Teaching International*, 44(4), pp. 349–362.

Coates, H. (2006) *STUDENT engagement in Campus-Based and Online Education: University Connections*. London: Routledge.

Confederation of British Industry and the National Union of Students (2011) *Working Towards Your Future – Making the Most of Your Time in Higher Education*. London: CBI.

Corner, A., Shaw, C. and Clarke, J. (2018) *Principles for Effective Communication and Public Engagement on Climate Change: A Handbook for IPCC Authors*. Oxford: Climate Outreach.

Day, T. (2012) 'Undergraduate teaching and learning in physical geography', *Progress in Physical Geography*, 36, pp. 305–332.

Dolan, E. and Collins, J. (2015) 'We must teach more effectively: here are four ways to get started', *Molecular Biology of the Cell*, 26, pp. 2151–2155.

Doran, G. (1981) 'There's a S.M.A.R.T. way to write management's goals and objectives', *Management Review. AMA FORUM*, 70(11), pp. 35–36.

European Forum for Enhanced Collaboration in Teaching (EFFECT) (2017), *Enhancing the Education Mission of European Universities: A Proactive Response to Change*. Brussels: European University Association. http://eua.be/Libraries/default-document-library/web_effect-principles-one-pager16102017.pdf.

Fenneman, N. (2009) 'The circumference of geography', *Annals of the Association of American Geographers*, 9(1), pp. 3–11.

Fouberg, E. (2013) '"The world is no longer flat to me": student perceptions of threshold concepts in world regional geography', *Journal of Geography in Higher Education*, 37, pp. 65–75.

Fouberg, E. and Moseley, W. (2015) *Understanding World Regional Geography*. New York: Wiley.

Fung, D. (2017) *A Connected Curriculum for Higher Education*. London: UCL Press.

Gerstein, J. (2012) *Flipped Classroom: The Full Picture for Higher Education*. User-generated education web page 5 May. Available from: usergeneratededucation.wordpress.com/2012/05/15/flipped-classroom-the-full-picture-for-higher-education/ (accessed 01 June 2018).

Heffron, S. and Downs, R. (eds) (2012) *Geography for Life: The National Geography Standards*, Second Edition. Washington, DC: Geography Education Implementation Project (GENIP).

Healey, M. and Jenkins, A. (2009) *Developing Undergraduate Research*. HEA Publication. Available from: http://www.heacademy.ac.uk/assets/York/documents/resources/publications/DevelopingUndergraduate_Final.pdf.

Hockings, C., Cooke, S., Yamashita, H., McGinty, S. and Bowl, M. (2008) 'Switched off? A study of disengagement among computing students at two universities', *Research Papers in Education*, 23(2), pp. 191–201.

IPCC (2014) *Climate Change 2014: Synthesis Report. Contribution of Working Groups I, II and III to the Fifth Assessment Report of the Intergovernmental Panel on Climate Change* (Core Writing Team, R.K. Pachauri and L.A. Meyer, eds). Geneva, Switzerland: IPCC, pp. 1–151.

Jenkins, E.W. (2000) 'Research in science education: time for a health check?', *Studies in Science Education*, 35(1), pp. 1–25.

Johnston, R. (2009) 'Geography and the social science tradition', in Holloway, S., Rice, S. and Valentine, G. (eds), *Key Concepts in Geography*. Second Edition. London: Sage.

Joughin, I., Smith, B. and Medley, B. (2014) 'Marine ice sheet collapse potentially under way for the Thwaites Glacier Basin, West Antarctica', *Science*, 344(6185), pp. 735–738.

Lage, M. and Platt, G. (2000) 'The internet and the inverted classroom', *Journal of Economic Education*, 31(1), p. 11.

Lage, M., Platt, G. and Treglia, M. (2000), 'Inverting the classroom: a gateway to creating an inclusive learning environment', *Journal of Economic Education*, 31, pp. 30–43.

Maunder, R. (2015) 'Working with students as partners in pedagogic research: staff and student experiences of participating in an institutional bursary scheme', *Journal of Educational Innovation, Partnership and Change*, 1(1), pp. 1–7.

Mercer, J. (1978) 'West Antarctic ice sheet and CO_2 greenhouse effect: a threat of disaster', *Nature*, 27, pp. 321–325.

Neumann, R., Parry, S. and Becher, T. (2002) 'Teaching and learning in their disciplinary contexts: a conceptual analysis', *Studies in Higher Education*, 27(4), pp. 405–417.

Noddings, N. (1995) *Philosophy of Education*. Colorado: Westview.

O'Flaherty, J. and Phillips, C. (2015) 'The use of flipped classrooms in higher education: a scoping review', *Internet and Higher Education*, 25, pp. 85–95.

Pappas, S. (2016) 'How big is the internet, really?' *Live Science*, 18 March 2016. http://www.livescience.com/54094-how-big-is-the-internet.html.

Pierce, R. and Fox, J. (2012) 'Instructional design and assessment: vodcasts and active-learning exercises in a "flipped classroom" model of a renal pharmacotherapy module', *American Journal of Pharmaceutical Education*, 76(10), pp. 1–5.

Pring, R. (2001) 'Education as a moral practice', *Journal of Moral Education*, 30, pp. 101–112.

Quality Assurance Agency for Higher Education (QAA) (2014) *Subject Benchmark Statement. Geography*. Gloucester: QAA.

Richards, K. (2009) 'Geography and the physical science tradition', in Holloway, S., Rice, S. and Valentine, G. (eds), *Key Concepts in Geography*. Second Edition. London: Sage.

Rignot, E., Mouginot, J., Morlighem, M., Seroussi, H. and Scheuchl, B. (2014) 'Widespread, rapid grounding line retreat of Pine Island, Thwaites, Smith, and Kohler glaciers, West Antarctica, from 1992 to 2011', *Geophysical Research Letters*, 41(10), 3502–3509.

Stewart, M., Stott, T. and Nuttall, A. (2011) 'Student engagement patterns over the duration of Level 1 and Level 3 geography modules: influences on student attendance, performance and use of online resources', *Journal of Geography in Higher Education*, 35(1), pp. 47–65.

Vaughan, D. (2008) 'West Antarctic Ice Sheet collapse – the fall and rise of a paradigm', *Climatic Change*, 91, pp. 65–79.

Walkington, H., Dyer, S., Solem, M., Haigh, M. and Waddington, S. (2018) 'A capabilities approach to higher education: geocapabilities and implications for geography curricula', *Journal of Geography in Higher Education*, 42(1), pp. 7–24.

16. Conveying geographic concepts through issues-based inquiry

Phil Klein, Karen Barton, Jessica Salo, Jieun Lee and Timothy Vowles

INTRODUCTION

This chapter offers suggestions for instructors for incorporating structured inquiry activities into courses to help improve students' grasp of geographic concepts. Deep conceptual knowledge is an important building block toward construction of a set of geographic capabilities for students (Walkington et al., 2018). In this chapter, we use the term *concepts* to refer to specific disciplinary terminology, including those terms representing more complex geographic processes and the discipline's essential perspectives. The activities described here employ a pedagogy of *guided issues-based inquiry*. These are brief activities, some of which can be completed within a single class as an exercise. Each utilizes diverse forms of geographic data as the basis for student exploration and discovery. In so doing, they follow a more constructivist pedagogic vision than teacher-centered information transmission. While bearing similarity in spirit to project- or problem-based learning (see Pawson et al., 2006 and Chapter 24 in this volume by Pawson and Poskitt), the activities here are not focused on detailed analysis or resolution of a single geographic problem. Guided, issues-based inquiry activities are best seen as supplements to expository lectures and other methods, a way of introducing or advancing student understanding of foundational and more advanced geographic concepts.

The chapter begins with an overview of the importance of teaching and learning disciplinary concepts. We then briefly summarize salient points about inquiry-based teaching, describing a model of guided, issues-based inquiry pedagogy. A central point of this chapter is that inquiry activities that build student comprehension should build from their local experience. Finally, we provide examples of five inquiry-oriented activities used by geography faculty at the University of Northern Colorado, a mid-sized, public university. We close by considering how using inquiry activities to supplement presentation of disciplinary concepts may foster a more powerful form of geographic knowledge.

DISCIPLINARY CONCEPT KNOWLEDGE

For a student in any discipline, part of becoming a practitioner is developing what Howard Gardner (1999) referred to as 'the disciplined mind'. This is a deliberate pun, combining a traditional aim of higher education – to sharpen students' critical-thinking abilities – with the specific goal of constructing students' expertise within a particular field. Writing in the context of history education, Downey and Long (2016, p. 6) noted that 'for students to be knowledgeable in any particular field, they must know how those who work in that area think as well as understand the subject-matter content that is the product of that thinking'. Emerging recently within geography education is the consideration of geography as a form of 'powerful' knowledge (Lambert et al., 2015). This extends the conceptualization of 'thinking like a geographer' beyond outcomes-based competencies, such as cognition of its content and abilities with its analytical tools. To think geographically also incorporates an array of affective learning outcomes. Following Hanvey's (1975) notion of a 'global perspective', learning geography may help one better appreciate not only the world system but also one's place in that system (Klein et al., 2014). Geography education can also help develop in students a set of *capabilities* that help contribute to their perceptions of well-being and self-efficacy. Walkington and her colleagues (2018, p. 14) identified five such geocapabilities as outcomes for geography students, including developing their 'geographical imagination . . . the capability to see and think like a geographer'. Accomplishing this means learning to think across multiple scales and to examine connections among diverse variables, a perspective that shapes the way the geographer conceives of and addresses problems. Developing a geographical perspective enables students to analyze how spatial processes both create unique localities in particular places and simultaneously expose those places to changes reflecting their connections with other places.

At the foundation of this edifice of desirable learning outcomes, of competencies and capabilities, is acquiring the very language of the discipline: the concepts around which the subject-matter content is structured. The term *concept* is, itself, a concept, with several dimensions. It is a noun, used to denote a generalized mental construct about some phenomenon, a notion defined by classifying under that term a set of essential particulars, called attributes, shared by instances of that term. The concept noun may also embody a set of relationships that are expected to occur in a general process or, beyond that, be shorthand for the complex ways of thinking that lie at the very heart of a discipline's perspective. Teaching concepts effectively involves four elements (Tennyson and Cocchiarella, 1986; Toumasis, 1995): (1) its *definition*, a general statement that summarizes the structure of the concept's attributes; (2) expository *examples* that systematically organize and delimit the essential attributes embedded in the concept; (3) guided *inquiry* that refines student comprehension of the concept through questions, to differentiate the concept from its related terms and non-examples; and (4) analysis of the *significance or importance* of the concept through exploration of further examples or connections to related concepts.

Within geography, Gersmehl (2014) offered a useful 'three-strand' model for placing knowledge of concepts within the goals of geographic education. In the model, each strand is woven together to form a consistent and coherent body of knowledge. Conceptual knowledge is evident in each of these strands. First, concepts include discipline-specific terms, part of the basic language of geography along with the images of places that geographical study provides. In this simplest sense, a concept may be a word used to convey a set of similar circumstances. These may be relatively straightforward, invented or borrowed by geographers to describe a common feature (for instance, *megalopolis, rain shadow* or *urban heat island*). These might, for example, comprise the list of terms in a textbook glossary. Such concepts may be effectively conveyed through succinct definitions and photographs that show examples of the term.

The second strand of this model is analysis; for this, geographers create concepts to denote more complex spatial processes. In this analytical strand of the model, concepts are geography's 'big ideas'. Some examples might include *migration, nation, demographic transition,* or *climate change.* Understanding these enables one to evaluate the significance of spatial processes in shaping human and physical landscapes. That outcome – evaluation – is Gersmehl's third strand. Analytical concepts are, in the terminology of Meyer and Land (2003), the discipline's 'core' concepts, the building blocks learners need to comprehend spatial relationships. Defining, analyzing, and evaluating complex concepts requires some engagement with the contested or contextual nature of what may at first glance seem to be innocuous words. Within the USA, for instance, most undergraduates initially understand the term 'state' to refer to the 50 smaller units of political organization that comprise the country rather than how *state* is more commonly used in political geographic studies. Teaching the simplest type of concepts fits well with expository teaching, but to communicate the relationships embedded in more complex concepts requires further exploration and reiteration.

Slinger (2011) identified three types of conceptual change, ranging from basic changes related to knowledge of core concepts (for example learning to identify and differentiate among related terms), through what he called 'disciplinary and procedural' conceptual changes. The latter two reflect incorporation of discipline-specific perspectives and methods into the learner's mental constructs. Acquiring this more complex conceptual framework enables the novice geographer to undertake a 'structured exploration of place', another of the geocapabilities identified by Walkington et al. (2018). These deeper concepts for geography include *place, space, interactions, sustainability, change,* and *scale* (Maude, 2013).

These kinds of nouns, called 'threshold concepts', are at a yet deeper level of complexity, and thus more challenging to teach, but they embody the uniqueness of the geographic perspective (see Chapter 6 in this volume by Erin Fouberg). Meyer and Land (2003, p. 1) describe a 'threshold concept . . . as akin to a portal, opening up a new and previously inaccessible way of thinking about something'. Learning threshold concepts enables one to identify, formulate, and analyze problems within a particular disciplinary framework. Threshold concepts, in contrast to 'core concepts', represent transformational learning. Once these conceptual thresholds are crossed, learners undergo a shift in their perspective, their way of thinking about the world. Such shifts permanently alter learners' perspectives and help them recognize previously hidden relationships among related concepts. But such learning can also be 'troublesome', because threshold concepts may challenge existing mental constructs (Meyer and Land, 2003). Geographers have considered the threshold concepts that could help structure curricula for elementary and secondary geography and for GIS (Slinger, 2011; Srivastava, 2013; Enser, 2017). Teaching these involves more than simple textbook-style definitions or isolated examples. As will be discussed later, inquiry-based learning is a tool that can help overcome students' preexisting misconceptions to build new conceptual frameworks.

To summarize, learning geographic concepts is an essential building block toward building a student's deeper disciplinary awareness. What the optimal sequence is for teaching those building blocks remains a matter for investigation. In the USA, the 'road map' for geographic literacy calls for initiatives to study such 'learning progressions' (Bednarz et al., 2013). More systematic analysis of how students best learn geographic concepts (for example, Larsen and Harrington, 2016) may yield deeper understanding of how geography education can better develop students' conceptual frameworks. We turn now to an overview of inquiry teaching, which is a long-established strategy for developing a stronger conceptual framework among geography students.

INQUIRY-BASED TEACHING AND LEARNING

Inquiry pedagogy is a broad term, encompassing a range of approaches with origins in science and mathematics education (Schwab, 1966). It is rooted in the pragmatic and instrumentalist approach to education advocated by John Dewey (1938), in which students' experiences are recognized as the foundation for learning. As summarized by Tillman et al. (2017, p. 386), 'every experience enacted modifies the person who acts and ... this modification affects the quality of subsequent experiences'. Spronken-Smith and her colleagues (2008) provided a thorough introduction to the use of inquiry (or *enquiry*) within geography education. They classified inquiry-based learning (IBL) as a subset of the broader notion of *active learning*, in that it is student- rather than teacher-centered (see also Klein, 2003). Inquiry pedagogy is question-driven, with the goal of challenging students to refine and develop their understanding of concepts and exercise of skills through guided practice activities (Slater, 1982). The goal is to inspire curiosity in students: a desire to answer questions, getting them to appreciate that, even though the process of finding answers is tentative (maybe even a little 'messy') and leads to more questions, the journey of inquiry is inherently worthwhile (Mohan, 2018, p. 3). The value of inquiry is recognized in precollegiate curriculum frameworks used in both England's National Curriculum (Department for Education 2013) and the USA's National Geography Standards and C3 Social Studies Framework (Heffron and Downs, 2012; NCSS, 2013).

In contrast to pedagogy based on the direct transmission of information from expert (instructor) to novice (student), inquiry approaches rely on a constructivist model of learning (Pawson et al., 2006; Walkington et al., 2018). Constructivists view the acquisition of new knowledge as additions to preexisting mental constructs ('schemata'), unique to each individual learner, based on the collectivity of lived experiences that she or he brings to the classroom setting. The value of discovery-based learning for helping students shape new conceptions is well established in science education; indeed, Taba (1963) traced roots of that idea back to the early 1900s. Writing about inquiry within science education, Wheatley (1991, p. 10) offered that 'knowledge is not disembodied but is intimately related to the action and experience of a learner – it is always contextual and never separated from the knower'. Inquiry is an inductive approach to learning (Walkington et al., 2018), in which students process information about a topic and discover for themselves key concepts or generalizations. Done well, inquiry can help students challenge their preconceptions, develop empathy, and clarify their own values about a topic (Slater, 1982).

Frances Slater (1982) advanced a model of geographic inquiry that begins with a focused inquiry question, around which specific discovery activities are developed that lead students to the formulation of generalizations as major learning outcomes. Her inquiry model stressed the value of building activities using real data and situations. This model also inspired the structure used in major inquiry-materials projects aimed at K-12 education in the USA in the 1990s (Gersmehl and Young, 1992; Hill et al., 1995). Hill's (1990) adaptation of Slater's work is shown in Figure 16.1; this model, which Hill called

```
┌──────────────────────────────────────────────────┐
│          Goals (Desired Learning Outcomes)         │
│                         │                          │
│                         ▼                          │
│                       Issues                       │
│                         │                          │
│                         ▼                          │
│               Geographic Questions                 │
│                         │                          │
│                         ▼                          │
│   Critical Thinking → Data ← Procedural Skills     │
│                         │                          │
│                         ▼                          │
│           Generalizations (Actual Outcomes)        │
│                         │                          │
│                         ▼                          │
│                     Assessment                     │
└──────────────────────────────────────────────────┘
```

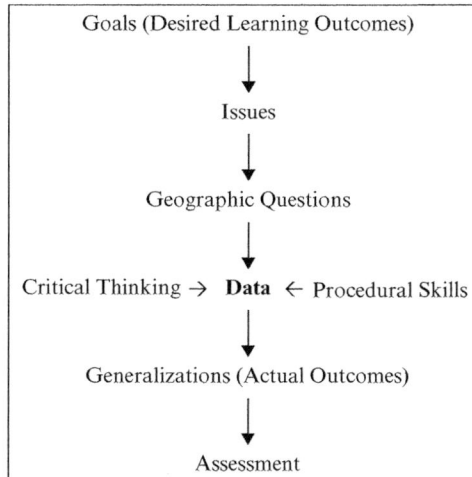

Source: Adapted from Hill (1990), as modified from Slater (1982).

Figure 16.1   Model for issues-based inquiry

issues-based inquiry, has also been called the 'case method' for teaching geography (Grant, 1997). Following Slater's approach, the data and examples in issues-based inquiry are real, not hypothetical. *Issues-based* refers to a focus on a particular issue, such as migration, development, or sustainable agriculture, developed through investigation and analysis of the issue's occurrence in specific places (the case study). Hill's (1990) formulation of what makes an issue 'geographic' is that it occurs in multiple places and at multiple scales; has long-term or perennial status; can be analyzed with diverse forms of spatial data; and that the nature of its occurrence varies according to local site and situation factors. Thus, issues-based inquiry is distinctly place-based, using case studies of various lengths as the focal point for investigation.

Hill's (1990) adaptation situates Slater's inquiry process within a set of defined goals. These can range from broad learning outcomes for an entire course, such as gaining deeper understanding of threshold concepts, to narrower outcomes, such as understanding a specific core concept. Analysis of the case-based issue provides the inquiry question, while analysis of geographic data germane to that place and issue serves as the locus of exploration and discovery. In data analysis, the student exercises both procedural skills of working with data, cognitive skills required to identify and analyze spatial relationships (Jo and Bednarz, 2009; Gersmehl, 2014), and critical-thinking about the nature of the data itself. The model of inquiry leads to tentative answers to the original inquiry questions. It's a cycle, so those answers (should) lead to new questions. Assessment of those outcomes leads to further inquiry, or perhaps a reformulation of the process, to assist students in reaching the outcomes. In inquiry, the role of the instructor is as a facilitator and guide, rather than the source of all answers. However, in Hill's (1990) inquiry model, the instructor acts as a rather firm guide, defining the questions, specifying the desired learning outcomes, and providing the data to be analyzed, rather than having students acquire it. This is *structured inquiry*, not free, open-ended, inquiry.

Crucially, the data utilized may take a variety of forms. Maps, obviously, are essential components, particularly in order to develop student awareness of the cognitive elements of spatial thinking through guided practice (for instance, see activities in Gersmehl, 2014). Tabular spatial data can also be effectively employed as data sources. For example, the wealth of demographic and socioeconomic data available on the internet can be the crux of activities designed to familiarize students with complex conceptual relationships like the demographic transition model or the international spatial division of labor. News and feature stories, photos, and first-person accounts are also rich data sources.

In terms of instructional design, an inquiry lesson may reverse the sequence of an expository concept presentation, such as the four-step process of Tennyson and Cocchiarella (1986) mentioned previously. In the inquiry sequence, the data-based activity *precedes* the explanation of the concept and exploration of its significance. Through working with data, students come to formulate a clearer understanding of the conceptual relationships. The method does, however, require more time than a lecture. The instructor needs to allow students adequate time to make the key discoveries and conceptual connections. Having students work in small groups, whilst helping each other construct understanding of relevant concepts and connections can facilitate this. The benefit of spending the extra time on inquiry comes from its distinct advantage of empowering students to learn key ideas through discovery, collaboration, and reinforcement. Group assignments can be simple or more elaborate. For example, the CGGE project (Solem et al., 2010) has students in two countries examine common issues, such as migration or national identity, collaboratively. The effort occurs simultaneously at two scales, with local groups at each university teamed with a student group from the other university. Evaluations suggested that groups were better able to compare and contrast the issues if they began by analyzing local and familiar cases before tackling the comparisons with team partners in other countries (Klein and Solem, 2008).

Inquiry-based learning need not be structured around analysis and resolution of a single complex case study. It can also be employed in more narrowly scaled, briefer activities. We turn now to description of several inquiry-oriented activities to illustrate the variety of possible approaches for teaching concepts to geography undergraduates. They range from short reading and mapping assignments to more involved role-plays. Other forms of inquiry illuminate how conceptual knowledge helps students appreciate local landscapes or the workplace requirements of professional geographers.

EXAMPLES OF LOCALLY-FOCUSED INQUIRY ACTIVITIES

It is a central tenet of geography that 'place' matters (Massey 1994). Far from being a rigid phenomenon with a litany of static characteristics, *places* are ever-evolving complexes of dynamic interactions, featuring actors engaged in their own personal geographies who intersect at that site at that moment. Educational activities occur in this milieu. Each classroom is situated within its particular nexus of geographic 'conditions and connections' (to use Gersmehl's helpful 2014 terminology). Universities are – fully in the geographic sense – *places*: situated within their own specific environmental, socioeconomic, and political contexts (Brasher et al., 2017). In precollegiate settings, mixed-methods research (for example, Goodlad, 1984; Klein, 1995) showed that the

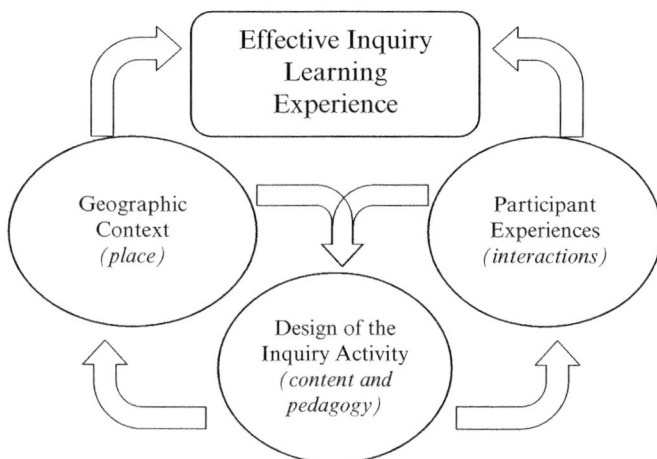

Figure 16.2   Place-based model of effective inquiry pedagogy

effectiveness of a learning activity depends on three factors, represented in Figure 16.2 above. Achieving designated learning outcomes depends on the activity's *content and pedagogical delivery* as mediated by *the setting* in which the learning activity takes place. Consider the latter factor itself as having two dimensions: the lived experiences and *interactions* of the students (among themselves and with the instructor) and the broader geographic *context* of the institution. The outer arrows illustrate the importance of these two dimensions, whatever the activity's content (in this case, its conceptual structure), and however the instructor determines to teach it (discussions, role-plays, or other strategies to engage students). For higher education, the factors of geographic context and participant experiences may be even more critical. College students arrive from diverse places and backgrounds, unlike more locally-based precollegiate institutions. It is a central point of this chapter that effective inquiry-based activities are those informed by consideration of the students' personal geographies as well as their university's geographic relationships. Figure 16.2 represents these place-based aspects of the dynamic with the interior arrows.

The examples below represent real activities that each author has found to be effective in one particular *place*. We teach at what is, within the American context, primarily a teaching university, serving a student population that is predominantly from within the region. The University of Northern Colorado has 12,200 students, of whom 9,500 are undergraduates. Over 90 percent of undergraduates are residents of this diverse state, representing not only its large urban centers but also many of its remote rural communities. The vast majority attended high school in state. Two-thirds of all students who self-identify their race or ethnicity are white. Hispanics form the largest ethnic minority (<20 percent), with roughly equal (<4 percent each) percentages of multiracial students, African Americans, Asians/Pacific Islanders, and Native Americans. Families with military backgrounds are common. Over one-third of students are classified as first-generation – the first in their families to go into higher education. The activities described below represent examples used in both introductory and advanced courses for majors and minors; the introductory courses also serve a general education audience, for whom the course is usually their only exposure to geography in higher education.

Activity 1 – Mapping and Analyzing One's Personal Activity Space

Familiarity is an important attribute for student success in understanding spatial concepts. Connecting the known, whether it is through personal experience or through learned prior skills, to the unknown, new concepts or places, is a key component of geographic learning. A simple yet effective assignment allowing for students to participate in spatial data collection, spatial analysis, and spatial learning is 'Spatial Interaction and Activity Space Journaling'. This assignment encourages students to have a better understanding of their own personal activity space and how this space influences their perception of space in comparison to others. The use of the 'story map' application by Esri (see the Useful Resources section at the end of this chapter) also introduces students to the power of GIS as an archival, mapping, and visual narrative tool.

There are three basic components to the assignment: (1) data collection; (2) mapping, using the story maps application; and (3) analysis and connectivity to the concept of individual activity spaces. Data collection comprises students recording their movements through space, keeping track of such variables as time, distance, route taken between nodes, mode of travel, and purpose of journey, over an agreed period (week/semester). Other attributes may include why the path was selected, perception of path, and interactions and observations along the path. Students are also asked to collect pictures of their journeys throughout this stage to incorporate in both their story map and in their analysis.

Mapping their movement in Esri's story map application is the next stage. Story maps allow students to quickly learn a web-based GIS that can be useful for analysis and presentations throughout their academic careers and beyond. In this activity, story maps allow students to start to visualize their movements and activity spaces. The inclusion of photos taken during the data collection stage allows for a more robust analysis to take shape.

The analysis stage of the assignment has students thinking about and applying concepts discussed in class to their own personal interaction and passage through space. Students create their activity maps by applying concepts of perception based on the work of Lynch (1967), identifying key elements of city spaces, including land uses, nodes, paths and landmarks. Ideas surrounding movement through space, path and modal selection, the impact of technology, age and spatial perception, introduced during lectures, are then applied on a personal level by the students. This helps them grasp the concepts through their own experiences instead of through sanitized, unconnected examples. This type of analysis of their own activity space, and other observations they feel are important in describing their perception and movement through space, also allows students to see ways in which they interact or don't interact with their communities. This is a growing concern between universities and the communities of which they are a part. This activity directly connects to the model shown in Figure 16.1. Working with data they generate themselves, students learn the complexity of their own activity space, and by extension, gain deeper awareness of the nuances of this core concept. The students are challenged because there is no specific answer to this assignment; instead they really think about how they move through space daily and what the influences and drivers are on that movement. Students commented that the activity revealed to them how set in their ways and routines they were; some noted that it really showed them how 'boring' their pattern of movements had become, how they were on auto-pilot most of the time, not paying attention to their activity space (not remembering how they got from A to B), nor realizing how narrow it was. Through this interactive assignment students work with theory, spatial data, personal perception and technology, helping lead them to the root of geography: 'the why of where'.

Activity 2 – Reading About Local Landscapes to Explore Threshold Concepts

An introductory human geography course provides additional examples of activities designed to get students to appreciate their own geographical relationships. In this course, one of the major goals is for all students to become more aware of their own simultaneous and diverse spatial connections to places at multiple scales. The concept of 'relational scale' (Howitt 2008) forms the backbone of a series of activities throughout the course. It is an example of a threshold concept in geography. To truly grasp the depth of this term, one must appreciate a radically different conception of scale than most students know. Rather than thinking of scale purely as a mathematical ratio or as a set of nested political hierarchies (for example, city, county, or state in the US context), 'relational scale' asks students to envision the web of interactions and connections each of us has with other places and peoples. That web in turn is mediated by the varied socioeconomic and cultural spaces that we each inhabit. It is thus a challenging term that embraces notions quite central to human geography, such as place, space, and interaction.

Early in the course, students consider their networks of social relationships to other places as well as the sources of some of the common consumer goods they own (for instance, clothing or electronics). This takes the form of both individual posts to a discussion board and brief, in-class, small-group investigations about the locations of operations of a transnational corporation of their choice. Students also explore more local-scale interactions by investigating the sources of drinking water in nearby cities (we are in a semiarid region in which water rights and distribution are always critical issues) or the locations of landfills for handling solid waste. Later, a variety of short readings illustrate specific concepts that help illuminate the nature of relational interactions on landscapes. For example, to get a grasp on the concepts of supply chains (forward- and backward-linkages) and the principles of regional industrial development, students study how one basic industry's growth – craft brewing – affects related industries in this area. The basis of this in-class activity is to read a short article from a local newspaper (Young, 2016) explaining how a farming family expanded their barley-growing operation by adding a new malt-processing sideline. The brief reading also provides an entry point to introduce new concepts like *vertical integration* and review earlier concepts, such as *sense of place.* In this particular story, the family was seeking ways to make their farm remain profitable in an area where rising land prices for new housing developments put pressure on agricultural operations. Students thus recognize how a variety of geographic variables influence their local economic landscapes. Similar short reading activities help students understand sources of change to local cultural landscapes owing to international migration.

At the end of the course, students write an essay, with examples, in which they summarize what they have learned about the threshold conception of simultaneous and multiple scales of relations and their effects on places and spaces they know. Growth in the depth of understanding from the initial posts on the topic is evident for most students. Notably, it is not only the students who earn the highest marks on exams that show this growth. Connecting these concepts to frequent local examples throughout the semester enables students who otherwise struggle on traditional assessments to express their improved geographical awareness.

Activity 3 – Role-Playing Simulations in Learning GIS Applications

For learning GIS, inquiry-based activities offer students a nexus of applying data-driven GIS simulations and understanding a geographic problem from personal experience. Recently GIS scientists and educators have increasingly recognized the importance of GIS in addressing critical social and cultural issues (Elwood, 2006; McLafferty, 2002; Pavoloskaya, 2002; Sheppard, 2005; Warf and Sui, 2010). Within a college classroom, critical GIS learning can be achieved through role-playing simulations. Role-playing provides an effective way to expand an individual student's understanding of the socio-cultural background of a problem and its interconnected spatial context.

In GIS instruction, role-playing simulations offer the benefits of learning through 'critical reflection mapping' (Hawthorne et al., 2015). Critical reflection mapping enables students to spatially link place-based reflections to multiple, synergistic data in order to create maps. In class, students appreciate the intersection between personal experience and collaborative activities through GIS data and applications that are designed to solve a community's problem.

In an urban GIS class, students use GIS to explore critical urban problems, such as housing market and residential segregation, urban transportation inequity, and food deserts. A role-playing simulation was developed to understand the issue of food (in) accessibility. Accessibility to quality food outlets is necessary in order to foster healthy communities. Some neighborhoods are disadvantaged in terms of access to healthy food choices due to factors including income, race and ethnicity, and gender. Understanding the community's particular situation and needs offers a key to solve the problem.

While food access and consumption might be a mundane daily activity, students are not necessarily familiar with the social structure of food accessibility. The key task in this inquiry-based activity, therefore, is to help students understand the consequences of limited access to basic needs. Such exposure not only enhances their own knowledge of the importance of geographic access – a key concept of geography – but also enlightens them about socially just decisions and consequences. Students' own experiences and specific situation of the urban community reflect the inner arrows of the inquiry-based learning model (Figure 16.2).

The instructor provides students with various forms of information and data about the current need for additional food outlets in the community. Also, the instructor introduces multiple stakeholders associated to the problem – for example, resident representatives, municipal officials, commercial developers, food retailers and other local business owners and their particular interests. After reading guidance materials, students are assigned a role from the community. Each stakeholder group gathers information on their interests and potential conflicts for the central problem: locating a supermarket in the community. Students use GIS to visualize the interests and conflicts among these stakeholders through acquired spatial and sociodemographic data. Visualizing inequity in access to healthy food by sociodemographic factors helps students discover the structural cause of the spatial problem. So informed, students as stakeholder groups can understand which challenges their group faces in relation to other groups in the community. These challenges are inherently associated with the place and its people. In this inquiry-based learning process (the outer arrows of the Figure 16.2 model), each student experiences a shift in preexisting knowledge and consciousness. From doing this exercise, students appreciated that they learned the social impacts of locating a food outlet, with regard to fostering equitable access to healthy foods. Specifically, students expressed that the role-play simulation allowed them to broaden their perspectives through exchanging diverse opinions of stakeholders outside their own socioeconomic and political contexts. Urban GIS simulations can foster data-driven discussions among groups, allowing critical reflection to help students comprehend the issue and develop socially equitable solutions.

Activity 4 – Field Observations for Understanding Local Landscapes

Field trips are an important tool for issues-based inquiry because they allow students to analyze and interpret geographic concepts while experiencing local landscapes firsthand (Pierce and Widen, 2016). Useful field experiences can also be built into courses through brief, local field excursions. These can be done in an afternoon, and while they certainly involve extra logistics, there are several benefits to students and the university, including building local connections for potential community engagement partnerships.

Undergraduates enrolled in an agricultural geography course participated in several field experiences designed to fit within the course's central themes of food, people and place. Class content emphasized locally relevant geographic issues with broader global implications including genetically modified foods, food deserts, industrial and organic dairies, and the geography of hunger. A combination of delivery formats was utilized including the reading of food systems literature; discussion and group debate using the *Taking Sides* text (Colson, 2012); intensive field trips; and writing and reflection papers that followed the site visits. Although the university is located within a county long dominated by dryland agriculture, the majority of our students hail from metropolitan areas and have little direct contact with local farming landscapes. As noted in the effective inquiry learning model (Figure 16.2), building on student participants' experiences can help reinforce or challenge agricultural geography content gleaned from a traditional classroom environment. In order to teach about industrial agriculture, the instructor arranged visits to local livestock and dairy operations with the goal of teaching the geographic scale of agriculture through first-hand experiences.

Thus to better bridge connections between 'town and gown' the course's field itinerary included brief visits to: (1) one of the nation's largest meatpacking plants, which processes 5,700 cattle per day and employs over 2,500 individuals including migrant laborers from over 15 countries; (2) an artisanal dairy operation, which processes cheese curds and milk from 200 cows for regional consumption; and (3) the region's largest organic dairy, which serves as a combined farm and bottling operation with over 5,300 cows. Because it can be challenging to teach threshold concepts such as geographic scale in an abstract manner, firsthand experience in nearby agricultural settings better supports and operationalizes inquiry. Each field trip adhered to the place-based inquiry model by: (1) providing agricultural site visits that allowed more visceral, geographic context for students; (2) infusing pre-trip lessons with appropriate information on the scale of industrial or organic agriculture; and (3) most importantly, allowing ample post-field trip time to share participant experiences (discussion and debate) in an interactive classroom environment. Such follow-up sessions are vital for effective inquiry learning, since it is important that field visits are not merely 'look see' events but rather opportunities to internalize or challenge course content.

Students were required to participate in at least two field trips for the course; participation rates ranged from 72 percent to 84 percent, with the slaughterhouse site visit having the highest attendance at 94 percent. Likert-scale questionnaires were administered to students who visited the meatpacking plant, and the results underscored the ways in which field experiences help participants understand complex issues in conjunction with other teaching methods. Over 90 percent of students agreed or strongly agreed that visiting the slaughterhouse as part of the course challenged the way they thought about industrial food production. Some 87 percent of students noted that the site visit gave them a better understanding of the geographic scale of industrial meat production and allowed them to better explore the facility's high level of efficiency, something not always noted in reading materials on CAFOs (Confined Animal Feeding Operations).

While field trips are on the decline in many colleges and universities due to issues such as liability and increased enrollment, these experiences provide value to undergraduate populations who wish to engage directly with agricultural institutions. Forging community partnerships is important first step for making these learning opportunities possible since field visits require permission and reciprocity. Institutions that value civic engagement as part of their strategic core missions may be better positioned to promote these learning opportunities in the classroom.

Activity 5 – Inquiry-Based Approach to Geospatial Programming

Many entry-level GIS positions now require some degree of computer programming experience, resulting in an increase in the number of programming courses being offered within geography and GIS programs (Bowlick et al., 2016). To meet the needs of the profession, faculty members must develop innovative and effective assignments to reach students with diverse backgrounds who may not be well aligned with the logic required for successful programming. In highly technical courses, using inquiry-based learning in a team environment can improve students' understanding and retention of key concepts (Muller and Kidd, 2014). Further, focusing activities on the process of problem solving and using known geographic locations, real data, and personal experiences can decrease student anxiety about learning a highly technical skill and increase student comprehension and retention.

Here, we present an assignment from a geospatial programming course that employs problem- and team-based learning to solve a task using local data. The goal of this assignment is to determine the number of buildings within specific distances of walking and biking trails as a surrogate measure for access to recreational and exercise opportunities. However, implementing the task using geospatial programming without step-by-step instructions requires critical thinking skills and is challenging.

Students are provided with general guidance and requirements on how to solve the problem, including working in teams of three to develop flow charts using appropriate geospatial techniques before writing scripts. Students are given the freedom to select appropriate geoprocessing tools and steps, thereby requiring that they apply critical thinking skills to complete the assignment. In addition to skill-based activity, task requirements ensure that students get practice applying programming concepts necessary for geospatial professionals: defining and working with variables, incorporating different data structures, ensuring proper syntax, working with geospatial tools, and applying the use of lists and loops to automate repetitive tasks (that is, creating multiple buffers around the trails in a single step). Using a local example and dataset makes difficult concepts more relatable to students. In this case, the students are knowledgeable about the location of the trails and can connect the results of the activity to what they know and understand about the local community.

This assignment challenges students by forcing them to think through a complex problem and reduce it to individual steps and requiring geospatial programming to solve the problem. In many professional settings, GIS practitioners are faced with similar work, therefore preparing students for future employment. In addition, research has demonstrated (Muller and Kidd, 2014), and student comments confirm, that using local datasets and inquiry-based learning can ease the difficulty of developing technical skills. Multiple students reported that the activity enforced the need to use critical thinking processes while taking on challenging tasks, allowing freedom for individual problem solving in an authentic setting.

CONCLUSION

This chapter has proposed a model and provided examples of a place-based pedagogy to show how inquiry-based approaches may be used to help build the conceptual frameworks of geography students. The model of 'place-based issues-based inquiry' (Figure 16.2) presented here has both utility and flexibility. Its utility lies in its emphasis on building undergraduates' data-analysis and critical-thinking skills. Judicious use of inquiry activities can help geography students build their conceptual frameworks and begin the process of acquiring a 'geographical imagination'. Flexibility is provided by the diversity of geographic data and situations that can be analyzed and by the range of learning outcomes that issues-based inquiry can serve. A wide range of topics may be explored using varied spatial and textual data and activity types, including the examples suggested above. Issues-based inquiry is best seen as being a valuable tool for the instructor's kit, to complement both simple expository methods of transmitting information and logistically complex problem-based and experiential learning activities.

Several examples from a mid-sized, regional university in the USA illustrated the diversity of issues-based approaches within introductory and more advanced geography and GIS courses. These examples adhered in different degrees to the model described in Figure 16.2, but in each, undergraduates were encouraged to construct their own knowledge through exposure to materials and resources provided as a brief activity within a course. The most effective inquiry activities are situated within the local geographic context (cultures, politics, environments, and economics) of the university's student body. Such activities help students reach learning outcomes *about* geography's concepts, not only the core concepts that are essential pieces of an incipient geographer's grasp of disciplinary content but also the challenging threshold concepts that empower students to think geographically. Having students acquire, organize and interpret geographic data, in many variations, further develops the budding professional's skill set. The issues-based case method also involves teaching *with* geography. Building from students' experiences with their local geographies, inquiry activities may help students cultivate a deeper appreciation and sense of their own places and help reveal to them the power of geographic thinking for addressing multiple real-world situations. Beyond that, analysis and evaluation of issues in real places, with impacts on real people, may awaken in students a sense of greater global awareness and appreciation of diversity of peoples, places and environments. This might be considered teaching *for* geography. In affective learning, awareness is the first step toward advocacy and action. That goal will not be achieved with these kinds of brief activities alone, of course. But as part of a larger armory of teaching methods, frequent use of issues-based inquiry can help make geographic concepts relatable for students, helping them bridge past experiences to their future professional and personal growth.

USEFUL RESOURCES

Online inquiry-based projects and geospatial analysis tools:

- This style of inquiry supports 'vignettes' of case studies about geographic concepts in the teacher professional development materials created by the Geocapabilities Project (www.geocapabilities.org).
- The Esri story maps application (storymaps.arcgis.com/en/) introduces web-mapping and templates in which students can combine text, images, and maps on any topic.

REFERENCES

Bednarz, S., Heffron, S. and Huynh, N. (eds) (2013) *A Road Map for 21st Century Geography Education: Geography Education Research.* Washington, DC: Association of American Geographers.
Bowlick, F., Goldberg, D. and Bednarz, S. (2017) 'Computer science and programming courses in geography departments in the United States', *The Professional Geographer,* **69** (1), pp. 138–150.
Brasher, J., Alderman, D. and Inwood, J. (2017) 'Applying critical race and memory studies to university place naming controversies: toward a responsible landscape policy', *Papers in Applied Geography,* **3** (3/4), pp. 292–307.
Colson, J. (2012) *Taking Sides: Clashing Views in Food and Nutrition.* New York: McGraw-Hill, 2nd edition.
Department for Education (2013) *National Curriculum in England: Geography Programmes of Study.* At www.gov.uk/government/publications/national-curriculum-in-england-geography-programmes-of-study.
Dewey, J. (1938) *Experience and Education.* New York: Collier Books.
Downey, M. and Long, K. (2016) *Teaching for Historical Literacy: Building Knowledge in the History Classroom.* New York: Routledge.
Elwood, S. (2006) 'Critical issues in participatory GIS: deconstructions, reconstructions, and new research directions', *Transactions in GIS,* **10** (5), pp. 693–708.
Enser, M. (2017) 'Crossing the threshold', *Teaching It Real* (blog), at teachreal.wordpress.com/2017/10/22/crossing-the-threshold.
Gardner, H. (1999) *The Disciplined Mind: Beyond Facts and Standardized Tests, the K-12 Education that Every Child Deserves.* New York: Simon and Schuster.
Gersmehl, P. (2014) *Teaching Geography.* New York: Guilford Press, 3rd edition.

Gersmehl, P. and Young, J. (1992) 'Images, analysis and evaluation: a linguistic basis for a regional geography course', in A. Hill (ed.), *International Perspectives on Geographic Education*, Boulder, CO: Center for Geographic Education, pp. 229–240.

Goodlad, J. (1984) *A Place Called School: Prospects for the Future.* New York: McGraw-Hill.

Grant, R. (1997) 'A claim for the case method in the teaching of geography', *Journal of Geography in Higher Education*, 21 (2), pp. 171–185.

Hanvey, R. (1975) *An Attainable Global Perspective.* Denver, CO: University of Denver, Center for Teaching International Relations and New York: Center for War/Peace Studies, pp. 1–31.

Hawthorne, T., Solís, P., Terry, B., Price, M. and Atchison, C. (2015) 'Critical reflection mapping as a hybrid methodology for examining sociospatial perceptions of new research sites', *Annals of the Association of American Geographers*, 105 (1), pp. 22–47.

Heffron, S. and Downs, R. (2012) *Geography for Life: National Geography Standards.* Washington, DC: Geography Education National Implementation Project, 2nd edition.

Hill, A. (1990), 'A model for issue-based geographic inquiry in secondary schools', *GIGI Bulletin 1A*, Boulder, CO: Center for Geography Education, 11 pp.

Hill, A., Dunn, J. and Klein, P. (1995) *Geographic Inquiry into Global Issues* (20 modules). Chicago: Encyclopaedia Brittanica Education Corp.

Howitt, R. (2008) 'Scale', in J. Agnew, K. Mitchell and G. Toal (eds), *A Companion to Political Geography*, Blackwell Publishing, pp. 138–157.

Jo, I. and Bednarz, S. (2009) 'Evaluating geography textbook questions from a spatial perspective: using concepts of space, tools of representation, and cognitive processes to evaluate spatiality', *Journal of Geography*, 108 (1), pp. 4–13.

Klein, P. (1995) 'Using inquiry to enhance the learning and appreciation of geography', *Journal of Geography*, 94 (2), pp. 358–367.

Klein, P. (2003) 'Active learning strategies and assessment in world geography classes', *Journal of Geography*, 102 (4), pp. 146–157.

Klein, P. and Solem, M. (2008) 'Evaluating the impact of international collaboration on geography learning', *Journal of Geography in Higher Education*, 32 (2), pp. 245–267.

Klein, P., Pawson, E., Solem, M. and Ray, W. (2014) 'Geography education for "an attainable global perspective"', *Journal of Geography in Higher Education*, 38 (1), pp. 17–27.

Lambert, D., Solem, M. and Tani, S. (2015) 'Achieving human potential through geography education: a capabilities approach to curriculum making in schools', *Annals of the Association of American Geographers*, 105 (4), pp. 723–735.

Larsen, T. and Harrington, J. (2016) 'Mental maps and a community-based sense of place: a case study among Kansas third graders', *Research in Geographic Education*, 18 (2), pp. 86–111.

Lynch, K. (1967) *The Image of the City.* Cambridge, MA: Massachusetts Institute of Technology Press.

Massey, D. (1994) *Space, Place, and Gender.* Minneapolis: University of Minnesota Press.

Maude, A. (2013) 'The vision of geography underlying the Australian geography curriculum', *Review of Geographical Education Online*, 3, pp. 253–265.

McLafferty, S. (2002) 'Mapping women's worlds: knowledge, power and the bounds of GIS', *Gender, Place and Culture*, 9 (3), pp. 263–269.

Meyer, J. and Land, R. (2003) 'Threshold concepts and troublesome knowledge: linkages to ways of thinking and practising within the disciplines', Occasional Report 4, Enhancing Teaching–Learning Environments in Undergraduate Courses Project, University of Edinburgh: School of Education, At www.etl.tla.ed.ac.uk/docs/ETLreport4.pdf.

Mohan, A. (2018) 'Valuing student thinking in the inquiry process', *The Geography Teacher*, 15 (1), pp. 3–4.

Muller, C. and Kidd, C. (2014) 'Debugging geographers: teaching programming to non-computer scientists', *Journal of Geography in Higher Education*, 38 (2), pp. 175–192.

National Council for the Social Studies (2013) *The College, Career and Civic Life (C3) Framework for Social Studies State Standards.* Silver Spring, MD: National Council for the Social Studies.

Pavoloskaya, M. (2002) 'Mapping urban change and changing GIS: other views of economic restructuring', *Gender, Place and Culture*, 9 (3), pp. 281–289.

Pawson, E., Fournier, E., Haigh, M., Muñiz, O., Trafford, J. and Vajoczki, S. (2006) 'Problem-based learning in geography: towards a critical assessment of its purposes, benefits and risks', *Journal of Geography in Higher Education*, 30 (1), pp. 103–116.

Pierce, J. and Widen, H. (2016) 'Visceral pedagogy: teaching challenging topics emotionally as well as cognitively', *Journal of Geography*, 116 (2), pp. 47–56.

Schwab, J. (1966) 'The teaching of science as enquiry', in J. Schwab and P. Brandwen (eds), *The Teaching of Science*, Cambridge: MA: Harvard University Press, pp. 1–103.

Sheppard, E. (2005) 'Cartography and power: the "poststructuralist turn" 1982–1991', *Cartographica*, 40 (1/2), pp. 85–111.

Solem, M., Klein, P., Muñiz-Solari, O. and Ray, W. (eds) (2010) *Center for Global Geography Education* (6 modules). Washington, DC: American Association of Geographers, www.aag.org/cgge.

Slater, F. (1982) *Learning Through Geography.* Oxford: Heinemann Educational Books.

Slinger, J. (2011) 'Threshold concepts in secondary geography education', Research report presented at The Geographical Association Annual Conference, Surrey, www.geography.org.uk/download/ga_conf11slinger.pdf.

Spronken-Smith, R., Bullard, J., Ray, W., Roberts, C. and Keiffer, A. (2008) 'Where might sand dunes be on Mars? Engaging students through inquiry-based learning in geography', *Journal of Geography in Higher Education*, **32** (1), pp. 71–86.

Srivastava, S. (2013) 'Threshold concepts in geographical information systems: a step towards conceptual understanding', *Journal of Geography in Higher Education*, **37** (3), pp. 367–384.

Taba, H. (1963) 'Learning by discovery: psychological and educational rationale', *Elementary School Journal*, **63** (6), pp. 308–316.

Tennyson, R. and Cocchiarella, M. (1986) 'An empirically based instructional design theory for teaching concepts, *Review of Educational Research*, **56** (1), pp. 40–71.

Tillmann, A., Albrecht, V. and Wunderlich, J. (2017) 'Dewey's concept of experience for inquiry-based landscape drawing during field studies', *Journal of Geography in Higher Education*, **41** (3), pp. 383–402.

Toumasis, C. (1995) 'Concept worksheet: an important tool for learning', *The Mathematics Teacher*, **88** (2), pp. 98–100.

Walkington, H., Dyer, S., Solem, M., Haigh, M. and Waddington, S. (2018) 'A capabilities approach to higher education: geocapabilities and implications for geography curricula', *Journal of Geography in Higher Education*, **42** (1), pp. 7–24.

Warf, B. and Sui, D. (2010) 'From GIS to neogeography: ontological implications and theories of truth', *Annals of GIS*, **16** (4), pp. 197–209.

Wheatley, G. (1991), 'Constructivist perspectives on science and mathematics learning', *Science Education*, **75** (1), pp. 9–21.

Young, C. (2016) 'Farmers launch malting business', *Loveland [Colo.] Reporter-Herald*, September 29, www.reporterherald.com/news/loveland-local-news/ci_30417727/farmers-launch-malting-business.

17. Learning and teaching about race and racism in geography
James Esson and Angela Last

INTRODUCTION

> Many of us teach courses that are shaped by anti-colonial and antiracist scholarship. . . We have compelling 'how-to' stories of what it means to incorporate race, ethnicity and anti-colonial perspectives into our classrooms. . . But I would argue that still, with all of this, for the most part, we are writing, teaching, and recreating white geographies: by 'we' I mean almost all of us (including me); by 'white' I mean ways of seeing, understanding, and interrogating the world that are based on racialized and colonial assumptions that are unremarked, normalized, and perpetuated. (Domosh, 2015)

This quote is from Mona Domosh, former President of the American Association of Geographers (AAG), in an essay provocatively titled 'Why is our geography curriculum so white?' Domosh highlights an issue that a relatively small group of geographers have spent decades trying to address, specifically; how learning and teaching in geography is shaped by and perpetuates racism (cf. Jackson 1989; Kobayashi, 1999; Mahtani, 2006). This scholarship connects to wider debates over racial oppression that transcends the discipline, and similarly Domosh's essay resonates with contemporary social movements seeking to challenge racism inside and outside the academy, for example; those asking and investigating 'Why isn't my professor black? and 'Why is my curriculum white?'; activism linked to Rhodes Must Fall in South Africa (Mbembe, 2016) and Oxford (Elliott-Cooper, 2017), and indigenous led movements such as the Standing Rock resistance to the Dakota Access Pipeline (Lane, 2018) and the Katribu resistance to mining in the Philippines (Simbulan, 2016). While we recognise that this chapter speaks from and primarily to the Western academy, we aim to situate our contribution to this volume within the above-mentioned efforts and movements seeking to dismantle the racist social classification of the world's population.

The main purpose of this chapter is to provide a resource for geographers wanting to learn and teach about race and racism; it is hoped that the insights provided will help counteract the reproduction of 'white geographies' in practical as well as epistemological terms. The next section introduces key ideas for geographers wanting to learn about race and racism, this is followed by a discussion about the presence of racism within the discipline. We then engage with Critical Race Theory (CRT) perspectives and decolonial approaches to outline how geographers can teach about the history and spatiality of racial oppression, as it intersects with wider structural inequalities, without reproducing 'white geographies'. We conclude by calling for geographers to embrace a *curriculum against domination* which, as argued by De Lissovoy (2010), pushes back against the epistemic and cultural violence that underlies the politics of learning, teaching and knowledge production in modern higher education.

RACE AND RACISM: A GLOBAL HIERARCHY OF SUPERIORITY AND INFERIORITY

Race, that is the categorisation of the world's human population according to markers, such as skin colour and head shape, was once considered a *natural* hierarchical framework for understanding differences among human beings verifiable by science (Back and Solomos, 2013). Racial sciences, such as eugenics, have been widely discredited and it is now acknowledged that racial categories and hierarchies are *ideological* constructions (Bressey and Dwyer, 2012). Yet the negative effects of a race-based social classification of the world's population remains, most notably, in the form of racialisation through the continued marking of some bodies as superior and other bodies as inferior. This results in *racism*, a global hierarchy of superiority and inferiority along the line of the human (Mignolo, 2014; Grosfoguel, 2016). Racism is relational and intersects with other ideological constructions, for example those connected to patriarchy and capitalism, which coalesce to generate oppressive relations around race, gender and class (cf. Crenshaw, 1989; Nayak, 2003; McKittrick, 2006; Raghuram et al., 2011; Ahmed, 2012; Woods, 2017).

Racism constitutes a 'metaphysical catastrophe', because it transforms the meanings associated with fundamental areas of thinking and being, particularly relations between the self and fellow human beings (Maldonado-Torres, 2018). Crucially, as noted by Grosfoguel (2016) drawing on the theorisations of Frantz Fanon and Boaventura de Sousa Santos, the people racially classified above the line of the human, as in they are fully recognised as human beings, have their humanity validated. Accordingly, they are able to enjoy better access to rights, resources, and social recognition of their subjectivities, epistemologies and spiritualities. Conversely, those people below the line of the human are racialised as subhuman or even non-human. In other words, their humanity is questioned and thereby negated. This dehumanisation means their access to rights, resources and the recognition of their subjectivities, epistemologies and spiritualities are invariably restricted or denied (the racialisation and exploitation of African people within the context of the transatlantic slave trade provides a good example of this).

A Grosfoguel–Fanon–Boaventura de Sousa Santos-inspired understanding of racism allows us to avoid the reductionism of many existing definitions of racism, particularly those related solely to skin colour, by recognising that different histories in diverse regions of the world will result in a range of ways to mark bodies and place them on a hierarchy of superiority/inferiority along the lines of the human. Racism can be marked by colour, but also other markers such as ethnicity, language, culture and/or religion. An example to illustrate this point is colonial relations in Ireland. Grosfoguel (2016, p. 11) notes how the British could not construct their racial superiority over the Irish through the marker of skin colour, because in this case the coloniser and the colonised shared the same skin colour. In order to maintain a social hierarchy of superiority/inferiority along the line of the human a different marker was needed. Therefore, what appears at first glance to be a religious conflict between Protestants and Catholics is in fact a racial/colonial conflict.

The establishment of racialised power structures, ways of knowing, and ways of being, cannot be disentangled from the coming together and expansion of three ideologies as part of the post-15th century colonial-modern era. These ideologies are white supremacy, capitalism and Eurocentrism. It is therefore important to note that while markers of difference between humans have long existed, the *racialisation* of these differences was a phenomenon driven by European colonialists seeking to establish degrees of being human. This was in order to position themselves as superior to the indigenous peoples they sought to subjugate (Mignolo, 2008; Walter and Butler, 2013). Martinot (2018) explains the colonial-modern era's role in establishing a racist global hierarchy of superiority and inferiority along the line of the human, and the intersectionality of indigeneity and race, as follows:

> In 200 years, the indigenous population of the Caribbean region, and much of Mexico and Peru, had been decimated, and the slave trade that replenished it with Africans had become the most profitable industry in the entire Atlantic economy. . . Racialization occurred in different terms in the Spanish colonies than it did in the English colonies, but the purpose and effect was the same. Its purpose was to create a system of social categorization that differentiated between who could own land and who would be forced to work on it; a distinction in social category between who could define, and who was to be defined. Mere military superiority does not interiorize; for the most part, it generates resistance. A more inclusive social process is required to consolidate conquest. It involves defining juridical structures, forms of spirituality and religion, and the nature of personhood for others. It is the power to define that divests others of the power to define themselves, to lay claim to juridicality or a spirituality of their own, and eventually results in a concept of racial difference. (Martinot, 2018)

Today, the concept of race and our relations as and to racialised subjects are still constituted through social institutions, meanings and practices that while differing from those of the colonial period are still nefarious and complex. This is because racialised meanings and practices are not always easy to recognise. On the one hand, they are often opaque, normative and mundane. On the other hand, they are able to maintain hierarchies of superiority and inferiority that are intensely painful and damaging. A key reason this is possible is *coloniality*, by which we mean the 'long-standing patterns of power that emerged as a result of colonialism, but that define culture, labour, intersubjective relations, and knowledge production well beyond the strict limits of colonial administrations' (Maldonado-Torres, 2007, p. 243). One of the main ways that coloniality manifests itself in society is through *institutional racism*, which constitutes:

> The collective failure of an organisation to provide an appropriate and professional service to people because of their colour, culture, or ethnic origin. It can be seen or detected in processes, attitudes and behaviour which amount to discrimination through unwitting prejudice, ignorance, thoughtlessness and racist stereotyping which disadvantage minority ethnic people. (McPherson, 1999, p. 369)

There are several working definitions of institutional racism, the earliest being from Kwame Ture/Stokely Carmichael and Charles Hamilton in the 1960s, but the definition above is particularly useful here. It acknowledges that while racism is in many cases based on a hierarchy of superiority–inferiority marked by physical attributes such as skin colour, processes of racialisation can as explained above be marked by ethnic, linguistic, religious or cultural identity also. Moreover, racism can but does not have to involve overt hostility and physical acts of violence. Rather, in the context of racism, violence is best understood as 'any relation, process, or condition by which an individual or a group violates the physical, social, and/or psychological integrity of another person or group' (Bulhan, 1985, p. 135).

In this chapter we focus on two approaches that have emerged to address coloniality induced institutional racism. The first is a *Critical Race Theory* (CRT) perspective, which emerged in the US in the post-civil rights era. A CRT perspective begins with the premise that racism is an endemic feature of society, and CRT 'sets out not only to ascertain how society organizes itself along racial lines and hierarchies, but to transform it for the better' (Delgado and Stefancic, 2017, p. 3). This transformation requires both scholarship and activism that addresses racism as a harmful force that manifests itself through seemingly mundane relations and practices, as well as institutional racism in fields such as law and policing, education and medicine. The second response is *decolonial* in nature, which denotes 'efforts at rehumanizing the world, breaking hierarchies of difference that dehumanize subjects and communities and that destroy nature, and to the production of counter discourses, counter knowledges, counter creative acts, and counter-practices' (Maldonado-Torres, 2016, p. 10). This decolonial imperative is not metaphorical, it entails the removal of ongoing colonial domination globally, thereby connecting moves to dismantle the racist social classification of the world population under Eurocentric world power (see Mignolo, 2008) to indigenous-led demands for radical restructuring of land, resources and wealth (see Tuck and Yang, 2012).

In the discussion that follows we draw on the ideas introduced in this section, such as institutional racism, violence and coloniality, to reflect on the issue of racism *within* geography. We then elaborate on how insights from CRT and decolonial approaches can improve how we learn and teach about race and racism in geography.

THE PRESENCE OF RACE AND RACISM IN GEOGRAPHY

Audrey Kobayashi's (2014) 'The dialectic of race and the discipline of geography' is a key resource for those seeking to understand race and racism in geography for many reasons, but two are worth highlighting here briefly: i) the biographical approach adopted provides a detailed overview of how major thinkers in the discipline, particularly geographers of colour, have engaged with the concept of race from the Enlightenment through to the 2000s; ii) Kobayashi points to a key, but often ignored, starting point for those wanting to learn and teach about race and racism in geography, which is to ensure there is scope within geography programmes to critically reflect on how participation in the academy reinforces racialised social privilege. Therefore, in order to generate a critical understanding among students and teachers that recognises racism as a social phenomenon, geographers should not objectify racism and treat it as an issue irrelevant to the structures and practices within our discipline (Dwyer, 1999; Delaney, 2002; Berg, 2012; Mahtani 2014; Esson, 2018). In other words, both students and teachers must begin efforts to learn and teach about race and racism by adopting a perspective in keeping with CRT, that is one that recognises the need to reflect critically on the endemic nature of racism in society and accordingly the *presence of race and racism in geography*. One way to do this is by interrogating the idea of the 'racial project'.

Geography as a field of study, a social institution, and a workplace, is underpinned by a 'racial project' that sought to privilege an ideology of Eurocentric-white superiority (Peake and Kobayashi, 2002). This 'racial project' was and is deeply shaped by colonialism and coloniality respectively. Readers can and should think about this in relation to their own context, but for the authors who are based in the UK the 'racial project' is apparent when we consider geography's role as one of the disciplines used as part of empire building and colonial endeavours. For example, British geography was directly involved with and benefited from the promotion of white supremacy as part of these activities. Bonnett (1997) summarises this situation as follows:

> It is difficult to underestimate the impact the ideologies and practices of empire have had upon the imagination of British geographers. Nowhere is this impact more evident than in their approach to race. Racial differences were seen by British empire builders as one of the greatest challenges to colonial expansion. Geographers interested in issues of race saw their task as the elucidation of the hierarchy of the world's races and the provision of informed speculation on the implications of White settlement and colonial government. (p. 193)

As noted previously, race is an ideological construction that varies both in its affects and effects according to geographical and historical circumstances (Jackson, 1989). Let us therefore continue with the case of British geography as an example to examine how the discipline both as a social institution and a workplace reinforces racialised social privileges. We can do so by drawing on insights from two recent articles that illustrate the profile of 'Black and Minority Ethnic (BME) students and staff in contemporary British Geography' (Desai, 2017), and the everyday experiences of racism encountered by academics racialised as non-white in a geography department (Tolia-Kelly, 2017).

Vandana Desai's (2017) article is a defining moment for discussions about racism in British higher education geography, and a useful teaching resource on this topic, because it makes plain the presence of *institutional racism* within the discipline and the predominance and reproduction of white privilege. Drawing on a range of national data sets, Desai (2017) illustrates the marginal and precarious position of people within geography who are racialised as non-white. For example, in terms of the undergraduate student body, where nationally 21.3 per cent of all UK-domiciled first degree undergraduate students are BME, for UK geography this is only 6.3 per cent (ibid., p. 320). UK BME geography students who are admitted onto geography programmes graduate with degree results significantly below those of their white peers. Of BME students, 11.2 per cent attained a first and 69.5 per cent attained an upper second or better (across the three years, 2013–15) as compared with 16.9 per cent and 80.0 per cent for white students respectively (ibid., p.321). To be clear this situation, which is not unique to geography and is known as the 'attainment gap', has been well-researched and the disparity is not attributable to an intellectual deficit in BME students (Tatlow, 2015; also see Chapter 13 in this volume by Annie Hughes and Nona McDuff).

British geography not only has a low proportion of undergraduate BME students, who leave with lower grades than their white peers, but it also fails to encourage BME students to go on to postgraduate qualifications. In the UK, 16.4 per cent of UK domiciled research postgraduate students are BME, yet when we look at a subject level it reveals that the proportion for BME UK domiciled postgraduate students in geography is only 4.4 per cent (Desai, 2017, p. 320). The situation is no better when we look at academic staff. Among all UK national staff in the UK, 8.2 per cent are BME, which is almost twice the 4.3 per cent of UK national geography staff who are BME (ibid., p. 322). The consequences of unfavourable and unsupportive environments for BME academic staff in geography make themselves manifest in lower levels of progression in the discipline (ibid., p.322). In the UK 7.3 per cent of UK professors are BME, but geography at 1.4 per cent is disturbingly low.

The findings from Desai's study are brought to life in Divya Tolia-Kelly's (2017) article 'A day in the life of a geographer: lone, black, female', which illustrates how these statistics take the form of racist relations, which intersect with other ideological constructions such as gender, and that have become part of the normative architecture of institutions and practices. Notably, given the context of this chapter, Tolia-Kelly highlights how for academics racialised as non-white, teaching about race and racism can be a painful practice in predominantly white institutions where some students contribute to the reproduction of racist thinking within learning environments. To be clear, the point is not that a white academic could not find themselves in a similar position where anti-racist teachings are challenged (see for example Jackson, 1989). It is rather that as a 'lone, black, female' who is already dealing with institutional racism, being in a classroom environment where an anti-racist message is being undermined by your pupils contributes to a sense of inferiority and not belonging in the academy. The following example was used to illustrate this point:

> Recently, a black academic was teaching about the myth of race based on Stuart Hall (1997) and recent debates in popular culture. The discussion was focused on the discrediting of racial science. In response, the students dismissed her argument. Their responses included 'it's proven scientifically, race does exist'. 'It is biological. Look at our skins.' Also to prove their point, students started 'Googling' for evidence while in the lecture theatre. 'Look here's the evidence!' said a throng, while looking at a sports piece arguing for recognition of biological differences between white and black runners in capacities for running (e.g. Isaksen 2013). In that space, her authority and expertise were placed on an equal or lesser platform to the students. (Tolia-Kelly, 2017, p.326)

The insights from Desai (2017) and Tolia-Kelly (2017) demonstrate why, in the context of British geography as an example, geographers need to remain attentive to the fact that racism can be seen at all levels of society *including* the institutions, policies and practices of higher education geography (see Jackson, 1989). Furthermore, given the inferior and marginal position of geographers of colour at undergraduate level through to faculty positions as illustrated within both papers, it becomes possible to comprehend how 'white geographies' are recreated, that is ways of seeing, understanding and interrogating the world that are based on racialised and colonial assumptions that are unremarked, normalised, and perpetuated (Domosh, 2015). But the two papers also confirm that if geographers want to critically reflect on race and racism then there is a 'need to extend that reflection to the classroom, a major site of antiracist struggle, where both teaching methods and the ways in which we forge relations with our students are strongly influenced by the processes of racialization that surround us' (Peake and Kobayashi, 2002, p.57).

TEACHING ABOUT RACE AND RACISM

In this section we draw inspiration from CRT and decolonial approaches to put forward three themes that can help geographers seeking to teach about the history and spatiality of racial oppression, as it intersects with wider structural inequalities, without reproducing 'white geographies'.

1. Know (Y)Our History

One of the reasons why 'white geographies' are being perpetuated through the curriculum is because of our engagement with colonialism and empire's role in shaping how geographical knowledge, modes of learning and assessing come into being is inadequate. This might seem odd given the public disdain shown by geographers for Bruce Gilley's 2017 essay on the 'Case for colonialism' suggests that blatant colonial-white supremacist thinking, which positions Europe as intellectually and morally superior, is widely considered unacceptable. But what we are calling for geography students and teachers to do, through the theme of *knowing (y)our history*, is to avoid engaging in a liberal humanism that includes colonial histories in teaching merely as *symbolic representations*. We have to remind ourselves that even core geographical concepts, such as space, had to be wrestled from imperialist and white supremacist notions such as *Lebensraum* – an understanding of space used by the Nazis that denoted containment, invasion and expansion. Instead, we need to encourage critical reflection that both exposes the costs of Western modernity and empire in the past and challenges us to address their consequences in the present (Desai and Sanya, 2016).

To know (y)our history, is to ask 'how do we narrate the history of our respective fields and methodologies within the curriculum?' For example, in geography we teach qualitative and quantitative methods, and connect their evolution to the history of science and forms of knowledge making, including cartography. This history invariably starts with Europe, yet science was shaped through global interactions and knowledge transfer (cf. Raju, 2017). We can see these influences on the development of today's science and technology all around us: we use a Hindu-Arabic numeral system, an Egyptian calendar, Babylonian time, Chinese compasses, et cetera. Furthermore, the European intellectual scene that is narrated is often, as historian Nell Irvin Painter (2010) remarks, *retrospectively* racialised as one full of white blonde ancient Greeks. This is not what intellectual life looked like at the time, yet these racialised reconfigurations of knowledge production in the past provide a good example of why it is important to pay attention to how knowledge is produced and portrayed today, and to keep reminding ourselves that knowledge is always geographically as well as geopolitically shaped. As McKittrick (2011, p. 947) notes 'a black sense of place, black histories, and communities are not only integral to production of space, but also that the analytical interconnectedness of race, practices of domination, and geography undoubtedly put pressure on how we presently study and assess racial violence'. Furthermore, scholars research *about* 'imagined geographies' (Said, 1993), 'imagined communities' (Anderson, 1983) and 'invented tradition' (Hobsbawm and Ranger, 1983) – we need to incorporate these critical perspectives into our praxis and teach *with* them.

Depending on where you are located, *to know (y)our history* will mean looking at the ground upon which you currently stand and admitting that it is territory that was violently taken from indigenous populations and settled upon by colonisers. Daigle and Sundberg (2017) give an example of how they do this on their Introductory human geography course: 'We start by acknowledging our hosts, the Musqueam nation, who are the legal caretakers of this place ʔəəlqsəən (Ulksun), otherwise known as UBC's Point Grey campus, located in Vancouver, British Columbia' (2017, p. 338). This introduction skilfully introduces to students how the places that we teach, live and work in today, cannot be disentangled from the above discussed colonial-modern era's role in establishing a global hierarchy of superiority and inferiority along the line of the human. Moreover, this approach invites students and teachers to see themselves as entangled in processes of colonialism irrespective of their positionality (Daigle and Sundberg, 2017), and therefore their role in maintaining racial hierarchies and structures.

Indigenous activists and scholars have also pointed to the emphasis on particular formats of learning and assessment and have argued that different ways of transmitting knowledge should be recognised, including different styles of written and oral history. Linda Tuhiwai Smith (2012) and Edouard Glissant (2010), for instance, highlight how indigenous forms of knowledge have been devalued as ahistorical 'traditions' or even 'natural history', that also translated into pedagogies of erasure, for instance, through compulsory and 'corrective' European education in residential schools. McCoy et al. (2016) have collected experimental pedagogies that are based on the concept of 'land education'. Their approach critiques what they perceive as a settler imposed – and settler benefiting – education centred around 'place'. Smith (2012) has suggested 'Twenty-five indigenous projects' in her book *Decolonizing Methodologies*, which include methods from story-telling to rethinking research ethics around 'sharing'.

To know (y)our history is to, as Mahtani (2006) notes, 'look at sites closer to home' and ask 'are we sharing with our students how gendered and racialised identities influence who is teaching in geography, and why?' (p. 22). Who is being considered and treated as the 'norm' and who is, often by simple structural continuity, excluded? How did we arrive at the current make-up of the discipline in terms of staff and students? One consequence of knowing this history should be to critically contextualise what is included/excluded in the curriculum. This can be further reinforced by providing visual representations on slides and hand-outs of the scholars being cited. Who are we showing as victims, decision-makers, experts, workers? This is not only relevant to race, but to gender, (dis) ability et cetera, so an intersectional lens needs to be applied. Where suitable, even short biographical sketches could be included, where information is known, to show the different paths of geographers into academia. For instance, there are blog posts written by black/working class/female/disabled/LGBT+ geologists and geographers that tell their stories (for example the Black Geoscientists blog). These biographical sketches are not meant to represent role models, but rather to disrupt normative understandings of who is able to the enter the academy and how.

2.   A Place for Environmental Justice

Engagement with activism in both theory and practice is relatively lacking in the geography curriculum, yet a key tenant of CRT is that we should not only aim to understand how society organises itself along racial lines and hierarchies but try and dismantle these hierarches also (Delgado and Stefancic, 2017, p. 3). We appreciate that this may seem like a daunting task, but one way to approach this subject in our learning and teaching is by examining the relationship between race and environment. For example, when it comes to 'nature', geographers frequently deconstruct Western notions of the concept and its apparent difference from culture. Here, race often comes into play when the history of the nature/culture binary is examined. Students are sometimes told how indigenous people have been naturalised or denaturalised in accordance with imperialist and genocidal goals.

What is addressed less is the contemporary white environmentalist lens. This lens has occupied environmentalists of colour who have often felt excluded by the 'white liberal' priorities that do not only treat issues that concern communities of colour as peripheral, but that also treat environmentalists of colour themselves as peripheral.

An example that shows how key geographers' engagement with race and environment are portrayed in racially biased terms is the work of the Detroit Geographical Expedition and Institute. In an interview with geographer Cindi Katz, Co-Director of the Detroit Geographical Expedition and Institute (DGEI) Gwendolyn Warren (Warren and Katz, 2014) brilliantly subverts the assumptions and methods of the white geographers who wanted to involve her in a mapping project on her black neighbourhood in Detroit. Although she credits the geographers with good intentions such as equipping poor communities to bring about changes in their environment, she also calls out the naivety of the geographers about the daily living and working conditions of the community that not only shape their lives but would also hinder their participation in the project. In the case of the DGEI this included struggle with transportation, education, work and substandard living conditions. On the other hand, Warren points to the ways in which the two parties in the project were invested in making the project work for each other so that both sides could benefit in the long term: the black participants would get educational opportunities that would enable them to get university education or better work, and the white participants would learn about the shortcomings of their methods and assumptions, and be able to publish challenging work. Amongst other things, the project resulted in jointly produced maps that document how race impacts on a range of issues from road safety to housing standards.

Given that communities of colour bear the brunt of environmental hazards, summarised in the term 'environmental racism' (Bullard, 1983), there is widespread anger at white environmentalists who accuse people of colour of lacking concern for environmental issues. Sociologist Robert D. Bullard, who coined the term 'environmental racism', is considered the 'founding father' of the US environmental justice movement. By introducing race, environmentalism becomes an issue of social justice, because it calls for answers to ethical and political questions of 'who gets what, when, why and how much' (Bullard, 1999, p. 7). In his work, Bullard (1999) identified race as the key factor that determined how likely an American would be exposed to environmental hazards such as air, water and ground pollution. This phenomenon extends beyond the United States, and also translates into relations between so-called 'developed' and 'developing' countries, as waste and polluting industries get pushed onto 'indebted' countries. Highlighting the impact of Bullard's work, and that of scholars and activists like him, in lectures and seminars on the environment and environmental movement would counter the impression that only white people notice and address environmental issues.

Decolonial scholarship also encourages academics to design their curriculum so that learners are made aware of the ways in which indigenous communities of colour have been protesting against environmental abuses for centuries. Students should be introduced to research highlighting that many indigenous peoples have been relocated to land or areas that are unsuitable for maintaining their livelihoods, and that they continue to be displaced without adequate compensation or offers of the possibility to return. It is little known, for instance, that Australia and New Zealand's 'agricultural miracle', that also saw their non-agricultural landscapes transformed to a more European style, was largely dependent on fertiliser mined from islands in the Pacific such as Banaba and Nauru. On

Banaba, for instance, people were forcibly moved, and did not even receive royalties. This population removal also included burial sites, which were sometimes destroyed in mining, the bones distributed as part of the fertiliser (Teaiwa, 2014, p. 198). Similarly, islands and islander communities were burdened with waste and radiation from nuclear weapons tests that either already have or will render their environments uninhabitable. This situation is aggravated by human induced climate change accelerating sea level rise, caused primarily by their former colonisers, which is leading to an increasingly large number of disappearing islands (Farbotko, 2010).

At the same time, a narrative of vulnerability is perpetuated that patronises local governments and activists. As writer Epeli Hau'ofa (1993) points out in his essay 'Our sea of islands': 'To acknowledge the larger reality would be to undermine the prevailing view, and to frustrate certain agendas and goals of powerful interests' (p. 14). Communities in the Pacific are fighting multiple battles that also include resources and space taken up by on-going military occupation and imposed detention centres, and also securing space for the time in which sea level rise takes their homes. Here, Katerina Teaiwa points out the irony that the same nations that are currently refusing immigration did not have any problems spreading the 'dust of [her] ancestors' over their lands (2014, p. 198). Here, teaching can show how indigenous people have fought back, including legal proceedings, international campaigns, indigenous data networks, participation in global social governance (such as the UN Declaration on the Rights of Indigenous Peoples), poetry and the performing arts. These case studies not only highlight the interconnectedness of racism and environmental issues, but also illustrate how struggles that seem far away in space and time are connected to on-going events and conflicts 'closer to home' (for those of us based in Europe).

3.   Mediating Discomfort

The final theme, *mediating discomfort*, may appear quite random. Yet it is crucial when trying to address race and racism effectively in our learning and teaching praxis. Audrey Kobayashi, in one of the few examples that exists on this theme in geography, provides telling insights on classroom dynamics on a course titled 'Race and Racism':

> I am deeply aware that racism is an uncomfortable topic and that students must, in some way, face its uncomfortable realities if they are to learn and if, as I hope, they are to change. In the charged atmosphere of the classroom the shift from the intellectual to the emotional is often swift and unexpected. . . I feel sometimes as though I carry a bomb into class, and if I am unsuccessful in establishing the right degree of comfort (or discomfort) it will explode with irreversible results. The most important concern is that what is comfortable for some is uncomfortable for others, depending on the experiences of the individuals and groups that make up the class. (Kobayashi, 1999, p. 180)

The quote points to issues of (dis)comfort but discussing the effects of racism can also induce a mixture of anxiety, anger, confusion, frustration and in many cases guilt (cf. Jackson, 1989; Dwyer, 1999), as can the topic of ongoing colonial relations (Daigle and Sundberg, 2017). This is true both when a course/module is compulsory, and students might therefore be unprepared or reluctant to critically reflect on race-related issues, and when the course/module is optional. It is important that students who have had their bodies racially marked below the line of the human and have experienced racial oppression, and might constitute the minority group within the class, should not feel objectified by their classmates and/or instructors. Kobayashi (1999) notes, however, that efforts to ensure that students never feel singled out, or obligated to share their experiences, has to be balanced with the likelihood that some students will want to share their most difficult experiences and that these personal accounts can be a 'powerful way of conveying how racism works. . .[and] the reality of racism in a way that no amount of reading and analysis could have done' (p. 180).

Are there any examples of approaches that both harness the potential of voice and narrative, while alleviating the pressure on students to disclose their own experiences of racial violence? Kobayashi (1999) found that students responded positively to being provided with opportunities to use dramatisations to act out situations of everyday/subtle racism. The use of storytelling and counter-storytelling is a key aspect of CRT because it allows for the interrogation of myths, assumptions and stereotypes thereby subverting dominant normative and racist values (Gillborn, 2006). Peake and Kobayashi (2002) point to the potential of non-academic literature as a way to give voice to people that have experienced racism. This can also be achieved using other textual forms such as art, dance, film, and music (see hooks, 1994). Meanwhile Daigle and Sundberg (2017, p. 340), as part of what they term 'an embodied and accountable pedagogical praxis', invited local community leaders and activists as well as emerging critical race scholars, to share their grounded expertise with students. This created a learning space where leaders and scholar-activists from groups that had been marginalised and 'treated as objects of analysis within academia become authorising subjects of knowledge production, autonomy and empowerment' (ibid., p. 340).

These approaches appear and are diverse, but what connects them is a conceptualisation of teaching and learning about race and racism as contextually situated. They simultaneously recognise the experiential knowledge of people racialised below the line of the human, and ground instructional practices in the present and past realities of students, teachers and wider society. This contextual and grounded instructional practice is a key reason why the classroom becomes a space of discomfort when teaching about race and racism in geography, because it can result in a sense of guilt amongst students. For example, many readers of this chapter will be working in settings where most students are racialised as white and at the top of a racial hierarchy. Therefore, while all participants on the programme will have suffered oppression in relation to ideological hierarchies linked to, for example, their gender, class and/or sexuality, the contextualisation of experiences should make it apparent that those racialised as superior live all those oppressions *mitigated* by racial privilege (cf. Grosfoguel, 2016). Kobayashi found that this realisation and associated sense of guilt usually leads to two responses: remorse-sadness and anger-resentment (see also Jackson, 1989), and argues that in both cases it is important to convey to students that their guilt-related responses are neither healthy nor productive. Although challenging, teachers need to mediate this discomfort and guilt and use it productively to 'guide students towards seeing how racism and the maintenance of racial hierarchies have structured space in ways that are detrimental to almost everyone's interests' (Delaney, 2003, p. 12). We hope that by trying to know (y)our history and by finding a place for activism in the geography curriculum, we can start finding ways to make this happen, and dismantle these hierarchies.

CONCLUSION: A CURRICULUM AGAINST DOMINATION

This chapter provided a reference point for geographers seeking to learn and teach about race and racism. Significantly, by doing so, we also contributed to efforts by geographers striving to tackle the reproduction of 'white geographies' via geography curricula (Domosh, 2015). Central to our discussion was highlighting how pedagogies and curricula informed by insights from CRT and decolonial approaches can aid geographers to recognise the subjectivities, epistemologies and spiritualities of racially marginalised groups as part of a concerted effort to recognise and address racism. CRT and decolonial approaches insist that we must challenge the intent, form and content of our teaching as part of moves to rectify oppressive social structures in educational institutions and learning environments, as well as supporting efforts to unsettle ongoing colonial legacies (cf. Tejeda et al., 2003). Such an approach to learning and teaching would do more than just open up counter spaces against the dominant, or create classroom conditions more welcoming to diverse perspectives; it would constitute a *curriculum against domination* (De Lissovoy, 2010).

A curriculum against domination is one that recognises that the decentering of the dominant content and viewpoint is not the end game. Instead, we must go further and strive to provide both staff and students with tools to begin building new ways of learning, teaching and being that are based upon coexistence and respect, as opposed to domination, separation and assimilation (De Lissovoy, 2010). A curriculum against domination appears to be what geography as a discipline is crying out for when its members ask 'why is our curriculum so white?'. This chapter provided examples of key elements that could be incorporated within geography degree programmes as part of efforts to create such a framework. The more difficult task is to go from calling for change, to engaging in activism to make change happen. RGS-IBG RACE hope this chapter will be of use to those who are willing to join us and take this challenge on.

USEFUL RESOURCES

- Global Social Theory https://globalsocialtheory.org/.
- Indigenous Education Network https://www.oise.utoronto.ca/ien/.
- The Disorder of Things https://thedisorderofthings.com/.

REFERENCES

Ahmed, S. (2012) *On Being Included: Racism and Diversity in Institutional Life*. Durham, NC: Duke University Press.
Anderson, B. (1983) *Imagined Communities: Reflections on the Origin and Spread of Nationalism.* London: Verso.
Back, L. and Solomos, J. (2013) *Theories of Race and Racism: A Reader*. London: Routledge.
Berg, L.D. (2012) 'Geographies of identity I: geography–(neo) liberalism–white supremacy', *Progress in Human Geography*, 36(4), pp. 508–517.
Bonnett, A. (1997). 'Geography, "race" and whiteness: invisible traditions and current challenges', *Area*, 29(3), pp. 193–199.
Bressey, C. and Dwyer, C. (eds) (2012) *New Geographies of Race and Racism*. Aldershot: Ashgate.
Bulhan, H.A. (1985) *Frantz Fanon and the Psychology of Oppression*. New York: Plenum Press.

Bullard, R.D. (ed.) (1983) *Confronting Environmental Racism: Voices from the Grassroots*. Boston: South End Press.

Bullard, R.D. (1999) 'Dismantling environmental racism in the USA', *Local Environment: The International Journal of Justice and Sustainability*, 4(1), pp. 5–19.

Crenshaw, K. (1989) 'Demarginalizing the intersection of race and sex: a black feminist critique of antidiscrimination doctrine, feminist theory and antiracist politics', *University of Chicago Legal Forum*, 1(8), pp. 139–167

Daigle, M. and Sundberg, J. (2017) 'From where we stand: unsettling geographical knowledges in the classroom', *Transactions of the Institute of British Geographers*, 42(3), pp. 338–341.

Delaney, D. (2002) 'The space that race makes', *The Professional Geographer*, 54(1), pp. 6–14.

Delgado, R. and Stefancic, J. (2017) *Critical Race Theory: An Introduction*. New York: New York University Press.

De Lissovoy, N. (2010) 'Decolonial pedagogy and the ethics of the global', *Discourse: Studies in the Cultural Politics of Education*, 31, pp. 279–293.

Desai, V. (2017) 'Black and minority ethnic (BME) student and staff in contemporary British geography', *Area*, 49, pp. 320–323.

Desai, K. and Sanya, B.N. (2016) 'Towards decolonial praxis: reconfiguring the human and the curriculum', *Gender and Education*, 28(6), pp. 710–724.

Domosh, M. (2015, June 1) 'Why is our curriculum so white?' Association of American Geographers Newsletter. Available at http://news.aag.org/2015/06/why-is-our-geography-curriculum-so-white/ (accessed 19 July 2018).

Dwyer, O.J. (1999) 'Teaching about race and racism in geography: classroom and curriculum perspectives', *Journal of Geography*, 98(4), pp. 176–179.

Elliott-Cooper, A. (2017) 'Free, decolonised education: a lesson from the South African student struggle', *Area*, 49, pp. 332–334.

Esson, J. (2018) 'The why and the white: racism and curriculum reform in British Geography', *Area*, DOI 10.1111/area.12475.

Esson, J., Noxolo, P., Baxter, R., Daley, P. and Byron, M. (2017) 'The 2017 RGS-IBG chair's theme: decolonising geographical knowledges, or reproducing coloniality?', *Area*, 49(3), pp. 384–388.

Farbotko, C. (2010) 'Wishful sinking: disappearing islands, climate refugees and cosmopolitan experimentation', *Asia Pacific Viewpoint*, 51(1), pp. 47–60.

Gillborn, D. (2006) 'Critical race theory and education: racism and anti-racism in educational theory and praxis', *Discourse: Studies in the Cultural Politics of Education*, 27(1), pp. 11–32.

Glissant, E. (2010) *Poetics of Relation*. Ann Arbor, MI: University of Michigan Press.

Grosfoguel, R. (2016) 'What is racism?' *Journal of World-Systems Research*, 22(1), pp. 9–15.

Hau'ofa, E. (1993) 'Our sea of islands', in Waddell, E., Naidu, V. and Hau'ofa, E. (eds), *A New Oceania: Rediscovering our Sea of Islands*, pp. 2–16. Suva: School of Social and Economic Development, University of the South Pacific and Beake House.

Hobsbawm, E. and Ranger, T. (ed.) (1983) *The Invention of Tradition*. Cambridge: Cambridge University Press.

hooks, b. (1994) *Outlaw Culture: Resisting Representations*. New York: Routledge.

Jackson, P. (1989) 'Challenging racism through geography teaching', *Journal of Geography in Higher Education*, 13(1), pp. 5–14.

Kobayashi, A. (1999) '"Race" and racism in the classroom: some thoughts on unexpected moments', *Journal of Geography*, 98(4), pp. 179–182.

Kobayashi, A. (2014) 'The dialectic of race and the discipline of geography', *Annals of the Association of American Geographers*, 104(6), pp. 1101–1115.

Lane, T.M. (2018) 'The frontline of refusal: indigenous women warriors of standing rock', *International Journal of Qualitative Studies in Education*, 31(3), pp. 197–214.

Mahtani, M. (2006) 'Challenging the ivory tower: proposing anti-racist geographies within the academy', *Gender, Place & Culture*, 13(1), pp. 21–25.

Mahtani, M. (2014) 'Toxic geographies: absences in critical race thought and practice in social and cultural geography', *Social & Cultural Geography*, 15(4), pp. 359–367.

Maldonado-Torres, N. (2007) 'On the coloniality of being: contributions to the development of a concept', *Cultural Studies*, 21(2–3), pp. 240–270.

Maldonado-Torres, N. (2016) 'Outline of ten theses on coloniality and decoloniality'. Available at: http://frantzfanonfoundation-fondationfrantzfanon.com/article2360.html (accessed 28 July 2019).

Martinot, S. (2018) 'The coloniality of power: notes toward de-colonization'. Available at: https://www.ocf.berkeley.edu/~marto/coloniality.htm (accessed 19 July 2018).

Mbembe, A.J. (2016) 'Decolonizing the university: New directions', *Arts and Humanities in Higher Education*, 15(1), pp. 29–45.

McCoy, K., Tuck, E. and McKenzie, M. (eds) (2016) *Land Education: Rethinking Pedagogies of Place from Indigenous, Postcolonial, and Decolonizing Perspectives*. New York: Routledge.

McKittrick, K. (2006) *Demonic Grounds: Black Women and the Cartographies of Struggle*. Minneapolis: University of Minnesota Press.

McKittrick, K. (2011) 'On plantations, prisons, and a black sense of place', *Social & Cultural Geography*, 12(8), pp. 947–963.

McPherson, W. (1999) *The Stephen Lawrence Inquiry*. Report of an Inquiry. United Kingdom: The Stationary Office. Retrieved at: https://www.gov.uk/government/uploads/system/uploads/attachment_data/file/277111/4262.pdf.

Mignolo, W.D. (2008) 'Racism as we sense it today', *Publications of the Modern Languages Association of America*, 123(5), pp. 1737–1742.

Nayak, A. (2003) 'Last of the "real Geordies"? White masculinities and the subcultural response to deindustrialisation', *Environment and Planning D: Society and Space*, 21(1), pp. 7–25.

Painter, N.I. (2010) *The History of White People*. London: WW Norton & Company.

Peake, L. and Kobayashi, A. (2002) 'Policies and practices for an antiracist geography at the millennium', *The Professional Geographer*, 54(1), pp. 50–61.

Raghuram, P., Bornat, J. and Henry, L. (2011) 'The co-marking of aged bodies and migrant bodies: migrant workers' contribution to geriatric medicine in the UK', *Sociology of Health & Illness*, 33(2), pp. 321–335.

Raju, C.K. (2017) 'Black thoughts matter: decolonized math, academic censorship, and the "Pythagorean" proposition', *Journal of Black Studies*, 48(3), pp. 256–278.

Said, E. (1993) 'Culture and Imperialism', Lecture, York University, Toronto, 10 February.

Simbulan, R.G. (2016) 'Indigenous communities' resistance to corporate mining in the Philippines', *Peace Review*, 28(1), pp. 29–37.

Smith, L.T. (2012) *Decolonizing Methodologies: Research and Indigenous Peoples* (2nd edition). New York: Zed Books.

Tatlow, P. (2015) 'Participation of BME students in UK Higher Education', in Alexander, C. and Arday, J. (eds), *Aiming Higher: Race, Inequality and Diversity in the Academy*, London: Runnymede, pp. 10–13.

Teaiwa, K. (2014) *Consuming Ocean Island: Stories of People and Phosphate from Banaba*. Bloomington, IN: University of Indiana Press.

Tejeda, C., Espinoza, M. and Gutierrez, K. (2003) 'Toward a decolonizing pedagogy: social justice reconsidered', in Trifonas, P. (ed.), *Pedagogies of Difference: Rethinking Education for Social Change*, London: Routledge, pp. 9–38.

Tolia-Kelly, D.P. (2017) 'A day in the life of a geographer: "lone", black, female', *Area*, 49(3), pp. 324–328.

Tuck, E. and Yang, K.W. (2012) 'Decolonization is not a metaphor', *Decolonization: Indigeneity, Education and Society*, 1, pp. 1–40.

Walter, M. and Butler, K. (2013) 'Teaching race to teach indigeneity', *Journal of Sociology*, 49(4), pp. 397–410.

Warren, G. and Katz, C. (2014) Gwendolyn Warren and Cindi Katz in Conversation [video], https://vimeo.com/111159306.

Woods, C. (2017) *Development Arrested: The Blues and Plantation Power in the Mississippi Delta*. London: Verso Books.

18. Teaching challenging material: emotional geographies and geographies of death
Avril Maddrell and Edward Wigley

INTRODUCTION

Emotional-affective geographies have developed as a sub-field within geography since Anderson and Smith's (2001) call for greater attention to such matters within the discipline, consolidated by publications such as Davidson et al.'s (2005) *Emotional Geographies*, Smith et al.'s (2009) *Emotion, Place and Culture*, Anderson's (2014) *Encountering Affect* and the journal *Emotion, Society and Space*. These developments mean that all students taking courses in human geography in the UK should encounter emotional-affective geographies at one or more points within their degree. Emotions may underlie and/or be explicitly addressed in relation to demography, political geography, studies of inequalities at global, regional or local scales, and modules on feminist geographies or geographies of gender, when students may be encouraged to reflect on their emotional-affective-visceral responses to data, case studies and field trip encounters (see Davidson et al., 2009; Pierce and Widen, 2017). The emotional-affective charge of geographical content merits further reflection and this chapter addresses the design and delivery of, and responses to, a new module with a clear emotional geography subtext: geographies of death. The study of death may prompt engagement with environmental or social justice issues, but also has the potential to evoke personal memories, fears or distress amongst students; and thus requires some care in its delivery. Whilst previously understudied within geography courses (except demography components), geographies of death have become increasingly visible within the wider emotional geographies sub-discipline in recent years, as evidenced by publications such as 'Shadowed ground' (Foote 2003), *Deathscapes* (Maddrell and Sidaway, 2010) and *Memory, Mourning and Landscape* (Anderson et al., 2010), *Geographies of the Holocaust* (Knowles et al., 2014) as well as a special issue of *Social and Cultural Geography* (Vol. 17, No. 2: Geographies of Dying and Death). The study of geographies of death can be integrated into related modules or taught as a standalone module in undergraduate and postgraduate geography degree programmes.

This chapter relates to a full module and draws on the reflections of students and staff in response to content, learning activities and assessment. One large-scale study on the learning styles preferred by geography students suggested that geography students tend to prefer an 'Assimilator' learning style, that is the combination of abstract conceptualisation and reflective observation, characterised by theorisation, logic, identifying problems and testing hypotheses (Healey et al., 2005). This would suggest that geography students would not typically be familiar with, or possibly open to, more reflective styles of teaching. However, more active, reflective and participatory approaches to teaching (for example see Maddrell 2007; Askins 2008) have been developed within the university sector in the interim, alongside the burgeoning of modules on cultural and feminist geographies which encourage reflexivity. The pedagogical successes and challenges of the geographies of death module are discussed, including the ways in which to utilise the subject's obvious emotional resonance for effective teaching through student engagement.

THE GEOGRAPHIES OF DEATH MODULE

I previously didn't see death as a study, especially in geography. However, now looking at the landscape it is clear that there is evidence of death within the landscape and there is room for it to be studied further. . . (Female, human and physical geography student)

When students enrol for a university degree in geography it is unlikely that a module on death and dying was uppermost in their expectations, or death and bereavement among the ideas that fill the prospectuses of higher education geography programmes. As the quote above illustrates, beyond demographics, death is neglected as a geographic study despite its obvious spatial qualities (Maddrell and Sidaway, 2010). Yet sites of tragedy, atrocity and holocaust regularly feature on undergraduate geography field trips to Berlin, Auschwitz, Cambodia and New York as part of wider urban, cultural or political geography courses (as well as earlier school trips, notably for history). These field trips can be seen as contributing to, as well as studying, what is labelled as 'dark tourism', a topic which has prompted reflections on teaching challenging and emotionally sensitive subjects. Despite the bleakness, and difficulty of talking about such horrors, students have tended to appreciate the need for such discussion (Hartmann, 2002; Hatt, 2011).

Creating a new third year module on geographies of death inevitably presented potential practical and experiential challenges for both students and teachers, as explored below after a brief introduction to the module. In addition to reflection on this particular module, this chapter aims to touch on a wider agenda within pedagogy, notably, the need for more discussion of challenges and strategies amongst those designing and facilitating learning with explicit emotional-affective dimensions (Fem-Mentee Collective et al., 2017). Building on the emerging interventions to date, such as commentaries on emotional-affective geographies of peer mentoring (ibid.) and fieldwork (Davidson et al., 2009), this chapter also responds to the need to share insights on teaching 'difficult' subjects, and to continue the conversation on the emotional geographies of education (Kenway and Youdell, 2011).

Geographies of death was taught for the first time at the University of Reading in the 2017/18 academic year. Whilst elements of this optional module, such as mortality and death rates within demographics, would be familiar to students on any human/combined geography degree course, and the field trip element had been taught on another course at another university, to our knowledge this was the first time a full 20 credit (10 ECTS) level 6 (final year) geography module had been delivered on geographies of death. The introduction of the module was motivated by the desire to: a) develop an innovative module capitalising on research-led teaching; and b) address an important topic that impacts on all of us, rephrasing Anderson and Smith's (2001, p. 7) call for greater attention to emotions within geography: 'to neglect [death] is to exclude a key set of relations through which lives are lived and societies made'.

Whilst there has been limited engagement with teaching death-related subjects within

---

BOX 18.1   LEARNING OUTCOMES FOR GEOGRAPHIES OF DEATH

Learning outcomes:
By the end of this module, students will have:

1. An understanding of concepts such as life expectancy, mortality, extinction, memorialisation, deathscapes, 'dark tourism', therapeutic environments and necropolitics.
2. An ability to apply these concepts to historical and contemporary case studies in the Global North and South.
3. An understanding of the contestation of sites of death and remembrance and a range of strategies that are deployed to address these issues in different contexts.
4. An appreciation of the planning issues associated with deathscapes in a multicultural society such as the UK.
5. An ability to reflect critically on attitudes to dying, death and associated spaces and practices in contemporary society.

---

geography, there are a number of other social sciences and healthcare-related subjects where these topics are mainstream. In the introduction to his edited collection, *Teaching Death and Dying*, Moreman (2008) identifies that such courses are often present within anthropology, sociology and religious studies. Other degree programmes include those relating to the 'caring' professions such as nursing, social work or psychology, where modules such as 'Children and death' are core topics that relate to employment-related skills and knowledge (Corr, 2016). However, ultimately as Moreman (2008) suggests, the study and discussion of death is relevant to all, particularly in societies where the final stages of dying are often separated from wider public view in hospital.

As can be observed from the Learning Outcomes in Box 18.1, whilst the module is mainly focussed on emotional geographies, these intersect with analysis of inequalities, the global economy, the politics of service provision and geopolitics, as well as covering a range of cross-disciplinary topics relevant to students within and beyond human geography. Students will have had some engagement with emotional geographies (for example in discussing place attachment or the plight of refugees) before the final year module 'Geographies of death', but may take more than one module in the third year which includes explicit aspects of emotional geographies. Students from outside geography, or who specialise in physical geography, may have very limited familiarity with the topics and learning activities. The module was team taught and delivered via a range of taught sessions, practical activities and fieldwork, and assessed by compulsory but ungraded group presentations, individual assessed essays and an examination.

The key challenges to teaching this module are the perceptions of the subject matter (influencing recruitment to the optional module in the first instance), delivering the content in a relevant and engaging teaching programme, and dealing with content and issues which may be sensitive to both students and staff. Death and dying are difficult topics for many people and students may encounter life-threatening illness themselves or within their circle of kith and kin, or experience bereavement at any juncture of their degree course. Bereavement is an ongoing process that has the capacity to confront grieving individuals in a variety of real world and virtual spaces and places (Maddrell, 2016). Death, dying and dead bodies are often sequestered within modern societies. Hospitals, hospices, funeral directors, cemeteries and crematoriums often hide dying and dead bodies from public view. Consequently, many young adults will not have first-hand experience of bereavement. Teaching staff on modules and courses centred around death will need to ensure that students are prepared for the challenging emotions that the subject may bring, necessitating sensitivity in how the content is presented and to students' *dynamic* personal relations and circumstances. Likewise, the sensitivities of the teaching team, *their* own dynamic personal relations and circumstances, and the emotional labour which may be associated with teaching such material, requires a degree of mutual responsibility and care within the teaching team.

The topics of dying and bereavement can be particularly sensitive, whether or not students have previously come into contact with death or experienced death amongst their network of family and friends. Student experience may vary with country of origin as well as family circumstances. Within the context of predominantly nuclear households and long life expectancy, many European students aged 18–24 years may have very limited experience of bereavement, which can heighten the sense of isolation when seriously ill or bereaved, and add to the 'shock value' of course content (Garces-Foley, 2008). Other international students may have had different experiences and bring different perspectives (for example those from cultures where multi-generational households are the norm, or from countries with low life expectancy and high mortality rates).

Although subject matter relating to death can often be saddening, even tragic, classes dealing with death are not necessarily gloomy affairs. Corr (2016, p. 175) reports that: 'Classes are often punctuated with laughter, perhaps because both humor (sic.) and death frequently highlight our limitations as finite and mortal creatures along with the absurdity of many aspects of everyday life.' Similarly Garces-Foley (2008) presents an anecdote where during one field visit to a funeral home a student jumps onto an embalming table and changes the mood of the visit altogether. As this incident illustrates, humour can be a useful mechanism for dispelling tension. Teaching such subjects may therefore include a spectrum of emotions from laughter to sadness, and instead of denying the emotion, it can be useful to actively engage with emotion in order to highlight the real-life significance of the issues outside of the classroom (Pierce and Widen, 2017). In their urban geography classes, Pierce and Widen (2017) have found the employment of graphic descriptions that confront students with the daily realities of urban poverty stimulates the imagination to attain a fuller understanding of life in such settings. However, as Pierce and Widen evidence, evoking intense emotional responses can have pastoral implications which may be challenging to support in the UK HE context of limited contact hours. Some examples of these pastoral implications are discussed later in the chapter with reference to the assessments for this module.

Reflections on Teaching Geographies of Death

The following sections present some reflections by the authors, and other members of the teaching team for the geographies of death module, on delivering a challenging emotional topic. Materials drawn on include research 'postcards' asking students brief questions along with some basic demographic information (a method devised and utilised widely by Maddrell (for example see Maddrell, 2011). These voluntary postcards, completed by approximately half of the class, were supplemented by data from standard university end of module feedback evaluation forms completed by the students, as well as notes made by the teaching team. The chapter will now discuss and reflect upon the student experience of the module, including motivations and expectations, the module content and modes of delivery and finally assessed work.

The Student Cohort, their Motivations and Expectations

The module attracted 37 students in total (fairly typical for a specialist optional third year module) the majority of the intake was composed of those on a human geography or combined human and physical geography programme, with a slight preponderance of female students (see Table 18.1). Six students were drawn from physical geography, international development, and economics and geography. Out of the 19 students who answered our postcard survey, 15 students identified the uniqueness of the module topic as the attraction to them enrolling. The remaining four respondents explained that their enrolment on to geographies of death was due to limited options in Year 3 resulting from the unexpected cancellation of two modules due to staff illness and relocation. This resulted in these students being enrolled on a very different type of module than they had expected, presenting additional challenges for the teaching team to relate the subject matter to students with a diverse range of disciplinary interests and to 'translate' concepts and approaches that this small group of students lacked grounding in and familiarity with, such as emotional-affective and embodied geographies.

Students had varying expectations of the module. The module description emphasised spatial enquiry, incorporating geographical studies of deathscapes, planning and tourism and this was identified by many students as highlights within the module. However, the student below discusses what attracted her to the module and how it varied from her expectation:

> *It sounded different and potentially interesting. I thought it might go into emotions and accounts of people who are dying/ the experiences of those who had a loved one die.* (Female, human and physical geography student)

The quote above implies this particular student wanted *more* direct engagement with the emotions around dying and bereavement and expected a more social care or wellbeing centred content, rather than a geographical approach, and subsequently experienced some disappointment with the module.

Table 18.1   Enrolled students by gender and degree programme

Programme	Female	Male	Total
Human Geography	8	4	*12*
Human and Physical Geography	10	9	*19*
Physical Geography	0	1	*1*
Geography and Economics	0	1	*1*
International Development	3	1	*4*
Total	*21*	*16*	*37*

Module Content, Pedagogical Approach and Reflections

Module content incorporated five broad topics in geographies of death and death-scapes: mortality and morbidity, memorialisation, diversity and planning, religion, 'dark tourism' and the idea of 'taboo' associated with death and remembrance. These topics link to the learning outcomes outlined above and reflect an effort to link with familiar geographical content but also to draw on recent research developments to push the boundaries of what was presumed to be 'geographical'. Students reported enjoyment across most of these topics and activities in their formal evaluation of the module and the research 'postcards'. 'Dark tourism' and the end of module session on 'death as taboo?' were identified as the most interesting/enjoyable sessions (which was also reflected in assessed essay and exam question choices taken by the students). Whilst the comments were generally brief, one student did provide a reason for their interest in dark tourism: '*Dark tourism – I like seeing how other people in different countries use death as a source of income/economy e.g. selling souvenirs at Ground Zero*' (female, human and physical geography student). Student contact time centred on a weekly two-hour 'Lectorial' (typically a lecture with some student-centred activities) and a one-hour seminar (which ranged from reading-based discussions to group poster sessions and craft activities).

At the centre of the module there were two local field trips: one tutor-led tour to Reading's old cemetery and the second, a small group self-guided field trip to Reading's main cemetery and crematoria which is in current use. These field trips enabled students to put the theory and taught material into practice and understand how it related to 'real world' deathscapes.

Alongside lectures, the seminar hour was used primarily for discussion of reading, debating issues and practical activities that could present the themes being discussed that week in a less formal, more discursive and 'hands-on' format. Such activities included making posters, outlining key discussion points around cremations for minority religious groups (Table 18.2 below summarises the points from one student poster), designs for online memorial websites (Figure 18.1a), and modelling physical memorials (Figure 18.1b) in plasticine and Lego. Reflecting on student engagement with the discussion of planning-related issues associated with diversity-ready cemeteries and crematoria in the UK illustrated in Figure 18.1, one of the teaching team commented: '*I was really surprised by students' engagement in the planning assignment during the Deathscapes and Diversity seminar, and think this worked well because it fitted with their own prospects [future employment], internships and other courses. Thus, the combination of academic insights, practice insights, and personal discussion was very valuable*' (Module Tutor 4 notes). This highlights student appreciation of meshing of their academic study with applied examples of contemporary issues and policy – and how this in turn related to future employment prospects/employability.

Fieldtrips to the cemeteries were an essential component of the module; allowing students to explore the theoretical ideas around memorialisation and deathscapes (for example Maddrell's (2016) Mapping Grief paper discussed at the outset the module), in a 'real world' setting. Cemeteries are often considered to be spaces of silence, solemnity and stillness. Yet as Deering (2010) identifies, there is a great variety of life and lifestyles being enacted in cemeteries from biodiversity in green spaces to dog walking and antisocial behaviour. The fieldwork enabled the traditional image of cemeteries to be destabilised

Table 18.2   *Student poster content summarising small group discussion on the provision of designated rivers for Hindu and Sikh cremation ash scattering in the UK*

Poster heading	Poster bullet points and labelled arrows
Key stakeholders	<ul><li>Councillors;</li><li>Sikh and Hindu communities;</li><li>Residents of chosen local site location;</li><li>Environment Agency (specific river catchment)</li></ul>
Possible obstacles	<ul><li>local residents might not want ashes spread in river near them;</li><li>providing suitable parking facilities (plus wheelchair or pram access at the river) alongside privacy for the ceremony;</li><li>geographic location may not meet all requirements;</li><li>mobility/public transport;</li><li>approval from Environment Agency (water quality);</li><li>local development plan doesn't meet requirements;</li><li>communication between religious community and council.</li></ul>
Bad practices	<ul><li>use of a boat – accessibility and safety issues;</li><li>lack of communication between communities and local council;</li><li>potential lack of understanding of specific religious requirements (last rites).</li></ul>
Suggestions for improvement	<ul><li>communication between stakeholders – bereavement conference style;</li><li>diversity in deathscape in local community plan, e.g. time limits;</li><li>consider all aspects of accessibility, e.g. wheelchair, pram, public transport, and all aspects of intersectionality.</li></ul>

through practical exploration of the site. Indeed, several students reported evidence of drinking, drug-taking and homelessness within the older, less used cemetery, evoking a range of emotional responses for the students. Part of the task of the two cemetery field trips involved identifying and analysing the changes in site organisation and memorialisation styles between the older cemetery and the contemporary cemetery-crematorium in Reading. Like other large towns and cities in the UK, in Reading the demographic profile and social attitudes towards death has changed considerably during this timeframe, notably with the shift from burials to cremations as the predominant mode of bodily disposal, a growth in both individualised and secular memorials, and a more culturally diverse population. The two sites evidenced and illustrated these transformations, noted as highlights on the module by several students:

> *Cemetery exercise – found that it was useful to compare and made me think independently.* (Female, human and physical geography student)

> *Going to see the graves and putting theory to practice.* (Female, human and physical geography student)

> *Visiting the cemeteries to see the changes in real life.* (Female, international development student)

One of the module tutors with little experience of geography and geography students commented:

> *During the cemetery visit . . . they were not merely seeing things but really observing and questioning the place. I thought that their observations at the cemetery, as they were discussing what they were encountering, were actually much richer than the points that they brought back in their presentations.* (Module Tutor 4 notes)

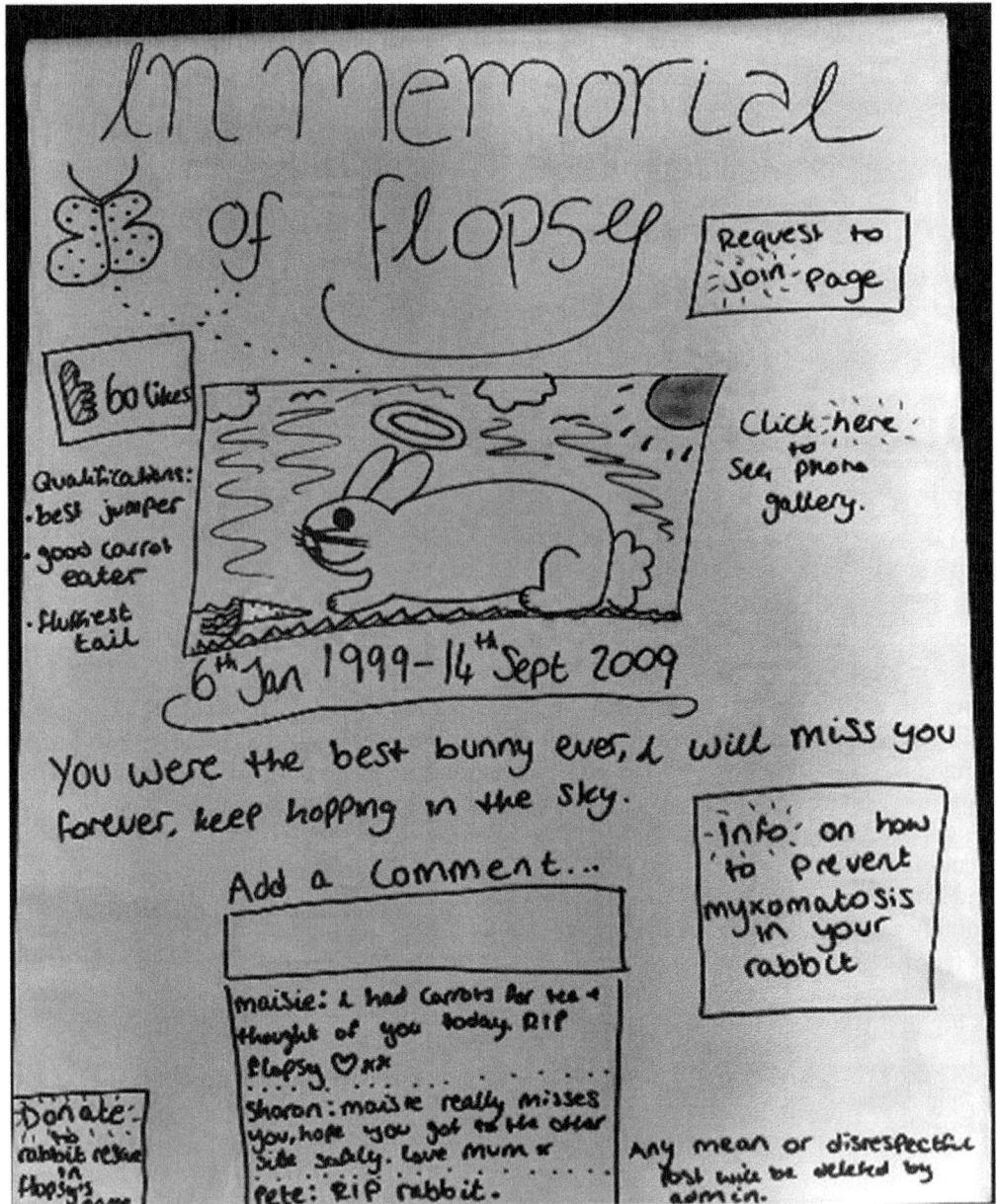

Figure 18.1a   Design for an online pet memorial website

Figure 18.1b   Model for a physical memorial site 'Letters to You', where individuals remove a brick from the wall and place a message inside to the deceased

Whilst crediting the students' insights it raises questions about study skills and effective recording of field observations and use in subsequent work. As students were asked to produce a presentation based on the fieldwork, in future iterations of the module further guidance could be provided on making and analysing fieldnotes to maximise the learning potential of the cemetery trips. Assessment in the field could also be considered.

These field work activities raise issues of sensitivity to cemetery visitors as well as students and staff. Given the minimal number of visitors to the old cemetery, this was deemed an appropriate place for the initial whole group tutor-led field trip, confirmed by health and safety review and liaison with local authority cemetery managers. Conversely, Reading's main cemetery-crematorium is in constant use for funerals, burials, cremations and regular visitors. Out of respect for current users and visitors, students were asked to visit this site in small groups of two to four and given clear guidance on being attentive to other users of the cemetery, especially if there was a funeral taking place, and to undertake their research sensitively (for example noise levels, taking photographs and moving to another area of the large memorial gardens if a funeral was taking place). One student reported their emotional response to the field work due to bereavement. '*In the past few months I have lost a family member and the cemetery visit had an emotional impact on me*' (male, human geography student). This illustrates the potential emotional vulnerabilities of such topics and activities (Garces-Foley, 2008), and it is important to remember that students have dynamic social lives which tutors are not always privy to, and that illness or bereavement can occur at any time, heightening those vulnerabilities. Sometimes even what appear to be less obvious topics may trigger upsetting thoughts or memories: '*Care homes upsetting* – [the topic was] *close to home*' (female, human geography student). This highlights that particular places and even minor reference to a sensitive topic (in this instance care homes) may be an affective trigger provoking an amplified emotional response (Maddrell, 2009, 2013, 2016). Teaching staff should therefore be sensitive to the variety of possible backgrounds and experiences of the students, as well as potentially changing circumstances between signing up for and undertaking/completing the module. At the outset of the module, these possible responses were identified and acknowledged, the module guide included contacts for university and bereavement counselling services, and students were encouraged to contact a member of the teaching team if the module content and activities proved personally challenging, which two students did.

The final taught session of the module exploring 'taboo' associated with death in Western societies included a short introductory lecture and activity-based workshop when students chose two of three activities: i) Mexican Day of the Dead craft; ii) 'death café' style discussion with refreshments; and iii) 'meet the ancient dead' skeleton analysis session with a forensic archaeologist. Both the content and the practical nature of the workshop proved popular with students, evidenced by student engagement and comments in class and the following feedback on aspects of the module that were found particularly interesting: '*Just having an informal conversation at the death café activity*' (male, physical geography student). This student, on a physical geography degree programme, also reported that the module had widened the scope of geography for him. This suggests that the fieldwork, applied topics and workshop activities in this module may have helped bridge the gap between human or cultural geography, often taught in abstract terms, and physical geography, often considered to be a more applied physical science subject. The majority of students opted to attend, and were fascinated by, the forensic archaeologist's workshop centred on two medieval skeletons, which included a research protocol for historic human remains, and identifying evidence of their lives and deaths from their bones. One student, who had been uncertain at the prospect of viewing the skeleton in the first instance, overcame those fears, but was then troubled about the ethics of keeping human remains in a scientific collection, a question which has prompted debate in many archaeological and museum collections, especially concerning colonial and indigenous remains (Cassman, Odegaard and Powell, 2007; Morton, 2017; also see Davidson et al.'s 2009 account by teaching staff and students on their visit to Gunther Hagen's Body Worlds 2 exhibition which centred on flayed and plastinated human remains placed in 'living' poses). During the 'Mexico's Day of the Dead' craft activity in the workshop, one teaching colleague was surprised that whilst the initial explanation of the activity at the start of the session was met with some amusement, many of the students chose the activity nonetheless. Furthermore, the practical activity relaxed students and created a time-space for informally talking about and reflecting on their experiences of death and bereavement, even if they opted not to participate in the more direct discussion of these topics in the death café group activity.

I asked at the start of the activity what motivated them to choose the module. One student explained that they had experienced deaths in the family over the past few years. This had made him and his family properly discuss death openly for the first time. He felt that it was difficult to do so at first, but that it is much more comfortable to now. Due to these experiences, he wanted to continue thinking and learning about death, and the module offered him this opportunity. One student remarked that the colouring-in was very relaxing, and they could understand why it had recently become popular with adults. (Module Tutor 3 notes)

This observation replicates other studies of young people's communication which suggest they may be more comfortable talking about experiences, concerns etc. in less direct settings and activities, for example talking while in the car or walking: 'contexts through which intimacies can be interwoven within narratives of the mundane ordinariness of the everyday' (Ross et al., 2009).

Whilst sensitivity is needed when asking students to reflect on their own experiences, beliefs etc., being overly-cautious in order to avoid possible distress is likely to restrict the emotional range of the subject matter or risk presenting overly-sterilised content. Indeed, the emotional weight behind some of the topics can help drive student engagement as its meaningfulness is more apparent, which, in turn, can lead to critical questions being raised and discussed.

For instance, the session on dark tourism was able to draw upon the emotional weight of the events at Auschwitz, in Poland or the World Trade Center Memorial, New York, and allows for the relationship between these events and subsequent commercialisation or sanitisation for a tourist market to be questioned by students. Additionally, socialist-materialist critiques of the unequal distribution of mortality and its relationship to the economy (for example Dorling, 2010; Tynor, 2016) is lent greater potency for students when applied to the topical contemporary issue of the working and living conditions and associated high mortality amongst migrants from the Indian subcontinent employed in the construction of Qatar's 2022 World Cup infrastructure.

Overall student feedback indicates that the balance and tone of the module seems to have been pitched appropriately and been well-received:

Sensitive – as it's a charged topic but I have enjoyed learning more. (Female, human and physical geography student)

All been approached sensitively. (Male, human geography student)

Not upsetting, thought provoking about personal experiences of death. (Female, human geography student)

However, the student who earlier reported expecting more emotional and personal accounts of death and dying in the module commented: '*thought it would be much more personal or upsetting which perhaps would have been more interesting*' (female, human and physical geography student). Whilst emotion was referred to in the student feedback on the module, it should be noted that generally very little emotion was visible amongst students in class. Indeed, a teaching colleague on the module remarked about the absence of emotion compared to similar content delivered in other disciplines at other universities. Whilst some students expressed shock at the working conditions and deaths of migrants at the Qatar stadium during a seminar and others reported some sensitivity regarding the fieldtrip, this was not always apparent *during* the sessions. However, students were more forthcoming in the 'death as taboo?' workshop at the end of the module, perhaps reflecting the environment offered by the nexus of the activities; the benefits from insights from across the module; and greater freedom for reflection, sharing and allowing emotional expression (including vulnerabilities) in the small group activities in this final taught session at the end of their degree course. It should also be noted that because students were drawn from four different degree course cohorts, they may not have been familiar with everyone or felt comfortable to express emotions within the wider group. In reviewing the first run of the module, the team has reflected on the content and timing of particular sessions, including the taboo workshop:

> *Crafts and death café worked brilliantly. I continue to wonder whether these activities fit better at the beginning or the end of the course. Before the module, I did wonder whether putting them at the beginning would add anything – in terms of making the topic more everyday or easier to discuss in relation to what students have encountered in their own lives. Now, I think it was perfect at the end of the module.* (Module Tutor 4 notes)

However, these do not need to be seen as mutually-exclusive options, a practical activity of this nature at the beginning of the module may facilitate and foster students' informal discussion of the emotional geographies of death and bereavement from the outset of the module.

Seminar activities throughout the module did engage students in a range of practical tasks and craft (such as designing memorials). The success of the final session with further craft and death café activities, as well as the field trips, suggest that varied student-centred active learning opportunities suited students with different learning styles, mapped on to as well as transcending notions of 'doing geography', enabled a consolidation of theoretical work, and diffused the emotional intensity of the module content.

Some vulnerabilities did surface in relation to assessments. Whilst for the majority of students the assessment took place without any issues, there were two students for whom the exam presented some challenges. The first student spoke to the teaching team regarding concerns about the exam and content as a family member had been diagnosed with a terminal illness; the combination of worry, stress and anxiety of final examinations and the module subject matter prompted concerns for this student. After discussions with the teaching team, personal tutors and student support services, provision was made for the student to complete the examination in a separate room from the main sitting, affording privacy and the opportunity to take a break if necessary.

The second student's experience only became apparent to teaching staff during exam marking when the student wrote at length of their own experience of bereavement with the loss of their grandmother. The student identified the sense of 'taboo' associated with death present within their own family who remained largely silent about the obviously impending death of the student's grandmother. Frustration was expressed at this silence and the student believed they had made the most of the relationship with the grandmother by being open about these events. Such accounts illustrate how the sensitive topic of death can amplify and allow for personal circumstances to travel and affect academic work (in the first student's case) and how academic work can travel, mobilising emotions and affect and impact on personal responses as well as providing analytical, theoretical and policy-oriented insight.

CONCLUSION AND RECOMMENDATIONS

This chapter has considered and reflected upon the teaching team's experience of delivering an innovative module, based on challenging material due to it containing potentially charged emotional-affective content. This content may go beyond many students' preconceptions of what does and doesn't constitute 'geography' *per se*. Students were clearly convinced of the geographical nature of death, dying and bereavement by the end of the module, but the range of geographical issues and analytical threads will be developed in future module runs. This will include enhancing teaching on environmental loss and extinction, and social justice issues locally and internationally, and reflecting this breadth in assessment topics. These topics will strengthen the module's roots in wider geographical scholarship, make more explicit links to pressing global issues, and provide those interested primarily in the physical environment or development issues to explore geographies of death in relation to their core interests through their own assignment-led research. It is hoped that this will enhance student motivation, engagement and ultimately learning on the course – whilst still leaving scope for students to learn through encountering unanticipated topics and modes of learning.

Teaching staff for such modules have to be sensitive not only to the emotional aspects of content, but also the more unanticipated affective responses, as well as any additional challenge of including students from other fields or related disciplines who may not have the grounding or disciplinary vocabulary with which to conceptually frame and articulate their studies at the outset. Applied case studies and activities can help here as most content covered in the geographies of death module could be identified in 'real world' case studies and datasets where theoretical approaches can be evaluated. The field trips were central to this process and well-received by students, but required careful logistical planning and preparation as it was important to be aware that this may be a students' first visit to a cemetery or conscious encounter with a deathscape, and may act as an emotional-affective trigger for those who have experienced bereavement.

The emotional dimension of the content is not unique to geographies of death – modules addressing homelessness, domestic violence, geographies of crime, human trafficking, refugees, gentrification, inequalities and other social justice issues are all examples of topics with emotional-affective impact; but death and bereavement ultimately affect us all and those most important to us. The subject of death is clearly something that has the potential to be off-putting to some students, but a draw to others. Whilst some of the module material was emotionally powerful for some, student responses indicate that emotional responses should not be seen as undesirable per se. Students taking geography modules dealing with challenging content will be able to reflect on and share personal views and experiences at times and in spaces where they feel safe to do so, and this should be respected rather than forced. The emotional intensity of the subject matter can also be employed to highlight the significance and value of the content, prompting engagement with topics and issues both within and beyond the university setting. Student feedback indicates that staff should not shy away from or attempt to neutralise the emotional dimensions of the content, instead staff should be sensitive to the variety of experiences and backgrounds of students and their reactions to topics and activities – particularly as these reactions may not always be immediately discernible. Varied small-group student-centred activities are effective in accommodating a variety of learning styles as well as accommodating student engagement, reinforcing the value of the content for students, and providing 'safe' spaces for students to share and reflect on the more emotional-affective dimensions of their learning and personal experience.

USEFUL RESOURCES

- Maddrell, A. (2016) 'Mapping grief: a conceptual framework for understanding the spatialities of bereavement, mourning and remembrance', *Social and Cultural Geography*, 17 (2), pp. 166–188 [https://doi.org/10.1080/14649365.2015.1075579] (Open Access).
- *Diversity-ready Cemeteries and Crematoria in England and Wales*, briefing note and visual resources at www.deathscapesanddiversity.org.uk

ACKNOWLEDGEMENTS

Our thanks to all the students who participated in the module, provided feedback and agreed to share examples of their group work activities; thanks also to Brenda Mathijssen and Danny McNally who contributed to and shared their reflections on teaching this module; and to Katie McClymont, co-developer of the original student-directed field trip activity.

REFERENCES

Anderson, B. (2014) *Encountering Affect: Capacities, Apparatuses, Conditions*. Farnham: Ashgate.

Anderson, B. and Smith, S.J. (2001) 'Editorial: emotional geographies', *Transactions of the Institute of British Geographers*, 26, pp. 7–10.

Anderson, E., Maddrell, A., McLouglin, K. and Vincent, E. (eds) (2010) *Memory, Mourning, Landscape*. Amsterdam: Rodophi.

Askins, K. (2008) 'In and beyond the classroom: research ethics and participatory pedagogies', *Area*, 40, pp. 500–509.

Cassman, V., Odegaard, N. and Powell, J.F. (2007) *Human Remains: Guide for Museums and Academic Institutions*. Lanham, MD: Rowman Altamira.

Corr, C.A. (2016) 'Teaching about life and living in courses on death and dying', *OMEGA Journal of Death and Dying*, 73 (2), pp. 174–187.

Davidson, J., Bondi, L. and Smith, M. (eds) (2005) *Emotional Geographies*. Aldershot: Ashgate.

Davidson, J., Huff, L., Bridgen, J., Carolan, A., Chang, A., Ennis, K., Loynes, K. and Miller, J. (2009) '"Doing gender" at Body Worlds: embodying field trips as affective educational experience', *Journal of Geography in Higher Education*, 33 (3), pp. 303–314.

Deering, B. (2010) 'From anti-social behaviour to X-rated: exploring the social diversity and conflict in the cemetery', in Avril Maddrell and James D Sidaway (eds), *Deathscapes: Spaces for Death, Dying, Mourning and Remembrance*. Farnham: Ashgate.

Dorling, D. (2010) 'All connected? Geographies of race, death, wealth, votes and births', *The Geographical Journal*, 176 (3), pp. 186–198.

Fem-Mentee Collective, Bain, A.L., Baker, R., Laliberté, N., Milan, A., Payne, W.J., Ravensbergen, L. and Saad, D. (2017) 'Emotional masking and spill-outs in the neoliberalized university: a feminist geographic perspective on mentorship', *Journal of Geography in Higher Education*, 41 (4), pp. 590–607.

Foote, K. (2003) *Shadowed Ground: America's Landscapes of Violence and Tragedy* (2nd edn). Austin: University of Texas Press.

Garces-Foley, K. (2008) 'Teaching outside the classroom', in Christopher M. Moreman (ed.), *Teaching Death and Dying*. Oxford: Oxford University Press.

Hartmann, R. (2002) 'Forum: "places of horror we should never forget" – approaches to teaching the holocaust, atrocity sites and pariah landscapes in the classroom', *International Research in Geographical and Environmental Education*, 11 (4), pp. 354–358.

Hatt, C. (2011) 'Teaching the holocaust through geography', *Teaching Geography*, 36 (4), pp. 108–110.

Healey, M., Kneale, P. and Bradbeer, J. (2005) 'Learning styles among geography undergraduates: an international comparison', *Area*, 37 (1), pp. 30–42.

Kenway, J. and Youdell, D. (2011) 'The emotional geographies of education: beginning a conversation', *Emotion, Space and Society*, 4 (3), pp. 131–136.

Knowles, K.A., Cole, T. and Giordano, A. (2014), *Geographies of the Holocaust*, Bloomington, IN: Indiana University Press.

Maddrell, A. (2007) 'Teaching a contextual and feminist history of geography through role play: women's membership of the RGS (1892–3)', *Journal of Geography in Higher Education*, 31, pp. 393–412.

Maddrell, A. (2009) 'A place for grief and belief: the Witness Cairn, Isle of Whithorn, Galloway, Scotland', *Social & Cultural Geography*, 10 (6), pp. 675–693.

Maddrell, A. (2011) '"Praying the Keeills": rhythm, meaning and experience on pilgrimage journeys in the Isle of Man', *Landabrefid*, 25, pp. 15–29.

Maddrell, A. (2013) 'Moving and being moved: more-than-walking and talking on pilgrimage walks in the Manx landscape', *Culture and Religion*, 14 (1), pp. 63–77.

Maddrell, A. (2016) 'Mapping grief. A conceptual framework for understanding the spatial dimensions of bereavement, mourning and remembrance', *Social & Cultural Geography*, 17 (2), pp. 166–188.

Maddrell, A. and Sidaway, J.D. (2010) 'Introduction: bringing a spatial lens to death, dying, mourning and remembrance', in Avril Maddrell and James D. Sidaway (eds), *Deathscapes: Spaces for Death, Dying, Mourning and Remembrance*. Farnham: Ashgate.

Moreman, C.M. (2008) 'Introduction', in Christopher M. Moreman (ed.), *Teaching Death and Dying*. Oxford: Oxford University Press.

Morton, S. (2017) *The Legacies of the Repatriation of Human Remains from the Royal College of Surgeons of England*. PhD Thesis. Oxford: University of Oxford.

Pierce, J. and Widen, H. (2017) 'Visceral pedagogy: teaching challenging topics emotionally as well as cognitively', *Journal of Geography*, 116 (2), pp. 47–56.

Ross, N.J., Renold, E., Holland, S. and Hillman, A. (2009) 'Moving stories: using mobile methods to explore the everyday lives of young people in public care', *Qualitative Research*, 9 (5), pp. 605–623.

Smith, M., Davidson, J., Cameron, L. and Bondi, L. (2009) *Emotion, Culture and Place*. Farnham: Ashgate.

Tynor, J.A. (2016) 'Population geography III: precarity, dead peasants and truncated life', *Progress in Human Geography*, 40 (2), pp. 275–289.

19. Geography as responsibility: sustainability through teaching and learning within geography
Zoe P. Robinson

INTRODUCTION

This chapter is underpinned by the questions of what are our responsibilities as educators of geographers within higher education and what are the responsibilities of our students as higher education trained geographers? Perhaps these are not the questions that we ask ourselves day to day, yet they are important questions on which we should regularly reflect and should be at the centre of the decisions we make as educators. Such questions are at the heart of the field of 'education for sustainable development' (ESD), which considers the contribution of education to support a more sustainable future for our global societies and the ecosystems upon which we depend.

This chapter explores the relationship between geography as a discipline and the growing sustainability agenda within higher education and broader society, how our work as educators in higher education may be positioned within the wider sustainability agenda, and the implications for our pedagogies and practice.

GEOGRAPHY AND SUSTAINABILITY

There are myriad definitions of both geography and sustainability and an exploration of these is necessary to understand the relationship between these two fields. Geography is traditionally recognised as an integrative discipline, spanning both the natural and social sciences. The Royal Geographical Society (2017) refers to geography as being 'unique in bridging the social sciences (human geography) with the natural sciences (physical geography)'. The QAA geography benchmark statement (2014a, p. 6) states that geography occupies 'a distinctive place in the world of learning offering an integrated study of the complex, reciprocal relationships between human societies and the physical, chemical and biological components of the Earth'. This breadth has been seen as both a weakness and a strength of the discipline. For example, Bennett (2013, p. 107) states that 'Geography has historically been and continues to be a pluralistic "big tent" discipline without a core identity', while this 'plurality of ways of knowing and understanding the world' is also described as 'a valued characteristic' (QAA, 2014a, p. 6).

The most often used definition of sustainable development is that of the World Commission for Environment and Development (1987, p. 44), often referred to as the 'Brundtland Report': 'development that meets the needs of the present without compromising the ability of future generations to meet their own needs'. There have been many critiques of this definition, including discussion of the oxymoron that it seems to encapsulate (Redclift, 2005). Some authors view the terms sustainable development as synonymous with sustainability, while others do not (Sartori et al., 2014). For the purpose of this chapter, the term sustainability will be adopted as opposed to sustainable development, and a definition of sustainability that puts the relationship between humans and the non-human environment at the core of our understanding of sustainability is used: 'sustainability represents a condition or set of conditions whereby human and natural systems can continue indefinitely in a state of mutual well-being, security and survival' (Jones et al., 2010, p. 19).

Geography is one of the most prominent and oldest disciplines concerned with the links between humans and the environment (Grindsted, 2013), and hence sustainability can be considered 'natural territory' for geography and geographers (Chalkley et al., 2010). David Harvey (1969, p. 115) wrote that the 'theme of man-environment relations has never been far from the heart of geographical research, and for many it has functioned as the overriding theme'. This long history of interest in human–environment relations is therefore seen by some as highlighting the important role of geography in contributing to creating better solutions to the complex socio-ecological problems that we face (Widener et al., 2014). Yet despite this long tradition, geography has increasingly suffered from what Grindsted (2015a, p. 322) refers to as 'ontological dualism', splitting itself into increasingly divergent human and physical geographies, and weakening the historical interdisciplinary view of the world necessary to understanding these complex inter-relations.

Emerging more recently is the term 'sustainability science', representing the emergence of what is seen as a new field of problem-driven interdisciplinary research grounded in 'seeking to understand the fundamental character of interactions between nature and society', and 'meeting human needs while simultaneously sustaining the life support systems of the planet' (Kates, 2001, p. 1). Sustainability science is said to be defined 'by the problems it addresses rather than by the disciplines it employs' (Clark, 2007, p. 1737), and hence aims to draw different disciplines together to address particular sustainability challenges. Sustainability science has tended to view this interdisciplinary space as something new (Bennett, 2013, p. 99), yet to a geographer, there may seem to be many similarities with what sustainability science aims to do, and the discipline of geography. For example, the QAA (2014a) benchmark statement for geography is permeated by sustainability concepts, and how geographers can contribute to these agendas, for example:

> Geographers can take a global view, but are able to inter-relate global and local perspectives. Geographers are aware of the relevance of geographical concepts, techniques and expertise to problem solving, wealth creation, poverty reduction and improving the quality of life and well-being, for example, in the context of climate change, urban and rural planning, hazard assessment, sustainability and environmental management. (QAA 2014, p. 10)

Yet there are many criticisms of how geography has failed to engage with or to take a leading role in sustainability science debates and this rapidly growing and societally important research agenda (for example Peet, 1985; Eflen, 2004). This perceived current failure for geography 'to exert itself in the birth of sustainability science" is seen as "the latest failure by geography to take its place as a discipline essential to solving pressing environmental problems' (Bennett, 2013, p. 99). For geography educators, as well as researchers, it becomes an issue of responsibility if we wish to ensure that geography is visibly at the heart of such pressing educational and research agendas.

GEOGRAPHY AND EDUCATION FOR SUSTAINABLE DEVELOPMENT

The role of education in working towards a more sustainable future is widely acknowledged, reinforced by myriad international initiatives starting with the UN Conference on Environment and Development in Rio de Janeiro in 1992, the United Nations Decade for Education for Sustainable Development (ESD) (2005–2014), the 2012 Higher Education for Sustainability Initiative for Rio+20, and the role of education in the UN's Sustainable Development Goals (SDGs) ratified in 2015. Although a major focus of the specific SDG of 'quality education' is on inclusivity and access to education, it includes a target for 'all learners [to] acquire the knowledge and skills needed to promote sustainable development' by 2030 (UN, undated).

Universities can contribute to a more sustainable future in different ways, including through the sustainability of their campuses, their research, their links with businesses and the wider community, and through their educational activities, and international ESD initiatives have had an impact nationally on higher education policy. For example, in England in 2005, the Higher Education Funding Council for England stated that 'within the next ten years, the higher education sector in this country will be recognized as a major contributor to society's efforts to achieve sustainability – through the skills and knowledge that its graduates learn and put into practice, and through its own strategies and operations' (HEFCE, 2005/28). Many authors have gone on to emphasise the importance of the educational role, and the potential for universities to provide large numbers of graduates with the knowledge, skills, and values to help business, government and society progress towards more sustainable practices (for example Chalkley, 2006). Indeed, HEFCE's original 2005 document went on to say that 'the greatest contribution education has to make to sustainable development is by enabling students to develop new values, skills and knowledge. The main (though not only) way to make this happen is through developments in curricula and pedagogy' (HEFCE, 2005/28, p. 20).

In response to growing interest in the field of ESD, and acknowledging a skills gap in teaching staff, in 2014, the Quality Assurance Agency, an independent body which oversees standards and quality in UK education, published a document entitled *Education for Sustainable Development: Guidance for UK Higher Education Providers* (QAA, 2014b). This guidance defines education for sustainable development as: 'the process of equipping students with the knowledge and understanding, skills and attributes needed to work and live in a way that safeguards environmental, social and economic wellbeing, both in the present and for future generations' (QAA, 2014b, p. 5). More specifically, the guidance goes on to say that:

education for sustainable development means working with students to encourage them to:

- consider what the concept of global citizenship means in the context of their own discipline and in their future professional and personal lives;
- consider what the concept of environmental stewardship means in the context of their own discipline and in their future professional and personal lives;
- think about issues of social justice, ethics and wellbeing, and how these relate to ecological and economic factors;

- develop a future-facing outlook; learning to think about the consequences of actions, and how systems and societies can be adapted to ensure sustainable futures.

(QAA, 2014b, p. 5)

The QAA also produces 'benchmark statements' for different disciplines, which like the ESD guidance are authored by the academic subject community, and aim to outline what can be expected from graduates of different disciplines.

Despite the strong synergies with geography and sustainability, the benchmark statement for geography only explicitly mentions sustainability twice (this is less than in many other subject benchmark statements, and considerably less than the cognate benchmark statement 'earth sciences, environmental sciences and environmental studies'). 'Sustainable development' is referred to only once, and specifically as a specialism under the strand of 'environmental geography' (a suggested third strand of geography alongside human and physical geography). One of the two times that sustainability is mentioned explicitly is in the context that geography students' knowledge base should be expected to include 'a critical evaluation of the concepts underlying development and sustainability' (QAA, 2014a, p. 9). Yet several aspects of the geography benchmark statement refer explicitly to areas covered by the QAA's definition and goals of ESD and are crucial in our tackling of sustainability issues, such as awareness of the global context of learning, inequality, understanding drivers of change, and the use of systems frameworks.

That sustainability is mentioned only twice in the closest thing to a geography higher education 'curriculum', including reference to a critique of the concept, chimes with findings elsewhere about how the concept of sustainability is engaged with by some geographers. A study of geography academics in three Danish universities found that some geographers 'are reluctant with using the concept of sustainability' (Grindsted, 2015b, p. 13), 'remain critical to the concept itself', and 'sometimes find it more suitable as an implicit notion' rather than an explicit notion (ibid., p. 22). Yet other geographers have argued that the geographical and cognate disciplines are the 'torch bearers' of sustainable development education (Chalkley, 2002), and that in the UK, geography and cognate disciplines have played a leading role in supporting ESD.

TYPOLOGIES OF EDUCATION FOR SUSTAINABLE DEVELOPMENT

Several different typologies of ESD exist, reflecting different outcomes and pedagogical approaches. Vare and Scott (2007) describe what they call ESD1 and ESD2. ESD1 relates to informing specific skills and behaviour to guide positive actions – the sort of environmental education advocated by policy makers, where there is a set of underlying values and behavioural outcomes, and the sustainability context is explicit. This contrasts to ESD2, which Vare and Scott (2007, p. 192) describe as building the capacity to think critically, emphasising that our longer-term future does not depend on 'our compliance in being trained to do the "right" thing now', rather it depends on our ability to analyse and question alternatives, and make sound choices in the face of complexity rather than roll out a set of 'pre-determined behaviours', and hence the sustainability context may be implicit. Vare and Scott's (2007) work builds on the threefold typology of Scott and

Gough (2003). Type 1 assumes that learning leads to change once facts are established and communicated, and that problems are essentially environmental; Type 2 assumes that problems are social/political with environmental symptoms, and that learning is a tool to facilitate choices between alternative futures; and Type 3 assumes that learning must be open ended because of inherent uncertainties and complexities, meaning that a desired end cannot be specified. Additionally, three stages of ESD have been outlined by Sterling (2003) corresponding to education *about* sustainability (that is knowledge of sustainability issues), education *for* sustainability (that is enabling students to make a positive contribution to change), and education *as* sustainability where the learning process itself adopts the principles of sustainability and epistemic change is sought. Mochizuki and Yarime (2016) map Sterling's (2003) typology onto three stages of sustainability science: 'multi-disciplinarity', assembling relevant knowledge from different disciplines; 'inter-disciplinarity', connecting and integrating disciplinary knowledge to advance understanding of complex human–environment system interactions; and 'trans-disciplinarity' which promotes active collaboration with different stakeholders in wider society, creating mutual learning between 'science' and society.

Engagement with these different typologies may be useful to the educator to frame reflection on how sustainability is, and can be, tackled within the formal curriculum, through their pedagogy and practice, as well as via more informal structured learning opportunities that complement taught courses (sometimes referred to as the co-curriculum). These typologies may also be useful in helping frame specific learning outcomes at different levels from the individual session, to module, to programme level, ensuring transparency about the desired educational goals.

OUR ROLE AS EDUCATORS: CASE STUDIES IN PEDAGOGIES AND PRACTICE

As geography educators, we have a responsibility to think about the wider impact of what we teach and how we teach it. In a study exploring the perceptions of geography students towards notions of environmental citizenship over seven years, Robinson (2014) shows that almost a third of first year students studying geography, environmental science, and geology reported being 'sick of hearing about climate change', and in some years, up to 10 per cent of first year students agreed with the statement 'humans are too insignificant to affect the global climate'. However, the positives from this study are that third year students showed no such disengagement with climate change despite many studying a dedicated third year module on climate change. This suggests that it is not the nature of the topic (climate change) *per se* that is problematic, but potentially the depth and detail of the coverage at different levels, an 'over-saturation' of coverage of climate change through school and media before reaching university, with potentially little additional depth offered in the first year to that which students have engaged with previously, and the danger potentially of too much of the ESD1, Type 1, or education *about* sustainability approaches, likely to be more dominant throughout school and media coverage, and potentially first year university teaching. Another positive finding is that over the course of the seven years of the study, the number of first year students questioning the anthropogenic influence on global climate decreased. This study also highlighted another element of responsibility, that students felt *they* had a responsibility as geography students – they felt more knowledgeable about sustainability issues than their peers, and hence felt a responsibility to educate others. Yet despite their acknowledged greater knowledge of sustainability issues, this seemed to have little effect on their (self-reported) behaviour, and hence their personal responsibility to a more sustainable world.

There are, however, many examples throughout higher education institutions across the world where students are engaging in sustainability in practical, action-orientated ways. This can occur separate to the formal curriculum through student-led societies for example, or can be strongly linked to the formal curriculum through action-based activities linked to formal outcomes and assessment, or such activity can sit in the informal (co-) curriculum but be inspired by the formal curriculum.

One method growing in popularity to link action and solutions-orientated sustainability education to the formal curriculum is through the use of students' independent projects (or dissertations) which form a part of most degree programmes. In the UK, the National Union of Students has established a scheme called 'Dissertations for good' (NUS, undated). This scheme, open to undergraduate and postgraduate students, creates a framework and 'matching service' between students and organisations, to enable students to undertake their formal curriculum research project requirements with an external organisation that would like research to be carried out on behalf of their organisation. This approach, providing students the opportunity to apply their learning to a 'real-world' context, and contribute to solving real problems, relates strongly to both the transdisciplinary and solution-orientated ethos of sustainability science, as well as to the growing interest in the educational outcomes that can be achieved through a 'living lab' approach. 'Living labs' within a higher education setting and sustainability context use the campus (and potentially wider community) as a test bed to trial and research sustainable solutions, thereby improving the sustainability of the campus and its operations (or an aspect of the wider community) while contributing to and utilising the research expertise of the institution, and creating educational opportunities for students (see, for example, the applied sustainability projects at Manchester University, living laboratory structures at Cambridge University and Leeds University, and living lab guidance produced by the Environmental Association for Universities and Colleges (EAUC, 2017).

Unstructured, student-led informal learning opportunities can also take place at the fringe of the curriculum, inspired and supported by, but occurring outside of, the requirements of the formal curriculum. For example, at Keele University four students created the opportunity to 'live what they were learning', through lobbying the university to be allowed to turn a residence on campus into a 'sustainable student house' and an exemplar of sustainable student living. Each year a new set of four students lives in the house and develops new sustainability initiatives, aimed at trying to live more sustainably and educate the wider student population about sustainable living. Over the years of the project students have built their own raised beds and erected a polytunnel for growing their own vegetables, installed composting and rainwater harvesting facilities, worked to minimise their waste and energy use, run regular communal vegan meals and cooking workshops, and have become a physical 'hub' of student sustainability activism.

Although this project sits firmly within the informal (or co-) curriculum, it was indirectly driven by the explicit coverage of sustainability within their formal curriculum. In this instance the curriculum was important in catalysing this initiative, bringing together like-minded students (in this case studying BSc Environment and Sustainability) and in encouraging an action-orientated mind-set through a module entitled 'Greening business: employability and sustainability' which has a broader aim of enabling students to be able to drive positive sustainability change in their current or future workplaces. This module also uses a 'living lab' approach, with students working on projects set by university environmental professionals to address the sustainability of different aspects of the institution's estate and operations. Such 'action' or 'activism' projects as the 'sustainable student house' provide fertile ground for learning how to enact change, and in developing agency. In particular, these informal curriculum spaces of learning are important in providing the opportunity for experimentation and failure without consequence to students' degree outcomes, yet they also prove challenging spaces for us as educators, being at the nexus between students' private and public lives. The informal curriculum, however, lacks the formal requirement of reflection where greater learning can take place, and therefore, developing reflective learners through the formal curriculum may also give added benefit to informal curriculum projects. The breadth of skills and experiences that learning through 'change projects' outside of the classroom can give, from lobbying, persuasion, working with people constructively and negotiating, to understanding organisations and different stakeholders, helps develop more skills than can easily be achieved through more traditional academic activities, and reflects 'Type 3' learning, that is open-ended and complex. Vare (2007) highlights the importance of 'learning as participation', emphasising how the act of engaging in a process can cause us to gain deeper understanding of the extent that we may feel we can influence it (Vare and Scott, 2007). Unless one takes the view that learners simply need to acquire information about the environment and the technical requirements for achieving a more sustainable society (ESD1, Type 1 learning), it is difficult to deny that enabling students to pursue activism projects in their communities beyond the classroom has powerful potential to generate the transformative education of 'true' ESD.

Learning is not confined to the university campus (Haigh, 2006), as so clearly highlighted by the important role of field work within geography, but also in the use of community-based projects for learning. In some fields, active learning goes further than focussing on the benefits for the students involved, to the benefit that such learning can create for others, and to the need to move from theory to action – areas which have strong resonance with education for sustainability. For example, Bubriski and Semaan (2009, p. 91) write that 'we must go a step further than consciousness-raising to encourage students to implement what they are learning about social inequality and social change into practice'. Although they write about the specific context of women's studies, the same arguments could be made for ESD, and equally could be argued to have a role in geography. Such an approach resonates with 'service learning' which has a long history in North America, and is defined as a:

> course-based, credit bearing educational experience in which students (a) participate in organized service activity that meets identified community needs and (b) reflect on the service activity in such a way as to gain further understanding of course content, a broader appreciation of the discipline, and an enhanced sense of civic responsibility. (Bringle and Hatcher, 1995, p. 112)

Although there are many critiques of the service-learning approach, this engagement in the educational process with wider stakeholders in society relates to the third 'trans-disciplinary' stage of sustainability science described by Mochizuki and Yarime (2016), ultimately necessary for effective mutual learning among 'science' and society. Such action-orientated learning can take many forms, from working on projects within local communities, to the development of student-led projects, and if carried out in a critically reflective way can contribute greatly to education for sustainable development.

As geographers it is all too easy to *assume* that we are educating for sustainable development. But are we? It is easy to assume that the implicit coverage of sustainability in our courses exonerates us from the responsibilities of explicitly considering the wider societal impacts of our teaching. Indeed, there are mixed views on how far we as geography educators should engage with these issues. On the one side, Widener et al. (2014, p. 714) talk of geographers' 'special responsibility' to 'provide future leaders of sustainability transitions with the knowledge and capabilities necessary to successfully enact changes at all levels in society', and Chalkley claimed in (2006, p. 235) that geography 'will obviously be expected to play a leading role' in the ESD agenda. On the other hand, a number of studies find that geographers have been reluctant to integrate sustainability issues explicitly in their curricula (Widener et al., 2014; Grindsted, 2015a). Geographers interviewed by Grindsted (2015a, p. 324) state that providing 'students with the skills that enable them to become change agents that serve the normative agenda of sustainability has no purpose in geography', while Widener et al. (2014, p. 710) report that some geography professionals do not see themselves as 'responsible for teaching applied or action-based sustainability'. Despite this seeming reluctance in parts of the geographical community to engage in such pedagogies, they are increasingly prevalent in higher education as we acknowledge the need for more active learning, with geography in particular having a strong record of pedagogic innovation and experiential learning (Chalkley et al., 2010; and see Chapter 25 in this volume by Brail and Whalen). The nature of sustainability means that effective teaching and learning in this area is supported by pedagogies that are student-centred and interactive, inquiry-based, active and experiential, inter- and trans-disciplinary, and make use of the local (and regional) environment (Cotton and Winter, 2010). In fact, in general, good sustainable development pedagogy is often simply good pedagogy (HEFCE, 2008).

THE RESPONSIBILITIES OF TEACHING AND LEARNING IN GEOGRAPHY

The issues explored above have implications for how we approach our roles as geography educators, and how we view our responsibilities to our students, to society, and to our discipline.

We have responsibilities to our students in many ways. Much of the contemporary discourse as educators is around our responsibilities to our students to enhance employability. Implicit within this discourse around enhanced employability is future enhanced individual wealth, indirectly linked to increased environmental impact (Hammond, 2006; Senik, 2014) and social inequality (Li and Wan, 2015), highlighting the need to balance a focus on employability with considerations of students' own responsibilities to the environment and society (see, in this volume, Chapter 29 by Shepherd, Chapter 30 by Arrowsmith and Cartwright, and Chapter 32 by Solem, Huynh and Kerski). Yet the employability and sustainability agendas are not as conflicted as they might at first appear, with many studies suggesting that today's business leaders see the triple bottom line of society, economy and environment, as essential to their core business, future longevity and a determinant of their financial success (Eccles et al., 2012; Bocken, 2015; Aldersgate Group, 2016), and many businesses wanting to employ those with expertise in sustainability (Cade, 2008).

We have a responsibility to ensure that graduates can flourish in a changing and uncertain world, adaptable to a future that cannot yet be envisaged. We have a responsibility not to tell students 'what to think', or to try and imbue our own values, but equally we have a responsibility to help learners develop the awareness to think critically about existing structures and the paradigms that have led to our current unsustainable practices in terms of growing social inequality and environmental degradation. We need to consider how we can provide our students with the tools to share their knowledge with others in wider society – to help them be more effective in an area according to Robinson (2014) in which they perceive their own responsibility. We also have a responsibility to ensure that highly topical and relevant issues are taught in a fresh and engaging way that we move beyond ESD1 and Type 1 learning, to ensure that our students stay engaged in important debates, and develop holistic, informed and considered views and understanding (Robinson, 2011).

Even the most stalwart supporters of the role of geography in ESD acknowledge that the subject has significant unfulfilled potential in this area and has not seen the shift in engagement necessary to fulfil Sterling's (2003) education *for* and *as* sustainability (Chalkley et al., 2010). The solutions focus of ESD is seen by some as inherently political – legitimising a given political agenda (Grindsted, 2015a), and may explain some of the reluctance to engage explicitly in sustainability. Yet, sustainability science, this 'new kid on the block', seems to suffer no such sensibilities. Therefore geography, rather than hiding under a false mask of political neutrality, should accept the impossibility of a neutral education, and encourage deeply critical thinking about the nature of education and the purpose of universities, embracing the concepts underpinning Sterling's (2003) education *as* sustainability. Widener et al. (2014, p. 700) write that 'teaching sustainability starts by demonstrating sustainability'. Perhaps part of the reluctance of some to engage in explicit sustainability education is underpinned by an awareness that our own behaviours are not as sustainable as they might be, and an unwillingness to hold ourselves up to critique. Our responsibilities as educators are therefore to engage with both the concept of what our students may learn from our behaviour, as well as to ensure that we do not shy away from areas, due to a fear of a mirror being reflected on us.

Vare and Scott (2007) do not prefer ESD2 over ESD1, rather they state that *both* are essential. In the same way, it can be argued that both implicit *and* explicit sustainability considerations are required in our teaching of geography in order to meet our responsibilities to students, society and to the discipline of geography. Further explicit coverage of sustainability can likely be achieved by a simple re-orientation and framing of existing teaching practices, and is an important foundation for developing education *for* and education *as* sustainability. More active pedagogies, that integrate practice and theory around sustainability, will also help address the more solutions-based learning required by sustainability education.

We have a responsibility to our discipline to ensure that geography is not left behind or left out of contributions to a more sustainable future. In order to do this, we need to embrace geography as an integrated discipline spanning the social and natural sciences. Bennett (2013, p. 100) argues that geography's 'divergent perspectives are not weaknesses of the discipline but important assets that . . . could provide geography's most meaningful contributions to sustainability science'. We also have a responsibility to society and the ecosystems upon which it depends, which we can support through enabling our students to make more sustainable decisions within both their personal and professional lives, ensuring that they have the agency to be part of positive future change, enhancing this agency through active and experiential pedagogies and embracing emerging areas of geographical enquiry such as the analysis of commodities and supply chains.

In certain areas such as the historic treatment of the aboriginal people in Australia, there is an increasing acceptance of responsibility for past actions. Gatens and Lloyd (1999 in Massey, 2004, p. 9) write that 'we are responsible for the past not because of what we as individuals have done, but because of what we are'. Massey develops this argument to extend beyond the temporal element to that of spatial relationships in the 'here and now' and our responsibilities to others who are at a spatial distance to us, but still linked to us through globalisation, stating that we are 'responsible to areas beyond the bounds of place' (Massey, 2004, p. 16). These spatial relationships are at the heart of much sustainability discourse, and as geographers with our work at the human–environment nexus, and our emphasis on spatial relationships between local and global systems, we should have a particular heightened awareness of these responsibilities, 'because of what we are'.

CONCLUSION

This chapter started by asking a series of questions in a call for us to consider our responsibilities as geographical educators to students, society, and our discipline. Vare and Scott (2007, p. 192) write of the need as educators to constantly challenge ourselves 'to understand what we are communicating, how we are going about it and crucially, why we are doing it in the first place', and Robinson (2014, p. 257) highlights the need to 'be careful not to "rest on our laurels" thinking that ESD is part of what we have always done'. The different typologies of ESD presented in this chapter provide a useful framework through which to reflect on the degree to which we engage in sustainability in our teaching: whether sustainability is explicit or implicit; whether we teach *about, for* or *as* sustainability; whether we approach ESD through facts, learning as a tool to make choices about alternatives, or open-ended learning driven by inherent complexities and uncertainties; and whether we adopt a multi-, inter- or trans-disciplinary approach. The area of education for sustainability lends itself to active pedagogies, with opportunities for collaboration with a range of stakeholders, and opportunities to practically explore sustainability, both within and at the fringes of the formal curriculum. As geographers, we have a responsibility to make sure that geography is part of the conversations about what a more sustainable future and sustainable education system may look like, and we also have a responsibility to ourselves and to those that we teach, to regularly consider our own responsibilities as educators. The ratification of the United Nation's Sustainable Development Goals in 2015 has prompted a shift in gear in society's engagement across the full breadth of sustainability issues. Geography has been at the heart of work in these different areas throughout its history and we are now at a critical time for the future role of the discipline. Will it and will we, through our education and research, be part of ensuring the place of geography at the centre of the most challenging questions that society has faced?

USEFUL RESOURCES

- EAUC (2017) 'Living labs – opportunities, benefits and challenges of different models globally'. Available at: http://www.eauc.org.uk/living_labs_opportunities_be nefits_and_challeng.
- NUS (undated) 'Dissertations for good'. Available at: http://dissertationsforgood. org.uk/.
- QAA (2014) *Education for Sustainable Development: Guidance for UK Higher Education Providers.* Available at: http://www.qaa.ac.uk/en/Publications/Documents/ Education-sustainable-development-Guidance-June-14.pdf.
- Stibbe, A. (2009) *The Handbook of Sustainability Literacy*, Green books. Multimedia version available at: http://arts.brighton.ac.uk/stibbe-handbook-of-sustainability
- UNESCO (undated) *Education for Sustainable Development*. Available at: https:// en.unesco.org/themes/education-sustainable-development.

REFERENCES

Aldersgate Group (2016) *Ten Years of the Aldersgate Group 2006–2016*, accessed 3 March 2018 at: http://www. aldersgategroup.org.uk/our-reports.
Bennett, D.E. (2013) 'Geography and the emergence of sustainability science: missed opportunities and enduring possibilities', *The Geographical Bulletin*, **54** (2), pp. 99–112.
Bocken, N.M.P. (2015) 'Sustainable venture capital – catalyst for sustainable start up success?' *Journal of Cleaner Production*, **108** (A), 647–658.
Bringle, R.G. and J.A. Hatcher (1995) 'A service-learning curriculum for faculty', *Michigan Journal of Community Service Learning*, **2** (1), pp. 112–122.
Bubriski, A. and I. Semaan (2009) 'Activist learning vs. service learning in a women's studies classroom', *Human Architecture: Journal of the Sociology of Self-Knowledge*, **7** (3), pp. 11–32.
Cade, A. (2008), *Employable Graduates for Responsible Employers*, accessed on 4 March 2018 at https://www. heacademy.ac.uk/system/files/esd-employable-graduates-responsible-employers.pdf.
Chalkley, B. (2002) 'Setting the sustainability scene', *Planet Special Edition*, **8** (1), p. 1.
Chalkley, B. (2006) 'Education for sustainable development: continuation', *Journal of Geography in Higher Education*, **30** (2), pp. 235–236.
Chalkley, B., J. Blumhof and K.V. Ragnarsdottir (2010) 'Geography, earth and environmental sciences: a suitable home for ESD?' in P. Jones, D. Selby and S. Sterling (eds), *Sustainability Education: Perspectives and Practice across Higher Education*, London: Earthscan, pp. 93–107.
Clark, W.C. (2007) 'Sustainability science: a room of its own', *Proceedings of the National Academy of Sciences*, **104** (6), pp. 1737–1738.
Cotton, D. and J. Winter (2010) '"It's not just bits of paper and light bulbs": a review of sustainability pedagogies and their potential for use in higher education', in P. Jones, D. Selby and S. Sterling (eds), *Sustainability Education: Perspectives and Practice across Higher Education*, London: Earthscan, pp. 39–54.
EAUC (2017) 'Living labs – opportunities, benefits and challenges of different models globally'. Available at: http://www.eauc.org.uk/living_labs_opportunities_benefits_and_challeng.
Eccles, R., I. Ioannou and G. Serafeim (2012) 'Is sustainability now the key to corporate success?' *The Guardian*, 6 January, accessed 3 March 2018 at: https://www.theguardian.com/sustainable-business/sustainabi lity-key-corporate-success.
Eflin, J. (2004) 'Geographers and sustainability: a missing connection?' in D. Janelle, B. Warf and K. Hansen

(eds), *World-minds: Geographical Perspectives on 100 Problems*, Dordrecht: Kluwer Academic Publishers, pp. 339–343.

Gatens, M. and G. Lloyd (1999) *Collective Imaginings: Spinoza, Past and Present*. London: Routledge.

Grindsted, T.S. (2013) 'From the human–environment theme towards sustainability – Danish geography and education for sustainable development', *European Journal of Geography*, **4** (3), pp. 6–20.

Grindsted, T.S. (2015a) 'Educating geographers in an era of the anthropocene: paradoxical natures–paradoxical cultures', *Journal of Cleaner Production*, **106**, pp. 320–329.

Grindsted, T.S. (2015b) 'The matter of geography in education for sustainable development: the case of Danish University Geography', in W. Leal Filho (ed.), *Transformative Approaches to Sustainable Development at Universities*, Dordrecht: Springer, World Sustainability Series, pp. 13–24.

Haigh, M. (2006) 'Promoting environmental education for sustainable development: the value of links between higher education and non-governmental organizations (NGOs)', *Journal of Geography in Higher Education*, **30**, pp. 327–349.

Hammond, G.P. (2006) '"People, planet and prosperity": the determinants of humanity's environmental footprint', *Natural Resources Forum*, **30**, pp. 27–36.

Harvey, D. (1969) *Explanation in Geography*. London: Edward Arnold.

HEFCE (2005/28) *Sustainable Development in Higher Education*, accessed on 3 March 2018 at http://webarchive.nationalarchives.gov.uk/20100303151747/http://www.hefce.ac.uk/pubs/hefce/2005/05_28/.

HEFCE (2008) *Strategic Review of Sustainable Development in Higher Education in England*, accessed on 4 March 2018 at http://www.hefce.ac.uk/pubs/rereports/year/2008/sdhefcestrategicreview/.

Jones, P., D. Selby and S. Sterling (2010) 'More than the sum of their parts? Interdisciplinarity and sustainability', in P. Jones, D. Selby and S. Sterling (eds), *Sustainability Education: Perspectives and Practice across Higher Education*, London: Earthscan, pp. 17–37.

Kates, R.W. (2011) 'What kind of a science is sustainability science?' *Proceedings of the National Academy of Sciences of the United States of America*, **108** (49), pp. 19449–19450.

Li, S. and H.Y. Wan (2015) 'Evolution of wealth inequality in China', *China Economic Journal*, **8** (3), pp. 264–287.

Massey, D. (2004) 'Geographies of responsibility', *Geografiska Annaler*, **86 B** (1), pp. 5–18.

Mochizuki, Y. and M. Yarime (2016) 'Education for sustainable development and sustainability science: repurposing higher education and research', in M. Barth, G. Michelsen, M. Rieckmann and I. Thomas (eds), *Routledge Handbook of Higher Education for Sustainable Development*, Abingdon: Routledge, pp. 11–24.

NUS (undated) 'Dissertations for good'. Available at: http://dissertationsforgood.org.uk/. Accessed on 30th July 2018.

Peet, R. (1985) 'The social origins of environmental determinism', *Annals of the Association of American Geographers*, **75** (3), pp. 309–333.

QAA (2014a) *Subject Benchmark Statement: Geography*, accessed on 3rd March 2018 at http://www.qaa.ac.uk/en/Publications/Documents/SBS-consultation-geography.pdf.

QAA (2014b) *Education for Sustainable Development: Guidance for UK Higher Education Providers*, accessed on 3rd March 2018 at http://www.qaa.ac.uk/en/Publications/Documents/Education-sustainable-development-Guidance-June-14.pdf.

Redclift, M. (2005) 'Sustainable development (1987–2005): an oxymoron comes of age', *Sustainable Development*, **13**, pp. 212–227.

Robinson, Z.P. (2011) 'Teaching climate change in higher education: barriers and opportunities', in S.K. Haslett, D. France and S. Gedye (eds), *Pedagogy of Climate Change*, York: The Higher Education Academy, pp. 36–50.

Robinson, Z.P. (2014) 'Are geography students good "environmental citizens?": a comparison between year of study and over time', *Journal of Geography in Higher Education*, **39** (2), pp. 245–259.

Royal Geographical Society (2017) *What is Geography?*, accessed 26 February 2018 at: http://www.rgs.org/GeographyToday/What+is+geography.htm.

Sartori, S., F.L. da Silva and L.M. de Souza (2014) 'Sustainability and sustainable development: a taxonomy in the field of literature', *Ambiente & Sociedade*, **17** (1), pp. 1–20.

Scott, W.A.H. and S.R. Gough (2003) *Sustainable Development and Learning: Framing the Issues*. London: Routledge.

Senik, C. (2014) 'Wealth and happiness', *Oxford Review of Economic Policy*, **30** (1), pp. 92–108.

Sterling, S. (2003) *Whole Systems Thinking as a Basis for Paradigm Change in Education: Explorations in the Context of Sustainability*, PhD Thesis, University of Bath accessed on 4 March 2018 at http://www.bath.ac.uk/cree/sterling/sterlingthesis.pdf.

Vare, P. (2007) 'From practice to theory: participation as learning in the context of sustainable development projects', in A.D. Reid, B.B. Jensen, J. Nikel and V. Simovska (eds), *Participation and Learning: Perspectives on Education and the Environment, Health and Sustainability*, Dordrecht: Springer, pp. 128–143.

Vare, P. and W. Scott (2007) 'Learning for a change: exploring the relationship between education and sustainable development', *Journal of Education for Sustainable Development*, **1** (2), pp. 191–198.

UN (undated) *Goal 4: Ensure Inclusive and Quality Education for All and Promote Lifelong Learning*, accessed on 3 March 2018 at http://www.un.org/sustainabledevelopment/education/.

Widener, J.M., T. Gliedt and A. Tziganuk (2014) 'Assessing sustainability teaching and learning in geography education', *International Journal of Sustainability in Higher Education*, **17** (5), pp. 698–718.

World Commission for Environment and Development (1987) *Our Common Future*. Oxford: Oxford University Press.

20. Enhancing internationalisation in the geography undergraduate curriculum
Ash Parton and Martin Haigh

INTRODUCTION

Internationalisation of the curriculum has three dimensions: international, global and intercultural (Knight, 2003). This chapter describes some pedagogic strategies that may help foster the development of international, global and intercultural thinking in geography undergraduates and considers the question: 'what does internationalisation of the curriculum really mean for my teaching?' (Jones and Killick, 2013). It outlines two contrasting case studies that have sought to implement internationalisation within the undergraduate geography degree curriculum at Oxford Brookes University, in the UK. The first case study uses geographical content as a vehicle to explore global, international, and intercultural concepts and to develop awareness of Western mind-sets. The second case study uses non-Western, Asian 'dharmic' pedagogies and methods to explore subjects of geographical concern, from a perspective that places the learner's 'self' centre stage.

These two case studies explore ways of showing how a geographical education may, simultaneously, be utilised to develop both key geographical concepts and, through internationalisation of the curriculum, more general 'graduate attributes', especially global citizenship (Clifford and Haigh, 2011). Both recognise that the concept of global citizenship, while it includes much ambiguity, is both a process of transformative moral cosmopolitanism (Lilley, Barker and Harris, 2017) and a way toward building a more ethically-aware, more conative and, more generally, transformative geographical education (Simm and Marvell, 2017).

GEOGRAPHY AND THE 'INTERNATIONALISATION OF THE CURRICULUM' MOVEMENT

Of course, the geography curriculum is international in content. Geography has always been about the world, its landscapes, nations and peoples. As far back as 1802, Scotland's John Pinkerton offered that: 'The chief object of modern geography is to present the most recent and authentic information concerning the numerous nations and states who divide and diversify the earth' (Pinkerton, 1802, p. 2). Pinkerton recognised four major themes, which persist to this day: the historical geography of countries, political geographies including statistics, civil geography, especially the geographies of cities, and the geographies of the natural world. However, while the content of geography curricula has always been international, this is not true of geography pedagogy nor of the mind-set of curriculum design, which has often been parochial and chauvinist (Winter, 2018). Geography has always been a subject with purpose and, frequently, that purpose has involved political domination and economic exploitation. Some of this legacy lives on, even in our largely post-colonial age, within the hegemonic ambitions of an elite group of nations and universities from former colonialist nations, who arguably seek to preserve their near monopoly of research and knowledge creation as well as their pre-eminence in determining the nature of what is real knowledge and what is worth teaching (Kumar, 2004).

In the UK, internationalisation of the curriculum is a modern movement driven by economic, pragmatic, educational and idealistic drivers (Killick, 2015). The international, global and intercultural dimensions are shown in Table 20.1 alongside other definitions. The challenge is to incorporate these dimensions into 'domestic learning environments' (Beelen and Jones, 2015).

Table 20.1   Definitions of key concepts linked to internationalisation

Internationalisation	'is defined as the process of integrating an international, intercultural, or global dimension into the purpose, functions or delivery of postsecondary education. . . International, intercultural, and global dimension are three terms that are intentionally used as a triad. . . . These three terms complement each other and together depict the richness in the breadth and depth of internationalization' (Knight, 2003, pp. 2–3)
International	relates to 'relationships between and among nations, cultures or countries' (Knight, 2003, p. 3)
Intercultural	relates to the 'diversity of cultures that exist within and between countries, communities, and institutions' (Knight, 2003, p. 3)
Global	'provides the sense of worldwide scope' (Knight, 2003, p. 3). Global citizenship involves self-identification with the global community of all living beings and active engagement in support of the values and goals of humanity, such as sustainability, intergenerational equity and social justice, at the global scale
Internationalisation at Home	'is the purposeful integration of international and intercultural dimensions into the formal and informal curriculum for ALL students, within domestic learning environments' (Beelen and Jones, 2015, p. 12)
(Education for) Global Citizenship	means learning to live together (plurality, cross-cultural awareness) and learning to live ethically (social justice, equity). It also means learning to live in harmony with our habitat: (eco-literacy, sustainability). The shift from a wholly anthropocentric to a more biocentric perspective requires 'Global Consciousness', a higher level of self-awareness (Haigh, 2014). Education for Global Citizenship involves helping learners connect with the needs of wider human society, the larger environment, and their ethical responsibility to the future welfare of all (Haigh, 2017)

In the UK, the history of internationalisation includes eight co-existing but competitive narrative layers, which reflect the interplay between institutional strategy and classroom pedagogy (Haigh, 2014). The original driver for internationalisation was economic. 'Layer 1': in a world of higher education 'massification' and decreasing government subsidies for many public universities, recruiting international students became a matter of survival. The higher fees paid by migrant international learners helped supplement funds received from other sources and subsidised the education of local learners. Consequentially, in

'Layer 2', internationalisation became a pedagogic issue. It concerned teachers' reactions to changing classroom dynamics when international learners began to struggle in courses and curricula designed for learners with local backgrounds. Meanwhile, the ongoing self-transformation of universities into higher education corporations, 'Layer 3', saw greater emphasis placed on education as a business, often a multinational business. When the goal came to be 'world class', this could be underpinned by displaying an international staff and student body as well as campuses in other nations. Of course, having international staff is different to listening or learning from international staff and students, who feel pressure to 'fit in' with local traditions in teaching and learning (Clifford et al., 2010). 'Layer 4' concerns competitive 'fair play' at the institutional level, the creation of a level playing field through the international accreditation of degrees and standards, and, more rarely, changes in the curriculum at classroom level. 'Layer 5' is also led by thinking about globalisation and the need for all graduates to be able to operate in a multicultural 'world of work'. This is the root of the 'Internationalisation at Home' movement (Beelen, 2011), which requires building self-awareness and cross-cultural intelligence through and across the curriculum in order to make all graduates more cosmopolitan. Ultimately, this fuelled the 'Education for Global Citizenship' movement, which Haigh (2014) identifies as 'Layer 6'. 'Layer 7' emerges from the digital internet revolution, which while further diminishing the status of local knowledge, has created a global space for all education. Finally, 'Layer 8' recognises the global environmental crisis, the need for sustainability and for a greater planetary consciousness in everyday life and work, something geography is particularly suited to provide.

Despite this complexity, internationalisation of higher education curricula remains a process through which curriculum designers attempt to meet the needs of all learners, irrespective of their national, ethnic, cultural, social class or gender identities, and that provides them with the knowledge and skills they need to cope in a globalised world of work (Callan, 2000; Haigh, 2002). This is achieved by incorporating international, intercultural and global dimensions to teaching, learning, assessment and curriculum design (Leask, 2014).

To some degree, this aligns with many geographers' understandings of the role of the discipline. Many geographical subjects are rooted in an international framework of discussion while its value systems often correspond to those deemed central to the promotion of global citizenship ideals (Walkington, 1999; Simm and Marvell, 2017). These include increasing awareness of: the wider world; socio-political-economic drivers of global change; global–local ('glocal') community interactions; sustainability; and both global and local environmental issues (for example Clifford, 2013). Indeed, such matters often provide the core of many geography curricula. The fact that geographical discourse routinely combines the discussion of global issues from both social and environmental perspectives means that the subject is uniquely positioned to engage with students about the world, its nations and environments (see Haigh, 2002 in the Useful Resources section). Certainly, in theory, the discipline spans both the 'hard pure' (natural sciences) and 'soft pure' (humanities and social sciences) through its human and physical geography branches (Clifford, 2009).

So, even without considering external pressure, it is no surprise that geography is engaged with Internationalisation of the Curriculum (for example Simm and Marvell, 2017 in the Useful Resources section). However, the challenge remains to move away from just international subject matter to consider 'the holistic, personal and academic development' of learners (Clifford, 2009, p. 142) and their need to be able to address alternative, including non-Western, ways of thinking (for example Haigh, 2009). Real internationalisation demands 'the incorporation of an international and intercultural dimension into the content of the curriculum as well as the teaching and learning arrangements and support services' (Leask, 2009, p. 209). The search is on to find approaches that effect deep, affective, transformative, and conative internationalisation (De Wit and Leask, 2015).

Meanwhile, several geographers have begun to explore the ways that teaching and learning can be facilitated and enhanced through internationalisation of the curriculum (for example Waddington, 2001; Kenna, 2017). Here, some geographical concepts have great potential for fostering the outward-looking and yet inclusive worldviews that characterise visions of global citizenship. Oxfam (2015) sees a global citizen as someone both aware of the wider world and their own role as a world citizen, who respects and values diversity, who understands how the world works and is committed to social justice; participates in community activities at all levels from local to global; works with others to promote equity and sustainability; and who takes personal ethically-informed responsibility for their actions. For application to curriculum internationalisation in higher education, Clifford (2013) refined these ideas into five sets of measurable global citizenship attributes that involve increased awareness of the: 1. wider world; 2. socio-political-economic drivers of global change; 3. global–local community interactions; 4. need for sustainability; 5. environmental challenges at all scales. These challenges include concepts such as climate change, biodiversity, sustainability, desertification and, perhaps more succinctly, the Anthropocene. Such challenges offer teachers valuable vehicles through which to engage students with global issues and, in so doing, foster internationalisation within the geography curriculum.

This process is enhanced when geography teachers are involved in international collaborative research, teaching and fieldwork. Fieldwork findings and other international experiences can be fed into course content through research-led teaching and lend increased immediacy and relevance to global, international and intercultural awareness. Engagement with such issues helps learners expand their consciousness of the challenges involved in working effectively and sensitively in international and other-cultural contexts, as well as to build awareness of the skills this demands (Haigh, 2002).

ENHANCING INTERNATIONALISATION IN THE GEOGRAPHY CURRICULUM: CASE STUDY 1 THE 'ARID ZONE ENVIRONMENTS' MODULE

The first case study describes the internationalisation of an Honours level (final year undergraduate) module called 'Arid Zone Environments'. Table 20.2 reveals how internationalisation and global citizenship concepts may be integrated into module content, in an otherwise typical environmental geography module comprising lectures, practical classes and workshops, tutorials and independent study. The module focuses on a range of scientific, social and cultural issues specific to dryland environments, many of which are found in less economically developed countries (LEDCs). Over the years, much research

Table 20.2 '*Arid Zone Environments*' *module topics employed for the integration of internationalisation and global citizenship concepts*

Topic, background lecture and discussion content	Scope for internationalisation and global citizenship
Desertification and desert reclamation Desertification appeared on the world stage in 1976, when severe drought in the Sahel, Africa, brought famine to the region. Initially, local farming practices were blamed. Alarmist rhetoric was employed by Western nations to highlight the plight of those affected, based on poor quality scientific data and a perceived superiority of Western knowledge. However, the primary cause of the 1976 drought is now understood to belong to a natural cycle of lower rainfall, while the value of local knowledge is now recognised as critical to the success of mitigation strategies. The principal underlying cause of severe land degradation in most dryland regions – intensive farming and deforestation driven by global agribusiness – remains largely unaddressed by the West.	An improved awareness of the bias towards Western science. Understanding conflict between local and global perspectives. Enhanced awareness of globalised agriculture and its effects on LEDC farmers. Improved understanding of the socio-political-economic drivers of global change.
Dust and dust storms Increased dust loading within the lower atmosphere is considered a major factor contributing to a number of respiratory illnesses. Since many arid region countries are considered poor and suffer from substantial income inequality, it is often the poorest people that are most affected by increased dust transport. In addition, one key cause of increased dust flux is desertification, which is closely tied to poor land management, driven by global economic demand.	Awareness of the disproportionate effects of climate change on LEDCs. Improved understanding of the connection between local production and global demand. Enhanced appreciation of the disproportionate effects of global climate change – LEDCs in dryland regions suffer more than MEDCs in temperate regions.

Table 20.2 (continued)

Topic, background lecture and discussion content	Scope for internationalisation and global citizenship
Water management Water scarcity is considered one of the key global challenges facing humanity and in arid regions this issue is at its most acute. In many regions groundwater is being over extracted resulting in land degradation, salinisation and major disruptions to agricultural practices. Again, the root cause is an intensive and continually expanding global agribusiness model that disproportionately affects LEDCs. Several recent studies identify water and subsequent food scarcity as a likely cause of major global conflict.	Awareness of global resource inequality. Reflection on the importance of resources such as water to other regions of the world, and how these may be taken for granted in countries such as the UK. Improved understanding of the socio-political-economic drivers of global change.
Climate and demography Dryland regions are the home to the first humans and the earliest examples of farming, water management, animal domestication, and some of the first large urban centres. Climate change in drylands through time has coincided with major socio-techno-cultural changes, as populations responded to changes in water availability. In some cases the lack of freshwater resources may have resulted in the collapse of civilisations while in others, it resulted in increased societal complexity. Understanding the underlying causes and cycles of climate change in drylands, along with the societal responses to water availability through time, is critical to evaluating present and futures responses to increased aridity.	An awareness of the history of the human–environment relationship. Understanding of how this relationship differs between arid (resource-limited) and temperate (resource-rich) regions. Understanding how cultural changes may be linked with resource scarcity. Awareness of the interconnectedness of all human populations, and our ultimate link to founder populations in Africa.

has been conducted in these regions and numerous controversies have arisen, that include recurrent motifs that provide useful tools for module level internationalisation of the curriculum.

The module comprises a weekly lecture, followed by a discussion session in which varying local–global perspectives are explored. Students are invited to reflect on their own understanding of the issue and compare their perspective before and after the lecture. This is done by small discussion groups followed by collective class discussion. In addition, throughout each lecture, an interactive mobile application, that is 'Socrative', is used to intersperse the lecture with quick quiz-style questions. These are multiple choice and along the lines of 'from which climatic region does the majority of the world's agriculture originate?' This allows the students to reflect on their preconceptions of global issues, while anonymously contributing to the wider group. An additional benefit of this technique is that it allows teaching and learning to evolve dynamically and cumulatively during each class as discussion reflects on the results of each question. Finally, students are asked to keep a journal of their thoughts and experiences through the module. They note initial thoughts (preconceptions) about each week's topic, and then reflect on how these change through the module. The aim is to develop learner qualities such as self-awareness, an international perspective, sensitivity to intercultural processes and openness to otherness (Leask, 2001; Haigh, 2002).

Table 20.3   How internationalisation and global citizenship are addressed in four key module themes

Module Theme	Internationalisation issues to be raised in discussion	Global Citizenship Concepts 1–5*
Desertification	Western-bias in scientific thought and its significance. Post colonialism and enforced worldview across scientific disciplines. Local–global: the products you buy helping to drive desertification.	1, 2, 3, 4, 5
Dust and Dust Storms	• Poorer countries are disproportionately affected by climate change • Anthropogenic processes drive increased dust flux? • Climate change and land degradation are linked to increased dust flux, so developed countries benefit from mitigation and the provision of support to lesser economically developed countries (LEDCs)?	1, 2, 5
Water Management	• Geopolitics and resource conflict. • Water rights and water scarcity. • Local–global: the products you buy help to drive water shortages in dryland regions.	1, 2, 3, 4, 5
Climate and Demography	• The drivers of prehistoric demographic exchange and the ways past communities responded to climatic change. • The resilience of dryland regions to future climate change and the responsibilities of the West toward helping to tackle the issue.	1, 3, 5

Note: * The global citizenship concepts of Clifford (2013), in the final column relate to increased awareness of the: 1. wider world; 2. socio-political-economic drivers of global change; 3. global–local community interactions; 4. need for sustainability; 5. environmental challenges at all scales.

Table 20.3 shows the relationship between four major module themes, the issues to be raised in classroom discussion, and five key measurable aspects of global citizenship, as suggested by Clifford (2013). The table also indicates the greater scope for internationalisation provided by the environmental development topics, compared to the more purely environmental science, aspects of the module.

ENHANCING INTERNATIONALISATION IN THE GEOGRAPHY CURRICULUM: CASE STUDY 2 'THE ETHICAL GEOGRAPHER AND THE GEOGRAPHICAL IMAGINATION' MODULE

The second case study concerns another honours module. This differs from Case Study 1 'Arid Zone Environments' in not being content-led. Instead, it begins with an internationalisation and global citizenship agenda and integrates geography content afterwards. This gives the curriculum a radically different emphasis, despite its construction from similar typical module structures: lectures, practical field-classes, workshops, tutorials, a supervised group-work project, assessed spoken and written presentations and an assessed learning journal.

The difference is made more overt by the module's (possibly) unique feature. It attempts to replace traditional Western/Eurocentric pedagogy and, in its place, employs hybrid pedagogies with strong roots in the dharmic traditions of South and East Asia, especially India's Samkhya-Yoga philosophy, the meta-futures ideas of Sohail Inayatullah and school (Inayatullah, 2004, 2017), and the integral education theories of Ken Wilber and Sri Aurobindo (Wilber, 2000; Partho, 2007). These roots place introspection at the heart of this module, which overtly addresses the learner's development of their own inner self, after the fashion of the larger contemplative education movement (Gunnlaugson et al., 2014). This, of course, complements the module's emphasis on ethics, empathy and fostering 'mindful' right action (dharma).

If the learner's self is the first focus, the second is 'understanding the other', meaning other ways of imagining, seeing and reacting to the objects and events in this world. It is argued that, since the world is made by people: their decisions, their actions, their feelings, and their many different views of what is right and wrong, all govern how they try to create the future. For this reason, there can be few topics more important for geography as a living and evolving tradition. Since, for many participants, the module took place in their final semester at university, much module content considered the future, especially the role of geographers, such as themselves, in imagining and affecting how that future will develop. So, the module aims to combine these foci and encourage learners to explore their own values and their own self-awareness, not least of their personal responsibilities and potentials as a citizen. The explicit goal is the development of global citizenship ideals, and in the process, to hone other graduate attributes, specifically critical self-awareness and an ability to see what lies beneath the surface of geographical subjects and situations (Haigh, 2016a; Inayatullah and Milojević, 2015).

Table 20.4 elaborates the main module themes and shows how motifs from its internationalised pedagogies provide useful tools for exploring geographical subjects. In brief, the curriculum moves from personal feelings and ethics to thinking about the 'other' and alternative ways of imagining the world. It then explores the cultural and attitudinal

Table 20.4 The 'Ethical Geographer and Geographical Imagination' module in relation to international and intercultural pedagogy, and their integration with geographical content

Topic background lecture: global and international pedagogic content	Intercultural pedagogic content	Scope for exploring geography	1–5*
Exploring Ethics, Empathy and Psychogeography Ethics, empathy and emotional intelligence are essential qualities for a moral cosmopolitan global citizen (Hill, 2000; Boyd et al., 2008). Sessions explore alternative ways of determining right from wrong through interactive classwork exercises. They also emphasise the importance of mindful compassion and emotional intelligence (Goleman, 2004). Psychogeography and the way emotions are manipulated by place is explored (Coverley, 2006).	Cross-cultural input comes from the use of Triguna Theory (Jacobsen, 1999). This deploys three qualities, mixed in different combinations, to describe the world. These 'three modes of Nature' are Sattva – harmony, serenity, purity; Tamas – inertia, dullness, sloth; and Rajas – dynamism, energy, urgency (Kumar, 2007). A self-paced field exercise asks learners to use these ideas to map the feelings evoked in selected places (Haigh, 2009).	This explores welfare geography and the relativist ethics of 'Moral geographies in a world of difference' (Smith, 2000). The aim is to develop emotional intelligence and empathy. Psychogeography, a subfield of cultural geography, explores the subliminal messages embedded in the built environment, which concern matters such as power, entitlement, safety and 'belonging'.	1, 2, 3, 5
Understanding Different Worldviews Globally, those who conceive their world in different ways live in different realities and, hence, seek to change their world in different ways. Here, Stephen Pepper's 'World Hypotheses' (Pepper, 1942), are reworked from a dharmic perspective to re-vision the history of environmental thought. These ideas are developed through a workbook that feeds both a class quiz and group discussion.	Building cross-cultural empathy involves helping learners feel the world from an 'other-cultural perspective'. This task involves decoding the emotional messages in a film, 'Rasa Yatra' using Triguna Theory as a key (Kumar, 2007). The film uses images, songs, sounds (but rarely words) to evoke the sensations of a Hindu pilgrimage (Haigh, 2012).	This extends from intercultural experiential games such as 'Bafa Bafa' (Swift and Denton, 2003), and environmental interpretation based on particular political or other philosophies, using either the field (Haigh, Revill and Gold, 1995) or, as here, film (Gold, Revill and Haigh, 1996). Pilgrimage is itself an important geographical phenomenon (Brunn, 2015).	1, 2, 3, 5

277

Table 20.4 (continued)

Topic background lecture: global and international pedagogic content	Intercultural pedagogic content	Scope for exploring geography	1–5*
Geographical Futures Causal layered analysis (CLA), a dharmic methodology from Futures Studies, argues that the future world is being created by the metaphors, language and cultural myths that provide the root narratives of the present. CLA offers a simple structure to help learners explore the deeper layers of meaning embedded in every discourse (Inayatullah, 1998).	The Dharmic traditions believe in the spiritual unity of all life. Secular Western thought may conceive reality as material and historically mitigated, but dharmic thinking tends to view the material world as a mirage created by deeper levels of consciousness.	The history of environmental geography is explored through representations in the media: maps, art, literature, etc. Such Geographical content is analysed using CLA (Haigh, 2016a).	1, 2, 3
Sustainable Development Humans share an interconnected world that is subject to many challenges: environmental, socio-political and ethical. People, working together, can create an acceptable habitat for future generations. However, learners have to (re)connect themselves with the needs of wider human society, the larger environment, and their ethical responsibilities to the future.	The intercultural pedagogy of this component is founded in Sri Aurobindo's transformative Integral Education, which invites: 1. self-knowledge, 2. realisation that the internal self is deeply embedded in its external environment and, 3. re-integration of the self within its world (Partho, 2007).	Geography is about making a positive difference, thinking globally but acting locally for the benefit of the world. Here, a tree-planting exercise combines practical action and reflection (Haigh, 2016b). This is encouraged by a 'participation' questionnaire that asks learners to consider what the activity means to themselves, to their module curriculum, in the minds of their teachers, to their local community, and, finally as (global) citizens, for their world.	1, 2, 3, 4, 5

Note: * The Global Citizenship concepts of Clifford in the final column relate to increased awareness of the: 1. wider world; 2. socio-political-economic drivers of global change; 3. global–local community interactions; 4. need for sustainability; 5. environmental challenges at all scales.

roots of the creation of future worlds and ends with a practical exercise that involves working in the community and reflection upon the meaning of such work from multiple perspectives (cf. Caruana, 2011). Haigh (2009, 2016a, b) describes how these ideas were developed, practised, assessed and evaluated by learners at various times.

Course assessment was based on a weekly learning journal called 'The Connections Reading Diary'. This included five discrete components:

1.   reflection on the class and fieldwork sessions;
2.   reflective answers on classroom and workbook exercises;
3.   reflections on outside reading in support of 1 and 2;
4.   reflection on reading connected to a self-set ethical question; and
5.   mindful discussion of a personal resolution to that ethical question.

A second assessment component involved a small team exploration of the theme: 'Future Worlds and the Geographical Imagination'. This involved the preparation of a formal proposal for a project involving an issue of international, global or multicultural significance, the presentation of a 15-minute spoken conference paper to a group of peers, and the submission of an individual written paper based on that presentation. Outcomes are detailed in Haigh (2016a) showing how using an approach called causal layered analysis (CLA) helped learners think more deeply about cultural myths and the use of language in the media concerning topics such as the Olympic Games, 'the taming of the American West', and the Danish social experiment of 'Freetown Christiana'. These outcomes may rest uneasily with Clifford's five global citizenship concepts, which, despite origins in educational thought, emerge from a Western perspective and do not have the same 'self in its world' emphasis as ideas from the dharmic traditions. So, part of the exercise also involved each learner applying CLA to their personal self (Haigh, 2016a). Table 20.4's blend of disciplinary and general educational outcomes, despite the all-pervading attention to global citizenship attributes, focusses on issues personal to the learner and constructs its geographical content upon these foundations.

DISCUSSION

The two case studies described approach internationalisation of the curriculum from contrasting directions. The first focuses on integrating internationalisation within a content-led curriculum. Its aim is to enhance the value of its geographical content by embedding emphasis on global, international and intercultural issues. The second focuses on integrating geographical content in an internationalisation-led curriculum by embedding geographical topics that lend themselves to exploration through 'other cultural' methodologies, and international and global perspectives. The first focuses on building learner understanding of important geographical subject areas. The second, as befits a final semester module, focuses on the inner character, ethics and imagination of the soon-to-graduate geographer. The first focuses on enhancing the breadth and depth of what a geography learner knows; its emphasis is international and global. The second focuses on enhancing the breadth and depth of what a geography learner understands about their self and about others; its emphasis is intercultural and personal. Both address all of the global citizenship concepts summarised by Clifford (2013) and most of the larger set of Oxfam (2015). However, the first case study focusses more strongly on Clifford's attributes 5 (environmental challenges), 4 (sustainability) and 3 (global–local community interactions) while the second focuses most strongly on 1 (increased awareness), 2 (socio-political-economic drivers) and 3 (global–local community interactions) and the personal values aspects emphasised by Oxfam (2015).

In truth, accepting the major differences in module subjects, the real differences between these two modules are quite subtle. Both modules involve research-led teaching, one by research in physical geography and development of Arid Environments, the other by research in geographical education and pedagogies suggested by the dharmic traditions of Asia, with their emphasis of the spiritual interior (Wilber, 2000). Both modules engage with active learning through discussion, reading and inquiry-based learning. Both modules, in their different ways, aim to be learner-centred, both aim to cross the artificial divide between human and physical geography and both modules are unusual, the first because it attempts to internationalise applied physical geography and the second because it attempts to internationalise geographical pedagogy.

CONCLUSION

An internationalised curriculum would appear, on the surface, to be an intrinsic attribute of the geography discipline. However, while the subject matter of geography curricula frequently deal with matters that pertain to other nations, occasionally other cultures, and sometimes the world as a whole, the mindsets and motivations that create geography curricula around the world have, traditionally, had a different agenda. Frequently, the driving motivations have been predatory and partisan, they have concerned promoting narrow national goals; cultural supremacy; the exploitation of resources and 'other' peoples; colonisation, both physical and economic; and expansionism by conquest, displacement, religious conversion and, regularly, the elimination of rival or just inconveniently located 'others'. While these 'us versus them' processes remain active into the present day, as everyday news reports witness, today's geography has the ambition to promote global harmony, environmental protection, sustainable living, in sum, the ideals of 'global citizenship'. It is this kind of internationalisation of the curriculum that this chapter has addressed; an internationalisation that aims to decolonise the geography curriculum (see Chapter 17 in this volume by Esson and Last) by contesting its Eurocentric parochialism, patriarchy and its cultural elitism in educational, ethnic and cultural terms.

Internationalisation of the curriculum concerns embedding the international, global and intercultural by design. Its challenge is to teach respect for human diversity, for cultural difference, and for sustainability of the global environment and to provide an education that fosters the ideals of active, participatory, global citizenship. This work can be done in almost any geography module at any level, but it is achieved mostly easily in modules that have an international component and involve interactions between different human societies.

This chapter has detailed curriculum internationalism in two modules. In the first, the 'Arid Zone Environments', module content takes centre stage and internationalisation issues are integrated through classroom discussion. In the second, 'The Ethical Geographer and Geographical Imagination', internationalised pedagogies and methodologies from the dharmic traditions of Asia take centre stage and geographical subjects are integrated to exemplify these approaches. In both cases, the curriculum designers aim to use the best available and most appropriate pedagogic means for the delivery of their respective module content while, equally, addressing all three of the dimensions of curriculum internationalisation: international, global and intercultural (Knight, 2003). However, the fact that both modules emerge from the same programme reinforces the key finding of Leask (2013a, b), which is that, to be effective, internationalisation of the curriculum should be carried out by disciplinary teams and coordinated at programme level.

USEFUL RESOURCES

- Haigh, M. (2002) 'Internationalisation of the curriculum: designing inclusive education for a small world', *Journal of Geography in Higher Education*, 26(1), pp. 49–66.
- Simm, D. and Marvell, A. (eds) (2017) 'JGHE Symposium: creating global students: opportunities, challenges and experiences of internationalizing the geography curriculum in higher education', *Journal of Geography in Higher Education*, 41(4), pp. 467–474.

REFERENCES

Beelen, J. (2011) 'Internationalisation at home in a global perspective: a critical survey of the 3rd Global Survey Report of IAU', *Revista de Universidad y Sociedad del Conocimiento* (RUSC), 8(2), pp. 249–264.

Beelen, J. and Jones, E. (2015) 'Europe calling: a new definition for internationalization at home', *International Higher Education*, 83, pp. 12–13.

Boyd, W.E., Healey, R.L., Hardwick, S.W., Haigh, M., Klein, P., Doran, B., Trafford, J. and Bradbeer, J. (2008) '"None of us sets out to hurt people": The ethical geographer and geography curricula in higher education', *Journal of Geography in Higher Education*, 32(1), pp. 37–50.

Brunn, S.D. (ed.) (2015) *The Changing World Religion Map: Sacred Places, Identities, Practices and Politics*. Dordrecht, NL: Springer Science and Business Media.

Callan, H. (2000) 'Higher education internationalization strategies: of marginal significance or all pervasive?' *Higher Education in Europe (UNESCO)*, 25(1), pp. 15–24.

Caruana, V. (2011) 'The challenge of Global Citizenship Education in the 21st century university: a case for service-learning and community volunteering?', Chapter 11 in Clifford V.A. and Montgomery, C. (eds), *Moving Towards Internationalisation of the Curriculum for Global Citizenship in Higher Education*. Oxford, UK: OCSLD, Oxford Brookes University, pp. 257–250.

Clifford, V.A. (2009) 'Engaging the disciplines in internationalising the curriculum', *International Journal for Academic Development*, 14(2), pp. 133–143.

Clifford, V.A. (2013) *The Elusive Concept of Internationalisation of the Curriculum*. Available at: https://www.brookes.ac.uk/services/cci/definitions.html (accessed 8 June 2017).

Clifford, V.A. and Haigh, M. (2011) 'Graduate attributes and education for responsible global citizenship', Chapter 5 in Clifford, V.A. and Montgomery, C. (eds), *Moving Towards Internationalisation of the Curriculum for Global Citizenship in Higher Education*. Oxford, UK: OCSLD, Oxford Brookes University, pp. 93–117.

Clifford, V.A., Adetunji, H., Haigh, M., Henderson, J., Spiro, J. and Hudson, J. (2010) *Fostering Interculturality and Global Perspectives at Brookes Through Dialogue with Staff: A BSELE Project Report*. Oxford, UK: Oxford Centre for Staff and Learning Development. Available at: https://www.researchgate.net/publication/322369260_Report_on_BSLES_Project_Fostering_Interculturality_and_Global_Perspectives_at_Brookes_through_Dialogue_with_Staff (accessed 10 January 2018).

Coverley, M. (2006) *Psychogeography*. Harpenden, UK: Pocket Essentials.

De Wit, H. and Leask, B. (2015) 'Global: internationalization, the curriculum, and the disciplines', *International Higher Education*, 83, pp. 345–347.

Gold, J.R., Revill, G. and Haigh, M.J. (1996) 'Interpreting the dust bowl: teaching environmental philosophy through film', *Journal of Geography in Higher Education*, 20(2), pp. 209–221.

Goleman, D. (2004) *Emotional Intelligence and Working with Emotional Intelligence*. London: Bloomsbury.

Gunnlaugson, O., Sarath, E.W., Scott, C. and Bai, H. (eds) (2014) *Contemplative Learning and Inquiry Across Disciplines*. Albany, NY: SUNY Press.

Haigh, M. (2002) 'Internationalisation of the curriculum: designing inclusive education for a small world', *Journal of Geography in Higher Education*, 26(1), pp. 49–66.

Haigh, M. (2009) 'Fostering cross cultural empathy with non-Western curricular structures,' *Journal of Studies in International Education*, 13(4), pp. 271–284.

Haigh, M. (2012) '"Rasa Yatra" – using film to teach cross-cultural empathy', *Planet*, 26, pp. 51–58. Available at: http://www.tandfonline.com/doi/full/10.11120/plan.2002.00080022 (accessed 16 January 2018).

Haigh, M. (2014) 'From internationalisation to education for global citizenship: a multi-layered history', *Higher Education Quarterly*, 68 (1), pp. 6–27.

Haigh, M. (2016a) 'Fostering deeper critical inquiry with causal layered analysis', *Journal of Geography in Higher Education*, 40(2), pp. 164–181.

Haigh, M. (2016b) 'Fostering global citizenship – tree planting as a connective practice', *Journal of Geography in Higher Education*, 40(4), pp. 509–530.

Haigh, M. (2017) 'Connective practices in sustainability education', *Journal of Applied Technical and Educational Sciences*, 7(4), pp. 6–30.

Haigh, M., Revill, G. and Gold, J.R. (1995) 'The landscape assay: exploring pluralism in environmental interpretation', *Journal of Geography in Higher Education*, 19(1), pp. 41–55.

Hill, J.D. (2000) *Becoming a Cosmopolitan: What it Means to be a Human Being in the New Millennium*. Lanham, MD: Rowman & Littlefield.

Inayatullah, S. (1998) 'Causal layered analysis: poststructuralism as method', *Futures*, 30(8), pp. 815–829.

Inayatullah, S. (2004) 'Causal layered analysis: theory, historical context, and case studies', in Inayatullah, S. (ed.), *The Causal Layered Analysis Reader: Theory and Case Studies of an Integrative and Transformative Methodology*. Tamsui, Taiwan: Tamkang University Press, pp. 1–52.

Inayatullah, S. (2017) 'Macrohistory and timing the future as practice', *World Futures Review*, 9(1), pp. 26–33.

Inayatullah, S. and Milojević, I. (eds) (2015) *CLA 2.0: Transformative Research in Theory and Practice,* combined with Inayatullah, S. (ed.) (2004) *The Causal Layered Analysis (CLA) Reader: Theory and Case Studies of an Integrative and Transformative Methodology*. Taiwan: Tamkang University Press. Available at: http://www.metafuture.org/product/cla-reader-and-cla-2-0-pdfs/ (downloaded 15 January 2017).

Jacobsen, K.A. (1999) *Prakrti in Samkhya-Yoga: Material Principle, Religious Experience, Ethical Implications*. Delhi: Motilal Banarsidass.

Jones, E. and Killick, D. (2013) 'Graduate attributes and the internationalized curriculum: embedding a global outlook in disciplinary learning outcomes', *Journal of Studies in International Education*, 17(2), pp. 165–182.

Kenna, T. (2017) 'Teaching and learning global urban geography: an international learning-centred approach', *Journal of Geography in Higher Education*, 41(1), pp. 39–55.

Killick, D. (2015) *Developing the Global Student: Higher Education in an Era of Globalization*. Abingdon: Routledge.

Knight, J. (2003) 'Updated definition of internationalization', *International Higher Education*, 33, pp. 2–3.

Kumar, K. (2004) *What is Worth Teaching?* 3rd edn. Hyderabad: Orient Longman.

Kumar, S. (2007) *Spiritual Compass: The Three Qualities of Life*. Totnes, UK: Green Books.

Leask, B. (2001) 'Bridging the gap: internationalizing university curricula', *Journal of Studies in International Education*, 5(2), pp. 100–115.

Leask, B. (2009) 'Using formal and informal curricula to improve interactions between home and international students', *Journal of Studies in International Education*, 13(2), pp. 205–221.

Leask, B. (2013a) 'Internationalization of the curriculum and the disciplines: current perspectives and directions for the future', *Journal of Studies in International Education*, 17(2), pp. 99–102.

Leask, B. (2013b) 'Internationalizing the curriculum in the disciplines – imagining new possibilities', *Journal of Studies in International Education*, 17(2), pp. 103–118.

Leask, B. (2014) 'Internationalizing the curriculum and all students' learning', *International Higher Education*, 78, pp. 5–6.

Lilley, K., Barker, M. and Harris, N. (2017) 'The global citizen conceptualized: accommodating ambiguity', *Journal of Studies in International Education*, 21(1), pp. 6–21.

Oxfam (2015) *Education for global citizenship: a guide for schools*. Available at: https://www.oxfam.org.uk/education/who-we-are/global-citizenship-guides (accessed 16 June 2018).

Partho (2007) *Integral Education: A Foundation for the Future*. Puducherry: Sri Aurobindo Society and UBS.

Pepper, S.C. (1942) *World Hypotheses: A Study in Evidence*. Berkeley, CA: University of California Press.

Pinkerton, J. (1802) *Modern Geography* (2 vols). London: A Strahan.

Simm, D. and Marvell, A. (2017) 'Creating global students: opportunities, challenges and experiences of internationalizing the geography curriculum in higher education', *Journal of Geography in Higher Education*, 41(4), pp. 467–474.

Smith, D.M. (2000) *Moral Geographies: Ethics in a World of Difference*. Edinburgh: Edinburgh University Press.

Swift, C.O. and Denton, L. (2003) 'Cross-cultural experiential simulation in the global marketing classroom: Bafa-Bafa and its variants', *Marketing Education Review*, 13(3), pp. 41–51.

Waddington, S.B. (2001) 'Working with the community: improving the learning experience for large classes', *Journal of Geography in Higher Education*, 25(1), pp. 67–82.

Walkington, H. (1999) *Global Citizenship Education*. Sheffield: Geographical Association.

Wilber, K. (2000) *Integral Psychology: Consciousness, Spirit, Psychology, Therapy*. Boston: Shambhala.

Winter, C. (2018) 'Disrupting colonial discourses in the geography curriculum during the introduction of British Values policy in schools', *Journal of Curriculum Studies*, pp. 1–20. Available from: http://www.tandfonline.com/doi/full/10.1080/00220272.2018.1428366 (accessed 16 February 2018).

21. Heutagogy, personal learning environments, and multi-path entry into GIS education
Michael DeMers

INTRODUCTION

This chapter concerns how we might deliver personalized learning and the evaluation of subsequent knowledge and skills in GIS in preparation for diverse career pathways. It introduces Merriam's (2001) five assumptions of andragogy for adult learners as a means of proposing a more self-directed and learner centred 'heutagogy' for the teaching of GIS in higher education. Beginning with a historical overview of developments in GIS education in the United States it outlines the many paths which learners take to arrive at and navigate through GIS education, and the increasingly important role of technology in enabling learners to take more control of their learning journeys. The chapter goes on to propose a system for the validation of GIS skills through a competency-based personalized learning tool.

Over nearly six decades of growth in geographic information systems (GIS), the diversity of both the discipline and its technology has been followed by an equal volume and breadth of workforce opportunities and career paths. GIS in higher education is not focussed solely on undergraduate and postgraduate qualifications, many lecturers also teach professionals through 'in-service' course provision. The growth in workforce needs has resulted in a renewed effort to provide multiple paths of entry into both formal and informal education and training. First voiced by Duane Marble in the mid 1980s, this need has become exponentially greater than it was when he formed the GIS&T (Geographic Information Science and Technology) Task Force in the United States (Marble et al., 2003; DiBiase et al., 2006, 2007). At that time, the vast majority of GIS learning was taking place in a relatively small number of universities in the form of formal advanced level courses. Only a few years later, the National Science Foundation-funded National Center for Geographic Information and Analysis (Abler, 1987) developed a set of formalized notes constituting the breadth of the discipline as it existed in the late 1980s. More than just notes, they also represented arguably the most structured sequencing of GIS&T knowledge for university programs of their day (Goodchild and Kemp, 1990).

Subsequently, the GIS&T Task Force developed what was to become known as the UCGIS GIS&T Body of Knowledge, a compendium of GIS&T concepts and knowledge areas combined with detailed learning objectives (DiBiase et al., 2006). Acknowledging that, while a major undertaking, it was clear that the final product was far from exhaustive and, as a result of the fast pace of disciplinary growth, was also dated upon print publication (DiBiase et al., 2007). Additionally, it was also clear that the level of learning objectives covered by the knowledge areas varied widely with regard to rigor as measured by Bloom's Taxonomy (DeMers, 2009). In tandem with the development of these two efforts, a growing number of GIS and related texts became available, some written by

Outcomes

GIS&T Body of Knowledge

Computer &
Information Science

Business &
Management

Quantitative
Methods

Humanities

Core

Physical
Science

Social Sciences

Engineering

General
Education

Learner

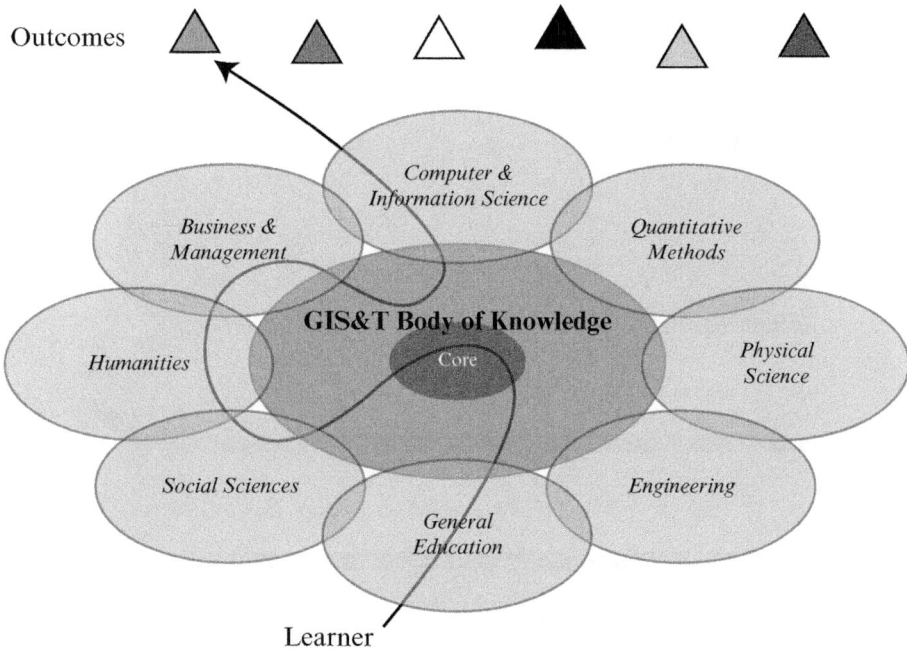

Figure 21.1   The multi-path entry into GIS first envisioned by Marble and redrawn by Di Biase et al. (2008)

those involved in both the NCGIA and UCGIS efforts, others quite removed from those efforts. A quick perusal of these texts indicates that whether comprehensive or not, they all focused on the college or university setting – some focusing more on the computational nature of the topic and others more on the use of the technology.

However, this college-centric approach to educational materials belies the increasing diversity of occupations and attendant learning paths that are indicating a new view toward GIS education (Marble 2006; Estaville, 2010). As Figure 21.1 shows, multipath entry may constitute the GIS learner previously coming to GIS from backgrounds as diverse as engineering, the physical sciences, general education, humanities and social sciences. Similarly, these pathways into GIS may be replicated as outcomes in a variety of disciplines. DiBiase et al. (2010), working closely with the geospatial industry and the US Department of Labor (2018), developed the first geospatial technology competency model (Figure 21.2) that included a framework of nine tiers. This tier system ranged from Tier 1 (Personal Effectiveness Competencies) through to Tier 9 (Management Competencies). What is critical about this approach is that, while not dismissing the role of university programs targeting the more academic aspects of GIS, this model focuses on the diversity of geospatial workforce occupations and illustrates the skills necessary for a variety of career paths. As the discipline continues to grow and mature it is highly likely that both the coverage of academic topics and workforce career paths will continue to expand.

As a general rule, GIS educators in higher education tend to focus not just on academic vocabulary for undergraduate students and theoretical concepts for graduate students,

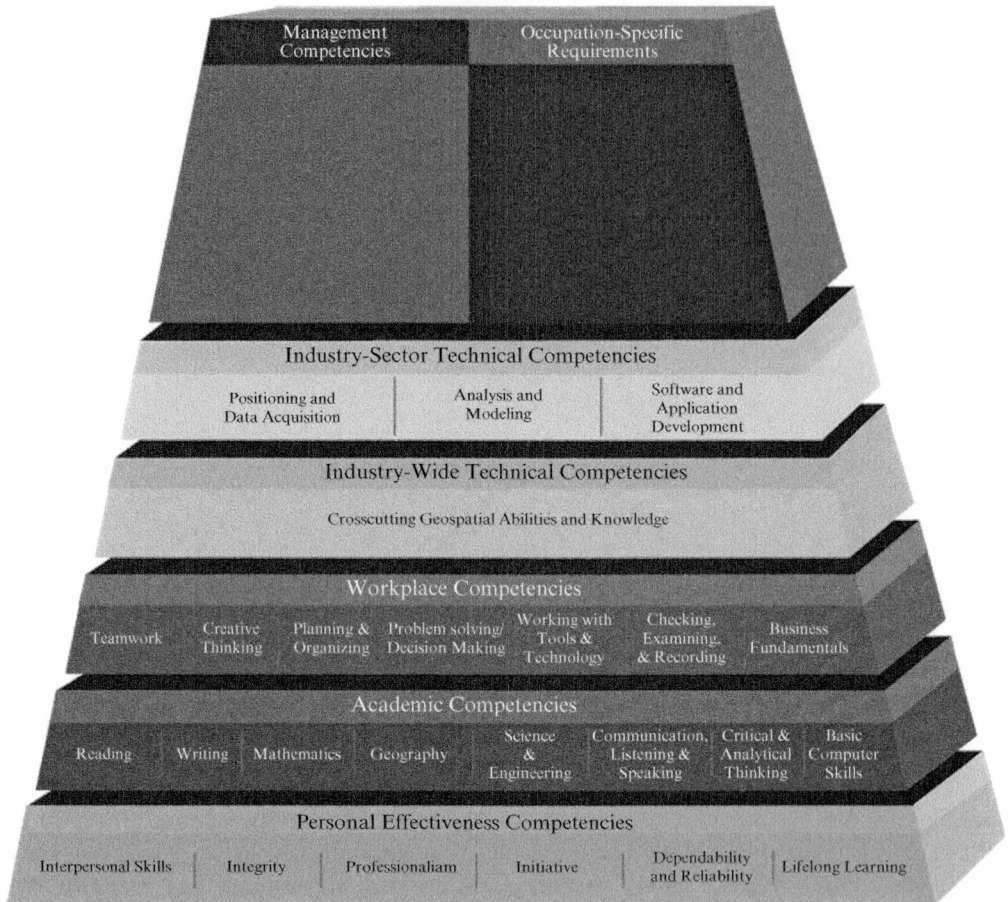

Figure 21.2   The US Department of Labor Geospatial Technology Competency Model

but also on workforce development for both. Many departments around the world offer workshops and certificate programs for in-service GIS professionals. Given this situation it becomes imperative that GIS educators at multiple levels begin to reconsider not just what is taught, as that will continue to change, but when and in what sequence it is most effective for learners. Not only will course sequencing within the conceptual academic setting need to be considered, but also the sequencing and learning paths of the broader workforce. This chapter therefore considers the varied circumstances in which GIS learning might be presented by thinking through the design of learning pathways for a range of existing and future GIS professionals. One must consider the *pre-service* academic track, focusing on research and development of new concepts and new geospatial tools and new ways of tool application. Another track is *in-service* learning whereby the focus is on learning the technology for immediate application. Some *extra-service* learners want to focus on programming to improve the GIS toolkit and add modules or change the user interface. Some learners will expect to come in from an organization but with little knowledge of the toolkit, while others may only need refresher courses as their initial education included GIS&T. Some learners will be perfectly comfortable with a linear path to learning GIS, while others may need special training in new tools, or current awareness of the tools their staff may use and which they are expected to direct. Some learners will come to the need for geospatial education both late and trained in other disciplines, while others may be well prepared for more advanced topics resulting from a full grounding in all the theoretical underpinnings of the technology. This is the situation that now confronts the geospatial educator. Where once there were limited career paths and limited learning opportunities, we now have an increasingly wide array of career paths, but still relatively limited learning paths.

TECHNOLOGY AND LEARNING CONCEPTS

When Professor Marble first envisioned the concept of multiple learning paths for GIS in the late 1980s (Marble, 2006; DiBiase et al., 2009), not only did the discipline lend itself to a more limited set of possible career paths, but also the options available for delivery of learning were far less abundant than they are today. Like education in general, colleges and universities largely mimicked the factory model; a method often referred to as the 'sage on the stage' that emphasized uniformity over innovation, and the transmission of knowledge from expert to novice through passive learning. The Internet was in its infancy and distance education for those unable to attend classes face-to-face was most often performed asynchronously using the postal system to pass assignments back and forth. Neither the instructional methods of the day nor the available technology would allow for the variety of career training needed in the 1980s, much less the vast variety of occupations available today.

In the past decade alone, the improved speed and efficiency of the Internet has allowed for both asynchronous movement of large files, including multimedia, and for the development of real-time interactive synchronous tools. As a result, online learning has become more commonplace, allowing learners to acquire knowledge, to interact with other learners and their professors, as well as engaging with content in a myriad of ways including video, audio, interactive computer models, 3-D visualizations, direct links to digital research and both synchronous and asynchronous lecture material. Learners can now see and hear their professors from afar, they can ask questions either during synchronous lectures via tools like Adobe Connect© or via asynchronous recorded lectures using such tools as VoiceThread© or LMS discussion tools. Faculty members can now be reached via e-mail, text chat, or video via tools like Skype© rather than being isolated behind office doors.

Another change that has the effect of providing more opportunities for multi-path learning involves the realization that adult learning (andragogy) is fundamentally different to the teaching of children. Malcolm Knowles (1980) proposed a new form of learning to distinguish it from pre-adult education. The European concept of andragogy, a form of learning that has become synonymous with adult learning, was substantially different than the art and science of pedagogy, a form of learning targeting children. The five assumptions of andragogy describe the adult learner as:

1. Self-directed
2. Possessing life experiences as a resource for learning

3.   Having learning needs closely linked to changing social roles
4.   Being problem-centered and interested in immediate application of learning
5.   Being self-motivated rather than being motivated by external forces (Merriam, 2001).

As one can see, the concept of andragogy dictates a different approach to teaching and learning. If one reviews the five assumptions above and applies them to GIS teaching in higher education, one should employ the following methods of teaching.

1.   Based on the concept of self-directed learning one should create learning experiences that provide minimum instruction and maximum autonomy. Adult learners tend to learn more effectively if they can build upon existing knowledge and if they are encouraged to explore a topic on their own. Group projects via project-based learning, scenarios, simulations and games with little instruction are considered applicable, but still require the educator to provide guidance as the learning takes place. This is the 'guide on the side' model of learning.
2.   While adult learners come to the table with more experiences upon which to draw, those experiences often vary. To take advantage of this, it is important to provide a wide range of instructional design models and theories to leverage those different experiences to make connections with the material they are learning. One useful method of linking learning to these varied experiences is to include a well-designed survey that indicates what the needs of the individual are. This is one limitation of andragogy, in that the review of past experiences may require some careful examination to be effective in personalizing every learner's curriculum.
3.   Regarding the assumption that adults are ready to learn it is beneficial to incorporate social media and collaboration tools that tie social development to learning. This approach allows the learners to enhance their learning community in support of their learning and to further develop their social network through interactions that expose and nurture similar interests.
4.   A characteristic of adult learners is that they often show a need to know why they are learning something before they begin. Their motivation springs not only from a desire to learn something new, but also from the need to learn something that will allow them to solve immediate problems. Real-world examples and scenarios, particularly those drawn from the learners' experiences themselves, provide them with the relevance of the material to assist them in solving problems that may have driven them to learn in the first place. The 'need to know' is a fundamental motivation.
5.   Finally, there should be a valid reason behind the learning, whether at the course, module, or activity level. Adults particularly want to know why they are doing what they are doing and are far less accepting of a black box approach to their learning. Clear goals are essential at all levels, and they should be linked to real problems requiring real solutions. This allows them to stay more involved in their learning and more focused on completing tasks, so they can clearly see how the process allows them to achieve desired outcomes.

What seems to separate andragogy from pedagogy is a shift away from dependency on the teacher as the source of knowledge toward the teacher as a facilitator, whereby learning is more self-directed. Heutagogy is a natural extension of andragogy wherein the adult learner has specific goals and objectives that are of immediate concern. This type of learning engages the learner far more intensely because they have an immediate need and are thus incentivized to learn. Heutagogy is far less teacher-centric, focusing more on the needs of the learner than on the assumption that the educator is more knowledgeable about what material is important than the learner. Kenyon and Hase (2001) suggested this new approach to adult education focused on vocational education for the 21st-century learner. Some have even extended the term from heutagogy to technoheutagogy whereby the learner-directed environment is enhanced by technology (Pelz, 2012). GIS and related technologies readily lend themselves to heutagogy because of its heavy reliance on project-based learning. This type of learning not only focuses on the learner but allows the learner to select the projects for which they need intense understanding, especially with a focus on doing things correctly, not simply accomplishing a task. For the current discourse I will constrain my discussion to the more well-established term heutagogy and will consider technological innovations consistent with that approach to learning.

What makes heutagogy so relevant to the current discourse in higher education is that it comes at a time of intense proliferation of career paths in the GIS industry. Where once one might limit a discussion of GIS jobs to GIS programmers and designers and GIS technicians and applications specialists, the list of career paths now includes everything from GIS librarian and spatial data archivist, institutional design specialists, GIS data conversion specialists and database designers, GIScientists and GIS software developers and many more. In fact, one issue that seems to be confounding the picture is the wildly differing definition of the career paths which seem to vary with the level of understanding of the employer. Importantly, heutagogy is often expressed as a learner-driven or learner-defined curriculum (Hase and Kenyon, 2003; Hase, 2011; Hase et al., 2006) with regard to the workforce, especially in vocational education. This places the importance of the selection of relevant course content clearly on the shoulders of the learner, rather than the educator. It also focuses on lifelong learning (Blaschke, 2012), a necessary component of such an ever-changing discipline. Finally, heutagogy empowers adult learners because it takes advantage of their own career-driven self-motivation.

In short, if it is difficult to arrive at a consensus on job descriptions, it is equally difficult to determine whether or not a 'path' really exists for learners. Rather than specific, linear, well-defined career paths and associated learning paths, instead specific skillsets in an ever-evolving discipline will require that we 'know whether, how, for whom and to what extent a GIS course helps careers' (Whyatt, Clark and Davies, 2011, p. 237). Importantly, this research concludes that there is a need to link theory with vocationalism. Research by Hong (2016) resulted in a prioritization of skills, competencies, and concepts identified from the content analysis of five GIS position descriptions. Such studies, if expanded to include more position descriptions, could yield a considerably more diverse set of skills, competencies and concepts.

Being able to provide meaningful learning experiences to the increasingly varied GIS learner audience presents a problem in that learning needs are not uniform. Instead learners need to be able to shape their own learning spaces in which they can form learning communities to consume, create, remix, and share what they have learned. This environment, called the personal learning environment (PLE), also allows learners to parse the information they consider necessary and even provide their own means of demonstrating their mastery of the material. This is at the heart of Marble's multi-path entry into GIS education and requires an examination of where the state of the GIScience curriculum and delivery are, and how current technology can be employed to develop personal learning environments.

CURRENT STATE OF GISCIENCE CURRICULUM AND DELIVERY

Today, GIS learners can be grouped into three distinctive classes based on experience and circumstance. *Pre-service learners*, for example undergraduates, are those who typically lack professional experience and are learning the basics of their discipline while in college, often prior to their first professional experiences. *In-service learners* are those who are working in the industry, typically in GIS software development, but also in high level applications and research. Finally, *extra-service learners* are typically those who most often employ the GIS technology for the solution of problems within their own discipline. These latter learners are most often found in government agencies, non-profit organizations, consulting firms and other industries that rely on geospatial information for successful performance of their day-to-day careers.

Universities largely provide education to pre-service learners emphasizing the conceptual nature of GIS especially as it relates to spatial and analytical thinking, and problem-solving capabilities (DiBiase et al., 2009; Bearman et al., 2016; Rip, 2016). However, other pathways to learning exist such as industry-specific software training, and community college competency-based instruction, which is more aligned with structures such as the US Department of Labor (DOL) competency model (Di Biase et al., 2010) and focused on in-service and extra-service learners. While providing some guidance for GIS workforce development, the DOL model specifies 74 essential competencies and 18 competency areas and is built on a foundation of non-GIS interpersonal skills, and general academic and workplace competencies, none of which are generally considered within current GIS curricula. As a foundational document, and one that is linked to the overall US DOL occupational analyses, this does provide direction for what is generally needed in the industry, as does the UCGIS Body of Knowledge (Di Biase et al., 2006) for the academic geographic information science portion of the industry. Recognizing, as did Di Biase et al. (2010), that the business and technical sides of GIS were largely being neglected in academic programs, Yen (2005) suggested a more supply chain management (SCM) model for structured GIS education. This SCM model proposed by Yen suggests a less structured, more customized system of education, tailoring the education to diverse professions that will result in better, more properly deployed and effective GIS. Yen (2005) used as his examples the Cisco Academy Training Centers (CATCs), with a tiered structure of regional and local academies, and Esri (the Environmental Systems Research Institute, a company building and supplying commercial GIS software) which uses authorized learning centers to produce certified professionals. Finally, Yen suggested the use of the theory of constraints as the overall tool for SCM implementation, which focuses on examining the needs and opportunities of the learner and relies on the vendors, developers, and applications users for guidance (ibid.). One drawback to the SCM approach is that it requires the educator to be up to date with new technology in a highly diverse environment. While this would be ideal, it is unlikely that the majority of educators would be able to stay equally current in all aspects of the discipline. Nor does this approach suggest a basic learning strategy by which either the instructors or the learners can remain fully prepared in such a rapidly developing environment.

Examining the relatively current approaches to GIS learning research (Baker et al., 2012), one is struck immediately by two distinct efforts at defining what should be learned, efforts not well aligned with one another. The first approach is that represented by collaborative attempts to classify and document bodies of knowledge, for example the University Consortium for Geographic Information Science's 'Body of Knowledge' (UCGIS BoK) (Di Biase et al., 2006) and its new incarnation (http://www.gistbok.ucgis. org see Useful Resources section); the European Geographic Information: Need to Know (GI-N2K) (http://www.gi-n2k.eu/); the US DOL Geospatial Technology Competency Model (Figure 21.1), and the GIS Certification Institute (https://www.gisci.org/). These valiant attempts at encapsulating the many disparate threads of GIS education all have merit and are all based on input from academia and industry (Wikle, 2015). They all have formal structures which hold them together, but, largely as a result of these very structures, are insufficiently adaptable to the extreme rapidity of industry change demanded by the industry learners.

The second approach, suggested by Yen (2005), relies on the industry itself to provide up-to-date learning opportunities for its customer base. This approach is currently most often delivered as topic-specific tutorials, either face-to-face or online. While this approach is neither part of a systematized strategy for learning the breadth of GIS, nor for rewarding the learner, it does have the advantage of being relatively current as it is most often driven by innovations developed by the vendor providing the training. Although it addresses an immediate need, because there is no overall coordination between vendors, nor any cross-platform evaluation structure, it is difficult for employers to be sure that the training is either effective or pertinent. This is perhaps where the GIS Certification Institute, ASPRS, and AGILE could play a role in providing professional credentials for the outcomes. Unfortunately, these and similar organizations emphasize different portions of the industry and demonstrate a notable bias in awarding certificates. Aspects that vary include academic coursework, experience, exams, paper presentations, etc. While all of these forms of evaluation have merit, one must by necessity choose which criteria are most important, which exam questions are most relevant, and which training centers, community colleges, or universities to rely on to deliver a quality program.

This brings the idea of heutagogy and GIS professional validation center-stage in the debate. It is important to note here that I use the term validation, rather than evaluation, grading or assessment. This is an important distinction as virtually all of the efforts outlined so far eventually focus on one of these measurement forms. Given both the increasing complexity and specialization of GIS, and the wide variety of program and training quality, it is less important that we know what was taught and instead more about what was learned and internalized. The usual measure for weighing a candidate's preparedness in course-related environments tends to forefront what was taught (that is what coursework) over what was learned, although letter grades provide a modicum of measurement of skill level. An employer will often ask not what one has taken for coursework, but more often what the potential employee can actually do, especially in the context of real-world applications.

A CASE FOR LEARNING VALIDATION

I propose one potential solution to this dilemma by adapting a new method of validation called NEXTREADY (Ferdi Serim, pers. comm., 2018), a data system being tested for K-12 learners of technology as well as being adapted for adult learners. Grounded in problem-based learning, employing a collaborative learner-educator selection of context-specific microcredentials and methods of demonstration, NEXTREADY is based on existing standards, such as those discussed previously (AGILE, GISP certification, etc).

NEXTREADY as it is currently operationalized is a competency and project-based learning platform that helps students 'learn to learn' and develop the skills necessary for employment. From a heutagogy perspective this means that the learners, in this case highly motivated adult GIS learners, will experience NEXTREADY as it is designed around the 'future of work', where candidates build upon a foundation of transportable skillsets (microcredentials), demonstrating the ability to apply their competencies rapidly, and often within teams, and delivering demonstrably high-quality products. NEXTREADY provides a foundation of evidence to improve employment, earnings, academic and soft skills allowing students to thrive in an economy that will continually evolve over the course of their careers.

NEXTREADY is a tool to support competency-based personalized learning, thus providing a high degree of learner flexibility while being linked to industry standards such as those found in GISP certification, AGILE standards, or the second-generation GIS&T Body of Knowledge (BoK). As a competency-based tool it provides not only measurable outcomes based on competencies, it also allows the learner to select the competencies they will demonstrate. Table 21.1 illustrates a selection of the BoK criteria as validated by NEXTREADY. As a computer system, it uses evidence to validate the learning outcomes and acts to direct competency-driven personalized learning, rather than relying solely on educators or industry. More importantly it may act as a source of evidence to help the learner achieve self-directed goals which they value and which they see as critical to their professional development.

NEXTREADY is a platform that makes project-based learning easy to establish, manage and evaluate. It was set up to help schools, colleges or private independent educational institutions collaborate with industry in the development of learner challenges. NEXTREADY ensures that learners are exposed to the tools and processes used in industry, that learners learn the soft skills required to be a productive member of a professional team, such as the non-technical skills of the US Department of Labor's geospatial workforce competency model, and finally that learners develop academic competencies while they complete a project. A hallmark of NEXTREADY is that it also allows the learner to demonstrate these competencies within the context of real-word problems which people are likely to encounter in the workplace. The software can be applied to validate specific skills suggested by industry, for example, Esri skills sets such as measurement, predictions, finding and patterns.

Table 21.1   Exemplar GIS core competencies validated in the NEXTREADY system

Geographic Information Systems & Technology Core Competencies Validated in NextREADY

Knowledge Area	Analytical Methods			GIS&T Code	AM
	Units		Core		AM
	Units	Academic and Analytical Origins	Core		AM1
	Units	Data Mining	Core		AM10
	Units	Network Analysis	Core		AM11
	Units	Optimization and Location-allocation Modelling	Core		AMI2
	Units	Query Operation & Query Languages	Core		AM2
	Units	Geometric Measures	Core	Y	AM3
	Units	Base Analytical Operations	Core	Y	AM4
	Units	Base Analytical Methods	Core	Y	AM5
	Units	Analysis of Surfaces	Core		AM6
	Units	Spatial Statistics	Core		AM7
	Units	Geostatistics	Core		AM8
	Units	Spatial Regression & Econometrics	Core		AM9
Knowledge Area	Cartography & Visualization			GIS&T Code	CV
	Units		Core		CV
	Units	History and Trends	Core		CV1
	Units	Data Considerations	Core	Y	CV2
	Units	Principles of Map Design	Core	Y	CV3
	Units	Graphic Representation Techniques	Core		CV4
	Units	Map Production	Core		CV5
	Units	Map Use and Evaluation	Core	Y	CV6
Knowledge Area	Conceptional Foundations			GIS&T Code	CF
	Units		Core		CF
	Units	Philosophical Foundations	Core		CF1
	Units	Cognitive & Social Foundations	Core		CF2
	Units	Domains of Geographic Information	Core	Y	CF3
	Units	Elements of Geographic Information	Core	Y	CF4
	Units	Relationships	Core		CF5
	Units	Imperfections in Geographic Information	Core		CF6
Knowledge Area	Data Manipulation			GIS&T Code	DN
	Units		Core		DN
	Units	Representation Transformation	Core	Y	DN1
	Units	Generalization and Aggregation	Core	Y	DN2
	Units	Transaction Management of Geospatial Data	Core		DN3

IMPLEMENTATION OF NEXTREADY AND PLE IN GIS LEARNING ENVIRONMENTS

The approach suggested here can be implemented in three broad environments that can be considered as encompassing the industry learning environments: Pre-service, in-service, and extra-service.

Pre-Service Environments

Pre-service environments are exemplified by traditional community college, college, or university programs where learners are focusing on GIS, GIScience, or Geospatial Technologies in the broadest sense as potential developers, programmers, applications experts, or managers. This group will most appropriately be considered the traditional GIS learner found in structured, mostly linear learning environments. While these learners can, and often will, pursue traditional coursework, the NEXTREADY system could be implemented into problem-based learning courses or individual exercises. One aspect of NEXTREADY that is often emphasized is the idea of group work, one of the soft skills considered in the DOL Geospatial Technologies Competency Model. This approach could be applied to project work in traditional, or even online courses (Canter, 2012). In this way NEXTREADY can act as a pre-service development environment in addition to the class itself. In an online GIS course I taught based on structural gamification (DeMers, 2018) I used a badging system that corresponded to the competencies of the DOL model, so there is a precedent for such an approach and an example is outlined in Box 21.1.

In-Service Environments

Among the most flexible environments is the in-service environment in which highly motivated learners, those most closely identified with the heutagogy learning environment, could best take advantage of the NEXTREADY approach to learning. This would especially be true in the case of online on-demand workshop courses. Unlike the traditional, linear, information-rich but context-poor online courses, such material should best be organized and structured around problems, perhaps even problems originating from the work environment of the employed learner. A robust form of this would be envisioned as a team of workers needing specific measurable skills to solve real problems collaboratively, thus improving both the skills and context of individual learners, but also strengthening the group working environment. To do this would require educators, perhaps 'geomentors' (Richardson, 2014/15) supported by academia and industry who have encountered similar problems in their own work place, and who would act as educational consultants to interact with the learners to devise both content and validation criteria.

Extra-Service Environments

Extra-service learners, those who are generally outside the mainstream GIS community but who need the skills and tools of the industry, are also adaptable to the heutagogical

BOX 21.1   QUEST-BASED LEARNING IN A GIS COURSE TO PROMOTE
LEARNER AUTONOMY

In the Fall semester I taught the 'Fundamentals of Geographic Information Science and Technology' course using a method of teaching called quest-based learning (QBL). The approach applies the structural framework of online gaming in which participants pursue quests and must achieve a particular score – usually 85 percent, before they win the quest. If they do not win the quest they must continue until they do, at which time they receive a reward. Operationally supported by a software system called 3D Gamelab which is embedded in the university's learning management system, the protocol allowed students to re-submit assignments (quests) until they achieved the requisite 85 percent at which time they received their reward, in this case full credit (100 percent) of the total points for the quest. In each iteration the learner receives copious feedback and encouragement. The primary feature of the quest grading is that learners are not punished, but rather are encouraged to learn from their mistakes.

A hallmark of QBL is that learners have options for what they learn. While some of the learning quests had requisite knowledge, and thus required prerequisite quests, the learners were free to pursue topics of interest to them. The course offered much of the same mechanics of online games as motivations for learning as well. These included a leader board to encourage competitive learning – a feature the learners could turn off if they were more self-motivated; game levels (advancing levels were always associated with additional points called rewards); rewards associated with superior work; and badges that were specifically linked to skills found in the US Department of Labor Geospatial Technology Competency Model (Figure 21.2). The badges could be saved via the Mozilla Backpack system and used as micro-credentials for the learner to demonstrate competency in selected areas. Additionally, some of the quests involved learners taking online short-courses from Esri which result in certificates that can also be used as micro-credentials.

Another hallmark of the QBL method is that grading is an additive process and certain levels, based on those points, are related to grade levels. Unlike traditional grading, where learners begin a course with the assumption of a perfect score of 100 percent of the available points and mistakes result in permanent loss of points, the QBL grading does not punish the learner for mistakes. This grading scheme, combined with the nature of grading for each quest, results in a positive learning environment that encourages learning and rewards attempts at assignments that are less than successful, because the learner is given ample opportunity to correct errors and learn from the errors.

approach I am suggesting via NEXTREADY. This group of learners is by far the most diverse of the three, coming from industries as varied as national security and law enforcement to environmental consulting and NGOs. Such diversity does present some problems in terms of identifying appropriate mentors but this is not insurmountable as the number of geomentors alone is growing rapidly and many of these disparate sister disciplines have been hiring GIS specialists to assist them. These latter could also act as mentors or in-house educators.

It is important to note that to make this work would require the integration of NEXTREADY professionals to provide professional development for those intending to become mentors to learners who will use the NEXTREADY system. The NEXTREADY company is currently devising a system of professional development revolving around several GIS courses. The professional development involves the creation of workshops to demonstrate the use of the NEXTREADY technology to build personal learning environments, construct measurable competencies, devise methods for validating the competencies, and the overall course delivery. One can envisage the collaboration between professional geography organizations and organizations like the geomentors group over an extended period of time. Indeed it might be time for all of the professional organizations with a vested interest in GIS and related geospatial learning to combine forces with state and regional GIS professional organizations and national certification programs to collectively approach the issue of GIS education, validation, and certification.

CONCLUSION

While the aspects of GIS continue to expand and the specialties grow, there is an increasing need to provide flexible, validated learning for practitioners. I have grouped the potential GIS learner community into three general groups: pre-service, in-service, and extra-service. The pre-service learners, especially those whose career goals are clearly GIS related, could take advantage of the heutagogy model of learning, combined with the power and flexibility of the NEXTREADY validation system to enhance their learning beyond traditional coursework. In-service learners would be a natural and perhaps the largest potential user-group for a NEXTREADY-based learning environment focused on real and immediate problems of the learners in a group setting, thus providing ample evidence of acquired skills plus the added advantage of solving problems directly related to their existing career goals. Finally, extra-service professionals, those who might best be described as the GIS application community, could reap the same benefits of the heutagogical model of learning proposed here as they too will be highly motivated to learn specific career-related aspects of GIS.

To ensure that this approach is successful will require an international effort from academia, practitioner volunteers (for example see Useful Resources section below for geomentors), state and regional GIS organizations, national geospatial professional organizations, and certification institutes. This approach may suggest a new era of collaboration in the GIS community that will not only provide better educational opportunities for all, but could provide the prospect for information sharing in general. One might further suggest that this level of cooperation in the GIS community is long overdue and the need for GIS professionals to stay current may be the needed impetus for such global collaboration.

USEFUL RESOURCES

- Geomentors http://www.aag.org/geomentors.
- NEXTREADY, Inc. https://imnextready.com/.
- The University Consortium for Geographic Information Science Body of Knowledge (2nd Edition): http://gistbok.ucgis.org/.
- US Department of Labor, Geospatial Technology Competency Model, available from: (https://www.careeronestop.org/competencymodel/competency-models/geo spatial-technology.aspx).

ACKNOWLEDGEMENTS

I would like to thank Ferdi Sermim, founder of CLARO consulting, for his help with the text relating to NEXTREADY.

REFERENCES

Abler, R.H. (1987) 'The National Science Foundation National Center for Geographic Information and Analysis', *International Journal of Geographical Information Systems*, 1(4), pp. 303–326.

Baker, T.R., Kerski, J.J., Huynh, N.T., Viehrig, K. and Bednarz, S. (2012) 'Call for an agenda and center for GIS education research', *Review of International Geographical Education Online*, 2(3), pp. 254–288.

Bearman, N., Jones, N., André, I., Cachinho, H., and DeMers, M. (2016) 'The future role of GIS education in creating critical spatial thinkers', *Journal of Geography in Higher Education,* 40(3), pp. 394-408.

Blaschke, L.M. (2012) 'Heutagogy and lifelong learning: a review of heutagogical practice', *The International Review of Research in Open and Distance Learning*, 13(1), pp. 56–71.

Canter, M. (2012) 'E-heutagogy for lifelong e-learning', *Procedia Technology*, 1, pp. 129–131.

DeMers, M.N. (2018) 'Structural gamification of a university GIS course', in Ahlqvist O. and Schlieder C. (eds), *Geogames and Geoplay. Advances in Geographic Information Science.* Switzerland: Springer, pp. 195–208.

DeMers, M.N. (2009) 'Using intended learning objectives to assess curriculum materials: the UCGIS Body of Knowledge', *Journal of Geography in Higher Education*, 33, pp. 1–8.

DiBiase, D., DeMers, M., Johnson, A., Kemp, K., Luck, A.T., Plewe, B. and Wentz, E. (2006) *Geographic Information Science and Technology Body of Knowledge.* Washington, DC: Association of American Geographers.

DiBiase, D., DeMers, M., Johnson, A., Kemp, K., Taylor Luck, A., Plewe, B. and Wentz, E. (2007) 'Introducing the first edition of Geographic Information and Technology Body of Knowledge', *Cartography and Geographic Information Science*, 34(2), pp. 113–120.

DiBiase, D., DeMers, M., Johnson, A., Kemp, K., Taylor Luck, A., Plewe, B. and Wentz, E. (2009) 'Supporting curriculum development in geographic information science and technology: the GIS&T Body of Knowledge', in Madden, M. (ed.), *Manual of Geographic Information Systems*. Maryland: American Society for Photogrammetry and Remote Sensing, pp. 1261–1271.

DiBiase, D. et al. (2010) 'The new geospatial technology competency model: bringing workforce needs into focus', *Journal of the Urban and Regional Information Systems Association (URISA)*, 22(2), pp. 55–72.

Estaville, L.E. (2010) 'Geospatial workforce trends in the United States', *International Journal of Applied Geospatial Research*, 1(1), pp. 57–66.

Goodchild, M.F. and Kemp, K.K. (eds) (1990) *NCGIA Core Curriculum in GIS.* National Center for Geographic Information and Analysis, Santa Barbara CA: University of California.

Hase, S. (2011) 'Learner defined curriculum: heutagogy and action learning in vocational training', *Learning and Action Research Journal*, 9(1), pp. 81–92.

Hase, S. and Kenyon, C. (2003) 'Heutagogy and developing capable people and capable workplaces: strategies for dealing with complexity', *Proceedings of The Changing Face of Work and Learning Conference*, Alberta, Sept 25–27. Available from: http://www.wln.ualberta.ca/events_con03_proc.htm (accessed 16 May 2018).

Hase, S., Tay, B.H. and Goh, E. (2006) 'Developing learner capability through action research: from pedagogy to heutagogy in the workplace', paper presented to Global VET: Challenges at the Global, National and Local Levels: Australian Vocational Education and Training Research Association (AVETRA) Conference, Wollongong, NSW, 19–21 April.

Hong, J.E. (2016) 'Identifying skill requirements for GIS Positions: a content analysis of job advertisements', *Journal of Geography*, 115(4), pp. 147–158.

Kenyon, C. and Hase, S. (2001) 'Moving from andragogy to heutagogy in vocational education', Proceedings of the 4th annual AVE. Available from: http://www.avetra.org.au/PAPERS%202001/kenyon%20hase.pdf (accessed 16 May 2018).

Knowles, M.S. (1980) *The Modern Practice of Adult Education: From Pedagogy to Andragogy* (2nd edn). New York: Cambridge Books.

Marble, D.F. (2006) 'Defining the components of the geospatial workforce – who are we?' *ArcNews*, 27(4), pp. 1, 6–9.

Marble, D.F. and members of the Model Curricula Task Force (2003) *Strawman Report: Model Curricula.* Alexandria VA: University Consortium for Geographic Information Science. Available from http://www.geo.upm.es/strawman/strawman_01.pdf (accessed 16 May 2018).

Merriam, S.B. (2001) 'Androgogy and self-directed learning: pillars of adult learning theory', *New Directions for Adult and Continuing Education*, 89, pp. 3–13.

Pelz, W. (2012) *Bill Pelz Reflects on the Term 'Technoheutagogy'*. Available from: https://www.youtube.com/watch?v=yry0YU8LBAQ&ab_channel=PhyliseBanner (accessed 25 March 2018).

Richardson, D. (2014/15) 'Give back – become a geomentor', *ArcNews*, Winter 2014/15. Available from: http://www.esri.com/esri-news/arcnews/winter1415articles/give-back-become-a-geomentor (accessed 1 June 2018).

Rip, F.I. (2016) 'Some thoughts on the possible benefits of using VirLaBoK for GI teaching design and locating GIS courses', *GI Forum*, 1, pp. 355–359.

United States Department of Labor (2018) *Geospatial Technology Competency Model*. Available from: https://www.careeronestop.org/competencymodel/competency-models/geospatial-technology.aspx (accessed 25 March 2019).

Whyatt, D., Clark, G. and Davies, G. (2011) 'Teaching geographical information systems in geography degrees: a critical reassessment of vocationalism', *Journal of Geography in Higher Education*, 35(2), pp. 233–244.

Wikle, T. (2015) 'A look at GIS certification programs and their challenges for higher education', *URISA Journal*, 27(1), pp. 5–10.

Yen, Matthew (2005) 'Customize GIS education with SCM model', papers of the Esri User Conference, San Diego, Paper number 253 Available from: http://citeseerx.ist.psu.edu/viewdoc/download?doi=10.1.1.198.5340&rep=rep1&type=pdf (accessed 20 March 2018).

22. Field-based pedagogies for developing learners' independence
Ian C. Fuller and Derek France

INTRODUCTION: THE PLACE OF FIELDWORK IN THE UNDERGRADUATE CURRICULUM

Fieldwork in the undergraduate geography curriculum has been described as being defining, distinctive, valuable, central, important, fundamental, intrinsic, integral and essential to the discipline (for example Haigh and Gold, 1993; Kent et al., 1997; Driver, 2000; Pawson and Teather, 2002; Stoddart and Adams, 2004; Fuller et al., 2006; Boyle et al., 2007; Maskall and Stokes, 2008; Hope, 2009; Herrick, 2010; Stokes et al., 2011; Krakowka, 2012; Leydon and Turner, 2013; Wilson et al., 2017). Hovorka and Wolf (2009) identified fieldwork as the subject's signature pedagogy and Fuller (2012) argued that fieldwork was the 'heartbeat' of teaching and learning in (physical) geography. The central place of fieldwork in the geography curriculum stems from what it contributes to that curriculum. A broad range of papers has been published on the contribution and value of fieldwork, since Sauer's assertion over 60 years ago that the principal training of geographers should be done . . . by fieldwork (Sauer, 1956). What, exactly, does fieldwork contribute to the undergraduate geography curriculum? The answer lies in a plethora of articles over the past ~30 years that have sought to demonstrate the valuable learning experiences provided, and skills developed, through this medium of learning (for example Kern and Carpenter, 1984, 1986; McEwen, 1996; Fuller et al., 2003; Fuller, 2006; Scott et al., 2006; Dummer et al., 2008; Hammersley et al., 2014; Walsh et al., 2014; Marvell and Simm, 2016; Friess et al., 2016; Mullens, 2016; Anđelković et al., 2017; Holton, 2017). A full review of these (and other) works is beyond the scope of this chapter, but the reader is encouraged to dip into this burgeoning literature on fieldwork in geography. Briefly, fieldwork provides opportunities to develop problem-solving, leadership, teamwork, organisation, and communication skills (Wilson et al., 2017). It also provides opportunities to connect students with research (for example Spronken-Smith and Hilton, 2009; Harris and Tweed, 2010; Fuller et al., 2010, 2014; Spronken-Smith et al., 2014); and is a means to integrate concepts taught in the classroom with practical experience, fostering holistic, experiential learning (for example Kent et al., 1997; Hill and Woodland, 2002; Fuller et al., 2003; Boyle et al., 2007; Wilson et al., 2017). Significantly, Boyle et al. (2007) demonstrate a positive link between fieldwork and learning in the affective domain (perceptions of a subject), which in turn can be argued to set students up for more effective learning in the cognitive domain (information processing and learning outcomes) by fostering deeper learning (cf. Entwistle and Smith, 2002; and see Hill and Woodland, 2002). As such, fieldwork is a pedagogic practice that is, can, and ought to be used to foster independent learning among students.

The place of fieldwork in the undergraduate geography curriculum should be prominent, especially with a view to developing independent learners, as it provides a ready medium in which students are encouraged to think (and 'do') for themselves. However, in some institutions, fieldwork may lack proper integration within the curriculum, or be lacking entirely in a student's degree programme (Mullens et al., 2012; Wilson et al., 2017). Certainly, learning cannot be assumed simply because students are taken on a fieldcourse (Lonergan and Andresen, 1988). Similarly, not all fieldwork models will foster independent learning, for example if the fieldwork comprises 'lectures on a bus' and/or any type of passive transfer of information (cf. Kent et al., 1997); or if the fieldwork is disconnected from the broader undergraduate geography curriculum (cf. Fuller, 2012). For fieldwork to be effective in fostering independent thinking it requires careful design and alignment within the degree programme (Fuller et al., 2006; Fuller, 2012). In this chapter we draw from our own research evidence and experience to provide examples that illustrate how fieldwork can be successfully embedded in the geography undergraduate curriculum from first to final year adopting specific pedagogies to develop, enhance, and refine students as independent learners throughout their undergraduate career.

DEVELOPING INDEPENDENT LEARNERS AT FIRST YEAR: LARGE COURSES, PADDLING AND PEDAGOGY

How can you use fieldwork to foster independent learning in large first year classes? For many this is in the 'too hard basket', resulting in students being corralled in buses and herded across landscapes (physical and human). However, fieldwork can and, given some of its wider pedagogic benefits rehearsed above, should foster independent thinking at this level. Friess et al. (2016, p. 546) comment that 'field trips are a particularly powerful tool in large, introductory undergraduate modules'. This is because fieldwork has been argued to help the transition into higher education and develop cohort identity (Leydon and Turner, 2013). A key feature of higher education is its development of independent learning and thinking. Appropriately-designed and delivered fieldwork can therefore aid that transition into higher level learning, notably where the fieldwork is properly aligned with the wider undergraduate curriculum.

At first year level Friess et al. (2016) reported that students perceived an enhancement of critical thinking skills simply from lecturer-led field activity. Fuller et al. (2000) compared student learning and perception between two groups of first year students completing field exercises. In both groups, students were conducting hands-on fieldwork, learning-by-doing (Race, 1993), measuring key parameters in a fluvial environment to answer a research question. One group was taught using a 'descriptive-explanatory' approach, while the other was taught using an 'analytical-predictive' approach (Church, 1988). The former group was essentially lecturer-led, while the latter group used student-led investigation. As such, this 'active learning' (Scheyvens et al., 2008) approach to fieldwork provided an introduction to research for both groups, with one receiving a greater degree of direction and guidance by the lecturer. Both cohorts were encouraged to think for themselves, and both developed independence in terms of conducting group-based data collection, analysis, and interpretation. However, a greater degree of direction by the lecturer at this level proved valuable, and aided student understanding of the topic and approach (Fuller et al., 2000). With the use of descriptive-explanation, the lecturer was pro-active in facilitating learning, drawing attention to key field evidence and generally offering advice through the field day; while in their application of 'analytical-prediction' the lecturer responded to requests for advice, but was much less pro-active in giving it (ibid., 2000). Interestingly both groups of students perceived their fieldwork equally favourably (Fuller et al., 2000), but an analysis of grades indicated that overall comprehension of the subject benefited from the scaffolded approach by the staff at this level.

At first year level it is important to provide clear direction, set the scene and context, draw out the linkages between processes and environment in the field, provide clear explanation of what is being measured, and why, and what the results might be suggesting. This approach provides a scaffolded framework for active, field-based learning at introductory level. As Fuller et al. (2000, p. 213) concluded, 'students require a good measure of direction in order to learn research skills, from which an analytical approach can then be practised'. Learner independence is thus enhanced at this level by clear direction and scaffolded learning, which also better prepares students for more advanced study beyond first year. Students undertaking this fieldwork were probably more active in their learning than those described by Friess et al. (2016), but incorporation of either active or observational fieldwork at first year level can develop students' thinking skills, and this should be encouraged. Field exercises of this nature do not need to be complicated. A simple, lecturer-guided activity that engages students is sufficient at first-year level to begin to develop critical thinking skills (Friess et al., 2016), and active engagement also fosters deeper levels of learning (Maguire et al., 2001), encouraging students to become independent learners. Where fieldwork is aligned in the curriculum, students value fieldwork as it is providing deeper understanding of course material (Leydon and Turner, 2013). In the example from Fuller et al. (2000), both groups of students were studying processes learned in the classroom and developing research skills for use in their second year, and as such, this fieldwork was well-aligned in the curriculum, setting these introductory-level students up for a greater degree of autonomy at a more advanced level.

Essentially the pedagogic approach to field teaching we advocate at this level is about developing learner independence through initially well-scaffolded approaches to fieldwork. Simple research projects, which test hypotheses making use of original field data collected by students can empower students in their learning and subject understanding (cf. Fuller et al., 2000; Leydon and Turner, 2013). Fieldwork is a valuable medium to introduce research skills and the research method, which is a key routeway to developing independent learners and original and critical thinking skills, and this can be successfully accomplished at first-year level, using both residential and campus-based fieldwork (see, for example, Fuller et al., 2000; Leydon and Turner, 2013).

Extending the remit of the traditional first-year residential field course beyond the faculty-led activities of a predefined excursion route with limited student autonomy (Friess et al., 2016), to a more active learning approach, will enhance the student learning experience (Fuller et al., 2000). Integrating digital technologies into fieldwork practice provides one such opportunity and the basis for geography students to personally develop their own research skills by initially undertaking simple data collection exercises, which culminate in the formation of small group research projects. As part of fieldwork assessment reported by France and Wakefield (2011) student groups were introduced to designing and creating their own digital stories (France and Wakefield, 2011). These digital productions were based around the fieldwork locale and students were encouraged to capture digital resources, such as videos and photographs with mobile devices. Capturing digital resources to support digital story development provides further opportunities for more independent learning and the production of student digital stories not only has the potential to increase the communication and presentation skills attained by the students, but can also foster group participation and understanding of the local environment (Fuller and France, 2015). The use of video in assessment has been reported by Mavroudi and Jöns (2011, p.18) 'to stimulate students' interest and critical thinking' and Dando and Chadwick (2014) note 'even if the videos are not perfect, learning happens' (p. 6). The process of working on video-based projects requires students to take responsibility for their own learning through knowing what content to include or exclude, and deciding the video structure. Student reflections on the video filming process as described in their field journals demonstrated that students were thinking independently as they engaged with the surrounding field environment (Mavroudi and Jöns, 2011).

In summary, fieldwork *can* and *should* be used at first year level to foster independent learning. Careful design of field activities can make effective use of readily available technologies in a meaningful way, and provide an early experience of research-based learning.

ENHANCING INDEPENDENCE IN SECOND YEAR FIELDWORK: MOBILE TECHNOLOGIES

How can learner independence be enhanced by use and incorporation of mobile technologies in fieldwork teaching? In an era of ubiquitous computing (Caudill, 2010) where mobile devices such as tablets and smartphones are becoming more affordable (Melhuish and Falloon, 2010) and more powerful than conventional desktop computers (Guy, 2010), many undergraduate students are still largely unaware of the potential that mobile devices have to support their own learning (Woodcock et al., 2012). Staff too are perhaps not making the best use offered by mobile devices. Mobile device is a term now commonly used to represent any device that can record, transfer or provide information to the user, in any location (Masrom and Ismail, 2010). Their use in the field can be complicated by remote fieldwork locations, limiting applications requiring data connectivity. Such devices are deemed useful to facilitate mobile learning (m-learning) allowing students to make the best use of limited time in the field. This would enable students, for example, not only to start primary data collection but also data analysis in the field, which would help them identify gaps in their field data (Welsh et al., 2018). However, faculty and staff must not assume that today's millennial students are equipped with the prior knowledge and experience to fully exploit the learning opportunities offered by mobile devices. Nevertheless, mobile device-based learning activities should be developed to realise their potential, and enhance learner independence, by empowering students to take advantage of their own or institutional devices for their own learning.

Students work in a range of educational spaces (Savin-Baden, 2008) and fieldwork provides one such learning space. A 'personal learning environment' (PLE) can be defined by an individual person, but can be greatly enhanced by the possession of a device such as an iPad and supplemented by 'the cloud'. Whalley et al. (2018) note 'The iPad alone is not the PLE but part of the knowledge network . . . which is mobile and can be personalised' (p. 4). Personalised devices offer the learner flexible, autonomous and individually tailored activities (Kearney et al., 2012) in which students can enjoy a high degree of independence in appropriately designed mobile learning experiences (Pachler et al., 2009). Even with institutional devices, the learner has autonomy in deciding pace and time when the mobile device and apps are used to support fieldwork outcomes. Mobile learning opportunities offer students the possibilities to interact in three-way connection between themselves, learning resources and a global-social network (France et al., 2015). Mobile devices such as smartphones and tablets are increasingly used by students for everyday social life and can be used effectively in the field (Welsh et al., 2013), whether internet-connected or not. The real potential for geography students is the ease with which students can work autonomously to capture geo-tagged data (including photographs) on their mobile device, synchronise automatically with 'the cloud' and share with a wider group as well as spatially present the results on a map (Welsh et al., 2012).

Building upon first-year fieldwork experiences can encourage staff and students to use their own mobile devices (BYOD: bring your own device) and/or departmental tablets in conjunction with a wide array of inexpensive mobile apps, to foster student engagement with small group research projects in second-year fieldwork. As an example, students are encouraged to use their device to share their day-to-day fieldwork reflections using short 140-character Tweets on Twitter. The use of Twitter in the field can lead to discussions in the evenings fuelled by the day's Tweets. One student suggested those discussions may not have been so productive if the comments had been locked away in a field notebook and not shared collectively. Hill et al. (2016) reported that Twitter was used successfully with second year human geography students doing local fieldwork to express their thoughts and feelings of the university campus. This innovative use of the digital learning space brought a personal touch to large group teaching. This was recognised by students as a way to encourage more meaningful student interactions and broke down the hierarchal relationship between staff and students.

Social media networks can be further used successfully to aid communication pre-, peri-, and post-fieldwork. Thomas et al. (2014) reported that the private closed group functionality of Facebook provided staff and students with the opportunity to direct student learning and promote critical thinking through communicating professionally on issues centred upon a multinational field course to Iceland. The group functionality enabled online discussion sessions, quiz style questions and provided an information portal for all fieldwork activities. Notably, these activities prompted a student to reflect in their blog that '*This encouraged me to think more independently about the oligotrophic environment from which I was extracting my samples from and observing the harsh conditions in person*'. Similar private group functionality within WhatsApp has provided a similar opportunity for staff and students to stay connected and communicate throughout the duration of a field course in New York.

Mobile technologies today provide an efficient and accurate way to capture, store, analyse and share data during fieldwork-based research. A tablet or smart phone in the hands of a student has the potential to be a multi-functional device where it could act as a camera, hand lens, compass and notebook (Whalley et al., 2018). Students have also recognised that the skills they learnt in the field through using mobile apps helped them develop graduate knowledge, skills and values and become more effective researchers (France et al., 2016). This can be illustrated by dissertation students who use their 'iPads as a *Vade Mecum*', that is a handbook or guide which is at hand for regular consultation

(Whalley et al., 2017). This enables students to work more efficiently as autonomous researchers using only one device to access research papers, record notes and observations and analyse field data. However, when recommending mobile apps for learning, teaching and research with students it is worth considering:

- the cost – are they free or have in-app purchases?
- access to data – are there any data protection issues?
- usefulness – what makes the app compelling?
- inclusivity – any web access options available beyond the device?

MacNeil (2015) provides an extended consideration of recommendations and scenarios to illustrate where apps can augment teaching practice. By using mobile devices and apps in fieldwork-based settings students are exposed to more opportunities to develop their learner independence through their personal mobile app choices and mobile device inter-actions during fieldwork-related activities and assessments. Mobile learning offers both benefits (outlined earlier in the chapter) and challenges for the new user of the technology. Staff can work proactively to support student access and work with mobile technology, not assuming prior knowledge. In order to promote self-directed learning staff must consider how best to scaffold the learning with clear guidance for the full duration of the activity. The nature of the learning activity needs to be considered and whether Wi-Fi or 3G/4G connectivity is required as well as the battery life of the mobile device.

REFINING INDEPENDENT LEARNERS IN THE HONOURS/ FINAL YEAR: LEARNERS AS INSTRUCTORS

Aristotle is attributed as saying, 'Those that know, do. Those that understand, teach.' Teaching, it is thus argued, is the highest form of understanding (for example Boyer, 1991). At third (final) year undergraduate level, as higher education practitioners, we are about to unleash our student cohorts into the world. Have we produced independent, critical thinkers? Have our students truly grasped the concepts we have taught them? They may be able to craft essays, write dissertations, construct reports, but have they *understood*? Adoption of student-generated digital video in fieldwork across a range of third year courses provides an opportunity to get a good measure of a student's grasp of key concepts and ideas. Presenting findings, ideas and concepts learned in the field in front of a camera, there is nowhere to hide, and the camera never lies. Can our students teach what they have learned? Use of digital video in final year courses provides the opportunity for students to become the instructors, refining them as independent learners and thinkers at this level. This approach provides a form of blended learning (Graham et al., 2017), which combines traditional face-to-face interactions between students and lecturers with those that are technology-mediated (Higgitt, 2014). Such an approach potentially promotes a more participatory and empowering learning experience (cf. O'Flaherty and Phillips, 2015) in fieldwork to refine students as independent learners and thinkers. This approach has worked in two ways.

Reporting Back Findings in Relation to Course Content and Context Using Digital Video

Where field experiments have been completed as part of both a third year campus-based course and residential fieldwork, rather than write-up a traditional report, students report back using digital video (see Fuller and France, 2014, 2016). The objective of incorporating digital video (or digital stories, *sensu*, France and Wakefield, 2011) into these field experiments was multidimensional. Initially, the intention was to increase the level of engagement and enjoyment involved in tedious data collection; and improve the level of understanding of the method employed, particularly where new and unfamiliar equipment was being introduced. In addition, the digital video is further enhanced by having students include a segment reporting back on their findings and how these relate to the course content and literature on the topic. This latter requirement firmly embeds the fieldwork in the wider course and literature context, helping the students to situate their specific work and findings conceptually and theoretically within the subject because the delivery of their video requires students to understand what they are doing, why, and what it means as they go along, and to discuss this as a group. An example from physical geography on pool-riffle analysis in rivers is included in Box 22.1.

Importantly, this learning activity very clearly provokes reflective thought, with a student comment reported by Fuller and France (2016, p. 200), stating '*[You] pushed us in a positive way with making the video diary, really beneficial to think about the site and situation, environment and what we had to achieve*'. This promotion of reflection and stimulation of thought is aligned with Fisher and Baird's (2006) findings, and in turn enhances levels of learning and engagement as found by (Jarvis and Dickie, 2010; Kemp et al., 2012), and supported by student comments reported by Fuller and France (2016, p. 200): '*Video diaries have been good . . . they take longer, but it makes us have a better understanding than we would have otherwise had.*'

While field experiments and digital video production were group-based, each student in a group was required to appear and/or narrate a part of the video, ensuring all students participated and engaged fully. The extent to which the objectives of introducing digital video into field experiments were achieved is reported in detail by Fuller and France (2014, 2016). To summarise, digital video in field experiments was shown to foster engagement, enjoyment, interest, and subject and methodological understanding. Further spinoffs included fostering a greater sense of group identity and cooperation. The overwhelmingly positive perception from a social, developmental, and learning perspective of the adoption of digital technology in this context is consistent with the findings of others (for example Jarvis and Dickie, 2010; France et al., 2013).

Digital Video as an Enhancement to Observational Style Fieldwork

Secondly, Fuller and France (2015) argue that the 'Cook's Tour' observation-based field course can still play an important role as an effective form of fieldwork, and digital video is a key component in this. Traditionally, the Cook's Tour model sees students bussed from site to site, with little interaction with peers, lecturers, or landscape (physical or human), and as such lacks much appeal for either lecturer or learner (Kent et al., 1997; Livingstone et al., 1998; Fuller et al., 2000). However, there remains a place for observational fieldtrips and Kent et al. (1997) described a variety of approaches that foster

BOX 22.1   VIDEOCAST: POOL-RIFFLE ANALYSIS

Context: In week 9 we will be considering the pool-riffle unit, particularly looking at the processes responsible for the maintenance of this mesoscale bedform in gravelly rivers. What you measure in the field is up to you. The following approaches are available:

- Grain size and compaction
- Velocity and resistance
- Bed structure
- Channel morphology (cross-section)

These techniques are described in the Field Technical Leaflets booklet available on STREAM (online learning platform).

Task: Produce a videocast which:

1. Introduces the group members you work with in the Turitea to analyse the pool-riffle characteristics in this stream.
2. Explains the method you are using: by explaining what you are doing and why you are using that particular method. What data are you generating and why? You may wish to comment on any limitations you find too.
3. Present the preliminary results of your analysis: is there a difference in the parameter(s) you measure between pool and riffle, if so why? This should be tied in with the literature on the topic.

The videocast is produced in a group. Please use a team member's smartphone or camera to record video and take photographs. You should edit your videocast using software such as Movie Maker, add subtitles/captions and voice-over audio. Each group member is expected to contribute to the video and provide commentary/voice-over. Personal appearance in front of camera is not required.

Note when working with digital cameras consider the following:
When speaking to camera, speak downwind, clearly and in a loud, audible voice. Oftentimes the clearest commentary is provided by the camera operator, especially if there is a lot of background noise, such as flowing water! In certain situations it may prove better to capture video or stitch together a series of still images and provide voice-over in (e.g.) Moviemaker subsequently.
Pointing the camera into the wind results in considerable noise interference.
Pan slowly, use a tripod if you wish.
Try not to zoom in and out too much.
You may prefer to capture a series of still images and provide voice-over and captions. Or use a combination of video and stills. The choice is yours!

The aim of this exercise is to help you to understand the techniques you are using in the Turitea in the analysis of pool-riffle characteristics, their application and limitation. If you can communicate clearly to camera, you have understood what's going on!

NB: You should include results in your video, and preface these with reference to the theory learnt in the relevant lecture.

Please note: the purpose of this exercise is to help reinforce the theory learned in the lecture preceding the fieldwork. It is therefore important to work-up your results and complete production of the video, which will include your commentary on how the results fit with the theory learned.

Course learning outcomes aligned with videocast assessment:
Students who successfully complete this course should be able to:

1. Discuss and critically evaluate principal theories and research in hillslope and fluvial geomorphology.
2. Discuss the interaction between flow hydraulics, sediment transport and channel form at a variety of spatial and temporal scales.
3. Implement and effectively communicate field-and-laboratory-based research in fluvial hillslope and fluvial geomorphology, using a range of techniques.
4. Work collaboratively and independently to collect, analyse, visualise, map, and evaluate hillslope and fluvial geomorphology data.

engagement of students, including critical assessments, map production, worksheets and self-paced guides, essentially meshing together 'look-see' and experiential fieldwork, as implemented by several practitioners (for example Higgitt, 1996; Friess et al., 2016). Using this pedagogic approach, the students become the instructors at sites visited in the field, refining their independence as learners. The intention and genre of the trip described by Fuller and France (2015) is observational, rather than hands-on measurement of process, with an emphasis on the relationship between evaluation of process and critical assessment of landscape management approaches within a broad spectrum of geomorphic topics (for example landslides, flooding and coastal erosion). Conceptually, the content of this course is at a high level, commensurate with final year undergraduate. Furthermore, the topics covered relate to courses taught in the second year of the curriculum, and are thus embedded within the overall degree. Underpinning the educational value of this approach is the idea that to communicate clearly and effectively, a succinct piece to camera requires that the students have recognised and understood the processes, issues, ideas and concepts at each site visited. The final digital video is a series of segments reporting on this content drawn from the full range of sites visited. Conceptually, students need to be able to understand both process and management issue, and come up with ideas to resolve the issue reported on. This requires quite a high-level of critical thinking and independent thought. Marks analysis reported by Fuller and France (2015) records a tangible effect on the quality of student work by introducing digital video. Significantly, the effects of digital video were more marked on weaker student cohorts. This suggests that engaging students using digital video has the greatest impact among students who have demonstrated lower levels of performance/achievement in their study to date, with less impact among higher-performing students. This is intuitive, since students who have higher levels of academic attainment tend to be more engaged with the learning process (which is why they have performed better), while the lower-achieving students are in need of greater help and encouragement. It is possible there is a learning-styles effect, and it is important to design course assessment that accommodates a range of learning styles to bring out the best across the range of student cohorts and abilities. As such, digital video in this context is a powerful learning tool, facilitating the engagement and learning of less able students in particular, and diversifying assessment beyond traditional written work (Fuller and France, 2015). This is important, because it suggests that the field class using this digital technology develops students in their critical thinking and fosters their independence as learners. Requiring students to become the instructors via digital video enhances their understanding. Comments from students reported by Fuller and France (2015) relating to the efficacy of use of digital video to foster learner independence and enhance students' understanding included:

> *[Video diary] reinforced my learning.* (p. 165)

> *[The video] helped me cement what we had learned on-site.* (p. 165)

> *Steep learning curve, but good fun and learnt a lot. We will utilise the skills in some form long after the fieldtrip.* (p. 166)

> *Took a little longer, however it made us have a better understanding than we would have had.* (p. 166)

> *Makes you think about the situation and environment and what you are trying to achieve [before filming].* (p. 166)

CONCLUSION: HOW TO PUT IT ALL TOGETHER

Fieldwork is a key sphere of learning in which subject-specific and generic skills are developed (Wall and Speake, 2012). However, fieldwork (courses, trips, exercises, experiments), must be aligned within the undergraduate curriculum to be effective, and to properly develop independent learners who are able to see for themselves and build upon linkages with courses back on campus. Key approaches to maximise the value of students' fieldwork experience and cultivate their independence and critical thinking have been described in this chapter. Hands-on research can be introduced at the outset in first year, and the application of digital video similarly can be incorporated at every level. At final year undergraduate level in particular, tools to enhance a learner-as-instructor pedagogy in field classes are powerful for student learning.

However, integrating digital mobile technologies into fieldwork practice takes planning, time and a good student-staff relationship to build upon existing good practice (for example Fuller and France, 2015; France et al., 2015). There may be resource implications for technological adoption, but these are not insurmountable. Even in times of austerity, positive learning outcomes can be achieved with limited investment. In an age when students have greater access to personal mobile devices, adopting a BYOD model to fieldwork has two main benefits 'familiarity with the device to enable [students] to focus on their learning and the ability to personalize their learning space' (Welsh et al., 2018, p. 18). A BYOD approach can enable students to be more independent learners, as they download their own preferred apps to fulfil their own personal research goals. However, as practitioners we need to be aware of the limitations and pitfalls of implementing a BYOD approach, which have been outlined by Welsh et al. (2018).

To put a coherent programme of fieldwork together in an undergraduate degree programme, in a way which utilises the best pedagogic approaches to graduate independent learners and thinkers, requires careful thought and planning. Care is required to align fieldwork within the undergraduate curriculum, and the suite of courses taught in the degree programme, so that the nature of fieldwork reinforces and extends class-instruction (cf. Fuller, 2012). Furthermore, planning is required to take advantage of best practice: how will field teaching be scaffolded and how might digital video be best incorporated? Ultimately, in mind must be the development of students as independent learners, and appropriate fieldwork pedagogies, as exemplified in this chapter, are a means of achieving this. Challenges such as ensuring equality of access for a potentially diverse student body will need to be met. Fieldwork brings with it resource implications, but exotic locations are not required for fieldwork to be effective. Embedded, local fieldwork is equally successful in developing independent learners as much as fieldwork run farther afield (Fuller, 2006), because it is the learning opportunity that is presented and utilised that is the key. Overseas fieldwork may have benefits, such as the opportunity to study a range of processes and landforms not available locally (see Braungardt and Ingram, 2012; Pearson et al., 2014). However, what matters is effective pedagogic design, regardless of location, and adoption of proven techniques and approaches that develop students as independent learners and thinkers. Effective pedagogic design, which we have focused on in this chapter, includes appropriate scaffolding of learning activities that are fully aligned to the wider curriculum. It seeks to encourage students as independent learners via active learning, incorporating research-based learning, and engaging students as instructors. Careful use and application of digital video can provide a powerful learning tool as part of this effective design, fostering autonomous learning at a range of levels throughout the curriculum, and whether this be fieldwork taking place for a few hours in the stream on campus, or over the course of a week at a distant location. Learner-focused activity, that actively engages students in a meaningful way, is the key to developing independent learners using field-based pedagogies. Fieldwork grounded on best-pedagogic practice and embedded in the curriculum will empower those who participate and constitute a key pedagogy for independent learning and thinking.

USEFUL RESOURCES

- Designing effective fieldwork guidance https://www.heacademy.ac.uk/system/files/gees_guides_jmas_designing_effective_fieldwork.pdf.
- Enhancing Fieldwork learning https://enhancingfieldwork.org.uk/.

REFERENCES

Anđelković, S., Dedjanski, V. and Pejic, B. (2018) 'Pedagogical benefits of fieldwork of the students at the Faculty of Geography in the light of the Bologna Process', *Journal of Geography in Higher Education*, 42, pp. 110–125.

Boyle, A., Maguire, S., Martin, A., Milsom, C., Nash, R., Rawlinson, S., Turner, A., Wurthmann, S. and Conchie, S. (2007) 'Fieldwork is good: the student perception and the affective domain', *Journal of Geography in Higher Education*, 31, pp. 299–317.

Boyer, E.L. (1991) 'The scholarship of teaching from: Scholarship reconsidered: priorities of the professoriate', *College Teaching*, 39, pp. 11–13.

Braungardt, C.B. and Ingram, S. (2012) 'Justifying long-haul field courses: the role of cultural learning', *Planet*, 26, pp. 23–30.

Caudill, J.G. (2010) 'A futurist perspective on mobile learning', in Guy, R. (ed.), *Mobile Learning: Pilot Projects and Initiatives*, pp. 253–271. Santa Rosa, CA: Informing Science Press.

Church, M. (1988) 'Problem orientation in physical geography teaching', *Journal of Geography in Higher Education*, 12, pp. 51–65.

Dando, C.E. and Chadwick, J.J. (2014) 'Enhancing geographic learning and literacy through filmmaking', *Journal of Geography*, 113, pp. 78–84.

Driver, F. (2000) 'Field-work in geography', *Transactions of the Institute of British Geographers*, 25, pp. 267–268.

Dummer, T.J., Cook, I.G., Parker, S.L., Barrett, G.A. and Hull, A.P. (2008) 'Promoting and assessing "deep learning" in geography fieldwork: an evaluation of reflective field diaries', *Journal of Geography in Higher Education*, 32, pp. 459–479.

Entwistle, N. and Smith, C. (2002) 'Personal understanding and target understanding: mapping influences on the outcomes of learning', *British Journal of Educational Psychology*, 72, pp. 321–342.

Fisher, M. and Baird, D.E. (2006) 'Making mLearning work: utilizing mobile technology for active exploration, collaboration, assessment, and reflection in higher education', *Journal of Educational Technology Systems*, 35, pp. 3–30.

France, D. and Wakefield, K. (2011) 'How to produce a digital story', *Journal of Geography in Higher Education*, 35, pp. 617–623.

France, D., Powell, V., Mauchline, A.L., Welsh, K., Park, J., Whalley, W.B. and Rewhorn, S. (2016) 'Ability of students to recognize the relationship between using mobile apps for learning during fieldwork and the development of graduate attributes', *Journal of Geography in Higher Education*, 40, pp. 182–192.

France, D., Whalley, B. and Mauchline, A. (2013) 'Using mobile devices to enhance undergraduate field research', *CUR Quarterly*, 34, pp. 38–42.

France, D., Whalley, W.B., Mauchline, A., Powell, V., Welsh, K., Lerczak, A. and Bednarz, R.S. (2015) *Enhancing Fieldwork Learning Using Mobile Technologies*. London: Springer.

Friess, D.A., Oliver, G.J., Quak, M.S. and Lau, A.Y. (2016) 'Incorporating "virtual" and "real world" field trips into introductory geography modules', *Journal of Geography in Higher Education*, 40, pp. 546–564.

Fuller, I.C. (2006) 'What is the value of fieldwork? Answers from New Zealand using two contrasting undergraduate physical geography field trips', *New Zealand Geographer*, 62, pp. 215–220.

Fuller, I.C. (2012) 'Taking students outdoors to learn in high places', *Area*, 44, pp. 7–13.

Fuller, I.C. and France, D. (2014) 'Fieldwork going digital', *Developments in Earth Surface Processes*, 18, pp. 117–130.

Fuller, I.C. and France, D. (2015) 'Securing field learning using a twenty-first century Cook's Tour', *Journal of Geography in Higher Education*, 39, pp. 158–172.

Fuller, I.C. and France, D. (2016) 'Does digital video enhance student learning in field-based experiments and develop graduate attributes beyond the classroom?', *Journal of Geography in Higher Education*, 40, pp. 193–206.

Fuller, I.C., Brook, M. and Holt, K. (2010) 'Linking teaching and research in undergraduate physical geography papers: the role of fieldwork', *New Zealand Geographer*, 66, pp. 196–202.

Fuller, I.C., Edmondson, S., France, D., Higgitt, D. and Ratinen, I. (2006) 'International perspectives on the effectiveness of geography fieldwork for learning', *Journal of Geography in Higher Education*, 30, pp. 89–101.

Fuller, I.C., Gaskin, S. and Scott, I. (2003) 'Student perceptions of geography and environmental science fieldwork in the light of restricted access to the field, caused by foot and mouth disease in the UK in 2001', *Journal of Geography in Higher Education*, 27, pp. 79–102.

Fuller, I.C., Mellor, A. and Entwistle, J.A. (2014) 'Combining research-based student fieldwork with staff research to reinforce teaching and learning', *Journal of Geography in Higher Education*, 38, pp. 383–400.

Fuller, I.C., Rawlinson, S. and Bevan, R. (2000) 'Evaluation of student learning experiences in physical geography fieldwork: paddling or pedagogy?', *Journal of Geography in Higher Education*, 24, pp. 199–215.

Graham, M., Mclean, J., Read, A., Suchet-Pearson, S. and Viner, V. (2017) 'Flipping and still learning: experiences of a flipped classroom approach for a third-year undergraduate human geography course', *Journal of Geography in Higher Education*, 41, pp. 403–417.

Guy, R. (2010) 'Mobile learning defined', in Guy, R. (ed.), *Mobile Learning: Pilot Projects and Initiatives*, pp. 1–7. Santa Rosa, CA: Informing Science Press.

Haigh, M. and Gold, J.R. (1993) 'The problems with fieldwork: a group-based approach towards integrating fieldwork into the undergraduate geography curriculum', *Journal of Geography in Higher Education*, 17, pp. 21–32.

Hammersley, L.A., Bilous, R.H., James, S.W., Trau, A.M. and Suchet-Pearson, S. (2014) 'Challenging ideals of reciprocity in undergraduate teaching: the unexpected benefits of unpredictable cross-cultural fieldwork', *Journal of Geography in Higher Education*, 38, pp. 208–218.

Harris, T. and Tweed, F. (2010) 'A research-led, inquiry-based learning experiment: classic landforms of deglaciation, Glen Etive, Scottish Highlands', *Journal of Geography in Higher Education*, 34, pp. 511–528.

Herrick, C. (2010) 'Lost in the field: ensuring student learning in the "threatened" geography fieldtrip', *Area*, 42, pp. 108–116.

Higgitt, M. (1996) 'Addressing the new agenda for fieldwork in higher education', *Journal of Geography in Higher Education*, 20, pp. 391–398.

Higgitt, D. (2014) 'Disruptive moments', *Journal of Geography in Higher Education*, 38, pp. 1–6.

Hill, J. and Woodland, W. (2002) 'An evaluation of foreign fieldwork in promoting deep learning: a preliminary investigation', *Assessment and Evaluation in Higher Education*, 27, pp. 539–555.

Hill, J., Thomas, G., Diaz, A. and Simm, D. (2016) 'Borderland spaces for learning partnership: opportunities, benefits and challenges', *Journal of Geography in Higher Education*, 40, pp. 375–393.

Holton, M. (2017) '"It was amazing to see our projects come to life!" Developing affective learning during geography fieldwork through tropophilia', *Journal of Geography in Higher Education*, 41, pp. 198–212.

Hope, M. (2009) 'The importance of direct experience: a philosophical defence of fieldwork in human geography', *Journal of Geography in Higher Education*, 33, pp. 169–182.

Hovorka, A.J. and Wolf, P.A. (2009) 'Activating the classroom: geographical fieldwork as pedagogical practice', *Journal of Geography in Higher Education*, 33, pp. 89–102.

Jarvis, C. and Dickie, J. (2010) 'Podcasts in support of experiential field learning', *Journal of Geography in Higher Education*, 34, pp. 173–186.

Kearney, M., Schuck, S., Burden, K. and Aubusson, P. (2012) 'Viewing mobile learning from a pedagogical perspective', *Research in Learning Technology*, 20, pp. 1–16.

Kemp, J., Mellor, A., Kotter, R. and Oosthoek, J.W. (2012) 'Student-produced podcasts as an assessment tool: an example from geomorphology', *Journal of Geography in Higher Education*, 36, pp. 117–130.

Kent, M., Gilbertson, D.D. and Hunt, C.O. (1997) 'Fieldwork in geography teaching: a critical review of the literature and approaches', *Journal of Geography in Higher Education*, 21, pp. 313–332.

Kern, E.L. and Carpenter, J.R. (1984) 'Enhancement of student values, interests and attitudes in earth science through a field-oriented approach', *Journal of Geological Education*, 32, pp. 299–305.

Kern, E.L. and Carpenter, J.R. (1986) 'Effect of field activities on student learning', *Journal of Geological Education*, 34, pp. 180–183.

Krakowka, A.R. (2012) 'Field trips as valuable learning experiences in geography courses', *Journal of Geography*, 111, pp. 236–244.

Leydon, J. and Turner, S. (2013) 'The challenges and rewards of introducing field trips into a large introductory geography class', *Journal of Geography*, 112, pp. 248–261.

Livingstone, I., Castley, A. and Matthews, M.H. (1998) *Fieldwork and Dissertations in Geography*, UK: Geography Discipline Network (GDN), Cheltenham & Gloucester College of Higher Education.

Lonergan, N. and Andresen, L.W. (1988) 'Field-based education: some theoretical considerations', *Higher Education Research and Development*, 7, pp. 63–77.

MacNeil, F. (2015) 'Approaching apps for learning, teaching and research', in Middleton, A. (ed.), *Smart Learning: Teaching and Learning with Smartphones and Tablets in Post-Compulsory Education*. UK: Media-Enhanced Learning Special Interest Group and Sheffield Hallam University Press, pp. 239–263.

Maguire, S., Evans, S. and Dyas, L. (2001) 'Approaches to learning: a study of first-year geography undergraduates', *Journal of Geography in Higher Education*, 25, 95–107.

Marvell, A.D. and Simm, D. (2016) 'Unravelling the geographical palimpsest through fieldwork: discovering a sense of place', *Geography*, 101, pp. 125–136.

Maskall, J. and Stokes, A. (2008) *Designing Effective Fieldwork for the Environmental and Natural Sciences*, UK: Higher Education Academy Subject Centre for Geography, Earth and Environmental Sciences, Plymouth.

Masrom, M. and Ismail, Z. (2010) 'Benefits and barriers to the use of mobile learning in education: review of literature', in Guy, R. (ed.) *Mobile Learning: Pilot Projects and Initiatives*, pp. 9–26. Santa Rosa, CA: Informing Science Press.

Mavroudi, E. and Jöns, H. (2011) 'Video documentaries in the assessment of human geography field courses', *Journal of Geography in Higher Education*, 35, pp. 579–598.

McEwen, L. (1996) 'Fieldwork in the undergraduate geography programme: challenges and changes', *Journal of Geography in Higher Education*, 20, pp. 379–384.

Melhuish, M. and Falloon, G. (2010) 'Looking to the future: M-learning with the iPad', *Computers in New Zealand Schools: Learning, Lending, Technology*, 22, pp. 1–16.

Mullens, J.B. (2016) 'Student perceptions of a recreation trail assignment as a valuable learning experience for geography undergraduates', *Journal of Geography*, 115, pp. 244–255.

Mullens, J.B., Bristow, R.S. and Cuper, P. (2012) 'Examining trends in international study: a survey of faculty-led field courses within American departments of geography', *Journal of Geography in Higher Education*, 36, 223–237.

O'Flaherty, J. and Phillips, C. (2015) 'The use of flipped classrooms in higher education: a scoping review', *The Internet and Higher Education*, 25, pp. 85–95.

Pachler, N., Bachmair, B. and Cook, J. (2009) *Mobile Learning: Structures, Agency, Practices*. New York: Springer.

Pawson, E. and Teather, E.K. (2002) '"Geographical expeditions": assessing the benefits of a student-driven fieldwork method', *Journal of Geography in Higher Education*, 26, pp. 275–289.

Pearson, S., Parr, J., Ullah, Z. and Omar, M. (2014) 'Supporting medical students to do international field research: a case study', *Innovations in Education and Teaching International*, 51, pp. 277–291.

Race, P. (1993) 'Never mind the teaching – feel the learning!' *Quality Assurance in Education*, 1, pp. 40–43.

Savin-Baden, M. (2008) *Learning Spaces. Creating Opportunities for Knowledge Creation in Academic Life*, Maidenhead: Open University Press.

Sauer, C.O. (1956) 'The education of a geographer', *Annals of the Association of American Geographers*, 46, pp. 287–299.

Scheyvens, R., Griffin, A.L., Jocoy, C.L., Liu, Y. and Bradford, M. (2008) 'Experimenting with active learning in geography: dispelling the myths that perpetuate resistance', *Journal of Geography in Higher Education*, 32, pp. 51–69.

Scott, I., Fuller, I. and Gaskin, S. (2006) 'Life without fieldwork: some lecturers' perceptions of geography and environmental science fieldwork', *Journal of Geography in Higher Education*, 30, pp. 161–171.

Spronken-Smith, R. and Hilton, M. (2009) 'Recapturing quality field experiences and strengthening teaching–research links', *New Zealand Geographer*, 65, pp. 139–146.

Spronken-Smith, R., Mirosa, R. and Darrou, M. (2014) '"Learning is an endless journey for anyone": undergraduate awareness, experiences and perceptions of the research culture in a research-intensive university', *Higher Education Research & Development*, 33, pp. 355–371.

Stoddart, D.R. and Adams, W.M. (2004) 'Fieldwork and unity in geography', in Herbert, D.T. and Matthews, J.A. (eds), *Unifying Geography: Common Heritage, Shared Future*. London: Routledge, pp. 46–61.

Stokes, A., Magnier, K. and Weaver, R. (2011) 'What is the use of fieldwork? Conceptions of students and staff in geography and geology', *Journal of Geography in Higher Education*, 35, pp. 121–141.

Thomas, B., Mauchline, A.L. and Jackson, R. (2014) *Facebook, iPads and 'Extreme' Microbes in Iceland*. Available from: http://blogs.reading.ac.uk/engage-in-teaching-and-learning/2014/08/27/facebook-ipads-and-extreme-microbes-in-iceland-by-dr-becky-thomas-dr-alice-mauchline-and-dr-rob-jackson/ (accessed 22 February 2018).

Wall, G.P. and Speake, J. (2012) 'European geography higher education fieldwork and the skills agenda', *Journal of Geography in Higher Education*, 36, pp. 421–435.

Walsh, C., Larsen, C. and Parry, D. (2014) 'Building a community of learning through early residential fieldwork', *Journal of Geography in Higher Education*, 38, pp. 373–382.

Welsh, K.E., France, D., Whalley, W.B. and Park, J.R. (2012) 'Geotagging photographs in student fieldwork', *Journal of Geography in Higher Education*, 36, pp. 469–480.

Welsh, K.E., Mauchline, A.L., France, D., Powell, V.W., Whalley, W.B. and Park, J.R. (2018) 'Would bring your own device (BYOD) be welcomed by undergraduate students to support their learning during fieldwork?', *Journal of Geography in Higher Education*, 42, pp. 356–371.

Welsh, K.E., Mauchline, A.L., Park, J.R., Whalley, W.B. and France, D. (2013) 'Enhancing fieldwork learning with technology: practitioners' perspectives', *Journal of Geography in Higher Education*, 37, pp. 399–415.

Whalley, W.B., France, D., Mauchline, A., Welsh, K. and Park, J. (2016) 'Every student use of iPads: a vade mecum for students' active learning', in Baab, B.F., Bansavich, J., Souleles, N. and Loizides, F. (eds), *Proceedings of the 2nd International Conference on the Use of iPads in Higher Education*. Newcastle, UK: Cambridge Scholars Publishing.

Whalley, W.B., Mauchline, A.L., France, D., Park, J. and Welsh, K. (2018) 'The iPad six years on: progress and problems for enhancing mobile learning with special reference to fieldwork education', in Crompton, H. and Traxler, J. (eds), *Mobile Learning in Higher Education: Challenges in Context*, New York: Routledge pp. 8–18.

Wilson, H., Leydon, J. and Wincentak, J. (2017) 'Fieldwork in geography education: defining or declining? The state of fieldwork in Canadian undergraduate geography programs', *Journal of Geography in Higher Education*, 41, pp. 94–105.

Woodcock, B., Middleton, A. and Nortcliffe, A. (2012) 'Considering the smartphone learner: an investigation into student interest in the use of personal technology to enhance their learning', *Student Engagement and Experience Journal*, 1, pp. 1–15.

PART III

CAPSTONE AND BRIDGING PEDAGOGIES FOR THE FINAL YEAR

23. Pedagogical partnerships, identity building and self-authorship in geography higher education
Niamh Moore-Cherry

INTRODUCTION

A marked shift in the paradigms of teaching and learning in higher education over the last decade, from teacher-centred, through student-centred, to 'discovery', has been accompanied by a radical re-thinking of roles, identities and responsibilities in the academy and beyond. This re-thinking has partly been driven by the emergence of a 'students as consumers' approach at policy level, and has evolved as a reaction against a culture that positions academic staff as information providers and students as passive consumers of knowledge. How students can be better engaged with their own learning is a critical issue across the international higher education landscape, particularly as new managerial frameworks link funding to student retention, progression and performance (Lynch, 2015; Kenny, 2017). While Kuh et al. (2008) define engagement as students' practical actions in terms of their own welfare and learning within a given system or institution, and the ways that these actions contribute to positive outcomes, other authors suggest that sustained engagement is produced more collaboratively and takes a more relational approach to learning (Cook-Sather, 2014).

This chapter focuses on one form of student engagement, namely partnership working. Developing a 'partnership' approach has become an aspirational goal for many institutions, policymakers, educators and student representative bodies as international evidence suggests that an ethos and culture of partnership in higher education, within and beyond the formal curriculum, impacts positively on student engagement (Cook-Sather and Luz, 2015). It assists in building a sense of academic identity and belonging, critical to retention and successful progression (Moore-Cherry et al., 2016). While meaningful partnership working faces some well-documented barriers, including resistance from some staff and students, and institutional norms (Bovill et al., 2016), it also has a transformative capacity. Effective partnerships have the capacity to foster higher-level learning for all stakeholders and re-shape learner identities. This is what Baxter Magolda (2004) terms 'self-authorship': the ability to author one's own life, knowledge and practices. Rather than simply accepting knowledge and adopting formulaic approaches to learning, self-authorship is a personally-referenced way of knowing that draws on experience, knowledge and values related to our own identities, and how that relates to others. Self-authorship comprises three inter-related dimensions: recognising that knowledge is socially constructed, and that meaning-making (*cognitive*) occurs within the framework of one's own goals and beliefs (*intrapersonal*) and those of others (*interpersonal*).

While much of the debate on partnership has taken place within the literature on academic development (Bovill et al., 2011; King and Felten, 2012; Cook-Sather, 2014; Curran and Millard, 2016), geographers have become increasingly visible in discussions around how the concepts and theories of partnership can be moved into disciplinary practice, and how geographers can be supported towards self-authorship (Moore et al., 2011; Marvell et al., 2013; Hill et al., 2016; Moore-Cherry et al., 2016). This chapter focuses on partnership and its impacts within pedagogical practice generally, before moving on to showcase current partnership working in geography and reflecting on how it can be extended in geography higher education.

PARTNERSHIP AS ENGAGEMENT

The lexicon of collaboration and engagement has permeated higher education for many decades but, in recent years, the discussion has gained momentum and significance and been reconceptualised as 'partnership'. A fairly well-worn term, student engagement has a direct correlation with levels of success but it is complex and shaped by a variety of factors, not just academic. Bozick (2007) and Quinn et al. (2005), for example, have found that students that commute and hold employment while in education are more likely to withdraw as they have less time to engage academically and socially within the university. This highlights the importance of both the cognitive and affective domains in understanding student experiences and the complexity of engagement, despite its instrumentalisation in recent years via performance tools such as the National Student Survey (UK), National Student Experience Survey (Australia), National Survey of Student Engagement (USA) and Irish Survey of Student Engagement (Ireland).

Meaningful engagement fosters a sense of belonging to the university through a feeling of connectedness, critical to student outcomes (Palmer et al., 2009; Hagenauer and Volet, 2014). This can be positively reinforced through the building of stronger relationships with faculty and peers (Bozick, 2007). Pedagogical practices such as collaborative and peer-learning approaches have demonstrated highly positive impacts on levels of student engagement (Nystrand and Gamoran, 1991). More reflective and collaborative approaches to pedagogy also help shift academic conceptualisations of teaching and learning away from ideas of 'pedagogical solitude' (Shulman, 2004) to something that is more of a joint effort or collective endeavour. Recent work has argued that rather than viewing teaching and learning as two separate processes, they should be conceived as inter-related, opening up a space where the boundaries between the two can become blurred. This 'fuzziness' challenges the notion of students as consumers to be fed information by academics and creates the conditions through which alternative approaches to education become possible. Within this more open context, students can be challenged to reject a view of 'education as a product that they can rate in terms of how satisfied they are', and rather to see it as 'a commitment to an intellectual endeavor' (Jensen and Bennett, 2016, p.43). Equally, academic staff can be challenged to re-think their roles and relationships both within and beyond the classroom. As traditionally-held beliefs about teacher and learner identities are broken down, the power structures underpinning these understandings are also subject to challenge, producing new ways of thinking and interacting. Rather than a consumer-based relationship of exchange, new transactional relationships based on partnership can emerge.

Critical to understanding the potential of partnership is to view it as a way of working; as a *process* rather than an outcome to be aspired to (Healey et al., 2014). Cook-Sather et al. (2014, pp. 6–7) define partnership as 'a collaborative, reciprocal process through which all participants have the opportunity to contribute equally, although not necessarily in the same ways, to curricular or pedagogical conceptualization, decision-making, implementation, investigation, or analysis'. Pedagogical partnerships can be diverse in nature (Bovill and Felten, 2016; Healey et al., 2016), involve students, staff and external stakeholders and be more or less 'structured' or controlled depending on context. Power dynamics shift when partnership is embraced but, depending on the structure, can be equal or weighted more towards particular stakeholders. Partnerships can develop in various contexts; curricular, extra-curricular and co-curricular, between:

- students and staff (tutors, library, student support services etc.);
- staff and staff (co-teaching, peer review of teaching);
- students and students (peer-mentoring, equal, longitudinal etc.);
- students and institution (external examiners, programme review, staff–student liaison committee, ambassador programmes etc.);
- students and the student union (their representative body);
- students and external bodies (employers, Professional Statutory Regulatory Bodies, outreach, public engagement, voluntary organisations etc.) (HEA, 2014).

A number of attempts have been made to conceptualise partnership working. Bovill et al. (2016) identify four key roles for students in partnership working: students as representatives, students as consultants, students as co-researchers and students as pedagogical co-designers. Although there is potential significant overlap across these roles, the latter domain is perhaps least well developed and thus pedagogical partnership might be considered an 'emergent practice' (Bovill, 2014). Healey et al. (2016) have recognised this in their conceptual framing of partnership, which highlights the diversity of learning and teaching activities within which it can develop across multiple scales from the module to the (inter)national level. Their model of partnership highlights two key domains: Learning, Designing and Developing; and Researching and Inquiring. While these models are generic, they do provide a sound basis on which to interrogate disciplinary partnership practices. Later in this chapter, a diversity of partnership approaches at the module, programme and institutional level, in a range of different contexts, are illustrated to highlight the practice and impact of students working as co-learners, pedagogical co-designers, co-researchers and consultants within the discipline of geography. This way of working is gaining significant momentum within and beyond the discipline and is broadly welcomed as a 'good thing' based on the extant impact data and evidential base. However, significant challenges can emerge in moving partnerships of any type from theory into practice.

PARTNERSHIP AS TRANSFORMATIVE PRACTICE

The challenges involved in grounding partnership ideas and theories in pedagogical practice have been likened by Cook-Sather (2014) to a disciplinary threshold concept: simultaneously troublesome, transformative, irreversible and integrative for both students and academic staff. Barriers to understanding (what it means and how it works), engagement (who should be involved, how and why) and progress (putting it into practice) create this threshold. Often it is a product of pre-existing internalised belief systems, cultures or long-held assumptions about teaching that doubt student capabilities to inform practice. On the other hand, it can be a product of students lacking confidence and opportunity to take control of their education and assume new responsibilities and identities. However, where there is an openness to working differently, and possibilities for new insights and working practices are embraced, partnership working has 'the power to transform the way educators understand the teaching and learning process and their role in it' (King and Felten, 2012, p. 5). Once all partners take a step forward together and cross the threshold into new learning spaces, ways and relationships, 'it is virtually impossible to un-know it; one cannot easily go back to a previous way of seeing or being' (Cook-Sather, 2014, p. 193). Partnership working thus has the potential to radically transform not just working practices but also identities, delivering both emotional and cognitive impact and transforming the wider student and staff experience. It is thus a critical way in which students can progress towards high-order independent thinking and meta-cognitive awareness about what is being learned (Bovill et al., 2016). Progress towards this type of self-authorship by the variety of partners (Baxter Magolda, 2004) has the potential to transform not just the space within which the partnership takes place but the wider learning environment and community. This is because it involves internalised shifts in identity that transcend specific activities or modules. Later in the chapter, these shifts in identity are illustrated through examples of both staff–student but also student–student partnerships.

Making such radical shifts is not easy but it can be productively disruptive, opening up liminal spaces as roles and identities are questioned and negotiated. Partnership working can thus be transformative, where there is a willingness to open up to other perspectives and where liminality is embraced rather than being viewed as troublesome and threatening to academic staff who may see themselves as the 'authorities'. While academic staff may be experts in the subject area, students are experts at being students (Cook-Sather, 2014). Instead of understanding or relating to students through our own frameworks, partnership working gives students a meaningful voice and academic staff an opportunity to see the learning environment through another frame. Embracing a more dialogic approach to the learning and teaching process positions students as partners in explorations of teaching and learning, shaping how they view their education and their roles and responsibilities within it. Their identity as a student is thus validated but their responsibility as a co-learner in an intellectual journey is heightened. For staff engaged in partnership, there is a liberation in realising that the achievement of learning outcomes, and ultimately student performance, is more of a shared responsibility.

Partnership between staff and students in the pedagogical domain is an empowering activity that enhances self-confidence and sense of belonging, supporting high levels of engagement and the emergence of an authentic learning community between those participating (Figure 23.1). However, the literature on partnership is dominated by models of partnership based on selection and is thus potentially exclusionary. Felten et al. (2013) and Moore-Cherry et al. (2016) have argued that if the benefits of partnership are as positive as much of the evidence would suggest, the time has come to engage in more 'inclusive partnership' and mainstream partnership working as pedagogical practice. The next section of the chapter highlights a range of ways in which this is being embedded in practice in the discipline of geography.

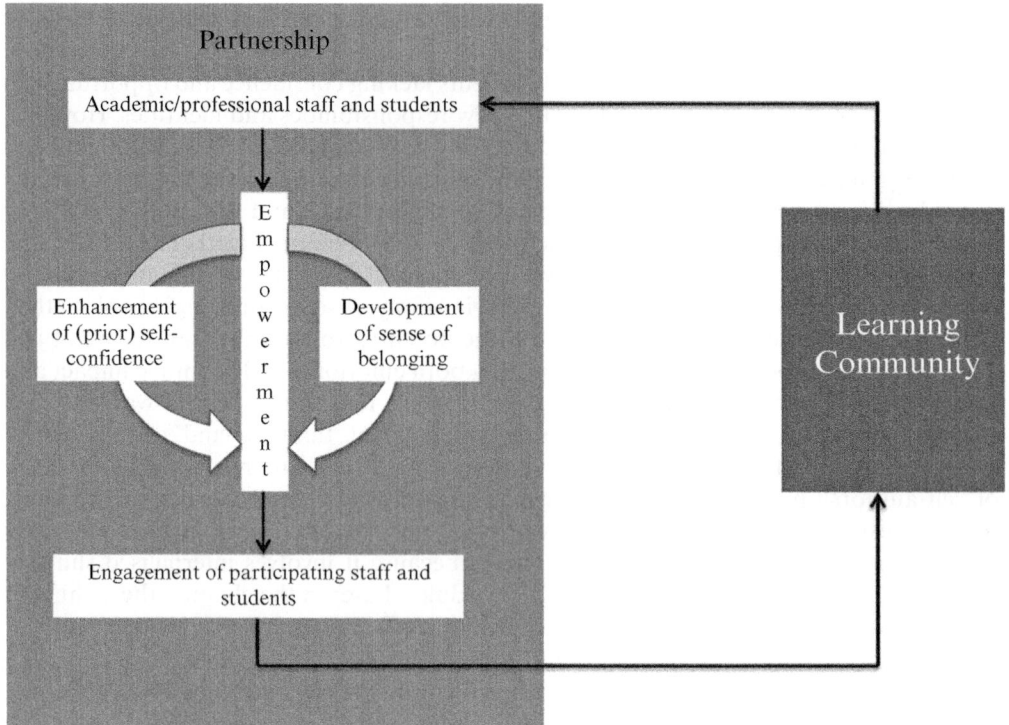

Source: Adapted from Moore-Cherry et al. (2016).

Figure 23.1   Benefits of partnership working

PRACTISING PARTNERSHIP IN GEOGRAPHY TEACHING AND LEARNING

In recent years, geographers have been among the most vocal advocates for, and early adopters of, partnership working within pedagogical practice. This may partly be attributable to the diversity of our subject and the diversity of learning spaces that we occupy, some of which, like fieldwork, lend themselves almost naturally to partnership working between academics and students. Yet even within more formal and traditional pedagogical settings like the lecture theatre or tutorial, Hill et al. (2016, Table 1) have identified ways in which geographers can, and do, engage in alternative approaches that create liminality, conceptualised as 'borderland spaces' within which partnership practices can emerge. This is not without its challenges, but they argue: 'persistence in these spaces can be affirming . . . perhaps the most important result for students can be a movement towards situating personal knowledge amongst alternative forms and a progression towards self-authorship through student-student and student-faculty partnership' (Hill et al., 2016, p. 379).

While geographers have demonstrated the possibility of partnership working in different physical spaces, there are also different curricular junctures where partnership can happen and is happening with some success. A range of examples and case studies from a variety of international contexts are now outlined to highlight the diversity of approaches to partnership working within the geography discipline, and the specific impacts on student engagement and learning. The case studies were collected collaboratively via the International Network of Learning and Teaching in Geography (INLT) and they outline practical examples of the different ways of partnership working that have been identified by Bovill et al. (2016).

Partnership working can begin as soon as students enter the university. For example, at Manchester Metropolitan University, orientation in week 0 embraces partnership approaches to inculcate an ethos of collaboration and co-learning. Students work in teams of five to prepare a pitch for an episode of a new, hypothetical BBC environment-focused documentary series. The activity is designed for students to work together to a common purpose, embed them within a community of university learning and support the development of their identities as geographers (Moore-Cherry et al., 2016). Students take on the role of *co-learners working in partnership* with each other, while tutors adopt a guiding supportive role.

One of the most challenging staff–student partnership practices is for staff to move away from an all-powerful and controlling sense of what should be taught, towards the *co-production of the curriculum with students*. For some, this kind of working may be perceived as an undermining staff authority or expertise and a drain on their already pressed time. Yet as case study 1 below illustrates (Box 23.1), rather than being an additional demand on staff and students, partnership working can be introduced into

---

BOX 23.1   CASE STUDY 1 – RESEARCHER DEVELOPMENT AND DESIGN, UNIVERSITY OF CHESTER

What is this course about?
This module is about preparing students to undertake independent research, and in particular the dissertation. It focuses initially on research philosophies and methods of collecting data (whether that is in the field or using other sources of data) and analysing it (for instance by using statistics).

What are the roles of each of the different partners and how do they interact?
This year we adopted a students as partners ethos to re-design the teaching of these research methods. Staff set the topic and five different readings were divided up amongst the class. On the basis of this, students were asked what aspects of the topic they thought were interesting and their ideas on the topic were recorded at the front of the class. Staff then categorised these into four over-arching themes. The class reviewed these categorisations and as a group came up with research objectives. Using these research objectives the class worked together (students and staff to produce an interview schedule). The students then each conducted one interview (19 in total – students given 5 per cent of their assignment to transcribe their interview). On the basis of the findings from the interviews the class worked together to produce a questionnaire. Each student was then asked to get at least 5 responses to the questionnaire (some students collected more – 107 in total).

What are the expected learning outcomes for students from this activity?
Students are expected to develop: detailed understanding of how to produce social science research tools (e.g. schedule and questionnaire); experience of conducting interviews and question-naires; and applied experience of analysing interview and questionnaire data.

existing courses as a way of structuring the learning experience differently. In this case, the partners were the lecturing staff and all 19 students taking the social strand of the module.

The outcome for the students is a more collaborative and authentic learning experience as they are actively involved in creating their own learning, building and developing as independent learners, feeding through into later learning experiences (see also Chapter 15 in this volume by Richard Hodgkins and Joanna Bullard). Students recognise this, with one commenting that: '*We're being prepared really well for doing our dissertations*' (student representative). Their understanding of the impact of their experience beyond the immediate environment indicates an enhanced meta-cognitive awareness.

While staff–student partnership in co-creating the curriculum may be considered challenging, *partnering students through support of peer-to-peer collaboration* may seem less daunting. This can occur in various spaces of learning: for example group collaborative learning is a common experience in small-group tutorials, in problem-based learning, in laboratory/practical classes and in fieldwork. Simm and Marvell (2015) have written extensively about the effectiveness of student-led peer teaching and learning on international fieldwork (Marvell et al., 2013), and its transformative capacity when students are pushed out of their comfort zone (Hill et al., 2016). While academic staff co-produce elements of the fieldtrip, students effectively author their field course. Students become responsible not just for their own learning but that of their peers. They also engage in different ways and at much deeper levels with the topic, each other and the place in which they are embedded.

Case study 2 illustrates that a similar but smaller-scale approach can be taken within the traditional classroom. The final year Social and Population Geography class at University College Dublin has an enrolment of 90 students and one course leader. Given the limited capacity of one lecturer to engage in depth with a group of this size, a partnership approach was taken to the development and undertaking of one piece of assessment. Students individually negotiated their assignment with the lecturer but then collaborated with each other to generate and collect data (see Box 23.2).

While students can be nervous about picking a project and some would prefer to simply be told what to do, for the most part the feedback was that they enjoyed leading and taking responsibility for a project from start to finish. This type of small-scale partnership activity can have significant benefits in promoting co-responsibility within the student body, but also developing an awareness of the research process, getting students to do geography in practice, and developing the skills to negotiate a bespoke project topic that links their academic learning to their personal experiences and awareness: '*The research essay was great, although I was very apprehensive about starting it. Once I chose a topic I liked, it didn't feel like work and was very interesting to find more info about the topic*' (student module feedback). Rather than doing an essay solely for grades, this student shows their sense of being purposefully engaged in an intellectual endeavour. The opportunity to take responsibility for their own learning and that of others was relished: '*I really enjoyed the assignment which allowed me to do my own research and analyses*' (student module feedback). These responses were represented across the majority of the student cohort in this module. Although not a specific learning outcome, this transformation in identity has the potential to influence how students approach their learning across and beyond the curriculum.

BOX 23.2   CASE STUDY 2 – SOCIAL/POPULATION GEOGRAPHY,
UNIVERSITY COLLEGE DUBLIN

What is this course about?
This module combines two distinctive geographic sub-disciplines; population geography and social geography. Drawing on current population statistics, the course begins by examining population composition and distribution before examining the physical, environmental and societal factors influencing spatial variations in populations and population movements. The social geography section refocuses attention on local communities and individuals, on understanding the spatial organisation of society and examines the factors which influence people's interactions, both positive and negative, with each other through space.

What are the roles of each of the different partners and how do they interact?
Part of the assessment for this module is an assignment on social geography. For this essay the students are given the opportunity to select any social geography research topic they are interested in and complete a miniature (2500 word) research project. In this way, the students can dictate their own assignment, but they are given detailed instructions in terms of layout, format etc. by the lecturer. The lecturer meets with each student individually or in small groups of 2/3 (whatever they are most comfortable with) to discuss their topic and make sure it fits within the remit of social geography. The students also work as partners together; each student is required to develop an anonymous questionnaire (using either survey monkey/hard copy) which is then sent to the other students for completion. Each student requires 20 responses to complete their results. All students are actively encouraged to buy into this part of the process, to support one another.

What are the expected learning outcomes for students from this activity?
Students are expected to enhance their research planning, critical thinking, information synthesis, analysis and writing skills. They are expected to develop a greater awareness of how lecture topics apply to an area of their own interest and they are expected to understand how their work fits within broader international, current research trends within social geography today.

While teaching and research are often conceived as two separate entities, the examples above highlight the close linkages between the two. The partnership literature provides clear examples where students work more explicitly with staff as 'co-researchers' (Bovill et al., 2016), playing a key role in bridging these domains of academic activity. This type of partnership working tends to be more selective than the types of partnership outlined earlier, with particular criteria being used to invite certain students to engage. For example, at King Saud University (Saudi Arabia), a new undergraduate research programme has been introduced aimed at supporting scientific research at undergraduate level in collaboration with staff. Although the programme is not geography-specific, geography academics have successfully partnered with geography students. Participating students are selected on the basis of high achievement. The model empowers students who are already doing well, and they must work collaboratively with staff to prepare a research proposal. If the project is approved they must sign a contract with the Research Deanship. The student is provided with small-scale financial support, as well as a recognition certificate once the research proposal has been accepted. In some cases, students have gone on to partner staff members in producing a research publication. Rather than just being a research assistant on a previously defined project, this is an example of where power and responsibility is shared from the initiation of the project.

Similarly, at the University of Staffordshire (UK), the Geography and Environment Research Assistantship (GRA) Programme creates partnership working opportunities between academic staff, students and sometimes external clients from industry, local authorities, schools, and other agencies. On some projects, the research is triggered by the needs of external clients who work in partnership with staff and the student. Interaction between all parties takes place at meetings at which research progress is reviewed and the next goals set. Students become not just co-researchers but also co-learners through research as they experience first-hand the iterative and dialogic practices of research. The GRA engenders a very real sense of 'practising geography' and of the participants (students, staff and external clients) taking ownership of the research work. This has had impact beyond just the functional elements of curriculum, such as the need for assessment (for more on this see Tweed and Boast, 2011). It has shifted identities as staff and students work together with a common purpose in a research environment where everyone is a learner, or as one student noted: '*a different relationship evolves – you become a co-worker*'. A liminal space of learning emerges as students and staff work collaboratively to question and review data to develop new knowledge. It is clear that this type of working and pedagogical environment enables significant leaps to be made towards self-authorship as student observations suggest this mode of working impacts their learning routine outside of the requirements of the RA. After their experiences on the programme, it is difficult to 'go back to a previous way of seeing or being' (Cook-Sather, 2014, p. 193), illustrating the transformative nature of this type of pedagogical experience.

While some of the previous examples illustrate how it is possible for students to work peer-to-peer within geography classes and to work with external stakeholders in a research capacity, there are other forms of partnership working that operate at the *intersection of students as co-researchers, pedagogical co-designers and consultants* (Bovill et al., 2016). At the University of Zaragoza (Spain), 155 undergraduate students studying economic geography, population geography and remote sensing and their lecturers work collaboratively with students and staff from the journalism programme in a partnership activity entitled *human geography in the media.* Through partnership working, students develop awareness of their skills and expertise as a geographer, understand their potential contributions to civil society and positioning as 'experts' on topics of societal importance, and enhance their ability to communicate their learning to other students and to those outside of the university (Box 23.3).

In the next section of the chapter, the specific impacts of these types of activity are discussed, together with their role in re-shaping identities and thus enabling progress towards self-authorship along the cognitive, intrapersonal and interpersonal dimensions.

IMPACTS OF PARTNERSHIP WORKING IN GEOGRAPHY HIGHER EDUCATION

Student engagement has never been a higher priority for institutions, staff and students. Partnership, as one form of engagement, has become a way of working that is associated with deeper learning and the development of a greater sense of belonging and connectedness to the institution and to others (Hagenauer and Volet, 2014). This is critical for integrating students with the institution, the subject and for their own development.

BOX 23.3   CASE STUDY 3 – HUMAN GEOGRAPHY IN THE MEDIA,
UNIVERSITY OF ZARAGOZA, SPAIN

What is this course about?
A range of subjects of contemporary relevance from the sub-disciplines of population geography, economic geography and remote sensing are chosen as the thematic foci for student learning and collaborative projects.

What are the roles of each of the different partners and how do they interact?
Geography students act as experts on various geo-economic, environmental and demographic topics on which the journalism students elaborate via audiovisual (podcasts, short TV reports) and visual (infographics) productions.

What are the expected learning outcomes for students from this activity?
Geography students improve their oral and visual communication competencies. Journalism students discover human geography as a key approach to understand the present world. All students reinforce the acquisition of significant content and improve their teamwork skills. The benefits of the project extend to society as a whole by publishing the results in university digital media: *Radio. Unizar.es* and *Entremedios*.

Cook-Sather and Luz (2015) have argued that partnerships embody Barber's (2012, p. 592) expanded definition of integration as 'extending beyond disciplinary boundaries to encompass multiple contexts, life experiences, and identity roles' and thus partnership has a significant role to play in developing more inclusive learning environments and progressing both students and staff towards self-authorship. Traditional roles within pedagogical practice of staff–student or expert–novice are socially constructed, but what the examples above illustrate is that these traditional roles can be de- and re-constructed into more collaborative relationships given the correct conditions and willingness. The examples here may not all have strengthened students' identities as geographers, but they have enhanced students' identities as co-learners, co-researchers and co-workers in geography with shared responsibility for the pedagogical environment. This empowerment leads to an enhanced sense of self, both intrapersonally and interpersonally, which ultimately supports progress towards self-authorship.

In case study 2, for example, the lecturer involved has found that the process of selecting a topic, which is unique to the individual student, involves a shift in gear for them; thinking about how to approach it, and what questions to ask and why, generates a different mindset and challenges their identity as a student. Through empowerment, students engage in meaning-making within the context of the specific module (cognitive dimension of self-authorship) shaped by their own interests, assumptions and identities (intrapersonal dimension), but mediated through their interactions with the lecturer and fellow students (interpersonal dimension). Similarly, in the example of peer-led fieldwork (Simm and Marvell, 2015), some of the greatest impacts of a partnership approach to the learning journey were a growing awareness of relationships with the 'other', sensitivity about 'invading' local space, and an acknowledgement of misplaced preconceptions. These interpersonal and intrapersonal identity shifts represent an enhanced metacognitive awareness of the situated nature and construction of knowledge. This was also particularly evident in case study 1. As students learnt more about the nature of questionnaires and interviews, they became more aware of the limitations of the method and their positioning as a researcher in influencing the nature of the data collected. This recognition of the socially constructed nature of knowledge and challenging of identities, through collaborative working, encourages personally referenced ways of knowing (Baxter Magolda, 2004). Although particular types of partnership working and activities might support specific dimensions of self-authorship, in general, partnership working encourages students to experience a sense of liminality enabling their progression to higher forms of learning.

The case studies and examples chosen highlight the diversity of partnership working at a range of scales; large/small classes, programmes, institutions, within and beyond the curriculum, and the various dimensions of self-authorship developed. Bovill et al. (2016, p. 199) suggest that: 'students at all levels can gain confidence and capacity when power relations within the educational environment shift to a more collaborative approach through which students have voice and an active role in their own and others' learning experiences'.

Whether in the field, research laboratory or lecture theatre, geographers have been creating spaces of liminality in 'traditional' learning environments suggesting that it is not the learning setting that is critical in harnessing these opportunities but what goes on within them and how it relates to the broader world, and broader identities and sets of beliefs. In the Geography and Environment Research Assistantship programme at the University of Staffordshire, the idea of students and staff as co-workers challenges established boundaries in higher education. This is a form of creative destruction; staff and students suggest that the work has meaning, impact and relevance beyond the needs of the curriculum and develops confidence, professionalism and enhances employability. This is precisely because it challenges how meaning is made and forces an evaluation of the researchers' positioning within the institution and relative to other researchers. Similarly, in the example from the University of Zaragoza, it was the connection beyond the curriculum to how geographers might, and have a responsibility to, play a role in civil society (the interpersonal dimension of self-authorship) that was one of the greatest impacts of the partnership between geography and journalism students.

REFLECTIONS ON PROGRESSING PARTNERSHIP WORKING IN PEDAGOGICAL PRACTICE

Partnership is clearly an emergent pedagogy, but one that remains a niche activity in many institutional contexts. Significant momentum has been gained in recent years in some contexts, but this mode of working and of building relationships still remains counter-cultural in the majority of higher education contexts. While geographers do appear to be at the forefront of innovation and in some cases are among the most vocal academics advocating partnership as an approach to working (Hill et al., 2016; Moore-Cherry et al., 2016, Cliffe et al., 2017), it is still very much a threshold concept. While it may be troublesome, the examples from geographic practice highlight that it can be transformative, integrative and that for many students in particular the impact of partnership working is irreversible and changes who they are as learners and members of wider society.

Cook-Sather (2002, p. 6) has argued: 'attitudes and institutional structures need to change if we are to more fully authorize students' perspectives on education and pursue challenging, and necessary changes, in educational policy and practice'. In geography, progress is happening but it remains slow and in many cases a 'niche' activity. If it is to become more of a mainstream practice and paradigm for geography in the 21st century, it is worth reflecting on a number of issues:

- Partnership working is dialogic and iterative. Successful practice requires acceptance that it is not a linear process and that there will be movement back and forth across a 'threshold'. Clear communication and a common sense of purpose between all stakeholders is key. While this may be easier within the setting of a course or module, a greater challenge may arise at institutional level where the idea of partnership working appears counter-intuitive or counter-cultural. Bovill (2014) has discussed in some detail the difficulty of moving partnerships from theory into practice but one strategy to encourage buy-in might be to start at the end point, articulating the benefits and opportunities that a partnership approach could bring to a particular activity, and then developing a pathway to operationalise it.
- Even where there is buy-in and a willingness to think differently, for partnership working to succeed, a shift in power relations is required. This can be a challenge, particularly where staff and students view staff as the only authorities and an 'expert–novice' culture is embedded. In each of the examples of partnership working and in the literature more generally, successful partnerships emerged where a liminal space was created, pushing all stakeholders beyond their comfort zone and facilitating more equal and collaborative working practices. For suggestions on how these liminal or borderland spaces can be created in our existing curricula and beyond, across different class sizes and sub-disciplinary areas, see Hill et al. (2016).
- One approach that can assist the development of new working practices is to view pedagogy from a different standpoint. Instead of seeing the curriculum and associated activities as 'doing geography', attention could be shifted to 'being a geographer'. Within this framework, a more collaborative, active approach automatically emerges and attention shifts away from content delivery and the privileging of particular authorised knowledges. In the examples of peer-to-peer fieldwork and students as co-researchers above, a sense of co-learning through the practice of geography was normalised.
- Geography is fundamentally about understanding the world of which we are a part. For partnership to be meaningful and authentic, staff and student experiences beyond the classroom need to be linked with academic learning. This can be supported by engaging a wider range of partners, perhaps other staff and students, as in the example from the University of Zaragoza, or engaging stakeholders who are completely external to the university. Creating collaborative working relationships with external agents helps shift attention away from the sometimes uncomfortable changing dynamics of the staff–student relationship but also enables students to develop more personally referenced ways of understanding the world.

A partnership approach to pedagogical practice has many positive impacts, but for the moment remains a threshold concept. Given its growing prominence in the literature and its positive relationship with student engagement, the potential is there for it to become instrumentalised, for example as university managers seek to enhance their feedback in student experience surveys. Nonetheless, the positive benefits are such that, as academic geographers, we should consider how we can practice partnership working within and beyond the curriculum to create professional, capable and independent geography graduates. As we move towards expanding or mainstreaming partnership working within our pedagogical practice, it is salient to consider the advice of Cook-Sather (2002, pp. 22–23) over a decade ago:

> From century-old constructivist approaches to education we must retain the notion that students need to be authors of their own understanding and assessors of their own learning. With critical pedagogy we must share a commitment to redistributing power not only within the classroom, between teacher and students, but in society at large. Keeping in mind postmodern feminist critiques of the workings and re-workings of power, we must be willing to take small steps toward changing oppressive practices, but we must also continually question our motives and practices in taking these steps.

USEFUL RESOURCES

- Centre for Engaged Learning, Elon University (USA), https://www.centerforen gagedlearning.org/doing-engaged-learning/students-as-partners/.
- International Institute for Students as Partners (McMaster University, Canada) https://macblog.mcmaster.ca/summer-institute/about-students-as-partners/.
- International Journal for Students as Partners, https://mulpress.mcmaster.ca/ijsap.
- Student Engagement through Partnership, Higher Education Academy (UK), https://www.heacademy.ac.uk/individuals/strategic-priorities/student-engagement.

ACKNOWLEDGEMENTS

Many thanks to the numerous colleagues from around the world who generously shared their examples of partnership working in geographical practice: Ali Al-Ghamdi (King Saud University); Arlene Crampsie (University College Dublin); Ruth Healey (University of Chester); Joseph Kerski (ESRI); Rebecca Theobald (Colorado Geographic Alliance); Fiona Tweed (University of Staffordshire); Ana Isabel Escalona-Orcao, Juan de la Riva-Fernández and María Zúñiga-Antón (University of Zaragoza, Spain); David Simm (Bath Spa University) and Alan Marvell (University of Gloucestershire).

REFERENCES

Barber, J.P. (2012) 'Integration of learning: A grounded theory analysis of college students' learning', *American Educational Research Journal*, 49 (3), pp. 590–617.
Baxter Magolda, M.B. (2004) 'Preface', in M.B. Baxter Magolda and P.M. King (eds), *Learning Partnerships: Theory and Models of Practice to Educate for Self-Authorship*. Sterling, VA: Stylus, pp. xvii–xxvi.
Bovill, C. (2014) 'An investigation of co-created curricula within higher education in the UK, Ireland and the USA', *Innovations in Education and Teaching International*, 51 (1), pp. 15–25.

Bovill, C. and Felten, P. (2016) 'Cultivating student–staff partnerships through research and practice', *International Journal for Academic Development*, 21 (1), pp. 1–3.

Bovill, C., Cook-Sather, A. and Felten, P. (2011) 'Students as co-creators of teaching approaches, course design, and curricula: implications for academic developers', *International Journal for Academic Development*, 16 (2), pp. 133–145.

Bovill, C., Cook-Sather, A., Felten, P., Millard, L. and Moore-Cherry, N. (2016) 'Addressing potential challenges in co-creating learning and teaching: overcoming resistance, navigating institutional norms and ensuring inclusivity in student–staff partnerships', *Higher Education*, 71 (2), pp. 195–208.

Bozick, R. (2007) 'Making it through the first year of college: the role of students' economic resources, employment, and living arrangements', *American Sociological Association*, 80 (3), pp. 261–285.

Cliffe, A., Cook-Sather, A., Healey, M., Healey, R., Marquis, B., Matthews, K.E., Mercer-Mapstone, L., Ntem, A., Puri, V. and Woolmer, C. (2017) 'Launching a journal about and through students as partners', *International Journal of Students as Partners*, 1 (1), https://mulpress.mcmaster.ca/ijsap.

Cook-Sather, A. (2002) 'Authorizing students' perspectives: toward trust, dialogue, and change in education', *Educational Researcher*, 31 (4), pp. 3–14.

Cook-Sather, A. (2014) 'Student–faculty partnership in explorations of pedagogical practice: a threshold concept in academic development', *International Journal for Academic Development*, 19 (3), pp. 186–198.

Cook-Sather, A. and Luz, A. (2015) 'Greater engagement in and responsibility for learning: what happens when students cross the threshold of student–faculty partnership', *Higher Education Research & Development*, 34 (6), pp. 1097–1109.

Cook-Sather, A., Bovill, C. and Felten, P. (2014) *Engaging Students as Partners in Learning and Teaching: A Guide for Faculty*. London: Wiley & Sons.

Curran, R. and Millard, L. (2016) 'A partnership approach to developing student capacity to engage and staff capacity to be engaging: opportunities for academic developers', *International Journal for Academic Development*, 21 (1), pp. 67–78.

Felten, P., Bagg, J., Bumbry, M., Hill, J., Hornsby, K., Pratt, M. and Weller, S. (2013) 'A call for expanding inclusive student engagement in SoTL', *Teaching and Learning Inquiry*, 1 (2), pp. 63–74.

Hagenauer, G. and Volet, S.E. (2014) 'Teacher–student relationship at university: an important yet under-researched field', *Oxford Review of Education*, 40 (3), pp. 370–388.

HEA (2014) *Framework for Partnership in Learning and Teaching*. Available online at: www.heacademy.ac.uk/students-as-partners. Accessed 28 February 2018.

Healey, M., Flint, A. and Harrington, K. (2014) *Developing Students as Partners in Learning and Teaching in Higher Education*. York: Higher Education Academy.

Healey, M., Flint, A. and Harrington, K. (2016) 'Students as partners: reflections on a conceptual model', *Teaching & Learning Inquiry*, 4 (2), pp. 1–13.

Hill, J., Thomas, G., Diaz, A. and Simm, D. (2016) 'Borderland spaces for learning partnership: opportunities, benefits and challenges', *Journal of Geography in Higher Education*, 40 (3), pp. 375–393.

Jensen, K. and Bennett, L. (2016) 'Enhancing teaching and learning through dialogue: a student and staff partnership model', *International Journal for Academic Development*, 21 (1), pp. 41–53.

Kenny, J. (2017) 'Academic work and performativity', *Higher Education*, 74 (5), pp. 897–913.

King, C. and Felten, P. (2012) 'Threshold concepts in educational development: an introduction', *The Journal of Faculty Development*, 26 (3), pp. 5–7.

Kuh, G.D., Cruce, T.M., Shoup, R. and Kinzie, J. (2008) 'Unmasking the effects of student engagement on first-year college grades and persistence', *The Journal of Higher Education*, 79 (5), pp. 540–563.

Lynch, K. (2015) 'Control by numbers: new managerialism and ranking in higher education', *Critical Studies in Education*, 56 (2), pp. 190–207.

Marvell, A., Simm, D., Schaaff, R. and Harper, R. (2013) 'Students as scholars: evaluating student-led learning and teaching during fieldwork', *Journal of Geography in Higher Education*, 37 (4), pp. 547–566.

Moore-Cherry, N., Healey, R., Nicholson, D.T. and Andrews, W. (2016) 'Inclusive partnership: enhancing student engagement in geography', *Journal of Geography in Higher Education*, 40 (1), pp. 84–103.

Moore, N., Fournier, E.J., Hardwick, S.W., Healey, M., MacLachlan, J. and Seemann, J. (2011) 'Mapping the journey toward self-authorship in geography', *Journal of Geography in Higher Education*, 35 (3), pp. 351–364.

Nystrand, M. and Gamoran, A. (1991) 'Instructional discourse, student engagement, and literature achievement', *Research in the Teaching of English*, 25 (3), pp. 261–290.

Palmer, M., O'Kane, P. and Owens, M. (2009) 'Betwixt spaces: student accounts of turning point experiences in the first-year transition', *Studies in Higher Education*, 34 (1), pp. 37–54.

Quinn, J., Thomas, L., Slack, K., Casey, L., Thexton, W. and Noble, J. (2005) *From Life Crisis to Lifelong Learning: Rethinking Working-Class 'Drop Out' from Higher Education*. Staffordshire, UK: Staffordshire University, Joseph Rountree Foundation.

Shulman, L.S. (2004) *The Wisdom of Practice: Essays on Learning, Teaching, and Learning to Teach*. San Francisco, CA: Jossey-Bass.

Simm, D. and Marvell, A. (2015) 'Gaining a "sense of place": students' affective experiences of place leading to transformative learning on international fieldwork', *Journal of Geography in Higher Education*, 39 (4), pp. 595–616.

Tweed, F. and Boast, R. (2011) 'Reviewing the "research placement" as a means of enhancing student learning and expanding research capacity', *Journal of Geography in Higher Education*, 35 (4), pp. 599–615.

24. Taking ownership: active learning and student engagement
Eric Pawson and Mark Poskitt

INTRODUCTION

We first encountered the idea of taking ownership at an undergraduate research conference in Australia, where it was the central theme of the opening keynote speech given by a doctoral student.[1] He described it as an active process of conscientiously engaging with, and assuming responsibility for, one's own research. It was intriguing how quickly the audience took to the notion, as if it was putting into words something for which many felt an intuitive need. Taking ownership in this context is about self-determination, and can be described as a decision, a mind-set, and a behaviour. It is not a one-off event, but rather a daily commitment to making one's learning one's own. Although it demands significant commitment, it has the potential to reap many benefits in terms of motivation and student engagement, which in turn may lead to greater understanding and enhanced learning (Marton and Säljö, 1976; Biggs, 1999). Throughout the conference, the idea was referenced many times by participants, becoming something of a cornerstone for the meeting. Our argument in this chapter is that 'taking ownership' is not limited to research contexts alone, but has both value and meaning in rethinking the educational experience more broadly.

Our approach here combines the reflections of both a current student and staff member to give a novel perspective on how students and teachers alike can participate at a deeper level with the learning process. In the first section, we consider the relationship between teaching and learning, and how taking ownership is enhanced through active student engagement in the construction of knowledge. Secondly, we examine the implications of this for both students and academic staff, as well as in the provision and use of learning spaces. Thirdly, we illustrate the argument with some case studies of specific learning practices for those who wish to try something different in or outside their classrooms. Fourthly, we draw the threads together to show how taking ownership enables lifelong learning and encourages the elastic and creative thinking skills required to navigate the challenges of a human-dominated planet in the Anthropocene. As a student–academic partnership, we draw on anecdotes that are sometimes specific to each of us, but it should be clear from the context who is speaking. In writing together we have also become acutely aware of the politics of authorship in relation to taking ownership. We address this issue at the close of the chapter in a coda.

LEARNING, TEACHING, AND THE CONSTRUCTION OF KNOWLEDGE

To understand the theme of taking ownership in the context of student learning, it must first be established what exactly is meant by 'learning'. Conventional educational theories have often tended to view student learning from a 'teacher-oriented' perspective. According to such approaches, student learning involves a one-way transmission of information from teacher to student (Trigwell et al., 1999). That is, a teacher, who is an expert in their field, imparts knowledge that is acquiescently received by a student. As the student is a passive actor here – at least within the classroom setting – it is the responsibility of the teacher to make sure this information reaches the student (Biggs, 1999). From this perspective, learning is reduced to the successful application of teaching, and the unidirectional flow of information from expert to student. Such teacher-oriented approaches are, for the large part, unhelpful for student learning (Steffe and Gale, 1995). They accentuate counterproductive hierarchies and power relationships within the classroom (Freire, 1972). They also fail to accurately depict the full picture of a university learning environment.

There are at least two key groups of actors directly involved in university learning: students and academic staff. Any definition of learning should therefore acknowledge both groups, and give a tangible explanation of what the learning process entails, and how the different actors involved in this process interact. Teacher-oriented approaches imply firstly that students are the only ones learning; and secondly that they need not actively engage with the content being presented in order to learn. The first of these implications is certainly false. Academic staff also regularly learn from classroom interactions with their students (Werder and Otis, 2010; Cook-Sather et al., 2014), and if they were not responsive to these, their teaching would be less likely to evolve. True, some academic staff may fit this category, but an inability to evolve surely inhibits learning rather than enhancing it. The second implication begs the question about what the learning process should look like. Critical student engagement is certainly desirable, and is widely viewed as an ideal outcome (Krause, 2005). Such an end goal would seem nigh impossible to achieve if learning is a priori defined as a process in which students are primarily passive actors within the classroom.

A more appropriate conceptualisation of learning then, is one where critical, active student engagement and student–academic interaction contributes to the learning process, whilst simultaneously being a desired learning outcome. According to a constructivist approach to learning, knowledge is not transmitted from one actor to another, but rather it is actively constructed, either by synthesising existing knowledge in new and novel ways for one or both actors, or by coming to joint discoveries previously inaccessible to either actor (Mercer, 1995; Steffe and Gale, 1995). That is, students and academic staff work together to build knowledge in the classroom – a social process in which both play a dynamic and salient role, and which 'affords students the power to co-create their learning' (Hill et al., 2016, p. 3). Teachers and teaching authority are no longer the primary focus of learning in the classroom. Rather, it is the dialogue and interactions between academics and students that take centre stage (Mercer, 1995) (see also Chapter 23 in this volume by Niamh Moore-Cherry).

It would be misleading, though, to claim that student–academic interactions are the only way knowledge is constructed. Classrooms are, in Splitter's phrase, 'communities of inquiry' (2009, p. 141) which sit within a wider social network of peers and mentors, as well as a landscape of learning spaces beyond formal settings. Interactions within these communities of inquiry are traditionally facilitated by teacher-like figures, but may occur between any of the actors within the space. For example, there is a substantial body of literature citing the importance of cooperative student–student interaction as an enhancer of learning, motivation, and academic achievement (Slavin, 1983; Panitz, 1999; Felder and Brent, 2007), and interactions of this sort indubitably play a key role in the construction of knowledge. Learning, then, in the context of this chapter, refers to the construction of knowledge which itself is a product of multifarious interactions between the actors who comprise a community of inquiry in an educational environment.

THE IMPLICATIONS OF TAKING OWNERSHIP

What does it mean to take ownership in the context of a community of inquiry, and what are the implications of such a move? In the following section we explore these implications for students, academics, and for the design and use of learning spaces.

A Student's Perspective

During the last year of my undergraduate studies as a Geography and Philosophy major in 2017, one of my favourite classes was with a philosopher named Diane.[2] One of the strengths of Diane's teaching was that she never asserted anything; we as the class could never tell where her true opinions lay. She would present different arguments to us, and we would dissect these through animated discussion and reasoned argumentation. If someone made a point, anyone else was free to challenge it. If the challenger had a strong argument, then good; if successfully rebutted, all the better. Either way, more debate would ensue, and we would begin to see for ourselves the strengths and weaknesses of each philosophical position, and construct notions about which positions we preferred and why. All of this occurred without Diane ever having told us 'this position is better than this one', or anything of the sort! We were able to construct knowledge, together, without ever feeling like we were 'disciples' of Diane (Barnett, 2017), or that she was forcing her epistemic framework and worldview on us. What I remember most about this experience is that everyone was actively involved – it was highly enjoyable and engaging.

There are many ways students can take ownership over their learning; the narrative of Diane's classroom depicts just one. With a little imagination, geography classes also lend themselves to different forms of active participation (Jenkins, 1984). However, this is unlikely to occur unless it is facilitated by the lecturer or tutor. For example, whilst Diane never participated in classroom arguments, she often encouraged these in subtle ways. If dialogue between students began to dwindle or become circular and unproductive, she would move the discussion along with another open-ended question, or allude to a potential argument or point that had been overlooked. This did not always guarantee that students would engage with the content being discussed, but it certainly optimised the likelihood of them doing so (Biggs, 1999). Being a student in a class like this made taking ownership over the construction of knowledge far easier.

Classroom discussions were conceptually stimulating, and made relevant to our lives, often through thought experiments and hypothetical or counterfactual scenarios. If we felt strongly about a philosophical position (which inevitably happened given the nature of the ethical and existential questions discussed), we would be more motivated to analyse its strengths and trade-offs, and familiarise ourselves with oppositional positions to refute these. This enabled us to gain a deeper understanding of specific concepts and ideas (Blumenfeld, Kempler and Krajcik, 2006), and to practice communicating this through dynamic debate and logical reasoning. These skills can be developed in numerous disciplines. Indeed, many of the theories I encountered in my geography classes provided opportunities for rigorous debate. Such skills are applicable to a range of social and professional contexts outside the classroom, including many modern work environments (Jackson, 1973; Roy and Macchiette, 2005). Additionally, engaging fully in such a learning environment generates peer interaction. Not only does this encourage students to work collectively, it also allows them to socialise and enhance interpersonal skills. Consequently, knowledge was not the only thing we constructed in our classes: building meaningful relationships was an equally important outcome of taking ownership over our learning.

The Teacher's Dilemma

There are clear implications for university staff of encouraging communities of inquiry. A shift away from a model that positions the teacher as *the* authority begins to re-shape the hierarchy of power within institutions. How can academics rethink their classroom practices to enable students to take ownership of their learning? Alan Jenkins (1985, p. 205) put it this way: 'One should be *an* authority; but seldom, if ever, should one act *in* authority'. The anecdote about the philosophy class in the previous section illustrates this well. But to trust students, by extending some of that authority to them, requires letting go. As one senior academic manager said to us:

> I remember vividly going up this learning curve in my own teaching . . . It is a hard one. But then 'Teaching how to trust' (which is something that arguably cannot be taught!) is one of the challenges . . . we have to model it ourselves: we cannot expect the students to do it if we can't.[3]

How to extend trust to students is one aspect of what has been called the teacher's dilemma (Edwards and Mercer, 1989).

As a young lecturer in the late 1970s, I was perplexed by the teaching environment of an antipodean suburban campus that was quite different from my own educational experience as an Oxford college student. One issue that concerned me was how to replicate in this massified and seemingly impersonal situation some of the socialisation into geography from which I had benefited. It was my responsibility to oversee a first year entry class of 300, taught in large lecture halls with supplementary lab classes. The tables in the dedicated laboratory room were in serried rows; the inherited practical exercises focused on individual effort and attainment. Students seemed anonymised, given minimal cues for mutual recognition or social engagement, and this on a campus where a high proportion lived at home, without the advantages of connections to each other that develop in a residential university. My solution was to rewrite the classes as group exercises, and to reconfigure the space (at no cost) by rearranging the tables to enable student groups to face each other, prompting them to learn socially.

This simple model is based on encouraging social relations that trust students to work together, to engage with each other, and to begin to know themselves and their own voice in a low risk situation. It is situation-specific, but can be reworked for many different contexts. It does have implications for assessment: lab work was no longer marked with individual scores after the class. Instead, students were given feedback at the time by tutors who recorded their satisfactory completion of each exercise. The scheme therefore models a redirection of teaching effort, away from the authority figure at the front of the room, towards facilitation and mentoring of small group learning. The negotiation of this is another aspect of the teacher's dilemma, that of being able to 'inculcate knowledge while apparently eliciting it' (Edwards and Mercer, 1989, p. 126). How something is taught is as important as what is being taught; through the extension of responsibility, or owner- ship, from teacher to student.

Learning Spaces

In an essay on peace education, Jenkins (1985) argued that it is necessary to attempt to model a classroom that is in some way 'a microcosm of the society one is trying to create' (p. 205). The key to achieving this is to think through the types of learning practices that align with the form of relations being sought, because as Savin-Baden (2008, p. 2) puts it, 'the creation and re-creation of learning spaces is vital for the survival of the academic community'. But as she indicates, such spaces are as much 'mental and metaphorical' as they are physical. Authoritarian relations are often writ large in the design of traditional teaching spaces. However, it is quite possible to turn conventional lecture halls into sites of active learning. This was a focus of the 'teaching larger classes' literature that emerged three decades ago in response to the beginnings of massification of higher education in the United Kingdom (Gibbs and Jenkins, 1984) (see also, in this volume, Chapter 4 by Matt Finn and Carrie Mott, and Chapter 5 by Bradley Rink).

More recently however there has been considerable enthusiasm for supplementing and to an extent replacing formal teaching venues with informal learning spaces. In an extended critique of the trend on many campuses to adopt learning 'cafes', 'streets', 'hubs' and 'pods' – a style sometimes caricatured as beanbag design – Boys (2011) argues against such an emphasis on representation, with space being treated as setting, and instead prioritising practices, where space is understood as process. Although informal learning spaces can be refreshing, they can be equally inhibiting, replacing one form of fixed capital investment with another, and quickly taking on an identity as yesterday's ideas about the future. Put another way, an expensively designed informal learning space may be no more 'cultivating' of student development and ownership of learning than a didactic class in a lecture hall, if used in ways that lack the challenge and support that characterise such examples as Diane's philosophy class.

A focus on practices suggests that a range of physical learning spaces is necessary. Those designed to be reasonably flexible, without expensive single use fixtures, can be well suited to students taking ownership in ways suited to their learning needs and styles. But this again intersects with the question of trust: students need to be entrusted with the design, use and management of student space (Brunsdon et al., 2012). Ironically, however, they are often the last people who are asked. Boys' (2011) analysis for example focuses on architects and designers, on educationalists and on estates managers; students barely feature. This is perhaps even more important for institutions that are largely commuter dependent, as there appears to be a relationship between higher levels of engagement and the residential nature of a campus (McCormick et al., 2009). The ability to make and claim learning spaces then matters even more for student belonging when a large proportion of them are non-residential, but can benefit from encouragement to learn together and socialise on campus in their own spaces.

CASE STUDIES

We have argued that the recognition of students as subjects capable of taking ownership has implications for teaching and learning practices as well as for the spaces, metaphorical and physical, within which education takes place. This argument can be illustrated through case studies of specific practices that encourage active learning and engagement. In this section, we explore the opportunities that open up for students, as well as the changing roles of academic staff and learning spaces, in problem-based learning, undergraduate research and in living laboratories. Each of these examples provide preparation for the world of work and lifelong learning.

Problem-Based Learning

Problem-based learning (PBL) has become increasingly popular in recent years: a critical assessment of PBL and how it can be used has become one of the most frequently read articles in the *Journal of Geography in Higher Education* (Pawson et al., 2006). PBL developed in medical schools as a means of contextualising and rendering learning more real and applicable for trainee doctors. It has multiple applications in geography, from classroom problem-focused debate through to research-driven capstone projects. It upends conventional beliefs in attempting to master knowledge before its application, by instead posing the 'problem' first up. The resolution of this problem requires a systematic, student-centred inquiry process, the purpose of which is to contextualise the learning of concepts and methods through encounter with specific situations. It presupposes that most students can more readily assume ownership when learning is purposeful, connected, active and challenging.

PBL is generally group-based, as it draws on the sharing of knowledge, ideas and experiences that students can bring to bear on the problem in hand. Its success depends on proper scaffolding, with development of clear objectives and provision of mentoring, to encourage research to be undertaken in the literature and often in the field, and for emerging insights to be pooled and considered through processes of discussion and reflection. It can require considerable effort from students, but simultaneously by actively engaging them tends to enhance participation; there is also some evidence that it can narrow the attainment gap between those who are committed to their studies, and those less committed, respectively (Biggs and Tang, 2011; O'Steen et al., 2011). The outcomes may be less predictable than those of conventional teaching but are almost certainly more memorable, and potentially more creative, as both students and their academic-mentors learn to trust the process.

PBL has interesting implications for spaces of learning. It relies conspicuously on the development of communities of inquiry, and can push students well beyond the comfort zone of individual study. Rather than attempting the answer, it encourages first a clear identification of the question. It can be translated into community-based learning, taking the university into civic spaces where students work on real-world problems with community partners (such as residents' associations, schools and not-for-profit organisations) to resolve specific research questions. It is one means of learning in classrooms 'without walls', literally and metaphorically (Bednarz et al., 2008; Pawson, 2016). Paradoxically, although it may seem to be a less formal way of learning than a lecture-based education, it requires a high degree of collective organisation amongst student participants. The references in this section provide helpful starting points for those academic staff wishing to incorporate PBL into their own practice. For many students, it can deliver an authentic encounter with undergraduate research.

Undergraduate Research

Like PBL, undergraduate research has been identified as one of a number of 'high impact' practices that generate student engagement (Kuh, 2008). 'Undergraduate research' has several potential meanings. For some, it may involve a summer internship project or a course-related research assignment. For others, it is an honours thesis or dissertation, or the findings of an independently researched topic. The various definitions are not overly important. What does matter is that undergraduate research holds meaning for students. The recent growth in dedicated undergraduate research journals and conferences hosted globally suggests that it is increasing in popularity (González, 2001). This raises several pertinent questions about the role of undergraduate research in student engagement and learning (see Chapter 14 in this volume by Helen Walkington). Perhaps most importantly in our context is whether undergraduate research provides an opportunity for students to take ownership over their learning, and by extension, access some of the tangible learning benefits associated with this. The answer to this question is often 'yes' (Kuh, 2008; Lopatto, 2008) but it is a pathway that has several challenges.

At the undergraduate conference we mentioned at the start of this chapter, there was a range of students presenting their research. Some were doing honours and wanted to discuss the findings of their theses. Some were undergraduates outlining the results from a significant project they had completed as part of their coursework or summer internships. And a small minority, including myself, were presenting the results of independent research undertaken in our own time. Despite these differences, we shared an important commonality: each student was there by their own choosing. As the sole New Zealand student at the conference, I had the opportunity to represent my institution on an international stage – something I am immensely proud of. I had taken ownership of my research, and was excited to share my work (Poskitt, 2017). This shared sense of 'ownership' was palpable throughout the conference, and unified us in a common community of inquiry despite the diverse nature of our research. The interdisciplinary nature of the conference gave us an insight into alternate realms of expertise (Hill et al., 2018). This enabled us to gain a fuller understanding of our own work; and to see it in an interdisciplinary context (Walkington et al., 2017). As a result, our research meant something real and meaningful to each of us, whilst letting us realise we were participating in something bigger than ourselves.

The practice of undergraduate research does however pose some challenges (Barnett, 2017). Adapting to new roles can cause uncertainty and anxiety (Hill et al., 2016). This can lead to confusion as to how to proceed, which may in the short term be a barrier to student engagement. Such liminality may be overcome if students are introduced to different elements of the research process early on. It is quite feasible to get first year students to begin to think like researchers. For example, they can be asked to formulate research questions in a particular context, to undertake brief literature reviews, or to outline simple step-by-step methodologies to achieve a given objective. Walkington et al. (2011) demonstrate that embedding research skill development early and scaffolding this throughout a degree programme supports geography students to become more independent producers of knowledge. Such strategies can be a rich source of experiential learning and development for both students and academic staff.

Living Laboratories

In reality students work all the time with the ambiguities of liminality, as they seek to understand and contribute to complex knowledge, face up to the challenges of group work, and move towards self-authorship, a critical imagination and independence of thought. These are some of the attributes or 'general cast of mind' (Warnock, 1989, p. 35) that prepare students for ownership of lifelong learning. One way universities can further encourage such preparation is through the development of living laboratories. These are organisational rather than physical spaces, and a good example of what Savin-Baden (2008) has called 'boundary spaces'. She defines them as 'within civic society . . . in-between spaces, between cultures and politics, between people and institutions and between diverse forms of knowledges' (p. 115). They are spaces within which students, academics and universities can engage with wider publics.

A decade ago Savin-Baden considered such spaces were often ignored. Since then the growing popularity of service learning in the United States, and student volunteering in many countries, is evidence that this is changing. The concept of a living laboratory, however, provides a more formal framework and can represent a step change in terms of research production. The term covers a variety of functional arrangements, from the instrumental innovation spaces shared between industry and the academy in particular contexts, to on-campus environmental initiatives that have become popular in the United Kingdom. There a living laboratory is 'where real-world sustainability challenges are formally addressed in stakeholder partnerships' (Waheed, 2017, p. 4), meaning between a university's general staff, its academics, students and often external interests as well. An example is the Cambridge living laboratory, which provides research and summer studentship opportunities, supported by Santander, a major European bank (University of Cambridge, 2018).

In contrast, the living lab at Massey University in New Zealand is described as 'a collaborative, research and innovation space, designed to co-create new knowledge'[4] which enables students and academics to work on funded projects, particularly with the local city and regional councils, but also with groups such as iwi, or Māori tribes (Massey University, 2018). A step on from this is the living laboratory in development for the post-earthquake city of Christchurch with which we have both been involved. It is envisaged as an intergenerational civic learning space focused on the question of 'How do we learn to live in a 21st century urban environment characterised by both uncertainty and opportunity?' It aims to create a partnership between higher education institutions, Māori organisations, local government, community groups, businesses and schools. This living laboratory is centred on the city's red zone, a vast area of former residential land in a coastal river corridor that had to be abandoned due to ground deformation in the Canterbury earthquakes of 2010–13. Learning themes include climate change, environmental monitoring, cultural narratives and social memories (Pawson, 2017). For students, the opportunity is to engage in research that may not only be transformational for the city and its communities but for themselves as well.

LEARNING FOR THE ANTHROPOCENE

Today we are living in a world under existential threat. The global footprint of human activities is expanding at a phenomenal rate. We have now reached an unprecedented epoch in our history where human activity is the single biggest driver of atmospheric, ecological and geological change within the earth system. The term 'Anthropocene' has been adopted to describe this new era (Crutzen, 2006). The Anthropocene presents a host of wicked problems that threaten to compromise the wellbeing of humankind, the rest of the animal kingdom, and the sustainability of our shared planet. An important question raised by these problems is what sort of learning will best prepare people for life in the Anthropocene; and how can the academy facilitate such learning (Pawson, 2015)? We have argued so far that taking ownership over one's learning can lead to a deeper engagement with the learning process, a greater understanding of complex concepts and ideas, interpersonal growth, and the development of creative critical thinking skills.

We now mean to take this argument one step further. The problems of the Anthropocene are global in impact, and complex and multifaceted in nature. Consequently, there is no simple solution that can be learned to solve these issues. Prescriptive approaches that focus on the acquisition and transmission of knowledge are therefore likely to be ineffectual in this context. It is only through a profound engagement with the learning process (Biggs, 1999) that students will gain the creative and critical thinking skills to enable them to navigate the complexities of the Anthropocene. Making it easier for students to take ownership over their learning is one way in which such a cast of mind can be encouraged. Another way of putting this is to escape 'the tyranny of present-mindedness' (Thomas, 1988, p. 16) that has brought humankind to its current crisis, and to generate instead new imaginative horizons or stories about the world. This ultimately is what is meant by 'taking ownership': not reproducing information or skills that are transmitted by teacher to student, but acquiring instead 'the possibility of envisaging a future different from either past or present' (Warnock, 1989, p. 37).

In much of the education literature, there is a heavy emphasis on the 'utility' value of different approaches to learning. Such emphasis suggests that 'learning' is only useful insofar as it provides graduates with 'market-ready skills' and prepares them for the workforce. It is little wonder then that many geography courses now emphasise utilitarian benefits such as 'employability', work-based experience and tangible graduate outcomes. Such a mentality can be unhelpful in that it reduces learning to a means to reach an end goal, rather than an end in itself. Such utility-oriented perspectives make it more difficult for students to take ownership over their learning. If students regard their learning as simply a tool, they will be preoccupied with what they can get from their learning, and what knowledge they can extract from the learning process; rather than how to take ownership and gain a deeper, more critical conceptual understanding of the ideas they come across in their studies. Students preoccupied in this way are less likely to become astute, elastic thinkers who can construct and apply knowledge to contribute to future solutions for some of the global problems facing our world. Yes, learning is a tool that will potentially equip graduates with 'useful', employable skills, but it does not finish once a student graduates, nor does it start at the door of the classroom. It is a lifelong process: something authentic and valuable in and of itself (Splitter, 2009). Seeing learning in this light enables one to more readily take ownership of learning, allowing students to develop the ability to critically and flexibly engage with the complex problems humanity faces in the Anthropocene.

In this regard the academy, as a community of inquiry, has a vital role to play. At its best, it can function as a 'partly-protected space' (Collini, 2017, p. 233) to give students an opportunity that most will not have again: 'the chance for serious exploration of complicated intellectual problems, the gift of time in an institution where curiosity and discovery are the source of meaning' for those prepared and enabled to own such opportunity (Worthen, 2018). For many, this will be the start of taking ownership over their own lives, in critically informed ways that are useful not only to them as individuals but also to human society as a whole in the challenges it increasingly faces.

CODA: THE POLITICS OF AUTHORSHIP

The prompt for this chapter was when we both, as student and academic, were drawn in by the opening address about 'taking ownership' at the conference we referenced at the start. We have since sought to make sense of the idea together, through reading and debate in ways consistent with the constructivist approach with which our chapter began. The initial invitation to write was to one of us only, but to be true to our theme, the section editor readily agreed that we could do this together. How student contributions to authorship are recognised is not, however, a simple matter. Articles in the educational press often comment on this. The title of one was 'Professors eat their own young', illustrating how the research of students can be downplayed or even appropriated without acknowledgement (Warren, 2018). Yet taking ownership must mean this in the fullest sense, rather than getting to do the research and seeing it published under another's name. To achieve this, as we have sought to emphasise, the power relations and social hierarchies that shape universities and classrooms have to be negotiated. The politics of authorship is part of this, yet is not often openly discussed between academics and students. Where are the 'rules' written down, and if they were, would they survive scrutiny?

Box 24.1 is our attempt to describe some rules, which we apply initially to this chapter (left-hand column). The first strategy would have been single (professorial) author, with student voice relegated to a footnote or acknowledgment. The second is equal voice, with authors listed in alphabetical order. Lead authorship is clearest when the first named is out of alphabetical order, as with (3). Then there could be a case for sole student authorship if the other party had contributed little (4), or we as authors may not have been able to settle on how or what to write, not producing a chapter at all (5).

The right-hand column reveals some of the difficulties that can emerge when students wish or are asked to publish their own research, for instance from a thesis. There is a risk that nothing will happen (1) if the rules of authorship, and those of 'authoring', that is

---

BOX 24.1   POTENTIAL AUTHORSHIP COMBINATIONS

Authoring this chapter
1 Pawson
2 Pawson and Poskitt
3 Poskitt and Pawson
4 Poskitt
5 no chapter

Authoring an article from student research
5 professor (has eaten their young)
4 professor and student
3 student and professor
2 student
1 no article

The numbers refer to the order of discussion in the text. They do not imply that certain choices are better than others (although clearly some are), but that the attribution and order of authorship deserves careful consideration. In the case of more than two authors, resolving the student research column can be even more challenging.

---

how to write for an academic outlet, are not openly explained. But academics may resist sole student authorship (2), arguing that supervision (and maybe a place in a lab team, or on a funded project) constitutes external input. In this case, (3) may be considered fair. Where the sequence becomes problematic is if a thesis supervisor overrules (4) or erases student ownership (5). There may be a case for (4) if, to get the work published, the supervisor has to write or re-write the text, or undertake additional research. But there is surely never a case for (5). That it happens reflects not only the power relations of academe, but lack of open discussion about what authorship means in relation to taking ownership. For us, this has not been an option. We have therefore written our own names into the left-hand column, as a small step towards encouraging others to think through these matters as well, and perhaps thereby to be forewarned and forearmed.

USEFUL RESOURCES

- Alan Jenkins and Mick Healey (2010) 'Undergraduate research and international initiatives to link teaching and research', *CUR Quarterly*, 30 (3), pp. 36–42.
- George Kuh (2008) *High-impact Educational Practices: What They Are, Who Has Access to Them and Why They Matter*. Washington DC: Association of American Universities and Colleges.
- Eric Pawson et al. (2006) 'Problem-based learning in geography: towards a critical assessment of its purposes, benefits and risks', *Journal of Geography in Higher Education*, 30 (1), pp. 103–16.
- Mary Warnock (1989) *Universities: Knowing Our Minds*. London: Chatto and Windus.

ACKNOWLEDGEMENTS

We are grateful to Jenny Hill for encouraging us to write this together, and would like to thank Denise Aitken, Neil Poskitt, Heather Purdie and Michele Slatter for their comments on an earlier draft.

NOTES

1. James Keal, keynote speaker at the Australasian Conference for Undergraduate Research, hosted by The University of Adelaide, September 2017.
2. The reference is to Professor Diane Proudfoot's 300 level undergraduate philosophy class, University of Canterbury, Christchurch, New Zealand, in 2017.
3. Professor Wendy Lawson, Pro-Vice Chancellor, Science, University of Canterbury. The opening of the quote refers to her teaching experience as a physical geographer.
4. We are Massey University living_labs*, publicity pamphlet, Palmerston North: Massey University, no date.

REFERENCES

Barnett, R. (2017) 'Some pathologies of undergraduate research – and how to cure them', *CUR Quarterly*, 37 (4), pp. 33–38.
Bednarz, S., Chalkley, B., Fletcher, S., Hay, I., Le Heron, E., Mohan, A. and Trafford, J. (2008) 'Community engagement for student learning in geography', *Journal of Geography in Higher Education*, 32 (1), pp. 87–100.
Biggs, J. (1999) 'What the student does: teaching for enhanced learning', *Higher Education Research and Development*, 18 (1), pp. 57–75.
Biggs, J. and Tang, C. (2011) *Teaching for Quality Learning at University* (Fourth edition). Maidenhead: Open University Press.
Blumenfeld, P.C., Kempler, T.M. and Krajcik, J.S. (2006) 'Motivation and cognitive engagement in learning environments', in R.K. Sawyer (ed.), *The Cambridge Handbook of the Learning Sciences*. New York: Cambridge University Press, pp. 475–488.
Boys, J. (2011) *Towards Creative Learning Spaces. Re-thinking the Architecture of Post-compulsory Education*. Abingdon: Routledge.
Brunsdon, N., Thomas, F. and Pawson, E. (2012) *Student Spaces Project*. Report prepared for the Senior Management Team, University of Canterbury: Christchurch, unpublished.
Collini, S. (2017) *Speaking of Universities*. London: Verso.
Cook-Sather, A., Bovill, C. and Felten, P. (2014) *Engaging Students as Partners in Learning and Teaching: A Guide for Faculty*. San Francisco, CA: Jossey-Bass.
Crutzen, P.J. (2006) 'The "Anthropocene"', in E. Ehlers and T. Krafft (eds), *Earth System Science in the Anthropocene*. Berlin: Springer, pp. 13–18.
Edwards, D. and Mercer, N. (1989) *Common Knowledge. The Development of Understanding in the Classroom*. London: Routledge.
Felder, R.M. and Brent, R. (2007) 'Cooperative learning', in P.A. Mabrouk (ed.), *Active Learning. Models from the Analytical Sciences*, 970, pp. 34–53.
Freire, P. (1972) *Pedagogy of the Oppressed*. Harmondsworth: Penguin.
Gibbs, G. and Jenkins, A. (eds) (1984) *Teaching Larger Classes in Higher Education*. London: Kogan Page.
González, C. (2001) 'Undergraduate research, graduate mentoring, and the university's mission', *Science*, 293 (5535), pp. 1624–1626.
Hill J., Thomas, G., Diaz, A. and Simm, D. (2016) 'Borderland spaces for learning partnership: opportunities, benefits and challenges', *Journal of Geography in Higher Education*, 40 (3), pp. 373–393.
Hill, J., West, H. and Kneale, P. (2018) 'Making the most of multi-disciplinary undergraduate research conferences', *Journal of Geography in Higher Education*, 42 (2), pp. 311–316.
Jackson, M. (1973) 'Debate: a neglected teaching tool', *Peabody Journal of Education*, 50 (2), pp. 150–154.
Jenkins, A. (1984) 'Active learning in structured lectures', in G. Gibbs and A. Jenkins (eds), *Teaching Large Classes in Higher Education. How to Maintain Quality with Reduced Resources*. London: Kogan Page, pp. 63–77.
Jenkins, A. (1985) 'Peace education and the geography curriculum', in D. Pepper and A. Jenkins (eds), *The Geography of Peace and War*. Oxford: Basil Blackwell, pp. 202–213.
Krause, K.-L. (2005) 'Understanding and promoting student engagement in university learning communities'. Paper presented as a keynote address, James Cook University Symposium 2005, *Sharing Scholarship in Learning and Teaching: Engaging Students*, Townsville, Australia: James Cook University, 21–22 September, pp. 1–15.
Kuh, G.D. (2008) *High-impact Educational Practices: What They Are, Who Has Access to Them and Why They Matter*. Washington DC: Association of American Universities and Colleges.
Lopatto, D. (2008) 'Exploring the benefits of undergraduate research experiences: the SURE survey', in

R. Taraban and R.L. Blanton (eds), *Creating Effective Undergraduate Research Programs in Science*. New York: Teachers College Press, pp. 112–132.

Marton, F. and Säljö, R. (1976) 'On qualitative differences in learning – I: outcome and process', *British Journal of Educational Psychology*, 46 (1), pp. 4–11.

Massey University (2018) *Living Labs at Massey University*. Available online at: www.massey.ac.nz/massey/initiatives/sustainability/research/living-labs/living-labs_home.cfm. Accessed 12 August 2018.

McCormick, A.C., Pike, G.R., Kuh, G.D. and Chen, P.D. (2009) 'Comparing the utility of the 2000 and 2005 Carnegie classification systems in research on students' college experiences and outcomes', *Research in Higher Education*, 50 (2), pp. 144–167.

Mercer, N. (1995) *The Guided Construction of Knowledge. Talk Amongst Teachers and Learners*. Clevedon, UK: Multilingual Matters Ltd.

O'Steen, B., Perry, L., Cammock, P., Kingham, S., Pawson, E., Stowell, R. and Perry, D. (2011) 'Engaging teachers and learners through service-learning', Wellington, New Zealand: Ako Aotearoa. Available online at: www.akoaotearoa.ac.nz/gppg-ebook. Accessed 12 August 2018.

Panitz, T. (1999) 'The motivational benefits of cooperative learning', *New Directions for Teaching and Learning*, 1999 (78), pp. 59–67.

Pawson, E. (2015) 'What sort of geographical education for the Anthropocene?', *Geographical Research*, 53 (3), pp. 306–312.

Pawson, E. (2016) 'Classrooms without borders: new spaces and places of learning', *Journal of Geography in Higher Education*, 40 (1), pp. 14–30.

Pawson, E. (2017) 'A living laboratory for Christchurch', *Undergraduate Research News Australasia*, 12, 6. Available online at: www.acur.org.au/about-acur/undergraduate-research-newsletter-urna/. Accessed 12 August 2018.

Pawson, E., Fournier, E., Haigh, M., Muniz, O., Trafford, J. and Vajoczki, S. (2006) 'Problem-based learning in geography: towards a critical assessment of its purposes, benefits and risks', *Journal of Geography in Higher Education*, 30 (1), pp. 103–116.

Poskitt, M. (2017) 'Shaping urban resilience: an analysis of post-earthquake recovery in Christchurch', *Macquarie Matrix*, 6 (1). Available online at: https://students.mq.edu.au/study/my-study-program/undergraduate-research-journal/acur2017. Accessed 12 August 2018.

Roy, A. and Macchiette, B. (2005) 'Debating the issues: a tool for augmenting critical thinking skills of marketing students', *Journal of Marketing Education*, 27 (3), pp. 264–276.

Savin-Baden, M. (2008) *Learning Spaces: Creating Opportunities for Knowledge Creation in Academic Life*. Buckingham, UK: Open University Press.

Slavin, R.E. (1983) 'When does cooperative learning increase student achievement?', *Psychological Bulletin*, 94 (3), pp. 429–455.

Splitter, L.J. (2009) 'Authenticity and constructivism in education', *Studies in Philosophy and Education*, 28 (2), pp. 135–151.

Steffe, L.P. and Gale, J.E. (eds) (1995) *Constructivism in Education*. Hillsdale, NJ: Lawrence Erlbaum.

Thomas, K. (1988) 'Perspective', *Times Higher Education Supplement,* 2 December, pp. 13–16.

Trigwell, K., Prosser, M. and Waterhouse, F. (1999) 'Relations between teachers' approaches to teaching and students' approaches to learning', *Higher Education*, 37 (1), pp. 57–70.

University of Cambridge (2018) *Living Laboratory for Sustainability*. Available online at: www.environment.admin.cam.ac.uk/living-lab. Accessed 12 August 2018.

Waheed, M.H. (2017) *Living Labs Brief. What Are They, and Why Are They Crucial for Post-16 Education?* Cheltenham, UK: Environmental Association for Universities and Colleges.

Walkington, H., Griffin, A.L., Keys-Mathews, L., Metoyer, S.K., Miller, W.E., Baker, R. and France, D. (2011) 'Embedding research-based learning early in the undergraduate geography curriculum', *Journal of Geography in Higher Education*, 35 (3), pp. 315–330.

Walkington, H., Hill, J. and Kneale, P.E. (2017) 'Reciprocal elucidation: a student-led pedagogy in multidisciplinary undergraduate research conferences', *Higher Education Research and Development*, 36 (2), pp. 416–429.

Warnock, M. (1989) *Universities: Knowing Our Minds*. London: Chatto and Windus.

Warren, C. (2018) '"Professors eat their own young": how competition can stifle good science', *The Guardian*, 29 January.

Werder, C. and Otis, M.M. (eds) (2010) *Engaging Student Voices in the Study of Teaching and Learning*. Sterling, VA: Stylus.

Worthen, M. (2018) 'The misguided drive to measure learning outcomes', *New York Times*, 23 February. Available online at: https://www.nytimes.com/2018/02/23/opinion/sunday/colleges-measure-learning-outcomes.html. Accessed 12 August 2018.

25. Examining the potential of experiential learning as pedagogy for senior undergraduate students
Shauna Brail and Kate Whalen

INTRODUCTION

This chapter begins from the premise that the integration of experiential learning into academic curricula can present significant, impactful and meaningful learning opportunities for geography students in their final year of undergraduate study (Rosenstein, Sweeney and Gupta, 2012). Experiential learning and experiential education are used interchangeably and defined here as a pedagogy that connects traditional, classroom-based study such as lectures and seminars with outside the classroom learning, the aim of which is to enhance student knowledge, understanding and skill development within the discipline.

Renewed emphasis on the role of building experiential learning into discipline-based curricular learning stems from three distinct forces reshaping undergraduate education: 1) reframing of the role of undergraduate education in building employment-related skills amongst graduates (Arrowsmith et al., 2011; Dowling and Ruming, 2013; Levkoe, Brail and Daniere, 2014); 2) emphasis on student experience as part of the changing competitive environment in which universities seek to both attract students and compete based on reputational rankings; and 3) changes to the ways in which universities are perceived to contribute to society (Breznitz and Feldman, 2012). This means that while universities have traditionally been seen as places of excellence in research and education, they are increasingly expected to contribute to a public mission of supporting knowledge and policy development within their immediate and extended surroundings (Addie, 2017; KPMG, 2017).

Over the past decade, there has been a discernible change in the overall approach to understanding the value of an undergraduate degree. A shift has taken place from thinking about universities as places of learning for the sake of learning, towards learning that builds a specific skill set and produces employable graduates who are well prepared to enter the workforce. Increasingly, emphasis is on the need to graduate students with job-ready skills, and experiential learning techniques can prepare students for a world of work post-university (Ives-Dewey, 2009). Furthermore, there is evidence to suggest that the global financial crisis of 2008 precipitated further emphasis of work-related skills in graduating university students alongside renewed focus on the role of the university as a community-builder (University of Toronto, 2017). As such, the promotion of experiential learning, regardless of specific pedagogy (for example community engaged learning, work integrated learning), has the potential to meet multiple institutional goals. First, it can help to produce graduates prepared to enter the job market, and contribute as engaged citizens. Second, the promotion of experiential learning can help position the university as an institution committed to economic and community development locally, nationally and globally (University of Toronto, 2017).

The environment in which universities operate has also shifted, with greater emphasis on the role of student experience. With increasing global mobility of students, and competition between universities to attract and retain students – notably for foreign students who typically pay higher tuition fees – experiential education has become a differentiating feature of undergraduate programs. The concept of high impact learning practices, or HIPS, comes from the National Survey of Student Engagement (NSSE). NSSE is a survey used by North American universities to assess university student participation through learning and engagement. Kuh (2008) identifies ten HIPS that improve student retention and engage students. Experiential learning is prominent, identified particularly through an emphasis on at least three HIPS that point to the value of experience: service learning, community-based learning and internships.

Finally, the role that universities are expected to play in society is expanding. While university mission statements traditionally focus on their role as centres of advanced, innovative research and centres of excellence in educating future generations, universities are being asked to play a wider societal role as anchor institutions (Goddard et al., 2014), to contribute to technology transfer and commercialization as place-based generators of economic wealth (Breznitz, 2014) and as drivers of knowledge production in an environment characterized by global urbanization (Addie, 2017).

Examining the role of universities as city-building institutions, KPMG (2017) concurs that their role extends beyond research and teaching to serving local and regional communities. The opportunity to engage students, through learning and building skills to take them into the workforce, is evident throughout strategies proposed in a report aimed at encouraging UK-based universities to leverage their 'superpowers' (KPMG, 2017). Crow and Dabars (2015) present a model for transforming universities to meet the needs of society, based on the transformation of Arizona State University. Crow and Dabars (2015, p. 56) suggest that:

> the objective of the new model is to produce not only knowledge and innovation, but also students who are adaptive master-learners, empowered to integrate a broad array of interrelated disciplines and negotiate over their lifetimes the changing workforce demands and shifts in the knowledge economy driven by continual innovation.

In addition to being driven by the desire to expand accessibility to a university education, the New American University model emphasizes the university's engagement beyond the walls of the classroom, office and laboratory. This model, and broader set of goals associated with the changing mission of universities, extends beyond the United States.

These three shifts – the emphasis on building employability skills amongst undergraduates, the focus on student experience and a shift in expectations of what a university ought to contribute to society, have all contributed to an environment in which the integration and expansion of experiential learning is promoted, encouraged and supported by university administrations. A process of filtering down through to faculties, departments, and individual instructors can result from articulating university priorities through policy statements and funding mechanisms. We suggest that this shift has been, at least in part, responsible for increasing experimentation and creative integration of experiential learning pedagogies as a component of curriculum renewal.

Going beyond institutional goals and directions, the next section demonstrates, by means of a review of scholarly literature, the pedagogical value of experiential learning as a key component of student learning. The remainder of the chapter focuses specifically on experiential learning connected to curricular learning as an important means by which to provide students with a set of skills and a knowledge base to become knowledgeable geographers, engaged learners and active citizens. This is accomplished by highlighting the value of experiential learning in undergraduate education, focusing on three sub-types of experiential learning: 1) Student placement courses that emphasize internships and service learning; 2) client-based studio courses; and 3) field study courses. Finally, the chapter concludes with suggestions and recommendations for embedding discipline-based learning into experiential, outside the classroom initiatives targeted to senior undergraduate learners.

EXPERIENTIAL LEARNING IN SCHOLARSHIP

The Association for Experiential Education (undated) defines experiential education as: 'a philosophy . . . in which educators purposefully engage with learners in direct experience and focused reflection in order to increase knowledge, develop skills, clarify values, and develop people's capacity to contribute to their communities.' Experiential educators can be instructors, coaches, practitioners, professionals and more. Experiential education can take place in a variety of settings and disciplines. While experiential education is a philosophy of education, it should not be assumed that all experiences are educative (Dewey, 1938) or that learning is the natural outcome of experience. Kolb (1984, p. 38) defines learning as 'the process whereby knowledge is created through the transformation of experience'. In Experiential Learning Theory and the associated Experiential Learning Cycle, Kolb and Kolb (2005) describe the process as a cycle or spiral where the learner engages in experience, reflection, thinking and acting.

Focusing on geography in higher education, Healey and Jenkins (2000) highlight that while different experiential educational techniques exist, what is important is that an educator guides the learner through each stage of the cycle, helping to make connections between stages. The role of the instructor in guiding students' experiential learning is important, as it is widely agreed that the most effective learning happens when classroom learning and experiential learning are connected and supported by an educator (Itin, 1999; Ballantyne and Packer, 2006 as referenced in Ballantyne and Packer, 2009; Kasimov, Chalov and Panin, 2013; Isaak et al., 2017; Wurdinger and Allison, 2017). When compared with traditional forms of learning, such as lecture and rote memorization, findings from a range of disciplines, learning environments and levels of study show that learning through experience, partnered with classroom-based academic learning and supported by an educator, offers a variety of benefits to support students' higher learning and their employability.

Two of the key benefits of experiential learning include students' positive perceptions of learning and development, alongside increased confidence to apply knowledge and skills. As an example, Hebert and Hauf (2015) studied undergraduate students enrolled in a second year psychology course, comparing students engaged in a service learning activity with those who were not. Measuring academic development through course grades, an assignment that tested for comprehension and self-reported improvement, their findings demonstrate that while there was no difference in final course marks, service learning students did demonstrate a better understanding of concrete course concepts and reported greater improvement in civic responsibility, interpersonal skills and the belief that they could make a difference in their community. Similar findings on the importance of student perceptions are identified by Hezel Associates (2015) in a study of students across disciplines, campuses and levels of study who had taken at least one experiential education course at SUNY university in the USA. Of the seven themes identified, three focused on the students' perception of value of their experiential education in relation to their future employment. The three themes were: identifying career goals and testing career paths; growing networks and gaining full-time employment; and being more prepared to enter the workforce. Responses also showed that the students believed they developed soft skills through their experiential education. Another interesting theme that emerged demonstrates that while students enjoyed learning through experience and appreciated the opportunity to gain skills for the workforce, they also recognized the importance of traditional classroom learning.

While we have demonstrated the importance of students' perceived value of their experiential learning, a note of caution is also warranted. Zhou, Smith and Spinelli (1999) present findings from a campus-wide survey of co-operative students from various disciplines, showing that a significant percentage of respondents reported their experiential education to be very helpful in obtaining practical experience and developing their professional skills. However, the authors caution that work experiences such as co-operatives and internships may cause students to focus narrowly on employment skills rather than broadening their perspective to capture the opportunities for rich learning experiences that will enhance their education.

As noted above, while caution is needed with respect to overly emphasizing students' perceived value of their education, especially in relation to tangible skills obtained or employment outcomes, inspiring students' positive feelings about education and learning should still be primary goals of experiential education. Boyle et al. (2007) describe the importance of focusing on student perceptions of learning and present findings suggesting that positive emotional responses to learning are an important antecedent to achieving learning goals. These authors explain that the affective domain deals with emotions, feelings and values, which impact students' perceptions of and approaches to learning, while the cognitive domain deals with processing information and constructing meaning. To demonstrate the importance of positive effects in the affective domain, Boyle et al. (2007) provided students from all levels of higher education enrolled in geography, earth and environmental sciences with a questionnaire before and after partaking in fieldwork. Their findings demonstrate that fieldwork inspired effective approaches to learning, independent of age, gender or social background, and it also supported students' social integration, confidence in working with peers and developing transferable skills. Furthermore, positive results in the affective domain are not only important in generating effective approaches to learning but also in triggering the development of skills in reflection and critical thinking, which could result in more responsible and ethical operation of knowledge (Golubchikov, 2015).

There is clearly a case for integrating experiential education techniques into higher education for the purpose of developing students' knowledge, skills and abilities that will support their learning and benefit them as they transition into employment. Much of students' learning in traditional settings of higher education takes place within relatively narrow disciplines using theoretical frameworks and applying an academic lens. As such, providing students with opportunities to work in diverse teams, develop and apply transferable skills in a practical setting, and understand how to employ their knowledge and skills in a responsible and ethical manner may be seen as an effective approach to complement traditional university education. Undertaken effectively, experiential education, which supports students' learning and relevant employment skills, is also likely to engage students and benefit society. As we describe next, there are a variety of approaches to experiential education. Determining which approach to take and how to effectively design and facilitate the experience depends on a number of factors, including pedagogical objectives, current trends in the discipline and related fields, available financial and other resources and relationships that can be leveraged.

EXPERIENTIAL LEARNING: PLACEMENT-BASED COURSES, CLIENT-BASED STUDIOS AND FIELD COURSES

As discussed, experiential learning can take a variety of forms. In this section, we emphasize three approaches to course design that highlight the value of embedding experiential learning in the curriculum. These include: placement-based courses, client-based studio courses and field courses. Examples drawn from our own teaching and research in this field illuminate ways in which experiential learning can be embedded in geography curricula and pedagogy on an ongoing basis. It should be noted that there are other valuable types of experiential learning that are not discussed in this chapter, including for instance: job shadowing; mentorship programs; and co-operative work placements. Furthermore, our focus on experiential learning emphasizes experiences that connect directly to curricular learning (following Bednarz et al., 2008).

Placement-Based Courses

What are they?
Placement-based courses include curricular activities in which student learning involves placement in a workplace or volunteer environment for a defined period of time. In placement-based courses, the types of activities in which students engage vary considerably (see Chapter 30 in this volume by Colin Arrowsmith and William Cartwright). Student placements can take multiple forms – two of the most common are student internships and service learning placements. A key distinction between internships and service learning, in theory, relates to outcomes and connection to social purpose. With an internship, the focus tends to be on learning rather than working (Sweitzer and King, 2014), while service learning by definition emphasizes a joint focus on service to the community alongside student learning (Furco, 2010). In practice, however, it is difficult to distinguish between the two, particularly when embedded in course-based curricula. Importantly, while value to the placement site may differ, value to the student can be indistinguishable.

How are they structured?
In best practice cases of student placements connected to curricular learning, discipline-based learning occurs alongside placement-based learning. The duration of a placement

can last weeks, months, a full term or a full academic year – though not on a full-time basis as students enrolled in these courses can be taking a full course load. There are regular class meetings with an instructor, and a course instructor or placement manager liaises between student and placement, facilitates learning by leading reflective exercises and ensures that the student placement provides a relevant learning environment for the student.

Case study
The University of Toronto's Urban Studies Program offers a year-long internship course in which 20 fourth year undergraduate students are placed in urban-focused organizations across the city, supporting the work of city councilors, city planning, research organizations and non-profit organizations. Within this course, there is no clear boundary between students whose work is more firmly embedded in service and those who are more focused on student learning. The class meets weekly throughout the academic year, organized into five modules: becoming an intern; local government; community; urban planning; and economic development. Students spend eight hours per week at their internship site, and assignments include three structured, reflective journals, an oral presentation and a major report connected to a challenge identified at the internship site. The course instructor receives half course release to account for the additional work required to develop and maintain relationships with 20 partner organizations, ensure student placements are productive and appropriate, manage expectations and insurance requirements, and act as the liaison between partners and students throughout the year.

Critiques and challenges
Critiques of placement-based courses emphasize challenges associated with short-term student placements versus long-term needs of community organizations, and resource and funding shortages. This is associated predominantly when partnering with non-profit organizations, and designing initiatives that benefit both student learners and an organization's mission, mandate or clientele (Allahwala et al., 2013).

Significant criticism surrounds internships that take place outside of faculty supervision or connection to curricular learning (for example Perlin, 2012). This is in large part due to the sense that internships with no curricular connection simply comprise a form of underpaid or unpaid labour. Furthermore, students who participate in unsupervized and unstructured internships or volunteer placements may develop a sense of inflated contribution to solving broader structural challenges (Holdsworth and Quinn, 2010, 2012). In the UK context, concerns around volunteering as learning suggest that, if not designed thoughtfully, they can take advantage of students as 'free labour' and make it increasingly difficult to stand out in a crowd when the expectation is that all students are encouraged to participate (Holdsworth, 2017).

Creating a boundary or dividing line between internships and service learning may be helpful for university administration in determining how best to structure and financially support engaged learning. The opportunity to imbue teaching with political or social justice aims can be appealing to activist scholars and students alike (Mitchell, 2008). However, increasingly the distinctions are less and less valuable from the perspective of promoting and understanding student learning and outcomes. Bednarz et al. (2008) suggest that narrow and restrictive definitions of community engagement are unhelpful and call for a broadened perspective on what constitutes community engagement and associated learning for university students. Debates about the differences between service learning and internships may have merit in considerations related to the types of organizations students work with, or the emphasis on balancing student learning with reciprocal benefits. However, at the end of the day, the outcome for students and their affiliated institutions is one of new knowledge, expanded networks and the potential for follow-on opportunity.

Enhanced learning opportunities
From a disciplinary perspective, and particularly in the field of geography where questions about space are both intrinsic to the field and inherently well-suited to experiential education, opportunities abound to develop best-in-class experiential learning opportunities. These can serve dual goals associated with enhanced student learning and societal contributions while at the same time contributing to the university's enhanced mission of engagement. One example of mutually beneficial outcomes is highlighted in a grades comparison of second year undergraduate urban studies students in which students who chose to partake in a service learning assignment received higher grades than those who opted to write a research paper (Brail, 2016). While the evaluation of student grades is a metric that might seemingly be associated primarily with academic knowledge, these findings suggest that higher grades also signal deeper subject-based learning and critical thinking promoted through application of service learning. Dale (1969) suggests that experiential learning supports knowledge retention and transfer so that critical thinking skills can be applied to solve related problems. Furthermore, co-operative and internship-based learning have been shown to increase student confidence, contribute to skills development and therefore enhance their attractiveness in the job market (Zhou, Smith and Spinelli, 1999).

Client-Based Learning

What is it?
Disciplines such as engineering and management have traditionally included courses that assign students to a client for the purpose of addressing and attempting to solve a problem. The opportunity to embed client-based problems into training for students in urban planning is also a feature of a number of professional Masters degree programs and seen as a way to impart professional skills while maintaining academic supervision over course content. Recent emphasis on job-readiness and employment-related skills appears to impact the inclusion and spread of client-based learning courses into other degree programs, including undergraduate geography. Sometimes referred to as workshop courses or studios, client-based learning creates the potential for improved intellectual development and creative freedom as a result of meaningful student engagement (Svinicki and McKeachie, 2011).

How is it structured?
In client-based courses, students are tasked with addressing a problem identified by a 'client', under the supervision of the course instructor and with varying degrees of contact and interaction with the client. An organizational and logistical difference of a client-based course, in comparison to a placement-based course, is that students are not

required to spend time at the client site other than for scheduled meetings or interviews. Students are not 'placed' at the client site, rather they are typically working on a structured project for the client. Furthermore, while the client does need to identify a lead that will work with the student(s) to provide them access to information and people, the level of supervision is minimized in comparison to a placement-based course. Traditionally, the end goal for a client-based course is a research report, program evaluation, presentation or some other combination of written and visual materials. This type of experiential course design may also enable greater creativity and 'outside the box' thinking on the part of students (Reimer and Douglas, 2003) as they work to solve problems outside the confines of the organization or client site.

Case study

McMaster University's Sustainable Future Program works with the city of Hamilton to understand current challenges faced by individuals, groups, organizations, businesses and the city. Together the partners curate project opportunities for small teams of students enrolled in a fourth year sustainability course. Students are able to preview project opportunities and meet with community leads before selecting a project that helps them meet individual learning goals. Students come from various faculties, which offers them the opportunity to identify and then tackle problems through interdisciplinary teamwork. Three hours of weekly class time is dedicated to delivering relevant content and facilitating dialogue on topics such as community engaged scholarship, research ethics and communicating in plain language. Throughout the course, student assignments include two formal written reflections on their learning through experience. With a small class size of between 8–12 students, the course is run by one instructor, without additional staff support or course release.

Critiques and challenges

Challenges of client-based courses include managing expectations about the amount of time as well as the knowledge and skills the students possess. With respect to time, it may be common for the community's timelines and the students' academic schedules to be misaligned. Such constraints can create challenges and impede the creation of a project that is of value to the community. This challenge can be exacerbated if the academy fails to ensure there is a point of contact to maintain continuity following student involvement.

Students that are not submerged in the environment and culture of the client's site, as is the case with most client-based projects, may not obtain a true appreciation of the challenges and unique qualities of the community in which they are working. Furthermore, without direct access to their community lead, they may not receive sufficient access to information, timely response to inquiries or guidance and mentorship, compared to those students who are working onsite for the duration of their experiential learning opportunity.

In cases where students are required to produce a tangible product or to action change, such as in Community-based Action Research, the level of the students' abilities to action what the client desires may be a barrier. Some of the specific challenges associated with time, resources, knowledge and skills include their ability to engage in sufficient and appropriate consultation with diverse stakeholders, to obtain relevant approvals, to secure required resources, and to satisfy health and safety requirements.

Enhanced learning opportunities

Client-based courses tend to be amenable to teamwork – an important and yet sometimes difficult skill to master. Client-based courses can also provide an opportunity for experiential learning that does not require additional legal paperwork on behalf of the university, since students are effectively not required to be onsite at a workplace.

Since client-based courses are for-credit and unpaid, they encourage students to focus on learning objectives, enable students to develop potentially innovative solutions under a low-risk environment and provide students with a professional experience that may help them in assessing future interests and pursuits. Client engagement typically includes advising students, participating in a series of meetings, reviewing draft reports or designs and attending a final presentation.

Kotval (2003) describes the need for professional urban and regional planners to possess practical training which can be delivered through planning studios and practicums. At Michigan State University, for instance, students are required to take a practicum course during their final semester. While student responses to a survey conducted immediately following the course were mixed, surveyed alumni say that their practicum was the most useful course in the curriculum. This suggests that transferable skills are valued even more once students graduate and begin to apply their skills professionally (Kotval, 2003).

Field Courses

What are they?

Field courses are perhaps the most traditional source of experiential learning for geography students, particularly for those studying physical geography as the opportunity to observe, test and learn is key to understanding physical processes (Kent, Gilbertson and Hunt, 1997). However, human and social geographers also study societies and spatial change in real time through field visits. Field courses enable students and faculty to spend intensive periods of time together in off-campus environments, enabling both scholarly and social interaction amongst participants, students and faculty alike. Furthermore, and especially when field courses take place in an international setting, they are deemed to aid in the university mission of student recruitment, meet student demand for international learning experiences and assist students in the development of a global, open outlook which can be an asset in postgraduate job searches (Glass, 2014).

How are they structured?

Field courses can take a number of forms (see Chapter 26 in this volume by Lisa Mol and colleagues). Typically, international or otherwise distant field courses are taught on a compressed schedule, and generally come with added expenses to cover student and faculty travel and accommodation costs. There are also examples of field courses that take place closer to home, and even in the same location as the university. Field courses that take place close to the university have the option of running either in a condensed time period or once weekly over the duration of the term. Aside from the fact that much of the 'class' time is spent in the field, field courses are managed much like other undergraduate courses. Seminars and lectures, in preparation for or following on from field work, and reflective written and oral assignments tend to characterize this type of course structure.

Case study

At the University of Toronto Scarborough Campus (UTSC), the Department of Human Geography offered a summer field course that engaged ten senior undergraduate students in learning about planning policies and issues in Tokyo, Japan and Toronto, Ontario. The UTSC students attended a series of lectures and seminars prior to the field trip component of the course. In Tokyo, they participated in a week of walking tours and seminars, led by urban planning students enrolled at the University of Tsukuba. The UTSC students visited a variety of neighbourhoods, used the extensive public transit system, and engaged with their counterparts from the University of Tsukuba in conversations about differences in planning, policy and culture amongst the two cities. Following the Tokyo field trip, the students from Japan accompanied the UTSC students on their return to Toronto and participated in a week-long set of tours and seminars (Quijano, 2016). The reciprocal field course model is one that leverages and builds relationships across universities, amongst faculty and between students. Furthermore, it can enable the sharing of labour in terms of setting an agenda that provides an authentic, insider look at an 'other' place. Students enrolled in the UTSC course not only prepared a reflective field trip report but also developed a workshop for University of Tsukuba students during their Toronto visit.

Critiques and challenges

Probably the greatest critique of field courses is that they can be expensive for students, particularly if they involve international travel. As such, field courses can exacerbate financial inequalities amongst students. However, universities can prioritize assisting students in obtaining international experiences through field courses by means of funding mechanisms supported by government, foundation or philanthropic funding or other sources. Those tasked with developing field courses must also consider how to create an accessible experience for students, with accessibility broadly defined to include race, gender, sexuality, physical ability and more. In this way, all students will be enabled to encounter 'other' places, with instructors paying additional attention to ensure that field courses do not reinforce misperceptions and misinform views of difference at the host site (Nairn, 2005). Furthermore, field courses are resource intensive to operate because of the need to cover instructors' travel costs. In addition, managing the logistics of field courses is a task that can be time-consuming and complicated.

Enhanced learning opportunities

Field courses provide teaching and learning opportunities that connect undergraduate students to one another and to their instructor(s) in ways that cannot be accomplished in a traditional classroom setting. Particularly in field courses that take place away from the home university, student–student and student–faculty interactions enable deepened relationship building and engagement and may also serve to humanize faculty members in the eyes of students. International field courses serve multiple purposes. They: assist students in developing work-ready skills; expand student engagement; encourage deep, active learning; and offer new ideas and experiences (Hope, 2009). In addition, field courses can act to stimulate student interest in a specific area of study, build confidence in students' social skills and assist in student retention (Salter, 2001). Finally, through reflexivity in field courses, or intentional thought and self-critique, Glass (2014) suggests that students can benefit from learning to question their own preconceptions of and in the field.

BEST PRACTICE RECOMMENDATIONS FOR EXPERIENTIAL LEARNING

Given what we know about the value of experiential learning to students, faculty, partners and universities, and in combination with challenges to successful implementation, we suggest five best practice recommendations as follows:

1. Curricular and discipline-based;
2. Scaffolded;
3. Reflective;
4. Flexible; and
5. Effectively resourced.

Each recommendation is expanded upon below.

1.   Curricular and discipline-based
In experiential learning, and particularly through service learning where the focus is on service to a community, it can be easy to lose sight of disciplinary connections unless they are intentionally built into the course design. For experiential learning to enhance learning for geography students, it must be discipline-based and connected to the course curriculum. In the case of urban studies students, this might mean that students are asked to make connections between readings and lectures on gentrification and observations about the impact of gentrification while volunteering at an inner city food bank (for example Brail, 2013). While it may require additional effort on behalf of all involved to deliver both an academically rigorous course and a practically-oriented experience together in one initiative, the opportunity to embed and connect these two variations on learning presents an unrivalled learning opportunity.

2.   Scaffolded
Scaffolding in educational terms essentially means that students construct a set of skills or knowledge over time with assignments building upon one another, or subsequent courses utilizing skills acquired in a previous course. Bednarz et al. (2008, p. 90) contend that 'where students are involved in more than one community engagement, the total learning experience can be more than the sum of its parts'. Offering students a variety of experiential learning opportunities throughout their degrees, and culminating with an intensive experience in the form of a placement, client-based workshop or field course, is an approach that supports the benefits of scaffolded learning. Furthermore, scaffolded experiential learning initiatives can enable continuity of relationships between the university, faculty, students and community (Allahwala et al., 2013).

3.   Reflective
While experience is important to learning, learning is not the direct result of having an experience. However, through critical reflection, students are able to engage in the meaning-making process involved in learning. Findings suggest that to be effective, students reflect best when they are guided through the reflection process (Moon, 1999), such as by employing guidelines and rubrics (Russell, 2005; Dummer et al., 2008; Ryan

2011, 2013). In addition, dialogue with educators and classmates helps students feel comfortable and helps them to make connections between course content and their experience (Moon, 1999; Golubchikov, 2015). An additional benefit of the connections created through experiential learning and reflection is that students may develop a stronger sense of belonging and allegiance to their alma mater – and it ties into the university's mission of improving the student experience.

4. Flexible

Flexibility is not only important to the diverse discipline of geography (Healey and Jenkins, 2000) and to a higher education that will prepare students for a rapidly changing society (Levkoe et al., 2014), but is also a critically important component of any academic experiential learning initiative (Wurdinger and Allison, 2017). Yet the very nature of the academic structure (that is timelines and timetables, prerequisites and institutional policies) is predominantly rigid, posing an additional challenge. Flexibility in any type of experiential learning is a constant, and affects students, partners, faculty and university administrations. There are a number of unknown factors that may affect the timing of an experiential learning activity, such as policy and governance changes, shifts in organizational leadership, changes in the funding environment and more. Beginning any experiential learning initiative with the knowledge that change and disruption are potential constants is an approach that may alleviate the stress and difficulty of challenges that will most certainly arise.

5. Effectively resourced

Although we present this at the end of our list, it is by no means a suggestion that it is the least important criterion – in fact, quite the opposite. While experiential learning is increasingly acknowledged by university administrations as an important learning practice that ought to be encouraged, Butin (2006) suggests that this emphasis has not consistently been supported by action. Experiential learning, embedded in an academic curriculum, requires resources in the form of staffing or faculty release time to build and manage relationships with partners, as well as to respond to challenges as they arise. Dedicated funds and an appreciation by university administrators and colleagues can go a long way towards ensuring that the value of experiential learning is not lost as a result of a weak funding opportunities.

CONCLUSION

We began this chapter with a discussion of a shift or 'turn' in the value of an undergraduate university education. This turn acknowledges a move away from understanding the university as a place where undergraduate students acquire knowledge through attendance at lectures and sustained reading and writing exercises. The addition of an experiential layer to undergraduate geography education is deemed to serve a variety of educational and civic purposes, while at the same time reflecting the continuous transformation of the university mission based on a changing set of institutional goals.

Understanding that the changing environment in which universities operate is connected to expanded interest in embedding experiential learning into undergraduate academic practices is important. Furthermore, and on academic grounds alone, experiential learning practices are valuable pedagogical practices. Based on a review of best practices in experiential learning literature we highlight the critical role of embedding experiential learning through curricular innovation, with an emphasis on reflection, faculty supervision and necessary resources, and connection to discipline-based learning. While the benefits of an increased emphasis on experiential education may accrue to students, the university and society more broadly, difficult questions remain regarding the impacts and implications for vulnerable communities and/or people if the manner of engagement causes harm; and for faculty and course instructors when time commitments are not appreciated in economic terms.

Nevertheless, experiential learning opportunities, and the educational and societal innovations that can result, present a stimulating path forward for learners, educators, universities and society. The potential for experiential learning to educate and engage all those involved in novel and impactful ways thus represents a key teaching and learning mechanism in geography education.

USEFUL RESOURCES

- Bednarz, S.W., Chalkley, B., Fletcher, S., Hay, I., Heron, E.L., Mohan, A. and Trafford, J. (2008) 'Community Engagement for Student Learning in Geography' *Journal of Geography in Higher Education*, 32(1), pp. 87–100.
- Brail, S. (2013) 'Experiencing the city: Urban Studies students and service learning' *Journal of Geography in Higher Education*, 37(2), pp. 241–256.
- Campus Compact. Global Service Learning Tools and Syllabi, https://compact.org/global-sl/toolsandsyllabi/.
- Higher Education Quality Council of Ontario (2016). A Practical Guide for Work-integrated Learning: Effective Practices to Enhance the Educational Quality of Structured Work Experiences Offered through Colleges and Universities, http://www.heqco.ca/SiteCollectionDocuments/HEQCO_WIL_Guide_ENG_ACC.pdf.

REFERENCES

Addie, J.P.D. (2017) 'Claiming the university for criticial urbanism', *City*, 21(1), pp. 65–80.
Association for Experiential Education (undated) *What is Experiential Education?* Available online at: http://www.aee.org/what-is-ee.
Allahwala, A., Bunce, S., Beagrie, L., Brail, S., Hawthorne, T., Levesque, S., von Mahs, J. and Spotton Visano, B. (2013) 'Building and sustaining community–university partnerships in marginalized urban areas', *Journal of Geography*, 112(2), pp. 43–57.
Arrowsmith, C., Bagoly-Simó, P., Finchum, A., Oda, K. and Pawson, E. (2011) 'Student employability and its implications for geography curricula and learning practices', *Journal of Geography in Higher Education*, 35(3), pp. 365–377.
Ballantyne, R. and Packer, J. (2009) 'Introducing a fifth pedagogy: experience-based strategies for facilitating learning in natural environments', *Environmental Education Research*, 15(2), pp. 243–262.
Bednarz, S.W., Chalkley, B., Fletcher, S., Hay, I., Heron, E.L., Mohan, A. and Trafford, J. (2008) 'Community engagement for student learning in geography', *Journal of Geography in Higher Education*, 32(1), pp. 87–100.
Boyle, A., Maguire, S., Martin, A., Milsom, C., Nash, R., Rawlinson, S., Turner, A., Wurthmann, S. and

Conchie, S. (2007) 'Fieldwork is good: the student perception and the affective domain', *Journal of Geography in Higher Education*, 31(2), pp. 299–317.

Brail, S. (2013) 'Experiencing the city: Urban Studies students and service learning', *Journal of Geography in Higher Education*, 37(2), pp. 241–256.

Brail, S. (2016) 'Quantifying the value of service-learning: a comparison of grade achievement between service-learning and non-service-learning students', *International Journal of Teaching and Learning in Higher Education*, 28(2), pp. 148–157.

Breznitz, S.M. (2014) *The Fountain of Knowledge: The Role of Universities in Economic Development*. Stanford, CA: Stanford University Press.

Breznitz, S.M. and Feldman, M.P. (2012) 'The engaged university', *The Journal of Technology Transfer*, 37(2), pp. 139–157.

Butin, D.W. (2006) 'The limits of service-learning in higher education', *The Review of Higher Education*, 29, pp. 473–498.

Crow, M.M. and Dabars, W.B. (2015) *Designing the New American University*. Baltimore, MD: Johns Hopkins University Press.

Dale, E. (1969) *Audiovisual Methods in Teaching* (Third Edition). New York: The Dryden Press; Holt, Rinehart and Winston.

Dewey, J. (1938) *Experience & Education*. New York: Simon & Schuster.

Dowling, R. and Ruming, K. (2013) 'Synergies between geography, planning and vocationalism in curriculum development and implementation', *Journal of Geography in Higher Education*, 37, pp. 204–219.

Dummer, T., Cook, I., Parker, S., Barrett, G. and Hull, A. (2008) 'Promoting and assessing "deep learning" in geography fieldwork: an evaluation of reflective field diaries', *Journal of Geography in Higher Education*, 32(3), pp. 459–479.

Furco, A. (2010) 'The engaged campus: toward a comprehensive approach to public engagement', *British Journal of Educational Studies*, 58, pp. 375–390.

Glass, M.R. (2014) 'Encouraging reflexivity in urban geography fieldwork: study abroad experiences in Singapore and Malaysia', *Journal of Geography in Higher Education*, 38, pp. 69–85.

Goddard, J., Coombes, M., Kempton, L. and Vallance, P. (2014) 'Universities as anchor institutions in cities in a turbulent funding environment: vulnerable institutions and vulnerable places in England', *Cambridge Journal of Regions, Economy and Society*, 7(2), pp. 307–325.

Golubchikov, O. (2015) 'Negotiating critical geographies through a "feel-trip": experiential, affective and critical learning in engaged fieldwork', *Journal of Geography in Higher Education*, 39(1), pp. 143–157.

Healey, M. and Jenkins, A. (2000) 'Kolb's experiential learning theory and its application in geography in higher education', *Journal of Geography*, 99(5), pp. 185–195.

Hebert, A. And Hauf, P. (2015) 'Student learning through service learning: effects on academic development, civic responsibility, interpersonal skills and practical skills', *Active Learning in Higher Education*, 16(1), pp. 37–49.

Hezel Associates, LLC (2015) *A Case Study Analysis: Student Perceptions of the SUNY Applied Learning Program*. Available online at: https://www.suny.edu/media/suny/content-assets/documents/applied-learning/CaseStudy-Student-Perceptions-of-SUNY-AppliedLearningProgram.pdf.

Holdsworth, C. (2017) 'The cult of experience: standing out from the crowd in an era of austerity', *Area*, 49(3), pp. 296–302.

Holdsworth, C. and Quinn, J. (2010) 'Student volunteering in English higher education', *Studies in Higher Education*, 35(1), pp. 113–127.

Holdsworth, C. and Quinn, J. (2012) 'The epistemological challenge of higher education student volunteering: "reproductive" or "deconstructive" volunteering?' *Antipode*, 44(2), pp. 386–405.

Hope, M. (2009) 'The importance of direct experience: a philosophical defence of fieldwork in human geography', *Journal of Geography in Higher Education*, 33(2), pp. 169–182.

Isaak, J., Devine, M., Gervich, C. and Gottschall, R. (2017) 'Are we experienced? Reflections on the SUNY experiential learning mandate', *Journal of Experiential Education*, 41(1), pp. 23–38.

Itin, C.M. (1999) 'Reasserting the philosophy of experiential education as a vehicle for change in the 21st century', *The Journal of Experiential Education*, 22(2), pp. 91–98.

Ives-Dewey, D. (2009) 'Teaching experiential learning in geography: lessons from planning'. *Journal of Geography*, 107(4–5), pp. 167–174.

Kasimov, N., Chalov, R. and Panin, A. (2013) 'Multidisciplinary field training in undergraduate Physical Geography: Russian experience', *Journal of Geography in Higher Education*, 37(3), pp. 416–431.

Kent, M., Gilbertson, D.D. and Hunt, C.O. (1997) 'Fieldwork in geography teaching: a critical review of the literature and approaches', *Journal of Geography in Higher Education*, 21(3), pp. 313–332.

Kolb, A.Y. and Kolb, D.A. (2005) 'Learning styles and learning spaces: enhancing experiential learning in higher education', *Academy of Management Learning & Education*, 4(2), pp. 193–212.

Kolb, D.A. (1984) *Experiential Learning*. Englewood Cliffs, NJ: Prentice-Hall.

Kotval, Z. (2003) 'Teaching experiential learning in the urban planning curriculum', *Journal of Geography in Higher Education*, 27(3), pp. 297–308.

KPMG (2017) *Universities: Harnessing Their Superpowers.* Available online at: https://assets.kpmg.com/content/dam/kpmg/uk/pdf/2017/11/universities-harnessing-their-superpowers.pdf. Accessed 23 January 2018.

Kuh, G. (2008) *High Impact Educational Practices: What They Are, Who Has Access to Them and Why They Matter.* Association of American Colleges & Universities.

Levkoe, C.Z., Brail, S. and Daniere, A. (2014) 'Engaged pedagogy and transformative learning in graduate education: a service-learning case study', *Canadian Journal of Higher Education*, 44(3), pp. 68–85.

Mitchell, T. (2008) 'Traditional vs. critical service-learning: engaging the literature to differentiate two models', *Michigan Journal of Community Service Learning*, Spring, pp. 50–65.

Moon, J.A. (1999) *Reflection in Learning & Professional Development.* New York: Routledge Falmer.

Nairn, K. (2005) 'The problems of utilizing "direct experience" in geography education', *Journal of Geography in Higher Education*, 29(2), pp. 293–309.

Perlin, R. (2012) *Intern Nation.* New York: Verso.

Quijano, B. (2016) *From Tokyo to Toronto: U of T Students Exchange Knowledge.* University of Toronto News. Available online at: https://www.utoronto.ca/news/tokyo-toronto-u-t-students-exchange-knowledge.

Reimer, Y.J. and Douglas, S.A. (2003) 'Teaching HCI design with the studio approach', *Computer Science Education*, 13(3), pp. 191–205.

Rosenstein, A., Sweeney, C. and Gupta, R. (2012) 'Cross-disciplinary faculty perspectives on experiential learning', *Contemporary Issues in Education Research*, 5, pp. 139–144.

Russell, T. (2005) 'Can reflective practice be taught?', *Reflective Practice*, 6, pp. 199–204.

Ryan, M. (2011) 'Improving reflective writing in higher education: a social semiotic perspective', *Teaching in Higher Education*, 16(1), pp. 99–111.

Ryan, M. (2013) 'The pedagogical balancing act: teaching reflection in higher education', *Teaching in Higher Education*, 18(2), pp. 144–155.

Salter, C.L. (2001) 'No bad landscape', *Geographical Review*, 91, pp. 105–112.

Svinicki, M. and McKeachie, W.J. (2011) *McKeachie's Teaching Tips: Strategies, Research and Theory for College and University Teachers* (Thirteenth edition). Belmont, CA: Wadsworth Cengage Learning.

Sweitzer, F. and King, M. (2014) *The Successful Internship* (Fourth edition). Belmont, CA: Brooks/Cole, Cengage Learning.

University of Toronto (2017) *Rethinking Higher Education Curricula: Increasing Impact Through Experiential, Work Integrated and Community Engaged Learning.* A White Paper for the University of Toronto.

Wurdinger, S. and Allison, P. (2017) 'Faculty perceptions and use of experiential learning in higher education', *Journal of e-Learning and Knowledge Society*, 13(1), pp. 15–26.

Zhou, Y., Smith, B. and Spinelli, J. (1999) 'Impacts of increased student career orientation on American college geography programmes', *Journal of Geography in Higher Education*, 23(2), pp. 157–165.

26. Fieldwork in the undergraduate geography curriculum: developing graduate skills
Lisa Mol, Michael Horswell and Lucy Clarke

INTRODUCTION

The role of fieldwork in student learning and development has been extensively discussed in academic literature, in particular focussing on geography degrees where fieldwork assumes a prominent place in the curriculum (Fuller et al., 2000). As Walkington et al. (2011) argue, the exposure of students to new environments and on-site learning methods can greatly enhance intellectual development throughout the degree course, especially early in the curriculum. The skills that students develop during fieldwork not only aid them in successfully completing their degree, but enhance their chances of securing employment post-graduation; the interpersonal, project management and time management skills gained from undertaking fieldwork are highly valued by employers. We explore three different types of undergraduate fieldwork here, and illustrate how students can gain skills which place them at an advantage in the graduate job market.

In the UK, particular emphasis is placed on the student experience, in which fieldwork is consistently highly rated in the National Student Survey (http://unistats.direct.gov.uk), although there is less evidence that this is the case globally (Wilson et al., 2016). The introductory section of this chapter aims to highlight how final year students engage with fieldwork and the role that this can play in developing graduate and personal attributes. Fieldwork at this level can take the form of group-based residential field trips and staff-led field trips set within the curriculum, or independent fieldwork which is student-led (either by individual students or small student groups) and completed without staff supervision in the field. Each approach has its own merits and limitations, facilitates different pathways to learning, and develops different student competencies and graduate skills.

There is no doubt that experiencing in real life the landforms and features discussed in the classroom enhances student understanding of earth surface processes and their role in shaping the landscape (Fuller, 2012). At its best, fieldwork is an extension of the classroom, where students observe and understand the direct link between the theory presented to them on campus and the landscape features in front of them (Hovorka and Wolf, 2009). At a deeper level, field settings can be used to demonstrate the complexities and non-linearity of many natural processes and to challenge the student to see beyond the simplistic approach (necessarily) taken in textbooks and conceptual models to explain these processes. This opens up avenues for problem-based learning, including the use of examples of the field sites to prepare for fieldwork, which encourages deep learning in students (Bradbeer, 1996).

Students view fieldwork as predominantly positive, as a valuable pedagogic tool for understanding the theoretical subject matter addressed in the classroom (Fuller et al.,

2010a; Stokes et al., 2011). The social interactions and bonds created during fieldwork are also highly rated by student participants (Fuller, 2006; Dunphy and Spellman, 2009).

Group-based student fieldwork can provide effective pathways of learning and assessment through presentation and collaborative skills (Haigh and Gold, 2007). That said, group work can also be fraught with conflict for students, where personal interests and varying levels of engagement with tasks can lead to frustration and non-cooperation (Huang, 2011). In challenging field situations, where students may be outside their comfort zone, this potentially poses a pitfall for effective learning, but it also challenges the students to learn to deal with potential future conflict in the workplace. Assessments and task division therefore need to be monitored by supervising staff, ensuring that students feel their efforts are rewarded irrespective of other group member behaviour. When this is achieved effectively, group work provides a pathway towards enhanced social and communication skills, work management and leadership (Andrews et al., 2003).

However, as students progress through their undergraduate degree they are encouraged to undertake independent fieldwork, and their learning and research skills are honed through challenges that need to be overcome in situ without the guidance of staff. While challenging, this experience can be immensely rewarding and lead to improvement not only in students' skills but also in self-esteem, social interaction and workload management, all of which are valuable to bring to the professional workplace after graduation (Nassar, Holmes and Mehta, 2016).

The rise in new and accessible technologies such as smartphones, commercially available drones and remote sensing techniques has led to new opportunities and development of advanced technological skill sets (see Chapter 22 in this volume by Ian Fuller and Derek France). Embedding the latest techniques of field research into the curriculum not only expands our learning methods but can also spark creativity and new approaches through student interactions, and it can also (literally) expand students' horizons (Stephens et al., 2016). The ubiquitous presence of smart phones amongst staff and students opens up further avenues of fieldwork preparation, especially for group work, where it is likely that at least one of the students will have access to a smartphone (Welsh and France, 2012). Integrating the latest technologies available to field researchers means that students can engage with field site metadata both remotely and whilst in the field, further enhancing their understanding of the site and its processes. The fieldwork educational journey thus becomes an amalgamation of preparatory and remote work, field data collection and post-field processing. Optimising each step means that educators can effectively engage students with fieldwork at every step while aiding them in developing a range of technological skills, which will increase their employability.

INDEPENDENT STUDENT FIELDWORK

This section explores the value of student-led independent fieldwork for their academic, personal and professional development. Student-led projects often take the form of the final year dissertation, but can also include smaller field projects carried out by students earlier in their studies to gain research experience. This work can take place in the student's home country or abroad, and be of any duration depending on student finances and the time available. It is therefore difficult to draw broad conclusions regarding the impact of this work on individuals. Although it is rare that students elect to undertake independent fieldwork in the early stages of their studies, it has been shown by Fuller et al. (2010b) that integrating students' field-based research early in the curriculum helps students prepare for the more substantial research work expected in the final year. Furthermore, the earlier students are exposed to research experiences and related skills, the more opportunities they have to practice and utilise the skills, increasing the likelihood they will continue using research skills post-graduation (Paterson et al., 2013). In an ideal world, the culminating effect of this early exposure to independent research is a cohort of students who are confident enough in their skills to take on more challenging field sites without direct supervision and to make the most of a potentially transformative opportunity. Exposure to hitherto distant cultures and environments can help students develop cross-cultural skills to successfully engage with an increasingly more globalised and mobile world (Killick, 2012). Thus, independent fieldwork is about much more than successfully passing a section of the curriculum; it is an opportunity for growth of skills, resilience and cross-cultural understanding, all of which greatly enhance employability post-graduation.

The wider literature (Fuller, 2006; Scott et al., 2006; Rydant et al., 2010), as well as the authors' personal experiences, shows that successful completion of independent research by students contributes as much to personal and professional growth as it does to their subject knowledge. Students participating in overseas independent fieldwork at the University of the West of England (UWE), UK have successfully competed for graduate schemes and competitive postgraduate study and one of the most frequently cited factors in their success was their participation in independent fieldwork abroad. Independent fieldwork helps prepare students for the complexities and ambiguities of an increasingly connected twenty-first century society. Interacting with people who do not share their ideas and values, who express dissenting opinions or live in circumstances radically different from those the student lives in all contribute to a more holistic and nuanced awareness of our global society. This immersion-based learning can transform the learning process from 'object-based' to a transformative process of unsettling students' prior experiences, understanding and imageries of the study site (Bhakta et al., 2015).

Independent fieldwork requires the students to take full ownership of the project; not just the short-term project preparation but the educational arch that leads to the particular project. It is not possible to motivate students to undertake intellectually challenging field research without a research culture within the department they can engage and identify with. Furthermore, in the current education system, where intensely monitored pass rates and expanding student cohorts necessitate a scaled-down approach to fieldwork, there is a substantial risk of fieldwork becoming a curriculum box to tick rather than an enhanced learning experience aimed at improving graduate skills and employability. As Bradbeer (1996, p. 12) notes: 'for many students fieldwork has come to mean data collection and its chief function is to generate unproblematic data from the "real world" which can be used to test generalised hypotheses and to apply hard-learned skills of statistical analysis'.

Curriculum-embedded fieldwork is therefore reduced to another process students go through to get the grades they desire. Independent fieldwork is an opportunity to counteract this trend, when staff can provide a mentoring role, setting the example with their own field research and creating space for students to participate in a research culture. In the curriculum, students can initially copy some of the staff approaches and then use that experience to develop their own projects. This is particularly fruitful when students are encouraged to follow their own interests and create a project that they feel is 'worthwhile', addressing societal or environmental problems in a constructive manner, an attitude that can be helpful in gaining fulfilling future employment.

Whilst this chapter predominantly focusses on enhanced employability gained from skills developed through final-year fieldwork, it should be kept in mind that this is the culminating stage of a trajectory that commences in the first year. Split across three years of undergraduate curriculum, the pedagogic curve should ideally resemble:

1.　Level 1: Introduction to field methods through carefully supervised field exercises. This is complemented with controlled experiments in the laboratory through practical sessions. This gives students an awareness of the possibilities as well as limitations of field- and potential laboratory follow-up work. It also engrains the idea that field research is a fundamental part of professional development, and a valuable way of gathering data.
2.　Level 2: Introduction to research methods, project development and execution under a reduced level of supervision. Students are responsible for defining research questions and methods to successfully complete a project in a pre-determined field location. This prepares them for project ownership, and provides an opportunity to practice their research design skills.
3.　Level 3: Opportunities to carry out fieldwork either alone, if field safety permits this, or in small groups. Students take full ownership of location selection, project design and execution. Staff provide guidance when called upon by the student. This can cover the final year dissertation, summer research projects or additional experience the student wishes to obtain. This independent work prepares the student for autonomous project development and execution in the workplace.

A misconception of independent fieldwork is that it necessitates being 'a lone researcher', which students especially at first year level may not be ready for (Garde-Hansen and Calvert, 2007). Independent fieldwork can equally take the shape of small teams of students designing and completing a field-based research project. These teams can be interdisciplinary, as shown in the case study discussed later in this chapter, or they can comprise small groups of peers from the same discipline. In fact, it is advisable that students do not undertake fieldwork by themselves in challenging environments where working alone can pose a significant risk to health and wellbeing. In locations such as Svalbard, for example, students are not allowed to undertake fieldwork by themselves because of the poor mobile phone coverage and threat of polar bear attacks. Coordination of projects within the same geographical area can greatly expand possible field locations and develop a student's collaborative, social and management skills.

Successful completion of an independent field project depends as much on student resilience in the field as it does on preparation prior to departure. To enhance the chances of success, supervising staff can use detailed risk assessments to guide students towards areas where successful completion of the work is most likely within the context of the individual student skills and experiences. Examples are countries where active partnerships exist, where students have travelled previously, or where a good infrastructure is present to help the students travel independently. Pre-departure meetings also provide additional check-points for students to prepare them for often-overlooked issues like homesickness and culture shock, as well as practical information such as emergency help, visa applications and financial security and access. The importance of these pre-departure meetings should not be underestimated as they increase student confidence in the undertaking, thus enhancing resilience in the field which will be a great asset when navigating difficulties in the workplace post-graduation. Furthermore, guiding a student through the full preparation process will give them valuable workplace skills in project preparation and planning across a wide range of industries and geographical areas, and instil a sense of 'good practice' in their approach to professional planning.

Case Study: Interdisciplinary Student Work in Uganda

To illustrate successful navigation of the issues outlined above and the benefits of the fieldwork to final year students a case study is presented here, which details the work of an interdisciplinary undergraduate team working in the Mubende district of Uganda on the impact of artisanal gold mining.

Independent final year fieldwork has been completed successfully by students under the umbrella of the Water Securities Project, based at UWE Bristol, UK. This scheme facilitates student travel abroad to tackle issues related to sustainable use of water. The work can be particularly challenging due to the remote and difficult nature of the field sites, and the complex issues associated with water politics and regulation. Students are therefore guided during the preparatory phase, ensuring they have all necessary logistics and health requirements in place and are aware of the social and emotional challenges they may encounter during their stay. They are partnered with an environmental organisation in the destination country.

As this scheme is open to all disciplines it offers a unique opportunity to create interdisciplinary teams of students who work towards a common goal, determined by the geographical location. In summer 2017 a team of six students spent five to six weeks in Mubende to investigate the impact of artisanal gold mining on the local environment and population, in partnership with the National Association of Professional Environmentalists (NAPE). The group consisted of a student from physical geography, human geography, environmental resource management, journalism, civil engineering and biomedical science. This unique combination of disciplines gave the supervising staff the opportunity to help shape a project that reached far beyond the individual student discipline. Working together gave the students an insight into the environmental damage caused by artisanal gold mining, the impact it has on the social structure and health of the local population and to attempt to design a system that can reduce the flow of mercury and cyanide into the environment. Moreover, this collaborative approach taught students how to evaluate approaches and methodologies from outside their subject area, thus preparing them for the multidisciplinary workspace they are likely to encounter post-graduation. The students gathered water, soil and plant samples and interviewed the local population to map the perception as well as the actual extent of the problem. Their results were a testament to the ability of undergraduates to show initiative, to tackle challenging situations and to see beyond the boundaries of their disciplines. Even more encouraging was the personal and academic growth resulting from this independent fieldwork, as evidenced by student testimony on their return:

My placement to Uganda has undoubtedly been the best experience of my life to date. It has changed my outlook as a human being.

Actively being involved in this research and meeting communities has given me more of an insight than any book ever could. It was a humbling yet incredible experience and one that I will never forget.

The research also underlined the importance of challenging students when they design their independent final year projects. Often, this project is seen as a burden, '*a scary big thing*' and something that is either put off as long as possible or causes upset at the end of the second year when students are asked to think about topics. As supervisors we are faced with the challenge of convincing the student to follow their interests rather than replicate something they have already done, to think outside the geographical boundaries of their daily life and to see the final year project as an opportunity for exploration and growth:

I have found my dissertation considerably more interesting and relevant since going to Uganda and experiencing a new country and environment for myself. I do not find my dissertation to be a burden but actually something I am excited to see the end result of and genuinely make a difference to those affected.

While the fieldwork was immensely valuable for scientific understanding of the environmental and health issues related to artisanal gold mining, it was not without risk to student wellbeing. Exposure to toxic substances, difficult infrastructure and unexpected government and army interference with the mining a week before the students arrival all contributed significantly to health and safety concerns. These challenges were met both through field preparation and improvisation during the field season, such as identifying useful local contacts and knowledge and adapting sampling strategy whilst in the field. The students were provided with all the required safety equipment to prevent accidental ingestion of the toxins, and trained in their proper usage. A member of staff travelled to Uganda three weeks before the students to ensure that the partners were fully prepared for the visit and that all accommodation and logistical arrangements met health and safety standards. During the field season, several members of staff were available for student support and kept regularly in touch with the partners to ensure the students were all safe and were progressing with the project. Arguably it was worth the effort and, at times, elevated stress levels of both staff and students:

I have been fortunate to undergo a unique and amazing experience, meeting some wonderful people and working within a completely new environment. Not only have I collected my dissertation data, but I have also had the opportunity to gain valuable experience of field research.

As shown in this section, independent student fieldwork can be a very valuable opportunity for academic, professional, and personal growth. While overseas fieldwork can be a challenge for staff and students alike, the trade-off is an enrichment of our graduate community, and well worth the effort if attention is paid to long-term (student through to professional work place) as well as short-term (project) preparation.

STAFF–STUDENT SMALL RESEARCH TEAMS

This section will focus on staff–student research teams and their role in undergraduate field teaching. Many academics in higher education are research active and geography fieldwork is often central to their research projects, and can be used to provide real-world training to students.

In the research–teaching nexus there is a desire to move from what Griffiths (2004) describes as *research-led* teaching (where students learn about staff research findings in the classroom) towards *research-based* teaching (where students learn as researchers through inquiry-based activities), and fieldwork offers an ideal opportunity to develop the latter. By involving students in their research projects, staff provide the opportunity to place the students as 'active stakeholders' in the academic research community (Healey and Jenkins, 2009) (see also Chapter 14 in this volume by Helen Walkington). This enables staff to pass on their knowledge and enthusiasm for their specialist subject in a fieldwork setting and use inquiry-based learning to enable students to participate in academic research.

The process of mentoring students in the field, linked to staff research, connects the students to real-world phenomena and helps them to apply theory in practical contexts (Resler and Kolivras, 2009). This can lead to the creation of research teams involving both staff and students, and enables the students to become 'trained researchers' (Thornbush, Allen and Fitzpatrick, 2014, p. 7). The transferable skills that are acquired by the students help to develop graduate attributes and are strongly valued by both the students themselves and future employers; as the following case study highlights.

Case Study: Staff–Student Field Research Collaborations

There are a number of modes by which students can become involved in staff research: by undertaking a dissertation on a specific staff project, through an internship, or through a formal/informal advertised opportunity to provide additional assistance. The latter has been used successfully at the University of Gloucestershire, UK in the form of a core geography final year module named 'Global Futures'. In this module, undergraduate students have to work in small groups to apply the skills they have acquired during their degree programme to answer a real-world geographical question, utilising a problem-based learning approach (Spronken-Smith, 2005). This provides an ideal opportunity for students to work with a member of staff on an active research project. The module is run over a single semester (12 weeks) and constitutes an introductory lecture in which project ideas are pitched to the cohort and they sign up to the one that interests them. Groups are then allocated (consisting of three to five students depending on the project), which have a planning meeting with the project lead (in this case the academic that they have been assigned to) and they then undertake fieldwork under the guidance of the staff member, before undertaking analysis of the collected data and writing a report for the remainder of the module hours.

The third author has a number of local research projects that have been utilised as part of the module and each year a couple of student groups work on different aspects of her research in this way. The primary research area is investigating flood risk and the use of Natural Flood Management and similar measures to mitigate flood impact around the Gloucestershire region. This is research collaborating with statutory organisations, local Government, charities and community groups and has an applied focus which appeals to the students. Research projects have varied in their focus, covering aspects of monitoring following the implementation of interventions, scoping exercises exploring new sites, as well as those looking at community engagement and education.

Key to ensuring a successful outcome, for both staff and students, is a clear description of the research project in the first meeting and stating the objectives for the work that the students will be involved in, including how this fits into the wider research aims. It should be noted, however, that the specific objectives and methods used have some flexibility so that they can be tailored to fit the skills and interests of the student group that sign up for the project. Arranging a meeting with some of the wider stakeholders can also be useful as it provides the students with the opportunity to gain different perspectives on the research that is being undertaken, and allows them to see the wider importance of the work they are doing. The first field visit is staff-led and used as a site introduction, with the aims of the research project reiterated and a walk through undertaken of the different aspects of a particular location and suggestions for data collection. The students then meet independently to discuss the project requirements and devise a sampling strategy and plan for their fieldwork, which they present to the member of staff for feedback. In this way, the students are involved in the design and development of their data collection allowing them to take ownership of their project whilst still being aware of the wider research goals and how they fit within these. Staff guidance is provided in the early stages of data collection to ensure that the data are being collected appropriately, but following this the student group works independently and part of the process is to update the staff member on their progress. In addition to the assignment itself, it is vital that the student group collate their methods and data at the end of the project and that this is stored in a shared drive, to ensure that all of their work is documented and can be used in the future.

The students benefit from these projects in a number of ways. They build a stronger relationship with the staff member involved and often with external organisations that they have come into contact with; providing network building opportunities and a collection of 'critical friends' that they can draw on for references in future job applications and for career guidance. The students develop an appreciation of the role of research in an academic workload and gain a deeper understanding of the specialisms of staff members. As part of the process they have to draw on their communication skills, both within the student team and to keep the staff member appraised of ideas and developments. They gain an understanding of the process of research, the importance of time management and how to work together to maximise individual strengths and enable optimum data collection. Most importantly, using enquiry-based learning (Healey and Jenkins, 2006) they get experience of applying their taught skills and knowledge as part of an active research project, which builds their confidence and showcases to them their own employability and graduate attributes at a time when they are searching for graduate-level jobs or furthering their studies post-graduation:

> . . .allowed me to apply skills and techniques that I learnt at university to a real-world project and gave me valuable insight into how this was achieved.

> I thoroughly enjoyed my [project] and it gave me valuable skills that I don't think I would have gained from a purely university-based environment.

This was very rewarding. . . As more people decide to study at university, employers are not looking solely at the degree you get any more and it is experiences like this what will help me.

The collaboration with students can be viewed as a risk for staff as it is part of their ongoing research and they have to ensure that the data collected are accurate and meaningful. It is therefore important for staff to have realistic expectations about what can be achieved by the students and ensure that they maintain oversight throughout the process. But, overall, if the process is managed correctly it can be beneficial to the staff involved. The input of additional researchers who bring with them a range of skills enables completion of a wider variety of tasks during the fieldwork. Discussions with the students often leads to the development of new methodologies or research avenues, which broaden the scope of the research and can provide new insight that can be valuable to the staff member. After the initial field site introduction and guidance on the sampling strategy and methods, the students develop autonomy and undertake data collection independently. This allows the project to progress with less time-input from the staff member than would otherwise have been possible. In this way, the fieldwork can progress from being staff-led at the outset to a joint collaboration, with knowledge and data sharing, once the students have grasped the aim and objectives of the research project.

In summary, staff–student fieldwork collaborations can be extremely valuable for both the staff and students involved. These need to be managed appropriately to ensure that the staff leading them take the time to inform the students about the wider research goals and the part that they can play in contributing to these, and the students fully engage with the process. If this is achieved, this *research-based* teaching technique can provide students with a range of graduate attributes and an experience that will improve their employability prospects, and enable staff to progress their research projects.

STAFF-LED GEOGRAPHIC EXPEDITIONS

As outlined in the introduction, fieldwork is a long-accepted and even identifying characteristic of geographic pedagogy (Sauer, 1956; Stoddart, 1986, Pawson and Teather, 2002; Holton 2017). However, one type of fieldwork that has become more prevalent in the undergraduate curriculum is the 'expedition' – staff-led group fieldwork that often takes place in the final year of the curriculum. Expeditions are a more complex incarnation of the traditional 'opportunity-to-rehearse-skills' field trips that characterise many undergraduate residential field trips. Leshem and Pinkerton (2018) demonstrate how the colonially-tainted 'expedition' can be appropriated and (re-)presented using a critical lens, and Holton (2017) argues that greater levels of autonomy in the 'field' allow students to become active, critical and reflexive learners, encouraging the development of valuable dispositional attributes. However, Marvell et al. (2013) question whether we can reasonably expect undergraduates to question their positionality within field contexts to any great depth.

If we accept the problematic character of 'expeditions', and engage with both the challenges and opportunities of theoretically informed geographic pedagogies, then we must consider our objectives and intentions, within the form, in a holistic way. We have to integrate our curricular responsibilities, our expectations of our students and their expectations of the module/trip, with preparing them both disciplinarily and affectively for the experience. Finally, we must align these considerations with the opportunities presented by the destination.

There seems to be a synergy between taking students to an unfamiliar geographic context and their willingness to cross both their perceived disciplinary boundaries and the subject boundaries of traditionally delivered modules, particularly when supported in the field by experienced staff. This may well arise as result of the experiential emphasis, where the messy 'real world' is engaged with rather than an idealised classroom example (Hall et al., 2002). Exploiting this new-found courage requires a cohesive, foundational narrative which is effectively integrated with an itinerary designed to meet both official learning outcomes and student expectations.

Case Study: The Advanced Geographic Expedition

In this section, we reflect on our experience of planning and delivering an expeditionary module. We will consider the learning outcomes of the module and our response to them, negotiating student expectations on a module for which they pay a considerable amount of money, and how we have tried to optimise the expeditionary learning opportunities.

The 'Advanced Geographic Expedition' is a final year optional module offered across a range of programmes at UWE Bristol, UK, including physical and human geography, civil engineering and environmental management. It consists of preparatory sessions (totalling 21 hours) and a 12-day expedition. Destinations usually change every two years or so, and have included Iceland, China, Kenya and South Africa. The learning outcomes of the module emphasise skills (research- and field-based) and critical engagement over knowledge acquisition. Tutors have a high degree of autonomy in shaping the student experience on the module, but they cannot avoid incorporating 'unconventional' outcomes into their pedagogy. Students engage from within their discipline *and* in response to the geographic context of the expedition. Assessment is by group presentation (based on a student-led project undertaken during the trip) and a portfolio of work, combining elements produced in preparation for the trip, and work undertaken during the trip, with reflexive practice.

The multi-disciplinary character of the student cohort requires a learning strategy that allows all students to participate effectively in field-based activities, and ensures none are advantaged or disadvantaged with regard to the assessment tasks they are asked to complete. Additionally, student engagement must be maintained, particularly when the activity is not obviously aligned with students' experience, interests or professional ambitions. This requires learning to be adequately scaffolded so that students, unfamiliar with concepts or approaches, never feel disempowered, disadvantaged, or unable to participate meaningfully. The expedition sets out to challenge students to think more widely than their disciplines, so our trip was framed as 'Places, people, problems and policy – wicked issues, contested ideas and post-normal science'. This determined the content, scope and nature of the material presented in the preparatory lectures, as well as the assessment activities.

The first two authors of this chapter have extensive experience of South Africa, so the expedition visited that country in 2018. The theoretical framework was based on post-normal science (Funtowicz and Ravetz, 2003), informing curriculum design, and combining an integrative and holistic view of science and knowledge with an explicit problem-solving emphasis. This enabled transdisciplinary synergies to be realised, leveraging the disciplinary diversity of the student cohort alongside the benefits of problem-based learning. Furthermore, it provoked engagement with some of the challenges offered by South Africa, which might otherwise have suggested it to be a less than ideal destination.

A key consideration was managing the personal safety and wellbeing of the students. There is a balance to be struck between permitting students to fully experience and enjoy being in a new country, and ensuring they do not put themselves at risk. Staff relied on information provided by the UK Foreign & Commonwealth Office to develop guidance for the students, but this was underpinned by a very thorough risk assessment, shared with the students at the start of the module. Honest communication about the risks fostered a relationship of trust between staff and students. Responsible self-regulation of behaviour during the trip was noted by students: '*I felt safe at all times and trusted by the staff.*' The trip centred on the coast and hinterlands of KwaZulu-Natal, on the eastern seaboard of South Africa. It was chosen as it presents a microcosm of the social complexities of South Africa, has a diverse range of landscapes, and offers touristic activities that could be woven into the expedition – the final element being important in meeting student expectations for the module. Such places also offer opportunities for students to consider their experience, in the context of debates about ethical tourism and authenticity.

None of the students had visited South Africa prior to the expedition, nor had it been a significant focus in any of the taught modules they had taken during their studies. A group-based, rich picture exercise was undertaken during the first taught session (which precedes the other sessions by eight weeks) to establish the knowledge baseline. This exercise highlighted that the students required specific support before they could engage meaningfully with the complex themes included in the module.

The social element of the module was consistently acknowledged in learning approaches, which included buzz groups, think-pair-share, as well as inter-group collaboration. This helped break down existing peer groups and prepared the students for travelling together. To foster a strong pedagogic relationship between tutors and students, when appropriate, staff participated in the group activities. This was extended in the field, with regular group discussions, to reinforce learning or prompt critical engagement with content and experiences, as well as informal (but planned) social events. Enhanced social skills, global citizenship and recognising the value of informal learning are outcomes of this approach. Student feedback consistently highlighted the value of the social elements of the expedition, such as events with staff and/or students of institutions or organisations we visited, or informal interaction with people during planned activities: '*the opportunity to talk to other university students at the BBQ was really good, informal – but I felt that I learnt a lot.*'

A chronological approach was used in the taught elements which introduced the students to the physical and human geography of the country, starting with Pangea and the geological processes that shaped the physical characteristics of places on the itinerary, and ending with consideration of socio-economic and environmental issues in post-apartheid South Africa. Environmental and resource management were explored through case studies, including governmental and para-statal initiatives, as well as community activism. Attention was paid to the social and cultural impacts of tourism, and the problematic endeavour of desiring an 'authentic' experience of the destination country, essential to helping students engage critically with their expedition experience. The purpose of this approach was to foster students' understanding of the complexity and challenges facing the country, but with an informed awareness of how they developed, and how knowledge about them is constructed and perpetuated. This allowed the students to grapple with the interrelatedness of the physical, social and political geographies of South Africa, tying back to the post-normal science paradigm of the trip.

The expedition ethos challenged disciplinary silos, drawing students out of their comfort zones and encouraging new ways of thinking. Two activities were developed for most destinations – one with a physical basis, the other with a social/human emphasis, and students were allowed to choose which activity to pursue. This was successful; students sometimes chose to pursue the familiar, and at other times chose to do something unfamiliar, for example all the physical geography and civil engineering students choosing an emotive landscapes activity over a geomorphology exercise. Feedback from students showed this choice to be an element they particularly appreciated, aligning strongly with the development of responsibility and autonomy: '*I never expected to write haikus as part of my engineering degree, but through it I learnt a new way of looking at the world.*'

Material presented in the assessed presentations showed students had made use of opportunities to engage with people across all elements of the itinerary, whether we expected them to or not. Both within the stated research approaches of their projects, and outside of them, students, more often than not, asked local people for their thoughts about some of the ideas they were exploring. The specifically problematising theme for the expedition required students to think about the opinions they had heard, and encouraged them to engage critically with the knowledges with which they were presented. This evidences the development of criticality, confidence and autonomy, reiterating the value of expedition modules in the development of dispositional attributes that contribute to employability upon graduating:

> *I never realised that apartheid would still be a driver of conservation initiatives [like iSimangaliso].*

> *The Zulus' story seemed to be missing from the battlefields visits.*

One of the problems with less tangible dispositional outcomes is that students are often unaware of developing them. The module learning outcomes emphasise such outputs, so assessment included opportunities for students to articulate an awareness of their personal development arising from the expedition. Reflexive writing was incorporated into the assessment strategy, with the expectation that students would write a short piece in response to each destination and activity, considering their experience in the context of the taught module content. This was a successful strategy, with students commenting on the value of being reflexive within their portfolios: '*By learning to be reflexive, I have come to know my weaknesses and strengths.*' There is little doubt that expeditionary modules offer students a different way to learn compared with the classroom. They offer opportunities to develop personally (confidence, self-regulation, autonomy, transdisciplinarity, criticality, reflexivity), while still being enjoyable. Student feedback attests that our integrative, social and theoretically informed approach, combined with a student-led assessment task that included a reflexive element, was very well received: '*The expedition was the best thing about my university experience.*'

CONCLUSION

The role of fieldwork in the curriculum can be diverse, inclusive and life-changing for students. The plethora of options available, both geographically and in terms of duration, academic level, topic and independence, means that any student can be facilitated in undertaking fieldwork. The positive role in the academic and personal development of students has been illustrated, using examples from the authors' personal experiences as well as the wider literature. We argue that fieldwork is an invaluable part of the geography curriculum, and that with sufficient preparation and staff guidance, fieldwork can be designed to suit all students. At final year level, when students are well-versed in subject matter, emphasis can really be placed on developing independent research and project development skills, interpersonal and time management skills and interdisciplinary approaches to problems, all of which are invaluable in preparing students for the professional environment post-graduation.

USEFUL RESOURCES

- Enhancing Fieldwork Learning: https://enhancingfieldwork.org.uk/.
- GeogSpace Fieldwork guide: https://www.geogspace.edu.au/support-units/fieldwork/fi-introduction.html.
- Geomorphological Techniques: http://geomorphology.org.uk/geomorph_techniques.
- RGS-IBG Advice and Training for fieldwork and expeditions: https://www.rgs.org/in-the-field/advice-training/.
- The International Association for Geoscience Diversity: https://theiagd.org/.

REFERENCES

Andrews, J.R., Kneale, P., Sougnez, Y.G., Stewart, M.T. and Stott, T.M. (2003) 'Carrying out pedagogic research into the constructive alignment of fieldwork', *Planet Special Edition*, 5, pp. 51–52.

Bhakta, A., Dickinson, J., Moore, K., Mutinda, D., Mylam, A. and Upton, C. (2015) 'Negotiating the responsibilities of collaborative undergraduate fieldcourses', *Area*, 47 (3), pp. 282–288.

Bradbeer, J. (1996) 'Problem-based learning and fieldwork; a better method of preparation?', *Journal of Geography in Higher Education*, 20 (1), pp. 11–18.

Dunphy, A. and Spellman, G. (2009) 'Geography fieldwork, fieldwork value and learning styles', *International Research in Geographical and Environmental Education*, 18 (1), pp. 19–28.

Fuller, I.C. (2006) 'What is the value of fieldwork? Answers from New Zealand using two contrasting undergraduate physical geography field trips', *New Zealand Geographer*, 62 (3), pp. 215–220.

Fuller, I.C. (2012) 'Taking students outdoors to learn in high places', *Area*, 44 (1) pp. 7–13.

Fuller, I., Rawlinson, S. and Bevan, R. (2000) 'Evaluation of student learning experiences in physical geography fieldwork: paddling or pedagogy?', *Journal of Geography in Higher Education*, 24 (2), pp. 199–215.

Fuller, I., Gaskin, S. and Scott, I. (2010a) 'Student perceptions of geography and environmental science fieldwork in the light of restricted access to the field, caused by foot and mouth disease in the UK, 2001', *Journal of Geography in Higher Education*, 27 (1), pp. 79–102.

Fuller, I., Brook, M. and Holt, K. (2010b) 'Linking teaching and research in undergraduate physical geography papers: the role of fieldwork', *New Zealand Geography*, 66 (3), pp. 196–202.

Funtowicz, S. and Ravetz, J. (2003) 'Post-normal science', *International Encyclopaedia of Ecological Economics*, pp. 1–10.

Garde-Hansen, J. and Calvert, B. (2007) 'Developing a research culture in the undergraduate curriculum', *Active Learning in Higher Education*, 8 (2), pp. 105–116.

Griffiths, R. (2004) 'Knowledge production and the research–teaching nexus: the case of the built environment disciplines', *Studies in Higher Education*, 29 (6), pp. 709–726.

Hall, T., Healey, M. and Harrison, M. (2002) 'Fieldwork and disabled students: discourses of exclusion and inclusion', *Transactions of the Institute of British Geographers*, 27, pp. 213–231.

Haigh, M. and Gold, J.R. (2007) 'The problems with fieldwork: a group-based approach towards integrating fieldwork into the undergraduate geography curriculum', *Journal of Geography in Higher Education*, 17 (1), pp. 21–32.

Healey, M. and Jenkins, A. (2006) 'Strengthening the teaching–research linkage in undergraduate courses and programmes', in C. Kreber (ed.), *Exploring Research-Based Teaching*. San Francisco, CA: Jossey-Bass, pp. 45–55.

Healey, M. and Jenkins, A. (2009) *Developing Undergraduate Research and Enquiry*. York: Higher Education Academy.

Holton, M. (2017) '"It was amazing to see our project come to life!" Developing affective learning during geography fieldwork through tropophilia', *Journal of Geography in Higher Education*, 41 (2), pp. 198–212.

Hovorka, A.J. and Wolf, P.A. (2009) 'Activating the classroom: geographical fieldwork as pedagogical practice', *Journal of Geography in Higher Education*, 33 (1), pp. 89–102.

Huang, K.-H. (2011) 'Learning in authentic context: projects integrating spatial technologies and fieldwork', *Journal of Geography in Higher Education*, 35 (4), pp. 565–578.

Killick, D. (2012) 'Seeing-ourselves-in-the-world', *Journal of Studies in International Education*, 16 (4), pp. 372–389.

Leshem, N. and Pinkerton, A. (2018) 'Rethinking expeditions: on critical expeditionary practice', *Progress in Human Geography*, https://doi.org/10.1177/0309132518768413.

Marvell, A., Simm, D., Schaaf, R. and Harper, R. (2013) 'Students as scholars: evaluating student led learning and teaching during fieldwork', *Journal of Geography in Higher Education*, 37, pp. 547–566.

Nassar, A.R., Holmes, K. and Mehta, K. (2016) 'Student outcomes of short-term international humanitarian engineering fieldwork', 2016 IEEE Frontiers in Education Conference (FIE), Erie, PA, USA, pp. 1–9.

Paterson, G., Rachfall, T. and Reid, C. (2013) 'Building a culture of research: using undergraduate research to advance the TR profession, build research capacity, and foster collaborative relationships', *Therapeutic Recreation Journal*, 47 (4), pp. 259–275.

Pawson, E. and Teather, E. (2002) '"Geographical expeditions": Assessing the benefits of a student-driven fieldwork method', *Journal of Geography in Higher Education*, 26 (3), pp. 275–289.

Resler, L.M. and Kolivras, K.N. (2009) 'A field-based technique for teaching about habitat fragmentation and edge effects', *Journal of Geography*, 108 (4–5), pp. 210–218.

Rydant, A.L., Shiplee, B.A., Smith, J.P. and Middlekauf, B.D. (2010) 'Applying sequential fieldwork skills across two international field courses', *Journal of Geography*, 109 (6), pp. 221–232.

Sauer, C. (1956) 'The education of the geographer', *Annals of the Association of American Geographers*, 46, pp. 287–299.

Scott, I., Fuller, I. and Gaskin, S. (2006) 'Life without fieldwork: some lecturers' perceptions of geography and environmental science fieldwork', *Journal of Geography in Higher Education*, 30 (1), pp. 161–171.

Spronken-Smith, R. (2005) 'Implementing a problem-based learning approach for teaching research methods in geography', *Journal of Geography in Higher Education*, 29 (2), pp. 203–221.

Stephens, A.L., Pallant, A. and McIntyre, C. (2016) 'Telepresence-enabled remote fieldwork: undergraduate research in the deep sea', *International Journal of Science Education*, 38 (13), pp. 2096–2133.

Stoddart, D. (1986) *On Geography*. Oxford: Basil Blackwell.

Stokes, A., Magnier, K. and Weaver, R. (2011) 'What is the use of fieldwork? Conceptions of students and staff in geography and geology', *Journal of Geography in Higher Education*, 35 (1), pp. 121–141.

Thornbush, M.J., Allen, C.D. and Fitzpatrick, F.A. (2014) 'Introduction', in M.J. Thornbush, C.D. Allen and F.A. Fitzpatrick (eds), *Geomorphological Fieldwork (Volume 18)* (First edition). Amsterdam: Elsevier, pp. 1–9.

Walkington, H., Griffin, A.L., Keys-Mathews, L., Metoyer, S.K., Miller, W.E., Baker, R. and France, D. (2011) 'Embedding research-based learning early in the undergraduate geography curriculum', *Journal of Geography in Higher Education*, 35 (3), pp. 315–330.

Welsh, K. and France, D. (2012) 'Spotlight on. . . smartphones and fieldwork', *Geography*, 97 (1), pp. 47–51.

Wilson, H., Leydon, J. and Wincentak, J. (2016) 'Fieldwork in geography education: defining or declining? The state of fieldwork in Canadian undergraduate geography programs', *Journal of Geography in Higher Education*, 41 (1), pp. 94–105.

27. Authentic assessment and feedback to develop lifelong learning
Jennifer Hill and Nancy Worth

INTRODUCTION

Assessment and feedback are fundamental to student learning and achievement and are arguably more influential to learning behaviour and learners' experience than teaching (Hattie and Timperley, 2007). A key debate in contemporary higher education, involving geographers and many other subject specialists, is how assessment and feedback can be constructed to maximise opportunities for meaningful student learning, moving beyond a summative conclusion about performance (Gibbs, 2003; Carless et al., 2006; Carless, 2007; McDowell et al., 2011). This focus on learning-oriented assessment emerges from a context in which assessment and feedback receive consistently low satisfaction scores in national student surveys around the world, irrespective of institution or discipline (Nicol, 2010; Yang and Carless, 2013). Moreover, this chapter is situated within wider calls from pedagogic research to improve student learning, performance and development (see summary papers of Li and De Luca, 2014; Medland, 2016; Winstone et al., 2017a).

Using assessment approaches to support students to focus on the processes of learning and self-development are typically viewed as secondary goals to the demonstration of learning outcomes, in spite of wide acknowledgement that these practices should be central to learning in higher education (Boud, 2007). As a consequence, a dominant discourse of assessment is perpetuated, which places students as passive subjects rather than active participants in the assessment process. Countering this discourse, this chapter encourages geography practitioners to productively reconfigure assessment in order to deliver assessment and feedback which promote the knowledge and skills needed not only for academic success but which are relevant for twenty-first century careers. The authors contend that this requires a foundation of authentic assessment, which situates learning in the context of immediate and future academic utility and prospective 'real-world' practice, promoting the learning dispositions required of graduates (Herrington and Herrington, 2006). Authentic assessment is achieved through active student engagement in a sustainable assessment process (Boud, 2000; Carless et al., 2011; Boud and Soler, 2016), which establishes relevant activity (Carless, 2007) and student–faculty dialogue (Nicol, 2010; Beaumont et al., 2011; Yang and Carless 2013). Dialogue is particularly important in feedback in order to co-create meaning and understanding between teacher and student, or student-to-student (Wegerif, 2006). In fact, feedback should aim to feed-forward, impacting upon an ongoing assignment or given post-assignment with specific direction on how this can be applied to future assignments, actions and behaviour (Carless, 2007; Orsmond et al., 2013). Authentic assessment and feedback should thereby be structured to develop learner responsibility (Hawe and Dixon, 2017; Winstone et al., 2017b), self-efficacy – a person's beliefs about their capabilities to accomplish specific tasks (Bartimote-Aufflick et al., 2016; Ritchie, 2016), and self-regulation – a person's ability to plan, monitor and evaluate their progress and adopt strategic approaches to learning and development (Nicol and Macfarlane-Dick, 2006; Hawe and Dixon, 2017).

Actively engaging students in the assessment process in order to build their skills of self-regulation and self-efficacy can take them into 'borderland' spaces for learning (Hill et al., 2016a). Such spaces are unfamiliar to students and, as such, their novelty and ambiguity are challenging. In such spaces, students' traditional roles are disrupted as they are invited to move from being passive recipients of information to active negotiators, evaluators and agents of change. This is a liminal position, which foregrounds in-betweenness and becoming (Turner, 1974), where students can evolve rather than 'play it safe' and remain passive as with traditional assessment processes. Moving into these spaces can be emotionally challenging, often taking students beyond their comfort zone and initiating feelings of uncertainty, vulnerability and discomfort (Cook-Sather and Alter, 2011). And yet persistence in these spaces can be affirming (see Chapter 6 in this volume by Erin Fouberg). When students negotiate shared understanding of assessment tasks, particularly with faculty, social hierarchies can be disrupted. The faculty–student relationship becomes more reciprocal as knowledge, understanding and standards are jointly explored and goals are co-constructed. As a consequence, these discursive spaces have the potential to be transformative (Mezirow, 2000). Students who engage in them begin to understand the shortcomings in their existing knowledge, perspectives and mind-sets (Meyer and Land, 2006). Through dialogue with others (faculty and peers), students can begin to reformulate their taken-for-granted frames of meaning by engaging in critical reflection.

This chapter presents two case studies that exemplify where geography faculty have worked purposefully to help their students transition into and learn from entering borderland spaces of assessment and feedback to engage in authentic practices. The case studies exemplify a social constructivist approach to authentic assessment (Rust et al., 2005), where students move beyond passive assessment approaches and actively and discursively use feedback in relation to explicit criteria. These approaches positively enhance the students' learning experience, improve their performance and develop their employability skills, supporting their transition into professional life. The first case study concerns making assessment relevant and interesting to students through its authenticity, building skills for employability, but also making a real-world contribution. The second case study explores student perceptions of dialogic feed-forward and charts the resulting impact on student behaviour, achievement and transferable skills. The chapter concludes by highlighting the positive results of such approaches, their inherent challenges and how they might be mitigated, and offers wider recommendations for practice.

CASE STUDY 1: DEVELOPING AUTHENTIC ASSESSMENT

This case study shares two progressive examples of authentic assessment, highlighting how it can be used to develop skills for lifelong learning. Authentic assessment in these examples has two registers: first, developing assessment (both formative and summative) that makes sense in the context of a module/unit and is meaningful to students – authentic to the module; second, teaching skills that students can use in the future, beyond the classroom, both as workers and participants in society – authentic in terms of real-world applicability (Herrington and Herrington, 2006).

The first example concerns formative assessment on a second year undergraduate geography module. In an early iteration of the module on citizenship taught in the UK, students responded to a government consultation about the future of citizenship education in the curriculum. This task was very 'real' as students sent their responses to the Department of Education. Box 27.1 shows the seminar task and a typical response from a group of students. Students received feedback from each other and from the tutor about how their consultation response made use of their knowledge of the module as well as how they integrated their own experiences. At the start, students were surprised and a little nervous that they would actually send their views to the consultation. Groups of students had animated discussions, comparing the curriculum documents with their own experiences of citizenship in the classroom. The example below includes the concept of local citizenship, a key area of concern in the module. Overall, the task was well received, with students working hard to provide workable suggestions for improving the proposed document. They viewed the assessment as relevant and worked together to negotiate relevant responses for what they recognised as an authentic audience.

The second example concerns summative assessment on the module. It involved students writing an article for Wikipedia, with the option to publish their work on the site. This assessment was 'authentic' in that it built up a resource for the module and developed skills of writing in a style suitable for the general public, including being accurate, concise and logical with content (Box 27.2), moving evaluation beyond a single academic assessor. We often dissuade students from using Wikipedia, with the dismissal that it is not an academic source. This message is conveyed much more powerfully (and is also contested) by students writing and publishing on the site. The assessment rubric explicitly cited Wikipedia's publication standards, while blending in other criteria, including critical analysis.

In a later version of the citizenship module taught in Canada, students wrote position papers – documents often created in government, business and social advocacy to make a case for change. Students responded to the prompt: What aspects of the geographies of citizenship should be taught in Ontario high schools? The aim of the assessment was for students to argue persuasively for a point of view, not in the style of an academic essay but in the style of a position paper. According to Hawe and Dixon (2014, p. 69): 'Participation in authentic evaluative activities not only facilitates deep engagement with subject matter . . ., such activities help students acquire requisite knowledge and skills for self-monitoring and self-regulation'. Importantly, for both the position paper and the Wikipedia article, what students wrote about was up to them. Each assessment was written in an open way that allowed students to follow their interests, but with specific assessment criteria so they knew how they would be evaluated. Critically, the tutor also worked to ensure assessment was authentic, for example by using language from Wikipedia about what makes a good entry. According to Swaffield (2011, p. 443): 'Sharing criteria with learners, developing classroom talk and questioning, giving appropriate feedback, and peer and self-assessment are accepted as being at the heart of assessment for learning'.

This example represents a novel assessment activity in which the students had to accept responsibility for developing outputs. The students moved from a position of being unsure about the task to negotiating content with each other and the tutor, and

BOX 27.1   SEMINAR ON CITIZENSHIP EDUCATION

In early debates about the new UK National Curriculum, citizenship education (CE) was at risk of being dropped – the focus seemed to be shifting toward a consolidated curriculum on core subjects of English, Maths and Science. Yet in the consultation documents released last month, citizenship appears for Key Stages 3 and 4. The goal of the seminar is to respond to the government's call for consultation, writing up a response form with your views on the proposed CE curriculum.

To prepare: Read 'Citizenship: Programmes of study for Key Stages 3–4' on the Virtual Learning Environment (VLE) as well as one background document of your choice (also on the VLE). Develop some initial comments, linking in your own experiences of CE from when you were at school. (Also reconsider the set readings/lecture for this week in the context of the consultation). Bring all this material to the seminar.

Seminar: Working in small groups, you will first share your notes/reactions to the proposed CE curriculum and your experiences of CE. Using the government's response form to organise your discussion, you will write up your group's views for submission to the Department of Education.

Some questions to consider

1. What is your critique of the new CE 'Aims'?
2. What other 'Aims' are needed?
3. Is the age range appropriate? [Key Stage 3: ages 11-14, Key Stage 4: ages 14-16] What about primary school education? What about A-Level?
4. What subject content would you change/add at Key Stages 3 & 4? Consider the kinds of material/concepts you have been working with on this module.
5. What advice would you give to teachers about implementing the new curriculum?
6. How might different groups of students react to this curriculum? Consider 'protected characteristics' including gender, race/ethnicity, age, disability, sexual orientation, and religion and belief.

At the end of the seminar, we will be sending response forms to the consultation to: NationalCurriculum. CONSULTATION@education.gsi.gov.uk

An excerpt from one group's submission:

Do you have any comments on the content set out in the draft programmes of study?

Student comments:
− *The curriculum is very focused on [the] democratic side of citizenship – it should be more focused on emotional and moral issues.*
− *The last bullet point in key stages 3 & 4 are good.*
− *There is little room for discussion – it presents citizenship as a very factual black and white issue when in reality citizenship is much more about moral/emotional issues.*
− *2007 report says you want knowledge, understanding, skills and participation but this curriculum only really wants knowledge.*
− *Students should be encouraged to reflect and discuss issues from their own situations, geographically-specific areas.*
− *Need to make it relevant and exciting!*

Practicalities:

− *From our personal experiences there was not an inherent focus on citizenship – we did not know we were being taught it – local experts should teach citizenship, or someone who has a passion for it.*
− *To make it more relevant and exciting could focus on local issues that actually affect the students/ could have an impact on them.*
− *For example, if an area has huge racial problems focus on this. Could also do the same with crime, get a policeman in to talk to the students.*
− *We believe citizenship is an important and memorable part of the curriculum but it needs to have more of a focus on what young people need [to be] educated on.*

BOX 27.2   ASSESSMENT RUBRIC FOR STUDENTS WRITING A WIKIPEDIA ARTICLE

Your submitted work should consist of:

- A 750 word article on a key term from the module, written as if it was for Wikipedia.
- The article should be about a *new* topic to Wikipedia, or a more specific *geography focused* or *UK focused* take of an existing topic.
- The article should include a succinct title, and include headings, references (using the endnote style of Wikipedia), further reading, external links and other styles common to the site. It may include one photo/image if you wish.
- http://en.wikipedia.org/wiki/Wikipedia:How_to_write_a_great_article is a helpful site for learning about Wikipedia style.
- *NB: Once your assignment has been marked and returned to you, you are welcome to upload it to Wikipedia. Do not upload a draft, or write directly on the site, as the open source technology allows others to edit your work.*

Learning objectives: (Modified from http://outreach.wikimedia.org/wiki/User:Awadewit/sandbox3#Research_skills)

- Gain experience writing for a diverse non-academic audience.
- Improve research skills of reviewing and fact checking, evaluating the reliability of sources.
- Understand the difference between fact-based and persuasive writing styles.
- Learn how to critically analyze content.
- Improve understanding of the relationship between Wikipedia and other sources, such as news outlets, other encyclopaedias, and academic research.

Assessment criteria: (http://en.wikipedia.org/wiki/Wikipedia:WikiProject_Alternative_education/Assessment#Assessment_Criteria and http://en.wikipedia.org/wiki/Wikipedia:WIAGA#What_is_a_good_article.3F to access hotlinks)

- Original, independent writing and research.
- Evidence of critical analysis and appraisal.
- Well-written:
  - o the prose is clear and concise, and the spelling and grammar are correct; and
  - o it complies with the manual of style guidelines for lead sections, layout, words to watch, fiction, and list incorporation.
- Factually accurate and verifiable:
  - o it provides references to all sources of information in the section(s) dedicated to the attribution of these sources according to the guide to layout;
  - o it provides in-line citations from reliable sources for direct quotations, statistics, published opinion, counter-intuitive or controversial statements that are challenged or likely to be challenged, and contentious material relating to living persons – science-based articles should follow the scientific citation guidelines; and
  - o it contains no original research.
- Broad in its coverage:
  - o it addresses the main aspects of the topic; and
  - o it stays focused on the topic without going into unnecessary detail (see summary style).
- Neutral: it represents viewpoints fairly and without bias.
- Stable: it does not change significantly from day to day because of an ongoing edit war or content dispute.
- Illustrated, if possible, by images:
  - o images are tagged with their copyright status, and valid fair use rationales are provided for non-free content; and images are relevant to the topic, and have suitable captions.

finally relating that content to real-world criteria. Refresh of the module has included experimenting with student peer review. Just as many work tasks involve seeking out and incorporating the views of others, peer review gives students a chance to both review and be reviewed, clarifying their own work while also helping others. This serves to disrupt their identities as students and shifts them towards the role of peer mentor evaluating work for improvement.

CASE STUDY 2: ITERATIVE DIALOGIC FEED-FORWARD ASSESSMENT

This case study highlights an assessment approach that was implemented in a second-year undergraduate geography module at a British university to support students' use of feed-back, to improve their performance and to develop their self-efficacy and self-regulation (Hill and West, 2019). Running over 12 weeks, the module, entitled 'Ecology', aims to provide students with the opportunity to study ecological principles and to begin to appreciate how these may be applied to problems in conservation biology. The students choose an essay to research from a selection included in the module guide (Box 27.3), which is made available in the first class. As such, the nature of the assessment is discussed with students from the very beginning of the module.

Students write a considered draft of their selected essay, which is discussed in an

---

BOX 27.3   CHOICE OF ASSESSED ESSAYS FOR A SECOND-YEAR ECOLOGY MODULE AS THEY APPEARED IN THE MODULE GUIDE (2015–16)

Assessment Component B
Coursework Essay

Answer one of the following questions using *no more than 2,500 words*.

1. With reference to a specific wetland type, explain the threats facing the ecosystem and the management techniques that have been implemented to address these threats.
2. 'Species distributions can be controlled by a combination of biological interactions and physical factors' (MacDonald, 2003: 77). Exemplify this statement.
3. 'Human impacts on ecosystems occur in all parts of the biosphere and at all temporal and spatial scales' (Dickinson and Murphy, 2007). Discuss.
4. With reference to different models, explain the significance of vegetation succession to the practice of nature conservation.
5. With reference to TWO of the following, explain the concepts and discuss their relevance to the practice of nature conservation:

    Food webs
    Guilds
    r and K life strategies
    Keystone species
6. With reference to specific examples, explain the role of disturbance in shaping the form and functioning of communities.

individual face-to-face meeting with the tutor. These feed-forward meetings start with open questions, asking students to explain their overall approach, to summarise the strengths/weaknesses of their essay draft, and to grade their draft. The tutor and student discuss how to discern key aspects of the question, and how to apply appropriate knowledge and skills to develop an effective answer. Where key weaknesses are identified, exemplar paragraphs of previous student work are used to demonstrate good practice (Handley and Williams, 2011; To and Liu, 2018). The meetings are audio-recorded (with permission) for students to listen to at their leisure. Towards the end of the module students take part in a seminar in which they discuss and grade two coursework essays from previous cohorts using the assessment criteria, comparing their judgments with those of the tutor (Rust et al., 2005).

In terms of summative assessment, students write a self-reflection of their essay progress (with a proportion of marks awarded for their verbal critique during the face-to-face meeting) and self-assess their essay draft (25 per cent of the module mark). A week later they submit their revised essays (75 per cent of the module mark). After final grading, the students are invited for a further individual feed-forward meeting, where their marked essay is discussed in relation to future assessments. This meeting is intended to support the development of long-term generic skills over and above those required for short-term achievement of assessment criteria. Dividing the assignment into these distinct phases generates an iterative feed-forward cycle which facilitates engagement with tutor comments and the prospect of improvement from one task to the next.

In the face-to-face meetings the students effectively learn 'head-on'. This is an affective encounter in which the students' work is being judged, often below their desired target level, and this requires emotional capacity to receive, process and build upon (Forsythe and Johnson, 2017). The students have coped well in this potentially unsettling situation, recognising the need to understand their weaknesses in order to improve their work. As one student commented: '*I don't want to learn from mistakes when I have a grade that I don't want. I would like to learn from mistakes, make [my work] better, and then get a grade that has been improved.*' Entering into dialogue compelled the students to engage critically with their work. They gained greater understanding of the written tutor comments through verbal clarification and use of exemplars: '*When I've had drafts handed back to me written over, I don't understand what they're trying to say. I can ask you questions if we're talking to each other about it, it's easier to see things.*' Gaining feed-forward before formal grading allowed the students to discover if they were tackling the essay appropriately. This motivated and empowered them: '*I didn't really know what direction I was going in. Then, after speaking and having the feedback, I spent more time on it because I knew where I needed to go with it.*'

The assessment approach worked to overcome the barriers preventing students from using feedback effectively, building their awareness of what feed-forward means, developing their understanding of appropriate strategies for implementing feed-forward, and building their sense of agency to implement these strategies (Winstone et al., 2017b). Students were given the opportunity to revise their work using individualised, task-specific commentary, related to criteria and standards and clarified through dialogue. The students perceived the feed-forward as highly useable as they could apply their understanding with immediacy (O'Donovan et al., 2016). They highlighted an improved ability to decode tutor comments through questioning and consequent explanation, allowing them to understand better the tutor's intentions (Orsmond et al., 2013). The dialogic meetings increased student confidence and motivation to act upon the feed-forward as they prepared their final submissions because they had a clearer idea of task expectations (Carless et al., 2011).

The students commented positively about the personalised nature of the feed-forward, noting it to be far more meaningful in helping them to improve their work and also saying that the individualised nature of the meeting made them feel cared about:

> *Because you are getting a one-to-one meeting, you are getting feedback just on your essay. So, you know, it is tailored to you . . . getting personalised feedback is really useful.*

> *I definitely felt like you cared about what I was getting.*

The educational alliance is clearly an important influence on student perceptions of feedback quality (Telio et al., 2015), offering an inclusive learning experience.

Students reported that they altered their behaviour after the meeting, both within-task and with respect to post-assignment self-regulation: '*It helped me to realise how to critique my own essays because I was able to go through the essay with you and know exactly why you were commenting on something . . . It allows me to see in other essays the same things I'm doing.*' Students self-avowed to increased self-efficacy, believing more strongly in their capabilities to accomplish assignments in future: –'*I understand what it means to be critical now; before I would read my work and think I am sure I have done that and then the tutor would say I hadn't!*' The students recognised that the academic skills they were developing were transferable beyond their university experience to the world of work. They commented on skills of critical reflection, planning and prioritising tasks, time management, and clear written and oral communication. Two examples are:

> *The feedback helped me see where my strengths and weaknesses were . . . being able to assess what you are doing is obviously a skill that an employer is going to want.*

> *Employability-wise it's important to take a lot of evidence and convert it into an argument. If I was to work for a conservation company . . . I could then feel confident in reading through all the literature and making a clear point.*

Student performance improved significantly after the assessment intervention. The mean module mark from 2011–2013 (n=69 students) compared with 2015–2017 (n=72 students) increased by 7 per cent from 56 per cent to 63 per cent. Students wrote less descriptively and built stronger arguments, offering more critical depth based on evidence from literature. Additionally, comparing the mean final year marks for the two cohorts prior to and post-intervention shows that those who took the ecology module performed, on average, 4 per cent better than those who did not. Whilst not a statistically significant increase, the results nevertheless highlight that the self-avowed changes in student learning behaviour are having a positive impact on their achievement.

This authentic assessment approach establishes feedback not as a single event but as a process that begins with teacher–student dialogue when a task is set, through guidance as the task is undertaken, to performance feed-forward accompanied by a verbal discussion informing the process of action-planning. Such a longitudinal approach to dialogic feed-forward, where teacher and student have a number of opportunities to engage, focuses on learners' progressive development. Whilst the positives to this approach have been highlighted in this case study, we will return to the inherent challenges and potential strategies for their mitigation later in the chapter.

INTEGRATING AUTHENTIC ASSESSMENTS ACROSS THE DISCIPLINE

In addition to the examples detailed in our case studies, geographers use authentic assessment in other ways. Often this is linked with real-world tasks such as students writing professional magazine articles or creating management plans related to, for example, environmental conservation, river and coastal management, climate change mitigation, smart transport management or ethical commodity production. The authenticity of these tasks can be increased by establishing them as 'live' projects, working with or for industry, third sector organisations and community groups (see Chapter 30 in this volume by Colin Arrowsmith and William Cartwright), and combining assessment by these external stakeholders with academic judgment (see Chapter 29 in this volume by Ifan Shepherd). We have also demonstrated in this chapter that assessment and feedback can be viewed as authentic when linked with traditional types of assignment, such as an essay, if the approach consciously develops, through student–faculty and student–student discourse, the knowledge and skills needed by graduates in the workplace. Crucial within this are skills associated with self-assessment and self-regulation, with writing following an authentic process of becoming through drafting, reflection and re-drafting. This approach requires students to be comfortable working through a state of 'unfinishedness', which we find in the borderland spaces of learning (Hill et al., 2016a).

CHALLENGES OF AUTHENTIC ASSESSMENT AND WAYS FORWARD

In this section we explore some of the challenges involved for geographers in delivering authentic assessment, suggesting possible solutions, or ways of addressing stakeholder concerns. It is helpful to think of authentic assessment in terms of a continuum (Herrington et al., 2014), rather than an all or nothing approach. We should not look to change our practice entirely, but to embed innovation as and where it is appropriate and to develop progressive interventions across programmes.

Dealing with Student Uncertainty

For students, moving beyond familiar assessment approaches can be unsettling. When students encounter a novel form of assessment there can often be anxiety as they are unsure about how to do well. Across a student's learning career, we teach the 'rules of the game' around assessment, and authentic assessment, especially when it moves away from expected formats, can at first seem to break these rules, taking students into borderland spaces of learning (Hill et al., 2016a). Engaging with student-focused assessment criteria and anonymised student exemplars from previous years are two ways to reduce students' uncertainty (Worth, 2014). When we write assessment criteria, they can often be generic and geared towards external examiners rather than students. Developing specific assessment criteria, or borrowing them from our case study (Box 27.2), allows students to get a sense of what is expected of them. Including a diverse set of exemplars is also helpful (Handley and Williams, 2011; To and Liu, 2018). Rather than being prescriptive, showing students that there are many pathways to success can encourage engagement (Jacobs et al., 2016).

Moreover, in authentic assessment tasks that involve peer learning and assessment, getting students to recognise these activities as learning opportunities can be challenging, as students often only see faculty as sources of knowledge about a module (Worth, 2013). This concern is not unique to authentic assessment, but developing the transferrable skill of working with others can be a valuable outcome (Boud et al., 2014). One way to get students to recognise peer learning is to prioritise it in the classroom and within assessments, making it an integral part of the learning process (Mutch et al., 2018). For example, taking time in a seminar for students to formatively assess drafts of work in progress allows students to receive more feedback and to practice giving meaningful feedback to others (Rust et al., 2003). Ideally, faculty can actively reinforce this critical engagement, 'validating' the process for students who initially only want to hear from their teacher. Building the confidence of students encourages them to access assessment discussions, appropriate understanding and ideas, and to refine their work more openly.

Impacts of Authentic Assessment for Faculty

For faculty, delivering authentic assessment approaches can involve additional planning and time. Our faculty–student dialogic example (case study 2) is a resource intensive scenario that would be best placed in a first year module when students arguably need the greatest direction from faculty. This model of delivery could be achieved by embedding the assessment in a module where there is less emphasis on large class delivery of content and more on skills development, privileging time for individual discussion with students across a team of tutors. This is assessment *for* learning (McDowell et al., 2011) in which the assessment process is afforded a prominent place within the teaching resource envelope, helping to ease the transition into higher education (Beaumont et al., 2016) (see Chapter 2 in this volume by Simon Tate and Peter Hopkins). As the process moves to the second and third years, peer-to-peer mentoring amongst groups of students can be increased vis-á-vis student–faculty interaction. Faculty might meet students individually to answer specific questions about their work in year two, following peer-to-peer discussion. By year three, peer-to-peer mentoring can be supported by optional group or individual meetings with the tutor. In this way, support is shifted from tutor to students as their skills of self-regulation improve. Authentic assessment can thereby be viewed as a large umbrella, with many different formats and 'intensities'. Williams (2007 in Carless, 2017) suggests developing faculty learning communities to support innovation in assessment, where participants can learn from and support each other. In practice, if this is too big a first step, most universities have a Centre for Excellence in Teaching and Learning to support professional development. The key is to adopt a gradual approach for changing assessment practice, making small adjustments that develop over time.

Authentic assessment encourages a more student-centred, constructivist approach that can initially feel challenging to facilitate (Herrington et al., 2014) as it is different from the style of 'direct instruction' that many of us experienced as learners and often adopt as teachers. Developing a dialogic approach in the classroom involves ceding authority in the learning process. Beginning with senior undergraduates is one option, as we already see them as more independent learners through the dissertation or capstone process. Building authentic assessment into the final year of a programme and working down can be useful. Alternatively, as noted above, running an undergraduate first year module that makes authentic discursive assessment compulsory offers early support for a diversity of students. Involvement in such participatory meetings would help students to appreciate the value they can bring to assessment and feedback discussion and potentially improve their self-efficacy. Finally, some colleagues may see authentic assessment as an instrumental response to institutional pressures around employability and graduate skills. Yet there is also an opportunity here to leverage graduate attributes and to 'move towards more participatory and self-regulatory teaching, learning and assessment' (Hill et al., 2016b, p. 161) by recognising how disciplinary knowledge and 'real world' skills reinforce each other.

A final point to note is that case study 2 highlights a role for geography faculty that moves beyond understanding of disciplinary content to embrace academic and assessment literacy (Price et al., 2012). In the faculty–student meetings described in this case study, much discussion centred on generic academic issues such as building argument, criticality and correct grammar, albeit in the context of ecology. Discussion also covered the nature and use of assessment criteria and judging standards in order for the students to comprehend the standard they were trying to achieve, how their progress compared to this standard, and what they might do to reduce the performance gap. This begs the question of whether we are prepared or have time to teach assessment literacy to our students, combined with our disciplinary knowledge and ways of doing. The authors of this chapter suggest that we should integrate these academic roles/purposes and the case studies we have presented demonstrate examples of how this might be achieved.

Operational and Strategic Challenges

Operational concerns about authentic assessment practices often centre on questions of rigour and reliability (Hathcoat et al., 2016). Yet, in practice, these concerns are for the most part unfounded (O'Neal, 2016). A broader challenge is that, similar to some faculty, there can be concern from middle and senior managers about what authentic assessment actually assesses. According to Chandler and Munch (2016, p. 2) the term authentic 'does not necessarily mean "real" (although it can) but it does serve as a term that separates the work that students typically do in schools (for grades) and the organised, purposeful application of knowledge in meaningful ways (for jobs and daily problem-solving)'. This 'real-world' view of the purpose of higher education, characterised by a focus on transferable skills, practical, professional and intellectual competence, is inherently difficult to measure and hence assess (Medland, 2016). At the institutional level, while faculty have to demonstrate quality assurance, their frameworks should not restrict assessment practices to pure measurement that will act as a barrier to the development of a learning culture (Bloxham, 2012). We can develop assessment criteria and marking schemes that allow the expression of diverse competencies, supported by co-curricular activities that exist beyond formal assessment. Such activities often entail more authentic peer and professional assessment, such as participation in institutional and national undergraduate research conferences (Hill and Walkington 2016; Kneale et al., 2016; Walkington et al., 2017).

Authentic assessment, which enhances student self-efficacy and self-regulation, might necessitate investment of resources and the adoption of innovative approaches that are viewed as carrying risk in an era when immediate student satisfaction bears so much weight. Equally, novel forms of assessment and dialogic feed-forward might work with new technologies in and beyond the classroom to support learning, courtesy of tools such as e-assessment and learner analytics. Such technologies should not stifle assessment engagement and dialogue for students. We must ask ourselves how committed, within current constraints, are institutions to explicitly restructuring and reconceptualising assessment and feedback? Academic staff are unlikely to change their assessment practices unless they are fully persuaded of the effectiveness of a new approach and are, moreover, supported by changed institutional policies and supportive management (Medland, 2016). A strategic approach might prove effective, in which enhanced resource is given at specific, critical feedback moments when students are most open to learning development or find it particularly challenging (O'Donovan et al., 2016).

CONCLUSION AND RECOMMENDATIONS FOR PRACTICE

This chapter has demonstrated the importance of faculty engaging with authentic assessment, developing the qualities, skills and competencies in students that are valuable in contexts within and beyond the immediate assessment environment. To help achieve this, faculty should strive to provide opportunities for students to monitor, regulate and attend to the quality of their work *during* its production. These conditions necessitate significant changes to deeply embedded practices that characterise much of teaching and learning in higher education.

We conclude by offering recommendations for practice if we are to rise to the challenge of delivering authentic assessment for lifelong learning in the future. We might consider: developing innovative assessments that aim to capture 'real' experiences (Chandler and Munch, 2016); meeting with students to undertake assessment dialogue or establishing peer feedback before and after formal grading (Nicol, 2010); offering students mastery experiences (Ritchie, 2016), developing phased tasks and giving verbal feedback and encouragement to improve student capabilities as experts in their community of practice; and delivering curricula that adopt coherent assessment objectives and standardised grading schemes in order to facilitate developmental feed-forward (O'Donovan et al., 2016). In short, if institutions recognise the importance of supporting student engagement with authentic assessment and offering developmental feed-forward opportunities, they can reimagine the transformative potentialities of the educational landscape and meaningfully prepare geography graduates for dynamic twenty-first century careers.

USEFUL RESOURCES

- Advance HE Feedback toolkit: 10 Feedback Resources for your Students: https://www.heacademy.ac.uk/knowledge-hub/feedback-toolkit-10-feedback-resources-your-students.
- ASKe (Assessment Standards Knowledge exchange) Centre for Excellence in Teaching and Learning (CETL) based at Oxford Brookes University: www.brookes.ac.uk/aske.
- Carless, D., Bridges, S.M., Chan, C.K.Y. and Glofcheski, R. (eds) (2017) *Scaling up Assessment for Learning in Higher Education*. Singapore: Springer.
- Herrington, A. and Herrington, J. (eds) (2006) *Authentic Learning Environments in Higher Education*. London: Information Science Publishing.
- Researching Assessment Practices (RAP) at the University of Southampton: https://www.southampton.ac.uk/rap/index.page.

REFERENCES

Bartimote-Aufflick, K., Bridgeman, A., Walker, R., Sharma, M. and Smith, L. (2016) 'The study, evaluation, and improvement of university student self-efficacy', *Studies in Higher Education*, 41, pp. 1918–1942.

Beaumont, C., Moscrop, C. and Canning, S. (2016) 'Easing the transition from school to HE: scaffolding the development of self-regulated learning through a dialogic approach to feedback', *Journal of Further and Higher Education*, 40, pp. 331–350.

Beaumont, C., O'Doherty, M. and Shannon, L. (2011) 'Reconceptualising assessment feedback: a key to improving student learning?' *Studies in Higher Education*, 36, pp. 671–687.

Bloxham, S. (2012) '"You can see the quality in front of your eyes": grounding academic standards between rationality and interpretation', *Quality in Higher Education*, 18, pp. 185–204.

Boud, D. (2000) 'Sustainable assessment: rethinking assessment for the learning society', *Studies in Continuing Education*, 22, pp. 151–167.

Boud, D. (2007) 'Reframing assessment as if learning were important', in D. Boud and N. Falchikov (eds), *Rethinking Assessment in Higher Education: Learning for the Longer Term*. London: Routledge, pp. 14–25.

Boud, D. and Soler, R. (2016) 'Sustainable assessment revisited', *Assessment & Evaluation in Higher Education*, 41, pp. 400–413.

Boud, D., Cohen, R. and Sampson, J. (2014) *Peer Learning in Higher Education: Learning From and With Each Other*. London: Routledge.

Carless, D. (2007) 'Learning-oriented assessment: conceptual bases and practical implications', *Innovations in Education and Teaching International*, 44, pp. 57–66.

Carless, D. (2017) 'Scaling up assessment for learning: progress and prospects', in D. Carless, S.M. Bridges, C.K.Y. Chan and R. Glofcheski (eds), *Scaling up Assessment for Learning in Higher Education*. Singapore: Springer, pp. 3–17.

Carless, D., Joughin, G. and Mok, M. (2006) 'Learning-oriented assessment: principles and practice', *Assessment & Evaluation in Higher Education*, 31, pp. 395–398.

Carless, D., Salter, D., Yang, M. and Lam, J. (2011) 'Developing sustainable feedback practices', *Studies in Higher Education*, 36, pp. 395–407.

Chandler, P.T. and Munch, D. (2016) 'Strengthening geography pedagogy with authentic intellectual work', *The Councilor: A Journal of the Social Studies*, 77, pp. 1–10.

Cook-Sather, A. and Alter, Z. (2011) 'What is and what can be: how a liminal position can change learning and teaching in higher education', *Anthropology and Education Quarterly*, 42, pp. 37–53.

Dickinson, G. and Murphy, K. (2007) *Ecosystems* (2nd edition). London: Routledge.

Forsythe, A. and Johnson, S. (2017) 'Thanks, but no-thanks for the feedback', *Assessment & Evaluation in Higher Education*, 42, pp. 850–859.

Gibbs, G. (2003) 'Editorial. Improving student learning through assessment', *Journal of Geography in Higher Education*, 27, pp. 123–132.

Handley, K. and Williams, L. (2011) 'From copying to learning: using exemplars to engage students with assessment criteria and feedback', *Assessment and Evaluation in Higher Education*, 36, pp. 95–108.

Hathcoat, J.D., Penn, J.D., Barnes, L.L.B. et al. (2016) 'A second dystopia in education: validity issues in authentic assessment practices', *Research in Higher Education*, 57, pp. 892–912.

Hattie, J. and Timperley, H. (2007) 'The power of feedback', *Review of Educational Research*, 77, pp. 81–112.

Hawe, E.M. and Dixon, H.R. (2014) 'Building students' evaluative and productive expertise in the writing classroom', *Assessing Writing*, 19, pp. 66–79.

Hawe, E. and Dixon, H. (2017) 'Assessment for learning: a catalyst for student self-regulation', *Assessment & Evaluation in Higher Education*, 42, pp. 1181–1192.

Herrington, A. and Herrington, J. (eds) (2006) *Authentic Learning Environments in Higher Education*. Hershey, PA: Information Science Publishing.

Herrington, J., Reeves, T.C. and Oliver, R. (2014) 'Authentic learning environments', in M. Spector, M.D. Merrill, J. Elen and M.J. Bishop (eds), *Handbook of Research on Educational Communications and Technology*. New York: Springer, pp. 401–412.

Hill, J. and Walkington, H. (2016) 'Developing graduate attributes through participation in undergraduate research conferences', *Journal of Geography in Higher Education*, 40, pp. 222–237.

Hill, J. and West, H. (2019) 'Improving the student learning experience through dialogic feed-forward assessment', *Assessment & Evaluation in Higher Education*, https://doi.org/10.1080/02602938.2019.1608908.

Hill, J., Thomas, G., Diaz, A. and Simm, D. (2016a) 'Borderland spaces for learning partnership: opportunities, benefits and challenges', *Journal of Geography in Higher Education*, 40, pp. 375–393.

Hill, J., Walkington, H. and France, D. (2016b) 'Graduate attributes: implications for higher education practice and policy', *Journal of Geography in Higher Education*, 40, pp. 155–163.

Jacobs, G.M., Renandya, W.A. and Power, M. (2016) 'Alternative assessment', in G.M. Jacobs, W.A. Renandya and M. Power (eds), *Simple, Powerful Strategies for Student Centered Learning*. Cham, Switzerland: Springer International, pp. 65–72.

Kneale, P., Edward-Jones, A., Walkington, H. and Hill, J. (2016) 'Evaluating undergraduate research conferences as vehicles for novice researchers and transferable skills development', *International Journal of Researcher Development*, 7, pp. 159–177.

Li, J. and De Luca, R. (2014) 'Review of assessment feedback', *Studies in Higher Education*, 39, pp. 378–393.

MacDonald, G. (2003) *Biogeography: Introduction to Space, Time and Life*. New York: John Wiley and Sons.

McDowell, L., Wakelin, D., Montgomery, C. and King, S. (2011) 'Does assessment for learning make a difference? The development of a questionnaire to explore the student response', *Assessment & Evaluation in Higher Education*, 36, pp. 749–765.

Medland, E. (2016) 'Assessment in higher education: drivers, barriers and directions for change in the UK', *Assessment & Evaluation in Higher Education*, 41, pp. 81–96.

Meyer, J.H.F. and Land, R. (eds) (2006) *Overcoming Barriers to Student Understanding: Threshold Concepts and Troublesome Knowledge*. London: Routledge.

Mezirow, J. (ed.) (2000) *Learning as Transformation: Critical Perspectives on a Theory in Progress*. San Francisco, CA: The Jossey-Bass Higher and Adult Education Series.

Mutch, A., Young, C., Davey, T. and Fitzgerald, L. (2018) 'A journey towards sustainable feedback', *Assessment & Evaluation in Higher Education*, 43, pp. 248–259.

Nicol, D. (2010) 'From monologue to dialogue: improving written feedback processes in mass higher education', *Assessment & Evaluation in Higher Education*, 35, pp. 501–517.

Nicol, D.J. and Macfarlane-Dick, D. (2006) 'Formative assessment and self-regulated learning: a model and seven principles of good feedback practice', *Studies in Higher Education*, 31, pp. 199–218.

O'Donovan, B., Rust, C. and Price, M. (2016) 'A scholarly approach to solving the feedback dilemma in practice', *Assessment and Evaluation in Higher Education*, 41, pp. 938–949.

O'Neal, C. (2016) 'Beyond authenticity: what should we value in assessment in professional education?', in P.F. Wimmers and M. Mentkowski (eds), *Assessing Competence in Professional Performance Across Disciplines and Professions*. Cham, Switzerland: Springer International, pp. 51–71.

Ormond, P., Maw, S.J., Park, J.R., Gomez, S. and Crook, A.C. (2013) 'Moving feedback forward: theory to practice', *Assessment and Evaluation in Higher Education*, 38, pp. 240–252.

Price, M., Rust, C., O'Donovan, B., Handley, K. with Bryant, R. (2012) *Assessment Literacy: The Foundation for Improving Student Learning*. Oxford: Oxford Centre for Staff and Learning Development.

Ritchie, L. (2016) *Fostering Self-Efficacy in Higher Education Students*. London: Palgrave.

Rust, C., O'Donovan, B. and Price, M. (2005) 'A social constructivist assessment process model: how the research literature shows us this could be best practice', *Assessment and Evaluation in Higher Education*, 30, pp. 231–240.

Rust, C., Price, M. and O'Donovan, B. (2003) 'Improving students' learning by developing their understanding of assessment criteria and processes', *Assessment and Evaluation in Higher Education*, 28, pp. 147–164.

Swaffield, S. (2011) 'Getting to the heart of authentic assessment for learning', *Assessment in Education: Principles, Policy & Practice*, 18, pp. 433–449.

Telio, S., Ajjawi, R. and Regehr, G. (2015) 'The "educational alliance" as a framework for reconceptualising feedback in medical education', *Academic Medicine*, 90, pp. 609–614.

To, J. and Liu, Y. (2018) 'Using peer and teacher–student exemplar dialogues to unpack assessment standards: challenges and possibilities', *Assessment & Evaluation in Higher Education*, 43, pp. 449–460.

Turner, V. (1974) *Dramas, Fields, and Metaphors: Symbolic Action in Human Society*. New York: Cornell University Press.

Walkington, H., Hill, J. and Kneale, P. (2017) 'Reciprocal elucidation: a student-led pedagogy in multi-disciplinary undergraduate research conferences', *HERD*, 36, pp. 416–429.

Wegerif, R. (2006) 'Dialogic education: what is it and why do we need it?', *Education Review*, 19, pp. 58–67.

Winstone, N.E., Nash, R.A., Parker, M. and Rowntree, J. (2017a) 'Supporting learners' agentic engagement with feedback: a systematic review and a taxonomy of recipience processes', *Educational Psychologist*, 52, pp. 17–37.

Winstone, N.E., Nash, R.A., Rowntree, J. and Parker, M. (2017b) '"It'd be useful, but I wouldn't use it": barriers to university students' feedback seeking and recipience', *Studies in Higher Education*, 42, pp. 2026–2041.

Worth, N. (2013) 'Experimenting with student-led seminars', *Planet*, 27, pp. 30–35.

Worth, N. (2014) 'Student-focused assessment criteria: thinking through best practice', *Journal of Geography in Higher Education*, 38, pp. 361–372.

Yang, M. and Carless, D. (2013) 'The feedback triangle and the enhancement of dialogic feedback processes', *Teaching in Higher Education*, 18, pp. 285–297.

28. Capstones in geography
Alice Hovorka and Peter Wolf

INTRODUCTION

A capstone is the culmination of an undergraduate program that offers an opportunity for praxis whereby students actively engage and apply disciplinary concepts and ideas first-hand. It allows students to reflect back on their years of study to consider and apply their acquired knowledge, skills and values as a whole. As such, it facilitates mastery of disciplinary tenets. It also offers students an opportunity to integrate and critically assess their undergraduate experiences, make sense and meaning of those experiences, and look forward to building upon them for the future.

The aim of our chapter is to offer a range of ideas and approaches regarding capstones in geography that challenge students to demonstrate mastery, as well as synthesize and reflect on their learning, particularly as applicable for the wider world. To do so, we provide an overview of geography capstone rationales and goals. We also highlight capstone formats and approaches that predominate in the discipline, namely field-based experiences, independent research projects, and disciplinary overviews. These reflect geography's signature pedagogy of hands-on experiential learning, as well as an emphasis on geography's importance as a scholarly and applied realm. We then provide examples of innovative capstones inspired by re-conceptualizing the field, re-framing the dissertation, and re-imagining geography's contributions to scholarship and practice. Our hope is to inspire creative capstone design and suggest various ways in which capstones may resonate with increasingly diverse groups of undergraduate students working towards engagement and success within an increasingly complex world.

We emphasize that geography capstone goals and design should begin by asking 'What are we capping?' And capstone positioning need not wait until the end of a student's program of study. Indeed, given the breadth and depth of geography, as well as the expanse of formal and informal learning that students engage in over a program of study, assisting students to master the desired geographical knowledge, skills, and values is best served through a 'linked model'. This means scaffolding capstone experiences through an intentional and coordinated pathway. For example, if academic writing of geography is a desired outcome, students might be required to write a novice-level essay in an introductory course, whilst a capstone experience in later years of study might have those same students review their first-year paper in the fourth year, re-write it and include a reflective report on what new skills they gained in terms of writing ability and how their geographical knowledge evolved. Linked capstones can play a vital role in student development and in solidifying geography graduate attributes and evaluating program learning outcomes.

CAPSTONE RATIONALE AND GOALS

A capstone is the culmination of an undergraduate career; a crowning experience coming at the end of a sequence of courses that allows students to 'put it all together' (Nilsson and Fulton, 2002; Fanter, 2006; Lee and Loton, 2015). One rationale for offering a capstone to graduating geography students revolves around the concern that students will graduate with no sense of what, if anything, was 'geographical' about their higher education. Given the breadth of geography course offerings in undergraduate programs, students easily lose sight of the big picture in light of specialist knowledge encountered (Castree, Rogers and Sherman, 2005).

As another rationale, students may grasp the vast array of knowledge offered but lack experience in putting the pieces together (Spurrier, 2001). Capstone courses offer students a look at geography as-a-whole (Castree, Rogers and Sherman, 2005), allow students to experience the complexity of the discipline, and provide a final mastery experience based on integration (Healey, 2014). Ideally, a capstone will bring to fruition years of disciplinary study and practice offering students the opportunity to synthesize prior knowledge, engage in free-flowing discourse, and create an undergraduate *magnum opus* (Schmid, 1993). Capstones viewed as 'advanced introductory' courses invite students to become part of an ongoing collaborative community of researchers and scholars (Davis, 1993). Asking students to revisit the basics of the discipline and to build on prior coursework can facilitate mastery of disciplinary knowledge and skills. With this mastery comes a deeper appreciation of geography as a means of addressing real world problems (Lee and Loton, 2015).

As a final rationale, a capstone provides graduating students opportunity to critically assess their undergraduate experiences (Troyer, 1993). As such, capstones provide an experience through which undergraduates look back over the curriculum in an effort to make sense and meaning of that experience and look forward to a life of building on that experience (Healey, 2014). Further, that only a small group of students will go on to graduate work in the discipline raises the question: 'What last academic experience can [instructors] provide graduating seniors that will be valuable for citizenship in the human community?' (Troyer, 1993, p. 247). In this context, the capstone can function as a broader socializing agent, designed to instill in students a sense of self and civic responsibility, as well as disciplinary understanding (Collier, 2000).

In sum, student mastery, synthesis, and reflection characterize the rationales for offering an undergraduate capstone. The specific capstone goals are identified in scholarly literature as follows: integration (pulling together three or four years of undergraduate study); breadth (providing a general education context on top of specialized study); application (engaging expert knowledge to examine a discrete issue and produce a substantial product); and transition (making meaning of this knowledge and skillset as related to future careers) (Castree, Rogers and Sherman, 2005; Healey, 2014). Ultimately, a capstone may be best defined as a 'culminating educational experience with a focus on the consolidation of prior learning, the development of graduate capabilities, and the transition to post-graduation settings' (Lee and Loton, 2015, p. iii).

Beyond this student development emphasis of capstones, culminating experiences have grown in scope, importance, and necessity as a result of higher education mandates for accountability and documenting learning outcomes at a broader scale (Rowles et al., 2004).

From an institutional assessment and quality perspective, capstones have the potential to demonstrate program-level learning outcomes, as well as evidencing student development of disciplinary and wide-range capabilities relevant to employability, social engagement, and lifelong learning (Lee and Loton, 2015). When used to assess program-level student learning outcomes, capstones provide valuable insights on what students know and what can they do so as to improve institutional practice, quality of instruction, programmatic offerings, and documented outcome assessments for a variety of audiences, including employers, accreditation officials, policymakers, society, and governments. Capstones are used increasingly to facilitate integration of learning within a program major and connect that learning back to institutional themes and mandates (Rowles et al., 2004).

CAPSTONE FORMATS AND APPROACHES

Capstones in geography and beyond are referred to by various terms, for example: senior experience, senior seminar, colloquium, or independent thesis in the USA (Jones et al., 2012); capstone course, field research course, or honours thesis in Canada (Hovorka, 2009); capstone project in North America; final project in Europe and Australia; and dissertation in the UK (Healey, 2014). Generally, capstones reflect the following core design principles: (1) integration and extension of prior learning; (2) authentic and contextualized experiences; (3) challenging and complex problems; (4) student independence and agency; (5) concern with critical inquiry and creativity; and (6) active dissemination and celebration (Lee and Loton, 2015).

Many capstones involve a significant amount of research, taking the form of inquiry-based projects, independent studies, or dissertations in the final year or semester of an undergraduate program (Healey, 2014). Geography capstones specifically feature (often residential) field-based and/or research-oriented experiences for graduating students to facilitate active engagement with scientific questions, subject-based and transferable competencies, and real-world problem solving (Hefferan, Heywood and Ritter, 2002; Healey, 2005; Paradis and Dexter, 2007; Hill et al., 2011). In a regional survey of geography capstones in North America, 43 percent of departments use field-based experiences, courses or internships, while 40 percent use an honours thesis or research study as a culminating experience (Hovorka, 2009). Similar trends exist for capstones in European and Australian contexts (Hill et al., 2011; Healey, 2014; Lee and Loton, 2015).

Fieldwork has long been viewed as geography's signature pedagogy (Shulman, 2005; Gurung et al., 2009) and vital for the development of students as qualified practitioners in all aspects of the discipline. The 'field course' is touted as a fundamental component of undergraduate learning experiences in geography (Lonergan and Andersen, 1988; Gold, 1991; Haigh and Gold, 1993; Bradbeer, 1996; Clark, 1996; Higgitt, 1996; McEwen, 1996; Kent et al., 1997; May, 1999; Robson, 2002; Fuller et al., 2006; Scott, Fuller and Gaskin, 2006; Hope, 2009; Hovorka and Wolf, 2009; Grindsted et al., 2013; and see, in this volume, Chapter 22 by Ian Fuller and Derek France, and Chapter 26 by Lisa Mol and colleagues). Not surprisingly, 'the field' features prominently as an appropriate – and perhaps ideal – site for capstone-based learning for undergraduate students. More often than not, the field is conceived of as a locale situated away from the classroom to which students travel and reside at for a period of time. Residential field courses in geography highlight particular intellectual, technical and personal development benefits to students as situated within the broader framework of constructivist pedagogy. Geographical field courses promote 'learning by doing' with students exploring a new context in which they can make meaning and construct knowledge through intensive interactions with peers, instructors, and the environment itself (Hovorka and Wolf, 2009).

In the field, students actively connect theoretical concepts with real-world scenarios, and discover principles and facts for themselves by applying intuitive, observational, and analytical skills (Ackerman, 1996; Grindsted et al., 2013). Here, students are encouraged to arrive at their own version of 'truth' influenced by their background and experiences. Learning in-the-field is an iterative process, involving discursive, adaptive, interactive and reflexive qualities (Green and Gredler, 2002) that are mediated through student–student, student–instructor, and student–environment interactions. Ultimately, learning experiences of residential field-based courses are summarized as follows: (1) apply theory in the 'real world'; (2) practice observing and interpreting phenomena and/or dynamics; (3) utilize field techniques and methods; (4) make personal meaning of course content; (5) engage in high-level thinking (for example analysis, synthesis, evaluation); (6) explore personal beliefs and values; (7) increase appreciation of 'real world' issues; (8) engage with a variety of learning approaches (for example lecture, discussions, reading, writing, exploring); (9) enhance proficiency of transferable skills (for example organization, communication); and (10) work as part of a collaborative/team effort (Hovorka and Wolf, 2009).

Field-based capstones may not always be possible or desirable on account of numerous issues. Specifically, they may be challenged by budgetary constraints, increasing student numbers, instructor preparatory demands, or socio-political student access based on financial means, academic performance, or conforming to gendered, raced, or ability-oriented norms (Haigh and Gold, 1993; Jenkins, 1994; Bradbeer, 1996; Kent et al., 1997; May, 1999; Nairn et al., 2000; Tueth and Wikle, 2000; Hefferan et al., 2002). As such, geography field courses are increasingly delivered through a variety of formats moving beyond traditional residential models with greater emphasis, for example, on specialized, local, or thematic field activities. There is also recognition that a number of learning objectives may be as easily met in the classroom through active learning approaches as in the field (May, 1999; Livingstone and Lynch, 2000; Haigh, 2001; Hanson and Moser, 2003; Healey and Roberts, 2004; Hovorka and Wolf, 2009).

Capstones are a means through which research (field-based or otherwise) is often integrated into undergraduate programs (Healey, 2014) (see Chapter 14 in this volume by Helen Walkington). Capstone 'projects' or dissertations at the final year of study have a variety of purposes, including promoting skills (for example critical thinking, analysis, evaluation, effective communication, independence) and employability; diversifying assessment; empowering learners; motivating students; promoting teaching–research links; and identifying potential graduate students (Marshall, 2009; Hill et al., 2011). Key characteristics focus on the production of scholarly work (for example research-oriented, contribution to knowledge, defined and justified methodology, and an extended piece of work; Healey et al., 2013). Often they take the form of traditional formats, 8,000 to 12,000 words in length, highlighting academic writing, and are viewed as training for budding academics; this has evolved into journal-ready manuscripts (thus reduced word length) and requiring a proposal and presentation (Hill et al., 2011). In some instances, information dissemination may extend into public fora such as research conferences (Hill and Walkington, 2016) or practitioner-based contexts (Hill et al., 2011).

Scholars, including geographers, have raised concerns as to the relevance of such capstones in the face of increasingly diverse student cohorts, complex societal challenges, and interdisciplinary analytical requirements; traditional formats are also viewed as limiting creativity for both instructors and students (Hill et al., 2011). Further, evidence suggests that the dissertation does not, in fact, encourage student stakeholders in university research or members of disciplinary research communities (Healey and Jenkins, 2009). While undergraduate geography students should engage with research, it must be relevant for the student, aligning with their academic and career interests (Hill et al., 2011). Moreover, research capstones – be they field- and/or dissertation-based – are not always formatted as capstones. They may emphasize research skills and focus on depth of geographic study in one area of interest rather than necessarily requiring students to look back at the whole of their geography program and experiences therein. As such, simply having a research offering within a program of study does not always 'cap' geographical knowledge, skills, and values in a holistic way.

Beyond field- and dissertation-based capstone offerings, capstones highlighting disciplinary overviews also prevail in geography programs. For example, 35 percent of geography departments in North America offer a classroom-based capstone focused on evolution of the discipline and, to a lesser extent, on the transition of students to the working world (Hovorka, 2009). Such geography capstone courses often connect to disciplinary overviews. Introductory or upper year textbooks implicitly couch discussion of capstone courses within explorations of the history, philosophies, and definitions of Western geographical thought. Such texts (for example Gregory, 2000; Holloway, Rice and Valentine, 2003; Johnston and Sidaway, 2004; Castree, Rogers and Sherman, 2005; Clifford et al., 2009; Aitken and Valentine, 2015) provide foundational reading for geographers and students alike as a way of exploring the discipline. They offer students opportunities to consider the contested, constructed geographical knowledge to which they have been exposed during their undergraduate programs. Broader scholarly literature characterizes the ideal culminating course as focused on a small number of students, where the instructor facilitates rather than lectures, where students learn from one another, and where team-teaching and learning do justice to disciplinary breadth (Spurrier, 2001). Capstone course structure should allow instructors to assess: knowledge (for example discipline content area, interdisciplinary connections); skills (for example writing, speaking, collaboration, critical thinking, synthesis, evaluation); and attitudes (for example openness to more than one position, distinction made between facts and values, reflective self-evaluation, reflective institutional-evaluation) (Smith, 1993).

Ultimately, field-based inquiry, independent research projects, and disciplinary overviews predominate as geography capstone experiences in practice and as discussed within existing scholarship. These particular formats and approaches align with signature pedagogies meaningful to geographers; notably 'learning through the soles of their feet' (McEwen, 1996 p. 379), with field- and research-based experiences viewed as vital for student development as qualified practitioners in the discipline (see Hovorka and Wolf, 2009). Course-based emphases on the evolution of geography concepts and methods also lends itself to disciplinary teachings. While these geography capstones offer effective and engaging means of achieving student mastery, synthesis and reflection of undergraduate geographical knowledge, skills and values, brainstorming on new and innovative capstone experiences can extend further the importance and impact of culminating moments within a disciplinary program.

INNOVATIVE CAPSTONES

Capstones in geography can be conceived of and delivered in various and innovative ways. In this section, we provide examples for instructors to step out of traditional capstone applications by re-conceptualizing fieldwork, re-framing dissertations, and re-imagining disciplinary contributions. These options are meant to stimulate instructors' creativity, novel design, and out-of-the-box thinking. They emphasize the idea of a capstone as praxis and building foundations for lifelong learning, as grounded in, yet pushing further, signature geography pedagogy.

Re-Conceptualizing Fieldwork

Geography capstones need not be limited to traditional residential field settings. Rather, classrooms themselves can offer first-hand, experiential learning opportunities. This requires reconceptualizing what may be considered the field in geography capstones and 'activating classrooms' to offer engaging capstones as part of the undergraduate curriculum. It also requires adapting the ten above-noted core design principles of residential field courses into classroom-based settings.

As an example, we present an innovative capstone design based on a third-year undergraduate classroom-based course on gender and environment (originally detailed in Hovorka and Wolf, 2009). This course conceptualizes the field as grounded in 'everyday life' and spans students' personal circumstances, media engagements, and spatial encounters through which gendered dynamics might be evidenced. In re-conceptualizing the field, the course reflects principles central to feminist philosophy and pedagogy. Feminist scholars have long touted the importance of everyday life as a significant and legitimate focus of research. Studying the already-given situations or taken-for-granted features of everyday life has revealed norms, assumptions, processes and dynamics that fundamentally sustain gender inequality (Fonow and Cook, 1991), including common courtesies, linguistic practices, media practices, spatial dynamics, and so on. Feminists 'trace the interconnections between all aspects of daily life' (Johnston et al., 2000, p. 259). The course format and learning outcomes are grounded in core elements identified for traditional residential field courses, most especially merging theoretical concepts with real-world scenarios, enhancing proficiency in field observation and analysis, and facilitating personal growth and development.

The course is designed for approximately 80 geography majors and is offered as an elective. The classroom serves as a home base learning environment and focal point for student knowledge construction. Class sessions bring students into a conversation about feminist geographical theories of, and perspectives on, men and women's experiences with the environment. The instructor is tasked to a certain extent with delivering course content on a number of interrelated themes, including gendered interactions with nature, gendered body politics, and gendered production and use of space. Students engage in discussions, be they plenary, small group or think-pair-share, and exercises such as journaling and focused free writing, which encourage peer learning and discovery grounded in feminist theorizing.

Using this active classroom as a springboard, students delve into 'the field' of childhood to gain initial insights on their personal experiences with gender dynamics. The first course assignment is a self-reflective journaling exercise whereby childhood becomes a learning environment in and of itself through which students investigate key questions regarding the extent to which their education, home life, extracurricular activities, and work spaces have been influenced by gender norms. Focused free-writing artefacts on each of these topics are used by students as data for a self-reflexive essay that identifies the extent to which and how exactly gender dynamics have manifested themselves (or not) into the students' everyday lives to date.

The second course assignment involves 'the field' of media whereby students actively explore the representations of men, women and nature through everyday messages communicated through newspapers, magazines, television, and the like. Students acquire proficiency in content and visual analysis techniques by applying them to investigations of gendered messages. Assembling evidence of advertisements or assessment of article content in these magazines helps students establish the everyday messages they subtly receive about masculinity and femininity. They are then tasked with linking their empirical investigations with feminist theories and concepts discussed in class; in particular, which ideas help them best explain what they 'see' in contemporary media. This assignment offers students a means of recognizing the power of information and how it can serve to (re)produce particular male and female identities that, in turn, shape gendered opportunities and constraints.

The third course assignment involves group work whereby students become participant observers gathering primary data on gender dynamics in 'the field' of everyday spatial encounters. The opportunity to examine taken-for-granted spaces of eating and drinking establishments, downtown streets, the transit system or even public washrooms provide new perspectives and insights on men and women's differential presence, use and behavior in the same space. Again, students are tasked with linking their empirical investigations with feminist theories and concepts discussed in class, and the group-work component means that knowledge construction takes place through negotiation amongst individual group members. This particular assignment draws in most explicitly collaborative activities and problem-solving characteristics of field-based courses, emphasizing leadership, teamwork, interpersonal dynamics and communication within the context of peer learning and discovery.

In a follow-up survey, students reported that the design of the simulated field course met many of the characteristics of a residential field course and fulfilled many of the goals therein. It was also reported that the assignments and activities allowed students multiple opportunities to apply theoretical learning to practical contexts in their immediate world, helping to make meaning of their world though a feminist geographic lens. As students noted: '*assignments involved taking "real world" observations instead of simply using texts*' and '*after completing the assignments for this course . . . I [look at my life] broadly. I am more conscious of my surroundings*'. Ultimately, this course design can be considered a specifically capstone experience in that it integrates multiple years of feminist geography learning, provides a framework for applying geographic theories and perspectives, and offers meaningful application of disciplinary knowledge and skills as related to post-undergraduate experiences and a lifelong lens through which to view the world.

Re-Framing Dissertations

Geography capstones need not be limited to traditional independent research projects or dissertations. Hill et al. (2011) propose re-imagining capstone projects that offer greater diversity, relevance, and alignment with student needs and interests. To this end, they detail numerous innovative geography capstone projects, inspiring and challenging students to think in new ways, to apply their expertise to explore and solve problems, and to share thoughts and experiences with peers. Key to these innovative applications involves students working with academic stakeholders in new ways, working with non-academic stakeholders beyond the university, and students presenting projects through various text-based formats or eschewing them altogether. Ultimately, these innovations aim at expanding possibilities (rather than diluting the importance or rigour of the dissertation project or experiences) to ensure that students gain disciplinary understanding alongside instilled sense of self and civic responsibility. Here, the capstone functions as a broader socializing agent as much as a disciplinary platform.

Specifically, Hill et al. (2011, pp. 336–338) propose innovative capstones featuring new ways for students to work with academic stakeholders. For example, the 'academic apprentice model' allows students to work with university research groups so as to engage students more integrally with research discussions and to mimic more closely the collaborative rather than isolationist work that academic communities of practice engage in. This context offers opportunities for undergraduate students to co-create knowledge by sharing knowledge and learning from others through a participatory approach to research design or problem solving. Undergraduate students bring to the group their own set of knowledges and skills, which may be integrated into cutting-edge research projects through academic collaboration. While such scenarios raise questions regarding assessment of jointly-produced capstone projects, they importantly offer students a 'voice' in their educational journey, as well as in scholarly work.

Additionally, Hill et al. (2011, pp. 338–340) propose innovative capstones through which students work with non-academic stakeholders beyond the university. For example, workplace, service-learning and charity sector projects integrated into a final-year dissertation provide opportunities to engage with 'real world' contexts, issues and problems. Undergraduate students are matched with various government, private-sector or civil society organizations. Stakeholders from these organizations identify issues or problems to solve, and facilitate a process whereby students lead the relevant consultation process, research or task design, and generate outputs. Projects may be solo or team-based – the latter allows for more complex issues to be tackled and more individuals to be involved while the former allows for more streamlined academic assessment of the process and final project.

Finally, Hill et al. (2011, pp. 340–341) propose innovative capstones with students presenting projects through various text-based formats or eschewing them altogether. For example, creative and visual forms, such as art and design, photograph, video, online technologies, or mapping products extend opportunities for student creativity and visioning when presented alongside a critical commentary or narrative. Certainly cartographic display is fundamental to geography and capstone emphasis on this particular skill can enhance mastery and encourage reflective practice in undergraduate geography programs. Hill et al. (2011) also stress that re-framing dissertations in these and other ways requires attention to changing assessment to push beyond traditional criteria for independent research projects. They draw attention to assessment of products that are summative, reflective, and often made up of more than a single 'output'. Assessment criteria must cater for the differences inherent in independent compared with collaborative knowledge production, taking into account differing levels of student engagement with research or creative scholarship.

Re-Imagining Disciplinary Contributions

Geography capstones based in classrooms need not be limited to courses highlighting the discipline's paradigm shifts featuring an historical trajectory (for example Greek foundations through to modern positivist, interpretivist, and critical paradigms) and included key geographical works (for example 'greatest hits' by prominent geographers). Indeed, such applications may not resonate with students in ways that inspire insights on the contributions of geography to scholarship and applications to broader society.

An alternative approach (originally detailed in Hovorka, 2009) stems from a classroom-based capstone example organized around 'ten geographic ideas that have changed the world' and Susan Hanson's (1997) advanced introductory text with its balance of theoretical elements and practical applications. For example, John Mather's chapter on water budget climatology reviews hydrologic cycle formulations and their applications to evaluating water resources and future climate change scenarios; Edward Taaffe's chapter outlines the concept of functional region, illustrating spatial organization and interdependence and linking it to settlement planning activities; and Robert Kates' chapter on human adjustment traces the human–environment realm of geography as a means of understanding people's everyday coexistence with nature (Hanson, 1997).

This capstone is designed for a class size of approximately 50–60 students. Class sessions include lectures with small-group and/or plenary discussions, in-class exercises, group presentations, and guest lectures. The level and quality of effort that students bring to taught sessions largely determines course success, given that students lead a substantial portion of the course. 'Geographic ideas' provide the centerpiece for student engagement and course assignments as grounded in capstone goals of mastery, synthesis and reflection. The first assignment requires student groups to select and lead a class session based on one of the geographic ideas presented in Hanson (1997). Notably, students present arguments as to why their idea stands as the most significant for geography as an academic discipline and for the 'real world'. This assignment focuses on constructing logical and substantiated arguments, strengthening oral presentation skills, and demonstrating understanding and application of a core geographical concept.

The second assignment tasks students with assembling an academic portfolio. Students choose six out of the ten geographic ideas and track how these ideas have evolved through their undergraduate degree program. They discuss specific courses or scenarios in which they had encountered each idea, in what ways they engaged with it, how their understanding or use of a particular idea changed during their four years, and how their knowledge of the idea may serve them in the future. The academic portfolio also includes a 1,000-

word reflective essay on what students learned about the world through a geographic lens. Here, students synthesize and reflect on common threads from their six chosen ideas to answer the overarching question of 'what is geography?'

The third assignment asks students to write 'Chapter 11' for Hanson's (1997) *10 Geographic Ideas that Changed the World* based on a pivotal idea encountered during their undergraduate degree. This research-oriented paper requires students to identify the idea and provide a rationale for its selection in terms of its place in geographical knowledge, its relevance to the real world, and its importance to the students themselves. Students must demonstrate original geographic thought by situating their idea within the historical evolution of the discipline and discussing its application to society. Students also reflect on how and why their selected idea changed their perspective on and understanding of the world, as well as how this may serve them in their future career. Students display enormous creativity in this assignment with an impressive range of potential chapters on geography theories and concepts (for example topophilia, chaos theory, overland flow, the watershed, environmental determinism, concentric zone model); sub-disciplines (for example feminist geography, political ecology, resource management, transportation geography); approaches (for example holism, environmentalism); and broad issues explored by geographers (for example globalization, climate change, sustainable development).

According to course evaluations, students like the capstone format and approach; they engage with the material and participate enthusiastically in pursuit of the course goals. Notably, student feedback reflects themes of mastery, synthesis, and reflection as central to their positive learning experiences:

> *[This is a] great course to have included in the final year for [geography] students! It really ties together everything we have learned over the years and drives home the importance of geography as a whole.*

> *I appreciated the personal reflection that was asked of in this course because it helped to capture what I have done as an undergrad in geography, as well as think about what my future ventures might look like, and the career possibilities that lie ahead.*

Importantly, the capstone approach allowed students the opportunity to package their own geographical training and knowledge in a scholarly and creative manner, and to extend their interest in the discipline.

CONCLUSION

Capstones in geography must be conceptualized in terms of student learning outcomes and grounded within goals of the broader program curriculum. Capstones are scaffolded, beginning ideally with an introductory course that identifies what students will be able to do at the end of their geography program. Subsequent courses continue to emphasize such learning outcomes, and specifically address along the way 'what is an ideal geography graduate'. This threading continues to the senior-level capstone offering, presenting an opportunity to reflect back but also to look forward. Thus, a course-only model for capstones (that is, add capstone and stir) is less ideal than perhaps a series of capstone 'experiences' throughout a program that are scaffolded and bookended. In geography, for example, you could offer an initial course outlining geography learning outcomes, with strategic positioning throughout the program of geography capstone experiences (including field courses for example), and then completed with a capstone. Capstone alignment with program learning outcomes is important to ensure student mastery, synthesis and reflection in disciplinary context.

Thus well-designed capstones can serve as appropriate mechanisms for quality assurance processes at program or institutional levels (Lee and Loton, 2015). On the one hand, capstones can be viewed as a final test of the knowledge, skills, and values gained through disciplinary learning (it is a test of a student's readiness to graduate). On the other hand, capstones can be viewed as data sources from which institutional program quality and student achievement standards may be benchmarked (Lee and Loton, 2019). Here, alignment with not only disciplinary and institutional but also socio-political and employment contexts may impact the ways in which capstone curricula are designed.

Designing and positioning capstones is a substantial and complex task. It requires that we simultaneously authenticate, integrate, and develop disciplinary academic knowledge, skills and values while establishing a wide range of personal and professional capabilities and connecting students to their future career paths. It also requires that we ensure quality assurance of both students and programmes throughout the process (Lee and Loton, 2019). It is our hope that this chapter inspires creative, innovative, and out-of-the-box thinking about geography capstones both in and of themselves and in terms of program learning outcomes. Ultimately, it is rich and robust capstone experiences that will equip geography students to thrive in the 21st century.

USEFUL RESOURCES

- Hauhart, R.C. and Grahe, J.E. (2014) *Designing and Teaching Undergraduate Capstone Courses.* San Francisco, CA: Jossey-Bass Wiley. Available online at: https://www.wiley.com/en-ca/Designing+and+Teaching+Undergraduate+Capstone+Courses-p-9781118761878.
- The Capstone Network Site: www.capstonecurriculum.com.au.

REFERENCES

Ackerman, E. (1996) 'Perspective taking and object construction: two keys to learning', in Y. Kafai and M. Resnick (eds), *Constructionism in Practice: Designing, Thinking, and Learning in a Digital World.* Hillsdale, NJ: Lawrence Erlbaum, pp. 25–35.

Aitken, S. and Valentine, G. (2015) *Approaches to Human Geography: Philosophies, Theories, People, Practices* (Second Edition). London: Sage.

Bradbeer, J. (1996) 'Problem-based learning and fieldwork: a better method of preparation?', *Journal of Geography in Higher Education,* 20 (1), pp. 11–18.

Castree, N., Rogers, A. and Sherman, D. (2005) *Questioning Geography.* Oxford: Blackwell.

Clark, D. (1996) 'The changing national context of fieldwork in geography', *Journal of Geography in Higher Education,* 20 (3), pp. 385–390.

Clifford, N., Holloway, S., Rice, S. and Valentine, G. (eds) (2009) *Key Concepts in Geography.* London: Sage.

Collier, P.J. (2000) 'The effects of completing a capstone course on student identity', *Sociology of Education,* 73 (4), pp. 285–299.

Davis, N.J. (1993) 'Bringing it all together: the sociological imagination', *Teaching Sociology,* 21 (3), pp. 233–238.

Fanter, A. (2006) 'Preparing for post-college life: capstone and keystone courses'. Available online at: http://www.worldwidelearn.com/education-articles/capstone-keystone-courses. Accessed 29 August 2007.

Fonow, M.M. and Cook, J.A. (eds) (1991) *Beyond Methodology: Feminist Scholarship as Lived Research.* Bloomington and Indianapolis: Indiana University Press.

Fuller, I., Edmondson, S., France, D., Higgitt, D. and Ratinen, I. (2006) 'International perspectives on the effectiveness of geography fieldwork for learning', *Journal of Geography in Higher Education*, 30 (1), pp. 89–101.

Gold, J.R. (1991) 'Fieldwork', in J.R. Gold, A. Jenkins, R. Lee, J. Monk, J. Riley, I. Shepherd and D. Unwin (eds), *Teaching Geography in Higher Education: A Manual of Good Practice.* Oxford: Blackwell, pp. 21–35.

Green, S.K. and Gredler, M.E. (2002) 'A review and analysis of constructivism for school-based practice', *School Psychology Review*, 31 (1), pp. 53–70.

Gregory, K.J. (2000) *The Changing Nature of Physical Geography.* London: Arnold.

Grindsted, T.S., Madsen, L.M. and Nielsen, T.T. (2013) '"One just better understands . . . when standing out there": fieldwork as a learning methodology in university education of Danish Geographers', *Review of International Geographical Education Online*, 3 (1), pp. 8–25.

Gurung, R.A., Chick, N.L. and Haynie, A. (eds) (2009) *Exploring Signature Pedagogies: Approaches to Teaching Disciplinary Habits of Mind.* Sterling, VA: Stylus Publishing.

Haigh, M. (2001) 'Constructing Gaia: using journals to foster reflecting learning', *Journal of Geography in Higher Education*, 25 (2), pp. 167–189.

Haigh, M. and Gold, J.R. (1993) 'The problems with fieldwork: a group-based approach towards integrating fieldwork into the undergraduate geography curriculum', *Journal of Geography in Higher Education*, 17 (1), pp. 21–32.

Hanson, S. (ed.) (1997) *10 Geographic Ideas that Changed the World.* New Brunswick, NJ: Rutgers University Press.

Hanson, S. and Moser, S. (2003) 'Reflections on a discipline-wide project: developing active learning modules on the human dimensions of global change', *Journal of Geography in Higher Education*, 27 (1), pp. 17–38.

Healey, M. (2005) 'Linking research and teaching to benefit student learning', *Journal of Geography in Higher Education*, 29 (2), pp. 183–201.

Healey, M. (2014) 'Integrating undergraduate research into the curriculum: international perspectives on capstone and final-year projects', *Council on Undergraduate Research*, 34 (4), pp. 26–32.

Healey, M. and Jenkins, A. (2009) *Developing Undergraduate Research and Inquiry.* York: Higher Education Academy.

Healey, M. and Roberts, J. (eds) (2004) *Engaging Students in Active Learning: Case Studies in Geography, Environment and Related Disciplines.* Cheltenham: Geography Discipline Network.

Healey, M., Lannin, L., Stibbe, A. and Derounian, J. (2013) *Developing and Enhancing Undergraduate Final-Year Projects and Dissertations.* York: Higher Education Academy.

Hefferan, K.P., Heywood, N.C. and Ritter, M.E. (2002) 'Integrating field trips and classroom learning into a capstone undergraduate research experience', *Journal of Geography*, 101 (5), pp. 183–190.

Higgitt, M. (1996) 'Addressing the new agenda for fieldwork in higher education', *Journal of Geography in Higher Education*, 20 (3), pp. 391–398.

Hill, J. and Walkington, H. (2016) 'Developing graduate attributes through participation in undergraduate research conferences', *Journal of Geography in Higher Education*, 40, pp. 222–237.

Hill, J., Kneale, P., Nicholson, D., Waddington, S. and Ray, W. (2011) 'Re-framing the geography dissertation: a consideration of alternative, innovative and creative approaches', *Journal of Geography in Higher Education*, 35 (3), pp. 331–349.

Holloway, S.L., Rice, S.P. and Valentine, G. (eds) (2003) *Key Concepts in Geography.* London: Sage.

Hope, M. (2009) 'The importance of direct experience: a philosophical defense of fieldwork in human geography', *Journal of Geography in Higher Education*, 33 (2), pp. 169–182.

Hovorka, A.J. (2009) 'A capstone course of "geographic ideas"', *Journal of Geography*, 108 (6), pp. 252–258.

Hovorka, A.J. and Wolf, P.A. (2009) 'Activating the classroom: geographical fieldwork as pedagogical practice', *Journal of Geography in Higher Education*, 33 (1), pp. 89–102.

Jenkins, A. (1994) 'Thirteen ways of doing fieldwork with large classes/more students', *Journal of Geography in Higher Education*, 18 (2), pp. 143–154.

Johnston, R.J. and Sidaway, J. (2004) *Geography and Geographers* (Sixth Edition). London: Arnold.

Johnston, R., Gregory, D., Pratt, G. and Watts, M. (eds) (2000) *Dictionary of Human Geography* (Fourth Edition). London: Routledge.

Jones, K.W., Barrow Jr, M.V., Stephens, R.P. and O'Hara, S. (2012) 'Romancing the capstone: national trends, local practice, and student motivation in the history curriculum', *The Journal of American History*, 98 (4), pp. 1095–1113.

Kent, M., Gilbertson, D.D. and Hunt, C.O. (1997) 'Fieldwork in geography teaching: a critical review of the literature and approaches', *Journal of Geography in Higher Education*, 21 (3), pp. 313–332.

Lee, N. and Loton, D.J. (2015) *Capstone Curriculum Across Disciplines: Synthesising Theory, Practice and*

Policy to Provide Practical Tools for Curriculum Design. Final Report. Victoria University, Australia: Office of Learning and Teaching. Available online at: www.capstonecurriculum.com.au.

Lee, N. and Loton, D. (2019) 'Capstone purposes across disciplines', *Studies in Higher Education*, 44 (1) pp. 134–150.

Livingstone, D. and Lynch, K. (2000) 'Group project work and student-centred active learning: two different experiences', *Journal of Geography in Higher Education*, 26 (2), pp. 217–237.

Lonergan, N. and Andresen, L. (1988) 'Field based education: some theoretical considerations?', *Higher Education Research and Development*, 7, pp. 63–77.

Marshall, S. (2009) 'Supervising projects and dissertations', in H. Fry, S. Ketteridge and S. Marshall (eds), *Handbook for Teaching and Learning in Higher Education.* Abingdon: Routledge, pp. 150–165.

May, J. (1999) 'Developing fieldwork in social and cultural geography: illustrations from a residential field class in Los Angeles and Las Vegas', *Journal of Geography in Higher Education*, 23 (2), pp. 207–225.

McEwen, L. (1996) 'Fieldwork in the undergraduate geography programme: challenges and changes', *Journal of Geography in Higher Education*, 20, pp. 379–384.

Nairn, K., Higgitt, D. and Vanneste, D. (2000) 'International perspectives on fieldcourses', *Journal of Geography in Higher Education*, 24 (2), pp. 246–254.

Nilsson, T.K.H. and Fulton, J.R. (2002) 'The capstone experience course in agricultural curriculum'. Presented at the annual meeting of the American Agricultural Economics Association (now the Agricultural and Applied Economics Association), 28–31 July, Long Beach, California.

Paradis, T.W. and Dexter, L.R. (2007) 'Learner-centered teaching and assessment in an undergraduate field analysis course', *Journal of Geography*, 106 (4), pp. 171–180.

Robson, E. (2002) '"An unbelievable academic and personal experience": issues around teaching undergraduate field courses in Africa', *Journal of Geography in Higher Education*, 26 (3), pp. 327–344.

Rowles, C.J., Koch, D.C., Hundley, S.P. and Hamilton, S.J. (2004) 'Toward a model for capstone experiences: mountaintops, magnets, and mandates', *Assessment Update: Progress, Trends, and Practices in Higher Education*, 16 (1), pp. 1–2, 13–15.

Schmid, T.J. (1993) 'Bringing sociology to life: the other capstone mandate', *Teaching Sociology*, 21 (3), pp. 219–222.

Shulman, L.S. (2005) 'Signature pedagogies in the professions', *Daedalus*, 134 (3), pp. 52–59.

Scott, I., Fuller, I. and Gaskin, S. (2006) 'Life without fieldwork: some lecturers' perceptions of geography and environmental science fieldwork', *Journal of Geography in Higher Education*, 30 (1), pp. 161–171.

Smith, W.L. (1993) 'The capstone course at Loras College', *Teaching Sociology*, 21 (3), pp. 250–252.

Spurrier, J.D. (2001) 'A capstone course for undergraduate statistics majors', *Journal of Statistics Education*, 9 (1), DOI: 10.1080/10691898.2001.11910643.

Troyer, R.J. (1993) 'Comments on the capstone course', *Teaching Sociology*, 21 (3), pp. 246–249.

Tueth, M.W. and Wikle, T.A. (2000) 'The utility and organization of a college field course: examining national park management', *Journal of Geography*, 99, pp. 57–66.

29. Learning for work
Ifan D.H. Shepherd

INTRODUCTION

In the author's lifetime, there has been a quiet revolution in the teaching and learning of geography in higher education. Over a period of some four decades, the subject has evolved from one that was largely studied for its own sake, with a heavy emphasis on content, to one that also prepares students for life and work after graduation. During this time, many approaches to fostering learning for work have been proposed and many experiments have been undertaken. As a result, a considerable literature has accumulated on the subject.

In order to provide an appropriate structure for this chapter, we turn to Jenkins and Healey's (1995) suggestion that preparing geography students for the world of work can be undertaken in two broad ways: by bringing the workplace into the classroom, and by taking students out into the workplace. We refine this distinction by defining five levels of student engagement with work and the workplace during their undergraduate studies (Table 29.1). At the lowest level, students engage in familiarisation activities about the world of work, while at the highest level, they learn about the world of work first hand, as temporary employees on placements or internships. Levels 1 to 3 represent classroom-based learning, while levels 4 and 5 represent off-campus learning.

It should be understood that few of the learning activities discussed in this chapter are uniquely associated with learning for work. For example, project-based learning, group work and field investigations (for example Hindle, 1993), are also frequently used to meet purely academic learning outcomes. It should also be noted that some of the activities discussed, such as active learning, experiential learning and reflective practice, can all play a part at several levels of student engagement with work.

Table 29.1   Work-related student learning activities arranged into levels reflecting degrees of work engagement

Level 5a: Part-time and vacation employment	Level 5b: Work experience and service learning
Level 4: Field projects with/for external organisations and communities	
Level 3: Simulating real world work activities	
Level 2a: Acquiring 'generic' skills	Level 2b: Acquiring discipline-specific skills
Level 1a: Learning about work and workplaces	Level 1b: Personal career planning and PDP

The main focus of this chapter is on the 'what' and the 'why' of learning for work rather than on the 'how', and the treatment of each level is roughly proportional to the number of published studies in the literature. In order to provide some boundaries for the chapter, several topics have been omitted, including: the preparation of geography students for work in the profession of geography, whether as teachers or researchers; the role of geographical curricula in fostering social responsibility, citizenship, sustainable development and ethical behaviour; and informal learning (for example during gap years), despite its significant implications for more formal learning, whether in an academic or work context.

REVIEWING WORK-RELATED STUDENT LEARNING ACTIVITIES

Level 1a: Learning About Work and Workplaces

Bringing the world of work onto campus as awareness-raising learning experiences has been achieved in several ways. A relatively simple approach has been to provide students with resource materials describing work roles (Kneale, 2004), which encourage students to think more broadly about how they might contribute in their own part-time jobs (level 5a). A more interactional approach was adopted by Heard and Farrington (1998), who invited employers to workshops to share information with students about skills in their field, and to encourage them to reflect on how their own skills might best be developed in readiness for employment. Geography alumni have also been invited onto campus to share their work experience with current undergraduates (Cubitt, 1995). Additionally, professionals have helped to raise student awareness of the world of work in other ways: by assessing students' oral presentations (Church and Bull, 1995); by providing students with project work (level 4); or providing work experience (level 5b).

Level 1b: Undertaking Personal Career Planning and Personal and Professional Development

Personal development planning (PDP) is intended to raise student awareness of career opportunities while they study for a degree. PDP modules are now widespread across UK higher education (QAA, 2009), and Piróg (2014) discusses the role of PDP in Polish geography curricula. PDP also involves students reflecting on past learning and planning for future careers. Study activities typically involve students in assembling portfolios of evidence of learning, which typically include reflective commentaries on their learning progress, and the development of an evolving personal career plan. The PDP process can also involve students developing their individual personal brands, in addition to writing CVs, as a tool for positioning themselves in the career marketplace after graduation.

Level 2a: Acquiring 'Generic' Skills

The need for an increased emphasis on student employability was signalled by a contributor to the very first issue of the *Journal of Geography in Higher Education*, who argued that geography courses 'should provide students with marketable skills as well as academic abilities. Even non-vocational students are normally seriously concerned with their job prospects' (Bleasdale, 1977, p. 71). Because geography is largely a non-vocational subject, its curricula have been particularly responsive to the introduction of a range of occupation-neutral or generic skills (Jenkins and Pepper, 1988; Buckingham-Hatfield, 1995; Church and Bull, 1995; Jenkins and Healey, 1995). Some of the early innovations in the UK were funded by the government's Enterprise in Higher Education initiative, which supported varied student activities aimed at the acquisition of generic skills (Healey, 1992; Slater, 1993). However, some rear-guard action appeared in some quarters, illustrated by Johnston (1997), who championed the development of geography students' 'critical intellects' rather than their acquisition of generic skills. Unsurprisingly, perhaps, critical thinking skills are now routinely included among employability skills.

During the past three decades, numerous buzzwords have been used to describe non subject-specific skills, including: transferable skills, key skills, generic skills, and employability skills. Such skills are also embraced in broader conceptualisations, such as capability (Stephenson and Yorke, 1998), enterprise skills (Clark, 1991; Jenkins and Healey, 1995), graduateness (Johnston, 1997), and graduate attributes (Mager and Spronken-Smith, 2014; Hill and Walkington, 2016; Hill et al., 2016). And yet, as Bridges (1993, p. 45) has observed, these and related terms 'are used rather loosely, often interchangeably, and it would be somewhat arbitrary to draw distinctions in any very hard and fast way'. Francis and Penn (1994, p. 223) go so far as to suggest that: 'There is no shared conception of skill among social scientists. The concept is both multi-valent and complex.'

These criticisms have failed to prevent the spawning of innumerable skills lists in geography curricula, most of which suffer from various flaws: the absence of a formal analytical or logical base; overlap or duplication; inconsistent relationships between skills defined at different levels (for example graduate attributes sometimes referred to as a subset of generic skills, and sometimes vice versa); and some being so broad as to make it difficult to evaluate them effectively. Because of the broadness of some generic skills (for example communication, ICT literacy and problem solving), there has been a tendency to deconstruct them into lower-level components. However, it is difficult to know where such reductionist practices should end, or how the resulting finely diced classifications might be embedded in geography curricula. Beyond these classificatory problems, there is also the problem that the perceptions of students and their teachers differ on the range of skills that are taught and assessed on geography courses (Haigh and Kilmartin, 1999), and also the uncomfortable fact that several studies reveal significant differences between what employers need and what academia delivers (Owen, 2001; Hennemann and Liefner, 2010).

The labelling of skills as generic tends to hide the fact that many should be treated as employment-specific. Thus, while 'communication skills' might be seen as a universal capability, and therefore something to be desired by all potential employers, the reality is somewhat different. This is because there is no such thing as *the* world of work, and skills are never independent of the context in which they are used. In customer-facing roles, for example, communication skills might involve being tactful, courteous and having a good bedside manner, depending on the sector. In a creative or marketing role, by contrast, favoured communication skills might include debate, argumentation, behind-the-scenes political manoeuvring, and maybe dogged persistence. Finally, management roles will probably require well-developed negotiation skills, the ability to nurture the skills of others, and perhaps recognition of the benefits of a diverse workforce. So, just as Hill et al. (2016, p. 156) propose that in implementing graduate attributes, academics in geography should 'take ownership of institutionally derived descriptors and . . . make them relevant to disciplines', so there is an equal need to make graduate attributes relevant to specific niches in the job market. But here, of course, we are confronted with the inconvenient fact that geography is largely a non-vocational subject, which makes it difficult to foster skills on campus suited to specific employment niches.

In addition to differentiating between different employment roles and niches, a distinction also needs to be made between skills whose enhancement might best fit individual students. For example, Barrow (1990, p. 23) argues that:

> it makes no sense to conceive of these as generic abilities, meaning abilities that people have and can exhibit, should they choose to do so, in any field. On the contrary, the truth is that people are gifted in some areas and not others, intelligent in some respects only, capable of being creative in some domains but not all.

At the risk of oversimplification, students with outgoing or extravert personalities might be better employed in front-of-house occupations, while those with more introvert personalities might be more suited to creative activities involving only episodic interaction with customers. (Many creative industries use the 'T' recruitment model to ensure that recruits have both capabilities.) The question then arises as to whether students should be required to acquire all generic skills, with an inevitable congestion in the geography curriculum, or whether skills acquisition should be segmented according to the strengths and/or weaknesses of individual students, perhaps through personalised curricula. Or maybe one should adopt the mantra of those organisations that 'recruit for attitude, but train for skill'.

A final comment is appropriate concerning the widespread separation in higher education of 'skills and other attributes' from 'knowledge and understanding'. Lave and Wenger (1991) use the estimable phrase, 'knowledgeable skills' to expresses the strong bond that exists between these two, and Krathwohl's (2002) matrix model attempts to bridge the knowledge–skills divide in relation to curriculum design. Although binary thinking is still much in evidence (for example Whalley et al., 2011), broader integrative approaches are also emerging. Arrowsmith et al. (2011, p. 369), for example, write that 'it is the sum of geographical knowledge, technical competencies and personal attributes assembled in appropriate ways, which define a graduate's "employment capability"'. In a similar vein, Spronken-Smith (2013, p. 318) suggests that a more appropriate way of describing what geography programmes should offer its students as preparation for the world of work might be 'ways of thinking and practicing', because this 'goes beyond terms such as graduate attributes, which tend to evoke lists of skills and attributes that may be desirable'.

Level 2b: Acquiring Discipline-Specific Skills

Although generic skills have received the greatest attention in terms of their employability potential, a case has also been made for the general career value of discipline-specific skills. Over the past couple of decades, GIS and related technologies have frequently been singled out for their job enhancement characteristics. In one of the few studies to test the claimed vocational credentials of GIS courses located within undergraduate geography degrees, Whyatt et al. (2011) sought comments from alumni from eight cohorts of students who had studied a final-year GIS option module concerning its value for their career to date. They conclude that in order for students to use GIS effectively in the workplace, they need to go significantly beyond the acquisition of mere technical GIS competence; both theory and practice are necessary. The linking of theory (obtained through lectures) and practice (obtained through practical work) helps to make students' learning occupationally relevant, especially in obtaining an initial position that involves GIS. The authors also conclude that: 'GIS's vocationalism changes as careers progress: the early value is more GIS-specific and directly vocational; the later value is more indirectly vocational, like the generic value of any degree scheme' (Whyatt et al., 2011, p. 242).

An interesting change has occurred in the past couple of decades, with GIS being routinely taught in degree courses in an increasing number of disciplines. More recently, members of the general public have come to consult spatial apps on personal digital devices (for example web maps, store location finders, and route navigation aids), on a regular basis and for a variety of purposes. These developments raise interesting questions about the definitional boundaries between subject-specific technical skills on the one hand and generic skills on the other. It could reasonably be argued that critical spatial thinking and familiarity with key spatial technologies are no longer simply 'discipline-specific' skills, but comprise generic knowledge and skills that merit inclusion in the general preparation of students for life and work after graduation.

Level 3: Simulating Real World Work Activities

During the 1970s and 1980s, there was a vogue for using simulation and role-play exercises in geography courses (Walford, 1981), a trend which accelerated with the advent of computer assisted learning (Shepherd et al., 1980; Shepherd, 1985). As with many educational innovations, these were strong on activity-based and experiential learning, but almost exclusively aimed at improving student understanding of geographical concepts and processes. In more recent decades, role playing exercises have been devised that bring elements of the workplace into the classroom. One of the first was Walker's (1993) use of mock job interviews to help students acquire and develop oral skills. He distinguishes between the contrasting contexts in which workplace communication occurs, and the demands these place on graduate employees. In order to exemplify these differences, he focused on presentation and interrogative skills, both of which are manifested in job interviews. In his mock interviews, the students played, in turn, the job applicants and members of the interview panel. Walker suggested that external professionals could also be brought into such exercises to increase their degree of workplace realism.

The UK's Environment Agency uses various role-play exercises in training their professional staff. In one example, McEwen et al. (2014) describe their application of role-play in improving staff ability to communicate the results of flood science. In training exercises run at the author's university, professional actors have been employed to play the role of riparian landowners, against whom EA trainee flood hazard inspectors have to pit their wits in simulated site visits assessing compliance with flood prevention responsibilities. In another published example, Smith (2012) describes a mock grant pitching exercise on an environmental management course, in which groups of students make competitive presentations to win one of five pseudo-government grants. To ensure a high degree of realism, the grants are based on actual examples, the pitch event is organised as a formal conference at a local conference centre, students are encouraged to dress formally and behave professionally, and two local council members act on the grant adjudication panel.

In a similar example, the author was involved in designing and running 'integrated' residential field courses, in which final-year geography students spent a week investigating the suitability of a UK greenfield site for the location of an opencast coal mine or a nuclear power plant. After a week of local research by students, the final day consisted of a mock public inquiry, in which the students were split into two role-play groups: one in favour of the proposed development; and one opposing the development. In order to inject some professional realism into the proceedings, a senior member of the local county council who was well versed in the procedures of such inquiries chaired the mock inquiry.

The emphasis on realism and authenticity in these examples is also found in recently developed computer geographical simulations. These are able to provide highly realistic replicas of the natural world, so that geography students can participate in work-related activities without having to leave the classroom. Bertolo and Clay (2006), for example, describe how students can undertake simulated environmental surveys of contaminated land of the kind frequently undertaken by property development or civil engineering professionals. However, for simulations that represent workplace interactions, there perhaps needs to be less emphasis on visual realism. Simulations that involve students in virtual social interaction frequently fall short of social and interpersonal realism. For example, the virtual placement system devised by Cornelius et al. (2008) involves students interacting with a virtual GIS consultancy, for whom they undertake assigned GIS projects as interns. However, due to software limitations, student interaction with virtual company employees was handled by university placement tutors using email. Recent developments in videogame and speech recognition technologies suggest that more realistic virtual placements may soon be possible.

Level 4: Field Projects with/for External Organisations and Communities

This level of work-related learning involves students engaging in projects provided by external organisations, and which, unlike geography fieldwork projects, primarily serve organisational needs (see also Chapter 30 in this volume by Colin Arrowsmith and William Cartwright). This type of project work is similar to work experience at level 5b, though in the latter case there is likely to be more continuous student interaction with the workplace, and less emphasis on discrete projects. The external organisations may include business, industry, public authorities, voluntary agencies and communities, and students typically operate as researchers or consultants, undertaking work individually or in teams on behalf of the external organisation or community. The external organisations' research needs will vary significantly according to the sector in which they operate. The potential benefits of these projects is that they introduce students to the kind of investigative work they may be required to undertake after they graduate, and the contexts in which they commonly take place.

Community and voluntary body projects can be both the most rewarding and the most challenging for students (Buckingham-Hatfield, 1995). Through a series of international case studies, Bednarz et al. (2008) reveal how community engagement can take a number of forms, and lead to a variety of curricular and/or community benefits. The authors identify three forms of engagement that are integrated into geography curricula: service-based community engagement, where students work primarily in volunteering activities of benefit to the community; research-based engagement, where students apply skills acquired on campus in local community projects; and work-based engagement, where students spend a period of time working with a local community. The last of these blends into work experience discussed at level 5b. These studies reveal that project engagement is not only concerned with skills, but also involves the two-way exchange of knowledge: geography-related on the part of the students, and community-related on the part of the external partners. Moreover, while in the majority of cases the students go physically into the community, in some cases members of the community visit campus to share their knowledge (level 1a).

Where a member of university geography staff negotiates and organises a project, students may lack direct engagement with the external organisation. This may be because undergraduates do not have the level of competence in GIS-related research to discuss project requirements with the organisation, or they may have insufficient time during a semester-long course for active interaction. Alternatively, it may be because the member of staff wishes to maintain a tight rein on project activities and timeframes. In the example discussed by Kim (2018), GIS projects were undertaken by undergraduates in a local area, in which the amount of research undertaken by them varied between projects. Academic staff identified the project problems, graduates were mentored to train and support the undergraduates, and the undergraduates focussed almost entirely on the technical project work.

A similar pattern is reported in Barcus and Muehlenhaus's (2010) study of 'community partnerships', where the external partners predefined suitable problems and outcomes of student projects. Moreover, although the students undertook the field research project work, their college instructors acted as intermediaries (or 'translators') between the student researchers and the external partners. A similar example is provided by Elwood's (2009) community project in Chicago. Although this project is described as participatory action research (PAR), students were not directly exposed to the action elements in the sense of negotiating and implementing action-oriented goals with community partici-pants, which were largely identified from within the community. This example indicates that care is needed when exploring the published literature for suitable exemplars, because journal paper titles often refer to a project from the author's general perspective, rather than in terms of the actual student learning experience. There are numerous papers, for example, that include key words such as 'participatory research', 'action research' and 'transdisciplinary research' where these particular research approaches do not figure in the student project experience.

There are interesting contrasts in the locations chosen for externally commissioned student projects. Because of the ease of access by students in relation to their university, local examples predominate. Mohan (1995), for example, reports on community projects linked to a long-term service-learning relationship with local communities in North America. In contrast, Pawson (2016) describes a project set up as a one-off response to a local emergency caused by an earthquake in Canterbury, New Zealand. While this kind of reactive project can be highly motivating and rewarding for students, episodic work-place or community engagement may be difficult to build into a permanent curricular offering. An example of more regular student engagement is provided by 'Consulting to Organisations', a module available on a number of undergraduate programmes at the author's university, on which students undertake a project at a local organisation, usually working in small teams.

More distant projects are less frequently undertaken. In one example, Thomas and Meehan (2010) describe how a dozen pre-selected students at an Australian university spent two weeks in Vietnam analysing data gathered at meetings with local individuals and organisations. However, field work was not undertaken because of the practical difficulties in organising and undertaking it in the limited time available.

Concluding this level, it should be noted that project work undertaken for and/or with external organisations frequently serve both academic and work-related goals. Elwood (2009) describes two projects undertaken in suburban Chicago which involved groups of students undertaking data-related GIS work in order to provide the community with digital maps to support local community planning. She contrasts the mainly 'conceptual learning' undertaken in class with the 'applied learning' undertaken as part of data gathering in the field. While the former was developed through lectures and laboratory work, the latter was achieved by students engaging in data gathering and analysis in response to unscripted technical problems that resulted from responding to community partner requests.

Level 5a: Learning from Part-Time and Vacation Employment

This level of work-related engagement involves students taking part-time or vacation jobs, in which they participate in the world of work in ways not experienced at previous levels. The main characteristic that sets this level apart from work experience (level 5b) is that the work activities are typically undertaken for monetary reward (though some are voluntary), and tend not to be integrated into a programme of study. Nevertheless, it is widely recognised that genuine learning can arise from part-time work, both through the enhancement of existing generic skills and the acquisition of new work-specific knowledge and skills. As with work experience, the knowledge and skills gained, whether generic or work-specific, will vary considerably. Thus, for example, a student who obtains a summer job taking visitors around a heritage site will be able to make far more connections to a course on, for example, tourism management than a student who is checking inventory at a supermarket. If self-reflection is built into the student's daily activities, then experiential learning can be documented and assessed for academic credit. At the author's university, for example, this form of assessment is undertaken on a generic employability module entitled 'Learning from Part-time Work'.

Level 5b: Work Experience and Service Learning

Work experience is one of the earliest and most frequently reported forms of learning for work reported in the geographical education literature (for example Foster et al., 1979). The activities associated with work experience are often very similar to the projects described at level 4. The main difference is that students undertaking work experience are embedded physically and socially with an external partner for a period of time, and are typically involved in activities beyond those associated with discrete research projects.

Workplace activities are typically included as part of a programme of study, though their experience may not always be assessed for academic credit. Work experience may involve not only the classic workplaces of industry, business and government, but also voluntary sector organisations and community groups. In North America, work experience is also frequently associated with service learning (Lemon, 1979; Mohan, 1995), which is defined by Dorsey (2001, p. 124) as community-based experiential learning, in which 'participants practice responsible citizenship while acquiring practical work experience'. For convenience, the phrase work experience is used here as an umbrella term, though it is recognised that a distinction is sometimes made between placements and internships.

Work experience provides students with numerous opportunities to: apply and enhance previously acquired skills in solving problems in authentic application contexts; acquire new skills and knowledge; understand organisational structures, processes and cultures from the inside; work both autonomously and as part of teams; and identify opportunities for future employment (Couch, 1995). Guile and Griffiths (2001) identify five models for learning through work experience: the traditional, experimental, generic, work process and connective. Although many early reports of geography work experience highlight its role in enabling students to apply and enhance generic skills acquired on campus (Shepherd, 1998b), other published reports indicate that subject-specific, technical and other skills are frequently involved (for example Couch, 1995; Bednarz et al., 2008). In the context of the cooperative education model, in which students engage alternately in study and work, Spinelli and Smith (1981) suggest that a synergistic relationship can be forged between academia and the workplace, whereby geography courses focus on providing students with generic skills, while work experience introduces them to more work-specific skills.

There is a considerable variety in the activities, durations, intensity, organisations, locations, and payment involved in work experience. Consequently, the learning outcomes are likely to vary considerably from student to student. The temporal patterns can vary from a one day per week visit to a workplace over a short period of time (Shepherd, 1995, 1998a), to an alternating pattern (one or more weeks on campus and in work), to full-time participation over a longer period, such as an entire year on a sandwich degree programme. On some geography degrees work experience is optional while in others it is mandatory (Sublett and Mattingly, 1995).

As with off-campus projects at level 4, most work experience is undertaken close to the students' home and/or university. In contrast, Rosser (2012) describes a six-week internship in Indonesia for Australian development studies students, reflecting the large international aid programme between the two countries. The students are placed with a local or international development organisation, and undertake various local projects in which they apply and enhance their research skills in authentic research contexts.

Work experience is commonly agreed to provide the most authentic opportunities for students to experience the world of work. It can also provide an opportunity to revisit the discourse of generic and transferable skills in an innovative way. Not only does work experience underline the fact that skills and knowledge acquired in university settings often require effort to apply them in work situations, but it also highlights the often highly situated nature of knowledge and skills acquired in the workplace (Lave and Wenger, 1991). Students therefore need to be helped to recognise the situatedness of their workplace learning, and to acquire the ability to transfer what they have learnt in the workplace, not only back into their academic environments, but also to other workplaces they are likely to encounter after graduation. At the author's university, a post-placement 'Return to Study' event is held at which students discuss the workplace situations in which they have been able to apply their so-called generic skills. They also learn from each other some of the idiosyncrasies of working in unique organisational environments. A complementary way of sharing this experience is for students to reflect in writing on their work experience (Eden, 2014).

There are, of course, several practical problems with this form of learning. For example, it can prove administratively arduous to organise, unless a university provides dedicated support. It can also be stressful where students are required to find their own placement or internship, and it relies on the goodwill and professional attitude of workplace liaison persons to ensure that students have appropriate induction on arrival, and are provided with meaningful work thereafter. Because of the diversity of student experience, it can also be extremely difficult to assess the work-related learning outcomes between students and programmes (Whalley, 2008).

CONCLUSIONS

Two broad conclusions can be drawn from this chapter. The first concerns the importance of one of the least discussed issues around skills and knowledge: their transferability. Transfer is important because, as Singley and Anderson (1989, p. 1) indicate, 'the problem of transfer [of training and learning] is perhaps the fundamental educational question'. However, most writing on the subject of skills and knowledge acquisition through geography degrees either ignores the transfer issue altogether, or adopts the received wisdom implied in the 'transferable skills' epithet, which presumes that such skills, along with broader capabilities and attributes, have transferability more or less built in. In other words, there is an almost universal assumption that when students acquire particular skills and knowledge, they are at the same time acquiring the ability to transfer them more or less automatically to new contexts, and especially to the workplace.

There is, however, a considerable literature on skills and knowledge transfer in both educational and training and people development circles, which rejects the assumption that generic or employability skills are somehow automatically transferable between academia and the workplace (Holmes, 2000), or indeed between training and application contexts within the workplace (Baldwin and Ford, 1988). From a geographical perspective, Saunders (2011, pp. 474–475) suggests that skill should be considered 'not as a possessable entity, but as a process that is always becoming'. Shepherd (2000) takes this a step further by suggesting that all skills are transferable, but that this cannot be taken for granted. Students must learn how to transfer skills, both during their acquisition, and also while they apply them to new contexts and situations. This implies that the emphasis in geography curricula should shift from the transferability of skills and knowledge to the transfer ability of students.

It is not necessary to wait until students graduate in order for them to acquire or practice their transfer abilities. There are at least half a dozen situations in which students can engage with the transfer of their learning: between study sessions within a course unit (for example lecture to seminar, or laboratory to field course); between course units; between academia and the workplace; within workplaces; between workplaces; and between workplaces and academia. It should, however, be recognised that evaluating transfer along some of these pathways can be difficult. Saunders (2011), for example, suggests that the modularisation of geography degrees makes it more difficult to assess the ability of students to transfer learning between modules.

The successful transfer of learning requires that the context within which the application of skills and knowledge takes place must be fully taken into account. Context not only refers to the organisational cultures and work pressures that exist in many workplaces, but also to the discourses that develop in individual workplaces. Because of these varying workplace characteristics, Saunders (2011, p. 474) suggests that skills and knowledge transfer 'is not simply a case of importing one way of doing things into another context, there is a need to recognise the particular ways of knowing that are prevalent within a given context'. In other words, it is necessary to understand the distinctive ontological, epistemological and methodological assumptions within individual workplaces, as well as local 'ways of working', before graduates can become truly effective in applying their knowledge and skills beyond the classroom.

A second broad conclusion is that student learning outcomes discussed in this chapter have rarely been subjected to formal evaluation, either during or immediately after the learning activity has occurred. Nor have many studies been undertaken on the comparative merits of the learning for work activities discussed in this chapter, or of cases where two more of these activities are undertaken together. There is also a lack of strong evaluative evidence that goes beyond self-reported studies of student satisfaction during or immediately after work-related learning activities. Rosser (2012, p. 345) suggests that 'student surveys are . . . an imperfect way of judging pedagogical effectiveness – they are more a measure of client satisfaction than of learning *per se*'. Without independent performance-related evaluations, much of what has been written about the fostering of work-related capabilities will continue to be strong on rhetoric and relatively weak on justification.

There is a particular need for studies that track geography students after graduation to determine the effectiveness of their degrees in enabling successful application of their prior learning in work environments. Mention has already been made of alumni-based studies of the vocational efficacy of GIS courses. One of the few other longitudinal studies, which explores a wider range of skills, was undertaken by Clark and Higgitt (1997), in which they surveyed geography students at one, five and ten years after graduating from two UK universities. Several of their findings highlight some of the practical difficulties in assessing skills and knowledge transfer. A more recent survey of all undergraduate geography degree courses in Poland elicited student views on the extent to which their degrees prepared them effectively for the world of work (Piróg, 2014). Students were interviewed at the end of their course, and six months later to determine the value of their degree in making a successful transition into employment. A significant number of those who had gained employment after graduating recommended that employers should be more involved in the design and implementation of the geography curriculum.

Perhaps it is appropriate to conclude on a somewhat political note. At the heart of curricular concerns with work-related learning are broader concerns with the impact of workplaces in serving societal needs. These have already been touched on in discussions of community projects and service learning. However, a key question remains: how far do we wish to provide students with so-called employability skills if these are applied in ways that are counter to the broader interests of society (Martin and Jucker, 2005; Wellens et al., 2006)? Geographers have long studied social inequality and environmental sustainability, and championed policies and practices that help to mitigate the worst effects of modern consumer societies in these domains. However, to these concerns must now be added the economically and socially disruptive behaviours of key players in the emerging digital economy (Taplin, 2017). If geography can lead directly and indirectly to modifying the knowledge, skills, attitudes and behaviours of students as they prepare to enter the workforce in a digitally connected world, in ways that contribute to a more sustainable global society, then those of us who are responsible for directing their learning in ways outlined in this chapter have a greater opportunity for shaping the future than we might previously have imagined.

USEFUL RESOURCES

- Bauer, T.N. and Erdogan, B. (2011) 'Organizational socialization: the effective onboarding of new employees', in S. Zedeck (ed.), *APA Handbook of Industrial and Organizational Psychology*. Washington, DC: American Psychological Association, Volume 3, pp. 51–64.
- Harteis, C. (2009) 'Professional learning and TVET: challenges and perspectives for teachers and instructors', in R. Maclean and D.N. Wilson (eds), *International Handbook of Education for the Changing World of Work: Bridging Academic and Vocational Learning*. Cham, Switzerland: Springer, Volume 3, pp. 1351–1366.
- *Journal of Education and Work*. Available online at: https://www.tandfonline.com/loi/cjew20.
- Tuomi-Grohn, T. and Engestrom, Y. (eds) (2003) *Between School and Work: New Perspectives on Transfer and Boundary Crossing*. London: Pergamon.

ACKNOWLEDGEMENTS

I would like to thank Jennifer Hill for her thorough and extremely helpful review of an initial version of this chapter; Alan Jenkins at Oxford Brookes University for insightful comments on its scope; and Anna Kyprianou at Middlesex University for checking a later draft for readability.

REFERENCES

Arrowsmith, C., Bagoly-Simó, P., Finchum, A., Oda, K. and Pawson, E. (2011) 'Student employability and its implications for geography curricula and learning practices', *Journal of Geography in Higher Education*, 35 (3), pp. 365–377.

Baldwin, T.T. and Ford, J.K. (1988) 'Transfer of training: a review and directions for future research', *Personnel Psychology*, 41 (1), pp. 63–105.

Barcus, H.R. and Muehlenhaus, B. (2010) 'Bridging the academic–public divide in GIS and cartography: a framework for integrating community partnerships in the classroom', *Journal of Geography in Higher Education*, 34 (3), pp. 363–378.

Barrow, R. (1990) *Understanding Skills: Thinking, Feeling and Caring*. London, Ontario: The Althouse Press.

Bednarz, S.W., Chalkley, B., Fletcher, S., Hay, I., Le Heron, E., Mohan, A. and Trafford, J. (2008) 'Community engagement for student learning in geography', *Journal of Geography in Higher Education*, 32 (1), pp. 87–100.

Bertolo, E. and Clay, S. (2006) 'Simulating environmental surveys using custom developed software', *Planet*, 17 (1), pp. 42–43.

Bleasdale, S. (1977) 'After the graduation ceremony: some thoughts on geography graduate careers', *Journal of Geography in Higher Education*, 1 (2), pp. 71–77.

Bridges, D. (1993) 'Transferable skills: a philosophical perspective', *Studies in Higher Education*, 18 (1), pp. 43–51.

Buckingham-Hatfield, S. (1995) 'Student–community partnerships: advocating community enterprise projects in geography', *Journal of Geography in Higher Education*, 19 (2), pp. 143–150.

Church, A. and Bull, P. (1995) 'Evaluating and assessing student oral presentations: a limited but effective role for employers in the geography curriculum', *Journal of Geography in Higher Education*, 19 (2), pp. 196–202.

Clark, G. (1991) 'Enterprise education in geography at Lancaster', *Journal of Geography in Higher Education*, 15 (1), pp. 49–56.

Clark, G. and Higgitt, M. (1997) 'Geography and lifelong learning: a report on a survey of geography graduates', *Journal of Geography in Higher Education*, 21 (2), pp. 199–213.

Cornelius, S., Medyckyj-Scott, D., Forrest, D., Williams, A. and Mackaness, W. (2008) 'The virtual placement: an alternative to the traditional work placement in the geographical sciences?', *Journal of Geography in Higher Education*, 32 (2), pp. 287–302.

Couch, I. (1995) 'Work experience: an alternative or a companion to the dissertation? A case study', *Journal of Geography in Higher Education*, 19 (2), pp. 212–216.

Cubitt, T. (1995) 'Graduates as a source of employer contacts for link days and a partnership scheme', *Journal of Geography in Higher Education*, 19 (2), pp. 223–226.

Dorsey, B. (2001) 'Linking theories of service learning and undergraduate geography education', *Journal of Geography*, 100 (3), pp. 124–132.

Eden, S. (2014) 'Out of the comfort zone: enhancing work-based learning about employability through student reflection on work placements', *Journal of Geography in Higher Education*, 38 (2), pp. 266–276.

Elwood, S. (2009) 'Integrating participatory action research and GIS education: negotiating methodologies, politics and technologies', *Journal of Geography in Higher Education*, 33 (1), pp. 51–65.

Foster, L., Jones, K. and Mock, D. (1979) 'Internships in the applied geography curriculum', *Journal of Geography in Higher Education*, 3 (2), pp. 8–14.

Francis, B. and Penn, R. (1994) 'Towards a phenomenology of skill', in R. Penn, M. Rose and J. Rubery (eds) *Skill and Occupational Change*. Oxford: Oxford University Press, pp. 223–243.

Guile, D. and Griffiths, T. (2001) 'Learning through work experience', *Journal of Education and Work*, 14 (1), pp. 113–131.

Haigh, M.J. and Kilmartin, M.P. (1999) 'Student perceptions of the development of personal transferable skills', *Journal of Geography in Higher Education*, 23 (2), pp. 195–206.

Healey, M. (1992) 'Curriculum development and "enterprise": group work, resource-based learning and the incorporation of transferable skills into a first year practical course', *Journal of Geography in Higher Education*, 16 (1), pp. 7–19.

Heard, S. and Farrington, J. (1998) 'Employer–student workshops: the Aberdeen experience', *Journal of Geography in Higher Education*, 22 (1), pp. 105–110.

Hennemann, S. and Liefner, I. (2010) 'Employability of German geography graduates: the mismatch between knowledge acquired and competences required', *Journal of Geography in Higher Education*, 34 (2), pp. 215–230.

Hill, J. and Walkington, H. (2016) 'Developing graduate attributes through participation in undergraduate research conferences', *Journal of Geography in Higher Education*, 40 (2), pp. 222–237.

Hill, J., Walkington, H. and France, D. (2016) 'Graduate attributes: implications for higher education practice and policy', *Journal of Geography in Higher Education*, 40 (2), pp. 155–163.

Hindle, B.P. (1993) 'The 'project': putting student-controlled, small-group work and transferable skills at the core of a geography course', *Journal of Geography in Higher Education*, 17 (1), pp. 11–20.

Holmes, L. (2000) 'Questioning the skills agenda', in S. Fallows and C. Stevens (eds), *Integrating Key Skills in Higher Education*. London: Kogan Page, pp. 201–216.

Jenkins, A. and Healey, M. (1995) 'Linking the geography curriculum to the worlds of industry, commerce and public authorities', *Journal of Geography in Higher Education*, 19 (2), pp. 177–181.

Jenkins, A. and Pepper, D. (1988) 'Enhancing students' employability and self-expression: how to teach oral and groupwork skills in geography', *Journal of Geography in Higher Education*, 12 (1), pp. 67–83.

Johnston, R.J. (1997) '"Graduateness" and a core curriculum for geography?', *Journal of Geography in Higher Education*, 21 (2), pp. 245–252.

Kim, M. (2018) 'Project-based community participatory action research using geographic information technologies', *Journal of Geography in Higher Education*, 42 (1), pp. 61–79.

Kneale, P. (2004) 'Teaching intrapreneurship: cases from business', *Planet*, 12 (1), pp. 8–9.

Krathwohl, D.R. (2002) 'A revision of Bloom's taxonomy: an overview', *Theory into Practice*, 41 (4), pp. 212–218.

Lave, J. and Wenger, E. (1991) *Situated Learning: Legitimate Peripheral Participation*. Cambridge: Cambridge University Press.

Lemon, J. (1979) 'Reflections on work experience and community', *Journal of Geography in Higher Education*, 3 (2), pp. 24–28.

Mager, S. and Spronken-Smith, R. (2014) 'Graduate attribute attainment in a multi-level undergraduate geography course', *Journal of Geography in Higher Education*, 38 (2), pp. 238–250.

Martin, S. and Jucker, R. (2005) 'Educating earth-literate leaders', *Journal of Geography in Higher Education*, 29 (1), pp. 19–29.

McEwen, L., Stokes, A., Crowley, K. and Roberts, C. (2014) 'Using role-play for expert science communication with professional stakeholders in flood risk management', *Journal of Geography in Higher Education*, 38 (2), pp. 277–300.

Mohan, J. (1995) 'Thinking local: service-learning, education for citizenship and geography', *Journal of Geography in Higher Education*, 19 (2), pp. 129–142.

Owen, E. (2001) 'What key skills do employers need?', *Journal of Geography in Higher Education*, 25 (1), pp. 121–126.

Pawson, E. (2016) 'Classrooms without borders: new spaces and places of learning', *Journal of Geography in Higher Education*, 40 (1), pp. 14–30.

Piróg, D. (2014) 'Do geography degree programmes facilitate a smooth transition to the job market? Reflections of working and job-seeking graduates in Poland', *Journal of Geography in Higher Education*, 38 (2), pp. 155–174.

QAA (Quality Assurance Agency for Higher Education) (2009) *Personal Development Planning: Guidelines for Institutional Policy and Practice*. Gloucester: QAA.

Rosser, A. (2012) 'Towards effective international work-integrated learning practica in development studies: reflections on the Australian consortium for "in-country" Indonesian studies' development studies professional practicum', *Journal of Geography in Higher Education*, 36 (3), pp. 341–353.

Saunders, A. (2011) 'Revisiting the skills agenda: a complicated geography', *Journal of Geography in Higher Education*, 35 (4), pp. 465–477.

Shepherd, I.D.H. (1985) 'Teaching geography with the computer: possibilities and problems', *Journal of Geography in Higher Education*, 9 (1), pp. 3–23.

Shepherd, I.D.H. (1995) 'Small is beautiful: a "short and thin" model for work experience', *Journal of Geography in Higher Education*, 19 (2), pp. 182–188.

Shepherd, I.D.H. (1998a) 'How long is short? Principles and practice in the delivery of work experience in geography', *Journal of Geography in Higher Education*, 22 (1), pp. 111–119.

Shepherd, I.D.H. (1998b) 'Work experience: who needs it?', *Journal of Geography in Higher Education*, 22 (1), pp. 135–145.

Shepherd, I.D.H. (2000) *Key Skills: Teaching and Learning for Transfer*. London: DfEE/Cheltenham: Geography Discipline Network.

Shepherd, I.D.H., Cooper, Z. and Walker, D.R.F. (1980) *Computer Assisted Learning in Geography: Current Trends and Future Prospects*. London: Council for Educational Technology, with the Geographical Association.

Singley, M.K. and Anderson, J.R. (1989) *The Transfer of Cognitive Skill*. Cambridge, MA: Harvard University Press.

Slater, T.R. (1993) 'Locality-based studies and the Enterprise Initiative', *Journal of Geography in Higher Education*, 17 (1), pp. 47–55.

Smith, M. (2012) 'Improving student engagement with employability: the project pitch assessment', *Planet*, 26 (1), pp. 2–7.

Spinelli, J. and Smith, B. (1981) 'Cooperative education versus internships: a challenge for an applied geography programme', *Journal of Geography in Higher Education*, 5 (2), pp. 163–168.

Spronken-Smith, R. (2013) 'Toward securing a future for geography graduates', *Journal of Geography in Higher Education*, 37 (3), pp. 315–326.

Stephenson, J. and Yorke, Y. (1998) *Capability and Quality in Higher Education*. London: Taylor & Francis.

Sublett, M.D. and Mattingly, P.F. (1995) 'Undergraduate geography internships in the United States: national survey and case study', *Journal of Geography in Higher Education*, 19 (2), pp. 240–249.

Taplin, J. (2017) *Move Fast and Break Things: The Dark Side of Google, Facebook and Amazon*. Boston, MA: Little Brown and Company.

Thomas, I. and Meehan, B. (2010) 'Student preparation for the international environmental profession', *Journal of Geography in Higher Education*, 34 (1), pp. 91–107.

Walford, R. (1981) 'Geography games and simulations: learning through experience', *Journal of Geography in Higher Education*, 5 (2), pp. 113–119.

Walker, G. (1993) 'Mock job interviews and the teaching of oral skills', *Journal of Geography in Higher Education*, 17 (1), pp. 73–78.

Wellens, J., Berardi, A., Chalkey, B., Chambers, B., Healy, R., Monk, J. and Vender, J. (2006) 'Teaching geography for social transformation', *Journal of Geography in Higher Education*, 30 (1), pp. 117–131.

Whalley, W.B. (2008) 'What should a (geography) degree for the 21st century be like?', *Planet*, 19 (1), pp. 36–41.

Whalley, W.B., Saunders, A., Lewis, R.A., Buenemann, M. and Sutton, P.C. (2011) 'Curriculum development: producing *geographers* for the 21st century', *Journal of Geography in Higher Education*, 35 (3), pp. 379–393.

Whyatt, D., Clark, G. and Davies, G. (2011) 'Teaching geographical information systems in geography degrees: a critical reassessment of vocationalism', *Journal of Geography in Higher Education*, 35 (2), pp. 233–244.

30. Embedding employability skills in the curriculum and extending into postgraduate programs
Colin Arrowsmith and William Cartwright

REVIEW OF EMPLOYABILITY SKILLS REQUIRED BY THE GEOSPATIAL SCIENCES INDUSTRY

Demands for higher education institutions (HEIs) to deliver graduates who are both work-ready and adaptable to a changing work environment have never been greater. A recently released national report shows that whilst university graduates fare well in the jobs market, 'Since the Global Financial Crisis graduates have taken longer to gain a foothold in the labour market' (Graduate Outcomes Survey, 2017, p. iii). The report goes on to state that full-time employment rates have fallen for all levels of graduates since 2008. Undergraduates from more vocationally oriented study areas tend to have higher levels of employment upon graduation, with medicine, pharmacy and dentistry the highest (Graduate Outcomes Survey, 2017). What does this mean for HEIs in developing strategies for improving graduate employment prospects? At present, there is a perceived concern from current and recently graduated students that there is a lack of preparedness for employment, partly due to a lack of knowledge of contemporary work practices by academics (Bennett et al., 2016). These authors see a need for interventions that enhance graduate employability, through 'developing self', by explicitly connecting student learning and the professional context, 'developing career awareness' by industry exposure through placements, and 'developing skills and knowledge', in particular generic skills to enable students to actively participate in the work place (Bennett et al., 2016).

So what are the particular generic and technical skills required by university graduates for professional employment? Cassidy (2006) notes that generic (or non-technical) skills are those that transcend different occupations and include basic communication skills, higher order skills such as strategizing, problem-solving and decision-making, through to dependability, attitudinal and interpersonal skills, self-discipline and self-management. Lim et al. (2016) reiterate the importance of these generic skills as essential for accounting professionals, where the role of the accountant has changed from accounting technician to knowledge professional. The same can be said for geography and geospatial science graduates whereby their respective roles have altered as technical advancements have necessitated a change in expertise. Arrowsmith et al. (2011) note that the most important skills required by graduating geographers are interpersonal and communication skills. This is supported by the findings from a survey conducted by Solem et al. (2008), who found that professionals need to be good managers, problem-solvers and communicators. These authors go further by suggesting that geography graduates possess skills in field management, work across disciplinary boundaries and are adept at spatial thinking (Solem et al., 2008) (see also Chapter 32 in this volume by Michael Solem and colleagues). Rather than professionals merely operating technical equipment, roles have advanced whereby the geographer/geospatial scientist takes on a managerial or organisational role working within an inter-disciplinary team on large scale projects. Of course, there is still a requirement that specific technical skills are acquired, but it is the generic skills that will stay with the individual employee through his or her working career.

So what are the implications for the development of curricula within HEIs? In general terms, there will need to be a shift from insular content delivery and assessment to one where the teaching and learning, whilst facilitated by HEIs, is enhanced through participatory involvement with industry. Arrowsmith et al. (2011) suggest that it is essential to integrate employability skills into curricula through active and experiential learning, such as project-based learning or through active involvement of employers into program and curriculum development. For these partnerships to be effective, all participants must have a clear picture of what they want to get out of the project, and they must understand and be empathetic to each other's needs (Arrowsmith and Goudey, 2007).

Having reviewed the employability skills required by the geospatial sciences industry, this chapter now overviews the requirements and accreditation standards specified by national and international professional organisations and accreditation boards and authorities. The chapter then reviews undergraduate and postgraduate programs in geospatial science and surveying at the Royal Melbourne Institute of Technology (RMIT University), an institution that historically has a focus on the development of curricula that accord to, and are in concert with, the needs of industry. Selected case studies are outlined, which are considered to be exemplars of good university-industry engagement, before general observations are made about the skills acquired through undergraduate and postgraduate partnership with industry, recognised within the broad constraints of these partnerships.

OVERVIEW OF REQUIREMENTS FOR ACCREDITATION STANDARDS

In Australia, the Spatial Education Advisory Committee has produced a workforce plan for the industry (Pupedis and Bellman, 2010). The Committee identified the employment of staff from industry as an important issue. Looking at the current academic staff at RMIT University, about half came to academia from industry. Programs offered in geospatial sciences in the School of Science at RMIT have, traditionally and currently, had close links with industry. This is formally guided by university policy. Practically, this is implemented through the Program Advisory Committee, whose members are drawn from industry, and they advise on course content and ensure that academic staff maintain close links with the industry. The outcomes of this engagement have been the inclusion of curriculum elements that address professional industry requirements and the demands of issues like accreditation.

Historically in Australia, there was a need to employ surveyors almost immediately after European settlement, to identify lands suitable for urban, agricultural and pastoral use. As land was alienated, that is transferred from the Crown to individuals or consortia, cadastral surveys were needed. Much later, surveying and mapping was needed for defence, natural resource exploration and development around growing metropolises. In contemporary Australia, it is a legal requirement for surveyors who undertake cadastral surveying to be registered/licenced in the state in which they operate. In the state of Victoria (in which RMIT is situated), the Surveyors Registration Board is responsible for the registration of Licensed Surveyors who undertake cadastral surveying. To become a registered surveyor, a candidate must complete an approved university degree, complete practical training in cadastral surveying after graduation (under the supervision of a Licensed Surveyor) and, finally, pass the Board's examinations in cadastral surveying.

The Bachelor of Applied Science (Surveying) (Honours), conducted at RMIT, is one of the programs approved by the Surveyors Registration Board. Graduates are also eligible to apply for membership of the Institution of Surveyors Victoria (ISV), the Surveying and Spatial Sciences Institute (SSSI) and the Royal Institute of Chartered Surveyors (RICS). The program is also accredited by the Land Surveyors Board of Malaysia. Students on the program undertake practical surveying during their studies and they engage directly with industry. The program includes a final-year research project that is industry-approved and reflects current best practice. In addition, it includes a vocational element, whereby students must complete 60 days of work experience, usually during vacation periods or as part-time employees, in order to be eligible to graduate. Graduates are able to undertake further qualifications via the Surveyors Registration Board of Victoria to become licensed cadastral surveyors. In addition, they are able to gain direct entry into a number of professional societies. Continued development of the degree is undertaken in concert with an Advisory Board, the membership of which includes individuals from the surveying profession.

THE ROLE OF THE AUSTRALIAN QUALIFICATIONS FRAMEWORK IN REGULATING QUALIFICATIONS IN AUSTRALIAN EDUCATION

Through the Australian Qualifications Framework (Australian Qualifications Framework Council, 2013, p. 50), the purpose of a bachelor honours degrees is 'to qualify individuals who apply a body of knowledge in a specific context to undertake professional work and as a pathway for research and further learning'. For postgraduate programs this extends to 'specialised cognitive and technical skills in a body of knowledge or practice'.

The Surveyors Registration Board requires a four-year degree as a minimum qualification for candidates who seek to enter into an agreement for training and subsequent licensing as a cadastral surveyor. As such, undergraduate programs in surveying and geomatics at RMIT are four years in duration. This also meets the requirements stipulated by the AQF that an Australian four-year degree must be an honours degree, which includes a self-directed, research-focused dissertation. This has necessitated the inclusion of a capstone project, containing an element of research, within the geospatial and surveying undergraduate honours programs. A dissertation is conducted and drafted over two semesters in the final year of the program and is submitted for formal examination. The 'Major Project' course guide notes:

> This course is a major component of the final year, providing an opportunity for you to develop your knowledge and expertise to a high level in an area of geospatial science, surveying, or

cartography of particular interest to you. The nature of the projects chosen for completion in this subject must contain some element of research. Projects based around industry needs are highly recommended. . . . The course includes feedback from industry.

CASE STUDIES THAT EXEMPLIFY UNIVERSITY–INDUSTRY ENGAGEMENT

This section documents recent projects at RMIT that demonstrate participation of undergraduate and postgraduate students in industry-focused research. Whilst we acknowledge that projects are not the sole means to engage industry with university curricula (see also Chapter 29 in this volume by Ifan Shepherd), the selected case studies exemplify good university-industry engagement, developing a range of learner skills within the broad constraints of these partnerships.

Zoos Victoria: Undergraduate- and Postgraduate–Industry Partnership

Context

This case study is based on work conducted by Arrowsmith, Zanon and Chhetri at Port Campbell National Park (Arrowsmith et al., 2005), and subsequent work by Shoval and Isaacson (2007) and Vazquez-Prokopec et al. (2009). It involves two students undertaking separate research projects with staff from Zoos Victoria. One student was an undergraduate undertaking an honours thesis, the other was a postgraduate master's student undertaking the final dissertation.

Zoos Victoria is one of the world's major zoo-based conservation agencies, operating three zoos in the state. The main site, where the two students conducted their projects, is based in Royal Park, about four kilometres from the centre of Melbourne and it attracts up to 8000 visitors per day. In collaboration with staff at Zoos Victoria, both students used a series of questionnaires seeking information on previous visits and some basic demographic variables linked to visitor itineraries collected using GPS travel loggers.

The project undertaken by the undergraduate honours student sought to determine the spatial and temporal characteristics of visitor movement throughout the zoo. The project conducted by the postgraduate student was focused on providing zoo education staff with a greater awareness of how secondary school students choose to spend their time and where they visit when on an excursion to the zoo. In addition, Zoos Victoria staff were interested to know whether or not students who had prepared for the visit were more likely to have a clear purpose than those who did not prepare. It should be noted that this student had a teacher education qualification.

Both projects required successful navigation of procedures that are important in developing employability skills. In terms of industry interaction, this took on six distinct phases. Firstly, a relationship had to be established between the students and Zoos Victoria staff. Several meetings between the supervisor, students and staff clarified the needs of both the students and the industry partner, where discussions centred on the research approach to be taken. Secondly, the students, under the guidance of the supervisor, had to submit applications to the RMIT Human Ethics Committee, and the postgraduate project required further ethics approval from the Victorian Education Department. Getting ethics approval was difficult and required a number of iterations in order to clarify the requirements of the committees. Whilst this led to an over-run in establishing the operational aspects of the projects, reducing the final data analyses, this process served to clarify the research aims and methodology, and enhance the students' written and verbal communication skills. Phase three of the exercise was equipment testing and purchase and both students managed to effectively assess and evaluate, and then purchase, the required number of GPS recording devices. The logistics of organising the field work (administering and collecting questionnaires and GPS devices) was the fourth phase. The fifth phase was downloading and analysing the respective data, whilst the sixth phase included thesis write-up and final presentation to peers and industry representatives.

Skills development from industry participation
Feedback from both students indicated that whilst the projects were challenging and time consuming, they presented a working environment in which the students took on responsibility for the outcome of a major research project that was authentic, fulfilling and engaging. The outcomes of project participation were that the students acquired both generic and specific technical skills. In terms of generic skills, the projects required both students to engage with Zoos Victoria staff and this developed their communication and interpersonal skills. The students were required to extract, through a user-needs study, the stipulated requirements necessary to meet the research objectives established by Zoos Victoria. This necessitated the development of organisational skills to set up meeting times with relevant staff, develop interview and participant questionnaires to ask appropriate questions, and to establish a method for collecting data from the public. Possibly the most challenging component for the students was successfully completing the ethics application approval process. This required both students to have clear and concise research objectives and an established approach to their field research. Additionally, they had to learn and follow guidelines regarding data storage and management.

The two students organised set days for surveys to be completed. They directed assisting staff from Zoos Victoria, practicing interpersonal and communication skills. In conducting their field-work, both students managed their respective projects in a professional and timely manner. While the undergraduate project required the student to interact with the general public, clearly articulating the aims of the research on behalf of Zoos Victoria, the postgraduate student had to engage with teachers and secondary students, explaining the rationale behind the research. Organising these projects was not always straightforward. There were a number of instances when zoo staff were unable to assist in the data collection, and a change of staff required one of the students to interact with new zoo staff. This uncertainty and variability developed learner skills of adaptability and resilience.

The projects also developed a number of technical skills developed through geographic enquiry, including field work and spatial thinking (Solem et al., 2008). Essentially, both projects required the systematic downloading and analysis of field data, using the technical skills built up through undergraduate and postgraduate formal training. These skills included the construction of geo-databases, linked to specific socio-demographic data, and spatial analyses undertaken using GIS and statistical software. Examples of heatmaps generated by the undergraduate student are shown in Figure 30.1 (Morris, 2017). Analytical skills were developed through pattern identification with respect to participant movements through time and space.

Both students successfully completed their respective programs. The undergraduate student has gone on to complete his master's degree in urban planning, whilst the postgraduate student has successfully acquired a full-time GIS analyst position in the Victorian State Government.

Bass Coast Drainage Study: Postgraduate Participation with the Australian Mathematical Sciences Institute and Industry

Context

Through the Australian Mathematical Sciences Institute (AMSI), an internship was established between AMSI, RMIT and Bass Coast Shire Council, a local government jurisdiction on the south coast of Victoria some 130 kilometres south east of Melbourne. The internship enabled a PhD scholarship to be funded by Bass Coast for a student to undertake research that was complementary to his research interests and also provided intellectual benefit to the local council. With three levels of government in Australia, responsibility for rubbish removal, planning, engineering and subdivisions, infant welfare and other local issues fall on local government. With its close proximity to Melbourne and the coast lifestyle, Bass Coast has experienced pressure from increased population moving from the city. This has led to problems associated with new development in low-lying areas, which are subject to increased runoff and coastal storm surges. Three consecutive internships were funded through the AMSI Scholarships Program with Bass Coast Shire Council. They related to the development of a flood modelling approach for local government based on new forms of digital data, including state government collected LiDAR data.

The three organisations involved with the internship had different responsibilities. RMIT provided the intern, a PhD student who would conduct the research, together with the supervisory and managerial responsibility for satisfactory completion of the research. Bass Coast Shire Council provided project data and direction from an industry perspective. In addition, the council provided funding to support the student for each of the four month projects and an AUD$5000 grant to the supervisor for each of the individual projects. AMSI provided administrative support and organisation.

This collaborative approach provided benefits to the three partner organisations. The industry partner gained access to specialist knowledge in the field of spatial data analysis, publication opportunities and access to recruitment opportunities. RMIT accessed industry-based research with a real-world focus. The student experienced the practicalities of working in an industry setting, enabling him to develop skills in team-working. Industry experts provided ongoing feedback on his performance and the industry also provided excellent employment opportunities. The student developed distinct phases to his research, with clear objectives and a commitment to complete these phases within a designated timeframe.

Heatmap (10am – 11am)

Figure 30.1   Heatmaps for Melbourne Zoo for two time periods

Skills development through external partnership

The student developed a range of generic skills through working with Bass Coast Shire Council and AMSI. He was required to interact with staff from both the operational and managerial teams at the council. He encountered initial reticence from operational staff, who were suspicious of a PhD student wanting to review processes undertaken by the organisation. However, through constant interaction and clear communication with staff, assisted by the student having a physical presence (he was assigned a desk in the offices),

Heatmap (12pm – 1pm)

Figure 30.1   (continued)

these barriers were overcome. Staff soon came to realise that the student was finding new and innovative ways of working with spatial data.

Significant technical skills were acquired through the research project. Specific spatial problems relating to flat surface terrains and overland flow determination, intersecting overland flow with existing underground drainage (Pourali et al., 2014), and identifying the issues of inappropriate subdivisions were enlightening to the student and managerial staff at the council alike. In fact, at the completion of the PhD, the student was offered a full-time GIS position at the organisation.

Parks Victoria, Wilsons Promontory: Postgraduate–Industry Participation and Inter-Disciplinary Research

Context

This case study demonstrates how an Australian Research Council and industry relationship was undertaken with postgraduate participation. It additionally demonstrates the effectiveness of undertaking interdisciplinary research. A project was conducted in partnership with Parks Victoria, a state government body. Parks Victoria is responsible for the management of four million hectares, or about 18 per cent, of the State of Victoria (Parks Victoria, 2018). The parks managed are national parks, state parks, metropolitan parks and marine parks and sanctuaries. Established in 1898, Wilsons Promontory National Park is located at the southernmost tip of the Australian mainland. Its 49,049 ha consists of mountains, forest, rainforest, beaches and coastlines (Parks Victoria, 2018).

In 2008, an application was made to the Australian Research Council for a research Linkage grant by an interdisciplinary team from RMIT University (Geospatial Science and Media & Communications). The Linkage Projects scheme promotes national and international collaboration and research partnerships between key stakeholders in research and innovation. These include higher education institutions, government, business, industry and end-users. Research and development is undertaken to apply advanced knowledge to problems, to acquire new knowledge and as a basis for securing commercial and other benefits of research (Australian Research Council, 2018). A successful application to this scheme supported two PhD students, funded in part by an Australian Research Council Linkage grant, in combination with an RMIT University postgraduate award. The research focused on the concept of 'Affective Atlas' (Cartwright et al., 2007), under the umbrella of the Geo-Placed Knowledge Research Initiative, which was part of RMIT's Design Research Institute. Two PhD candidates worked in close collaboration with members of Parks Victoria staff at the Wilsons Promontory National Park and at the head office of Parks Victoria in Melbourne. They specifically sought to develop theory and prototype tools using Web 2.0 to facilitate the better management of Australian parks. The research students each spent one day per week in the head office, with longer, focused periods at the park.

Activities undertaken by the students at the park were data gathering, discussions/interviews with stakeholders, and undertaking a visitor survey to elicit feedback on aspects of Web 2.0 and the methods for designing a geo-knowledge tool. The students conducted a mobile 'cultural probe' to better understand how park staff responded to and constructed knowledge of the environment after a major event. In March 2011, the park was inundated with heavy rain (370 millimetres fell over 24 hours), with floods causing extensive damage to the natural environment and built assets. The 'cultural probe' was used to find information, particularly geo-located information, which linked emotional responses from different park managers. At head office, the students were able to develop professional relationships with Parks Victoria staff and to obtain a greater understanding of how park management 'works'. The development of these relationships, and conducting data collection within the park in collaboration with park managers, enabled the students to develop a greater appreciation of how location influences knowledge building, and how this knowledge, in turn, can lead to better park management.

Skills developed through postgraduate–industry inter-disciplinary research

In terms of generic skills, both projects required the students to interact with Parks Victoria managerial and operational staff. User needs analyses required the students to listen, synthesise and develop strategies for the development of prototype products for evaluation. Additionally, the projects entailed undertaking surveys and questionnaires with park visitors, park rangers and management. The students were required to liaise with Parks Victoria head office and the local park office to arrange suitable times for visitor surveys and for meetings with park rangers. These tasks developed inter-personal skills through precise communication with Parks Victoria staff and with park visitors. The need to provide briefing documents before park visits, prepare surveys and questionnaires to be used at the park, conduct interviews with park managers and rangers, and undertake surveys with park visitors, demanded professional approaches to document preparation, the development of effective survey and interview techniques and accurate and timely assessment of results. This enhanced the research training objectives incorporated into the doctoral program.

With reference to the development of technical skills, one student constructed a prototype 'geo-knowledge tool' to provide data access based in part on the data's geographic attributes (Elsley and Cartwright, 2011). The prototype used a case study to focus the research. It was developed as a web platform with a wide variety of user participation (clients, visitors, staff) incorporated into its development. This process enabled completion of a prototype tool that was developed via a rigorous and systematic approach. In developing the 'cultural probe', the other student recorded the daily practices and experience of Parks Victoria staff using a mobile diary over the course of two months. A mobile application (app) was developed that allowed participants to construct mixed media entries. These were time-stamped and geo-located. A synchronous web-application was used to monitor, in real-time, park ranger entries. The student developed this application for use in the program, acquiring focused programming skills for location-based mobile devices.

Country Fire Authority of Victoria: input into firefighter training and operational logistics

The Country Fire Authority (CFA) is a volunteer and community-based fire and emergency services organisation in the State of Victoria. It is the organisation that coordinates and fights bushfires in the state. A doctoral research project entitled: 'Evaluating the potential for the use of commercial off-the-shelf computer games and mobile devices to deliver location and time sensitive spatial decision training tools' was motivated by involvement of the research student with the CFA as a volunteer firefighter. After devastating bushfires in 1983 (Forest Fire Management Victoria, 2018), research was undertaken by the Bushfire Review Committee (1984) on community engagement with bushfire safety programs and organisations. The subsequent report recommended that the CFA should inform people about the risks inherent in bushfires, how to prepare properties, and how to write and implement a safety plan (Quinn and Cartwright, 2011). The research student decided to respond to the challenge of how to better train and inform volunteer firefighters and citizens by creating a mobile location-based learning application.

Figure 30.2   Simulated spot bushfires from a student-devised computer game

The project investigated learning and time-critical decision-making in fraught cir-cumstances using scenes made with a commercial off-the-shelf game. The *Crisis Wars* Software Development Kit (SDK) (crytek.com) was used to make movies of bushfires set in a virtual reserve in Central Victoria. The movies were viewed in a location-based application called *CODE RED: MOBILE*, created with the *7scenes* framework and run on *iPad2* (Quinn and Cartwright, 2012) (Figure 30.2).

Forty firefighters from the Country Fire Authority Brigades in the Macedon Ranges undertook a scenario training exercise using *CODE RED: MOBILE*. They had to decide which of six virtual houses would be safer after a wind change affected a hypothetical bushfire. Participants' performances were assessed by the analysis of their GPS tracks, and in-the-field questions were answered using the mobile device as well as recall of the events in the virtual bushfire (Quinn and Cartwright, 2012).

This project was undertaken by direct engagement with volunteer firefighters. Whilst already a volunteer firefighter, the student was able to build on his substantial firefight-ing experience and develop useful and appropriate training tools. Here, the outcomes of the research were enhanced by immersion of the project in the volunteer firefighting community.

Skills developed through the project
Through his involvement with the CFA, the student was able to enhance his generic communication skills and further develop his standing within the CFA. As a volunteer CFA firefighter who had field experience, the student was able to develop and program an appropriate prototype for evaluation. Additionally, the student was a former high

school teacher, specialising in IT and the use of mobile hand-held location-based devices for educational programs. The combination of extended professional experience in firefighting and firefighting management and the development of educational programs using hand-held devices allowed for a specific and appropriate evaluation prototype to be programmed and used in the evaluation stage of research. The student furthered his existing programming and implementation skills through the development of this prototype. Organising and conducting in-field evaluation of the prototype with CFA firefighters demanded that the student manage a large evaluation program that needed to address in-field environmental and locational issues in order to ensure that the evaluation was professionally conducted.

Without doubt, the technical skills acquired by the student were substantial. His technical understanding of spatial fire propagation and his skills in fire training using IT were enhanced. Although the student had pre-existing skills in the development of prototypes using 'off-the-shelf' computer games software, he up-scaled his skills significantly to enable firefighters to use and evaluate the prototype in real landscapes and firefighting situations (Quinn and Cartwright, 2012).

GENERAL OBSERVATIONS OF SKILLS ACQUIRED THROUGH UNDERGRADUATE AND POSTGRADUATE PARTNERSHIP WITH INDUSTRY

In summing up, several generic and technical skills were common to each of the examples illustrated in the previous section. For the generic skills, communication, in particular with different levels of operational and managerial staff, were necessary. Interviewing and questioning staff about existing procedures and what aspects of their workplace needed addressing were commonplace. It was essential to clarify research objectives and methods to be adopted. This was particularly the case when completing ethics applications. All projects required meeting deadlines, whether they were academic timelines or timelines organised in conjunction with industry partners. Dependability and attitudinal skills were important. Knowing that an industry partner was dependent upon the outcomes of the research being conducted meant there was a need for students to invest significant time and effort in achieving positive outcomes. Problem-solving skills were required where projects met unforeseen obstacles. Finally, a report in the form of a dissertation generated by each student was an academic requirement. In addition, specific reports were required for the industry partners. In all cases, the students were required to present their findings in a symposium to their peers and industry representatives from the participating organisations.

Technical skills were developed through the contextualisation and implementation of technology in a work environment. Innovative approaches to extracting and analysing spatial patterns were common in all of the case studies. Field organisation and interaction with the public were also common skills utilised by the students. Finally, all the students worked with industry partners outside their particular area of expertise. The acquisition of interdisciplinary skills is readily acknowledged as a key capability in geographic disciplines (Solem et al., 2008).

CURRICULUM REVIEW AND MODIFICATION

A long history of running courses that involve students working with industry partners has enabled academic staff at RMIT to reflect on curriculum content and teaching approaches within the disciplines of geospatial science and surveying. New courses that emulate industry practice have been introduced, such as the first year Applied Geospatial Science course documented in Pupedis et al. (2007). In this course, students develop a holistic view of geospatial problem-solving through a simulated field exercise that incorporates data collection, collation and analysis. All students are required to complete work experience with an industry partner prior to graduation. Capstone courses are completed in the final year of undergraduate study, primarily with an industry partner, such as those documented in this chapter. Completed projects have given staff real-world examples that can be used to illustrate concepts learned in earlier years of study.

Specific courses that have been integrated into RMIT undergraduate degree programs include 'Scientific Communications', taught as a first year course to advance skills of academic writing, teamwork, time management, oral presentation, information literacy, critical thinking and creative thinking. Additionally, 'Professional Practice', offered to final year students, is designed to review business practices, workplace safety, dispute resolution, professional expectations and personal attributes for those entering professional work places. Finally, work-integrated learning is now promoted heavily in all RMIT taught programs and the case studies presented in this chapter demonstrate the ways in which the disciplines of geospatial science and surveying have enacted this process.

GENERAL OBSERVATIONS RELATING TO INDUSTRY-LINKED RESEARCH PROGRAMS

In terms of embedding employability into the research program, three main issues have been identified: timelines; success of research aims; and intellectual property and publication.

Timelines

First and foremost, there are often differing timelines for the student and the industry partner. Given the nature of research programs, results may take longer to acquire than an industry partner may want. Most industry partners want short-term projects that solve specific problems within several months. However, a research degree may take three to four years. For local government, for example, the trade-off of directing funding from capital works programs towards research into improving current decision-making, based on newly available data, may prove difficult to convey to the local community or other stakeholders (and possibly shareholders for private companies). Consequently, there needs to be clear outcomes with constant inclusion of senior managers, initially in the development of the project, through to delivering a clear report detailing the benefits accruing to the industry partner. In our examples, students at both undergraduate and postgraduate level worked with employees of the industry partners, and they would keep in constant contact either through meetings or actually working within the organisation.

Success of Research Aims

Research, by its very nature, does not always have known outcomes. Often things do not work out as anticipated, or one research question can unveil other (sometimes more interesting) research questions. Where an industry partner is involved, however, solutions to an existing problem need to be addressed and explicit benefits need to be conveyed to senior management. Provided the student and supervisor maintain constant contact with the industry partner, and keep that partner informed on the progress of the conducted research, no surprises need arise.

Intellectual Property and Publication

Whilst not an issue for the projects documented in the case studies, intellectual property rights and publication do need consideration prior to industry-linked research projects. In general, postgraduate students will own intellectual property rights for research work conducted within their own program. However, when funded by industry, the property rights for any outcomes in sub-projects conducted as part of a research program will reside with the industry partner. Provided clear contractual arrangements are documented these issues should not prove difficult to overcome. Further, in our experience, industry partners are keen to publish jointly in peer-reviewed journals under the guidance of the supervisor and student, to promote their particular organisation. Another consideration is where there may be conflicts of interest between the researchers and industry partner. For example, Eyre (2002) refers to the differing interests between industry and education in the role of the alcohol industry developing curricula for health education.

CONCLUSIONS

In this chapter, skills have been reviewed that are required in higher education to prepare undergraduate and postgraduate students for employment, especially with reference to the geospatial industry. Apart from basic verbal and written communication skills, geography graduates possess skills in field management, are able to work across disciplines, and are adept at spatial reasoning.

Through a series of case studies, it has been shown how undergraduate and postgraduate students have, to varying degrees, interacted with industry partners. These examples have demonstrated how students within a geospatial science discipline are building not only their research skills, but the ability to work professionally within a team structure. They are also able to obtain an authentic experience and acquire transferrable skills in order to move from university to industry.

USEFUL RESOURCES

- Australian Qualifications Framework: https://www.aqf.edu.au/sites/aqf/files/aqf-2nd-edition-january-2013.pdf.
- Graduate Outcomes Survey: https://www.qilt.edu.au/docs/default-source/gos-

reports/2017/2017_gos_national_report_final_accessiblea45d8791b1e86477b-58fff00006709da.pdf?sfvrsn=ceb5e33c_4.
- Surveyors Registration Board of Victoria: https://www.surveyorsboard.vic.gov.au/.
- Work Integrated Learning at RMIT: https://www.rmit.edu.au/students/student-esse
ntials/work-integrated-learning.

REFERENCES

Arrowsmith, C. and Goudey, R. (2007) 'Fostering a multi-faceted industry partnership'. Refereed conference paper for the AIC Conference 'Partnerships for World Graduates', 28–30 November, Melbourne, pp. 305–312.

Arrowsmith, C., Bagoly-Simo, P., Finchum, A., Oda, K. and Pawson, E. (2011) 'Student employability and its implications for geography curricula and learning practices', *Journal of Geography in Higher Education*, 35 (3), pp. 365–377.

Arrowsmith, C., Zanon, D. and Chhetri, P. (2005) 'Monitoring visitor patterns of use in natural tourist destinations', in C. Ryan, S. Page and M. Aicken (eds), *Taking Tourism to the Limits: Issues, Concepts and Managerial Perspectives*. Amsterdam: Elsevier, pp. 33–52.

Australian Qualifications Framework Council (2013) *Australian Qualification Framework* (2nd edition). Published by the AQF Council. Available online at: https://www.aqf.edu.au/sites/aqf/files/aqf-2nd-edition-january-2013.pdf. Accessed 1 March 2018.

Australian Research Council (2018) *Linkage Projects*. Available online at: http://www.arc.gov.au/linkage-projects. Accessed 28 February 2018.

Bennett, D., Richardson. S. and MacKinnon, P. (2016) *Enacting Strategies for Graduate Employability: How Universities can Best Support Students to Develop Generic Skill Part A*. Canberra, ACT: Australian Government, Office for Learning and Teaching, Department of Education and Training. Available online at: http://www.olt.gov.au/project-how-universities-can-best-support-students-develop-generic-skills-enacting-str ategies-gradua. Accessed 15 May 2018.

Bushfire Review Committee (1984) *Report of the Bushfire Review Committee on Bush Fire Disaster Preparedness and Response in Victoria, Australia, Following the Ash Wednesday Fires 16 February 1983*. Melbourne: Government Printer.

Cartwright, W.E., Miles, A., Morris, B., Vaughan, L. and Yuille, J. (2007) 'Affective atlas – constructing an atlas using Web 2.0 and social software', *Proceedings of the 22nd International Cartographic Conference*. Moscow, Russia: International Cartographic Association, August, CD-ROM.

Cassidy, S. (2006) 'Developing employability skills: peer assessment in higher education', *Education + Training*, 48, pp. 508–517.

Elsley, M. and Cartwright, W. (2011) 'Contemporary and collaborative web concepts as part of a geo-knowledge tool to assist park management', in A. Ruas (ed.), *Advances in Cartography and GIScience* Volume 1. Heidelberg: Springer-Verlag, pp. 261–277.

Eyre, L. (2002) 'No strings attached? Corporate involvement in curriculum', *Canadian Journal of Education*, 27, pp. 61–80.

Forest Fire Management Victoria (2018) *Ash Wednesday 1983*. Available online at: https://www.ffm.vic.gov.au/history-and-incidents/ash-wednesday-1983. Accessed 2 March 2018.

Graduate Outcomes Survey (2017) *2017 Graduate Outcomes Survey: National Report*. Published by the Quality Indicators for Learning and Teaching, January 2018. Available online at: https://www.qilt.edu.au/about-this-site/graduate-employment. Accessed 25 January 2018.

Lim, Y.-M., Lee, T.H., Yap, C.S. and Ling, C.C. (2016) 'Employability skills, personal qualities, and early employment problems of entry-level auditors: perspectives from employers, lecturers, auditors and students', *Journal of Education for Business*, 91, pp. 185–192.

Morris, M. (2017) *Investigating the Spatio-Temporal Dynamics of Visitor Movements in Melbourne Zoo*. Unpublished Honours thesis, RMIT University, December 2017.

Parks Victoria (2018) *Who We Are*. Available at: http://parkweb.vic.gov.au/about-us/who-we-are. Accessed 2 March 2018.

Pourali, S., Arrowsmith, C., Mitchell, D. and Matkan, A. (2014) 'Modelling and overland water flow path in an urban catchment using GIS', *Geoinformatica*, 4, pp. 1–19.

Pupedis, G. and Bellman, C (2010) 'Recruitment and retention of students in the geospatial sciences', *Scientific Journal of Riga Technical University*, Geomatics, 7, pp. 51–56.

Pupedis, G., Arrowsmith, C., Bellman, C. and Ramos, C. (2007) 'The implementation of an integrated introductory geospatial science course', in S. Catling and L. Taylor (eds), *Proceedings of the IGU Commission for Geographical Education 'Changing Geographies: Innovative Curricula'*. London April 2007, pp. 251–258.

Quinn, P.B. and Cartwright, W.E. (2011) 'Visualization development for "Code Red: Mobile": a location based scenario training tool for firefighters', in C. Arrowsmith, C. Bellman, W.E. Cartwright, S. Jones and M. Shortis (eds), *Progress in Geospatial Science Research, Geospatial Science Research Symposium*, GSR_1, 2011. Melbourne: School of Mathematical and Geospatial Sciences, pp. 373–389.

Quinn, P.B. and Cartwright, W.E. (2012) *Spatio-Temporal Analysis of GPS Tracks of an Experimental Mobile Scenario and Location Based Training Exercise* (CDROM). Geospatial Science Research Symposium, GSR_2, 10–12 December.

Shoval, N. and Isaacson, M. (2007) 'Tracking tourists in the digital age', *Annals of Tourism Research*, 34, pp. 141–159.

Solem, M., Cheung, I. and Schlemper, M.B. (2008) 'Skills in professional geography: an assessment of workforce needs and expectations', *The Professional Geographer*, 60, pp. 356–373.

Vazquez-Prokopec, G., Stoddard, S., Paz-Soldan, V., Morrison, A., Elder, J., Kochel, T., Scott, T. and Kitron, U. (2009) 'Usefulness of commercially available GPS data-loggers for tracking human movement and exposure to dengue virus', *International Journal of Health Geographics*, 8, 68. DOI: 10.1186/1476-072X-8-68.

31. Graduate attributes in geography higher education
Rachel Spronken-Smith

INTRODUCTION

In the last few decades, higher educationalists have become increasingly interested in, and focused on, what students are achieving through their higher education (for example Barr and Tagg, 1995; Barrie, 2006; Oliver and de St Jorre, 2018). This focus has been driven in part by the neoliberal agenda (for example Kalfa and Taksa, 2015), but also, and more importantly, through a promotion of more student-centred approaches (for example Richardson, 2005; Biggs and Tang, 2011). When taking a student-centred approach, the curriculum design process should begin with a focus on what students should know and be able to do when they graduate. This outcomes-based approach (Biggs and Tang, 2011), or backwards design, means that attention is first paid to what knowledge, skills and values students should be able to demonstrate upon graduation (that is the graduate outcomes), and then the curriculum is designed so that students should reach these outcomes. These graduate outcomes have been widely captured under the term 'graduate attributes', which have been defined as:

> the qualities, skills and understandings a university community agrees its students should develop during their time at the institution. These attributes include but go beyond the disciplinary expertise or technical knowledge that has traditionally formed the core of most university courses. They are qualities that also prepare graduates as agents of social good in an unknown future. (Bowden et al., 2000, p. 3)

However, with the growth of research on graduate attributes, which has occurred across several continents but particularly in Europe, the UK and Australia, there has been a variety of terms used to describe these outcomes. As well as graduate attributes, the terms 'graduate capabilities' or 'graduate competencies' have also been used. The descriptors are all outcomes-based and may encompass any institutional generic or transferable attributes – often referred to as a 'graduate profile', as well as programme or discipline-specific attributes.

Embedding generic attributes within curricula is key to successful engagement with graduate outcomes. Although it is increasingly common for institutions to try and embed their graduate profiles within curricula, the danger is that these profiles are, by necessity, divorced from the disciplinary context; they tend to be broad statements of generic or transferable skills that graduates should acquire. Moreover, as Barrie (2006) showed, academics may have varying perceptions of what this profile actually means. Barrie (2006, p. 229) found four qualitatively distinct understandings of graduate attributes:

- A *precursory* conception – in which academics assume students enter the programme with a set of generic attributes, so academics can focus on teaching disciplinary knowledge only;

- A *complement* conception – in which academics view generic attributes as useful skills, but see these as additional to disciplinary knowledge and thus not part of the core curriculum;
- A *translation* conception – in which academics see a mutual relationship between generic attributes and disciplinary learning outcomes, such that generic attributes are necessary for the application of disciplinary learning in new contexts;
- An *enabling* conception – in which academics view generic attributes as integral to disciplinary knowledge, rather than sitting alongside discipline knowledge. Thus the attributes are embedded in the curriculum, with an expectation that graduates will be able to reshape and construct knowledge in contexts outside the discipline.

Barrie's (2006) findings have implications for those undertaking curriculum change to embed graduate attributes. It is likely that geography faculty will hold varying conceptions of graduate attributes, so it is important to try and promote a translation or enabling conception of graduate attributes to ensure the attributes are embedded in disciplinary teaching and learning. Also, as de St Jorre and Oliver (2018) caution, it is important for disciplines to customise the institutional profile to make it relevant for their programmes. A case study at an Australian university found that students were more likely to engage with graduate attributes if they were embedded in teaching and assessment; graduate learning outcomes for the university were too generic to be meaningful.

Having discussed why graduate attributes or capabilities are used to drive curriculum design in higher education, this chapter now provides a synthesis of recent literature to identify which attributes or capabilities are relevant for geography graduates. Following this, some practical guidance is offered regarding how to embed graduate attributes in geography curricula, and then how to monitor attainment of graduate attributes. The chapter concludes with a summary of key points and important messages for readers.

GRADUATE ATTRIBUTES FOR GEOGRAPHERS

Whether the term attributes or capabilities is used, the focus of curriculum design in geography should be developing students to think and practise as geographers. The phrase 'ways of thinking and practising' means:

> the richness, depth and breadth of what students might learn through engagement with a given subject area in a specific context. This might include, for example, coming to terms with particular understandings, forms of discourse, values or ways of acting which are regarded as central to graduate-level mastery of a discipline or subject. (McCune and Hounsell, 2005, p. 257)

Hounsell and McCune (2002) pointed out that this notion of ways of thinking and practising involved students not just knowing disciplinary knowledge, but being able to apply this knowledge in new contexts. This idea resonates with the enabling conception of graduate attributes mentioned above. By having such a disposition, graduates can then 'cope effectively with uncertainty and complexity [that] they will meet both in employment and in society at large in the 21st century' (McCune and Entwistle, 2011, p. 309). Ways of thinking and practising reminds us why we are educating our students – we want to ensure that our graduates emerge with a geographical mind set, and can apply their knowledge and skills to new contexts.

But what does it mean to think and practise as a geographer? What attributes in terms of knowledge, skills and values should geographers have? Research concerning graduate attributes in geography has identified core knowledge that graduates should be familiar with, such as environmental/human impacts, citizenship, and social justice (for example Solem et al., 2008; Arrowsmith et al., 2011; Whalley et al., 2011; Hay, 2012; Spronken-Smith, 2013; Mager and Spronken-Smith, 2014). The notion of 'threshold concepts' (Meyer and Land, 2005) also provides insight into core knowledge for geographers, and readers should refer to Chapter 6 in this volume by Erin Fouberg for more detail. Threshold concepts are key ideas that are central to develop understanding in a discipline. They often concern troublesome concepts, which are difficult to grasp, but once understood, the student has passed a threshold. Their thinking is transformed and cannot be reversed, that is the concept is not easily forgotten (Meyer and Land, 2005). Spronken-Smith (2013) reported threshold concepts for geography including quantification and uncertainty, commenting these may be common to a range of disciplines, and more specifically sustainability and systems thinking.

In terms of skills, Hay (2012, p. 492) said geography graduates should be able to 'analyze and synthesize complex environmental, economic, social and political information to enable a geographical understanding of humans, environments and the dynamic relationships between them'. Whalley et al. (2011) advocated for spatial data analysis and geographical imagination as core geography skills, saying graduates need to be able to recognise relations in and between global and local processes. In an earlier study involving employers of geography graduates, Solem et al. (2008) reported the top five geographical skills sought by employers according to career type (Table 31.1). Spatial thinking, cartography and GIS were the most sought-after skills. However, we must treat these data with caution, as the types and nature of employment are rapidly changing, so what was relevant in the mid-2000s may not be as relevant now. Indeed, as Haigh and Clifford (2011) outlined, graduates now need to be educated to deal with personal responsibility towards the welfare of the whole planet. They argued that graduate attributes should not just be about employability skills, but must include attributes relating to personal integrity, and social and environmental responsibility.

Alongside identifying discipline-specific attributes that geographers should acquire,

Table 31.1   The top five geographical skills sought by employers across a range of organisations in the USA

Higher education	Government	For-profit company	Nonprofit company
Human–environment interaction	GIS Cartography	GIS	Interdisciplinary perspective
GIS	Spatial thinking	Cartography	GIS
Global perspective	Spatial statistics	Spatial thinking	Cartography
Cartography	Field methods	Spatial statistics	Spatial thinking
Spatial thinking	—	Economic geography	Diversity perspective

Source: Adapted from Solem et al. (2008, p. 369).

geography educators also need to elaborate on more generic attributes, to be clear about what these mean in a geographical context. Commonly espoused generic attributes include critical thinking, problem-solving, communication, time-management, creativity, sustainability, and teamwork. Although these skills are generic, and often expected as part of an institutional graduate profile, it is important to unpack what they mean in the disciplinary context. So, for example, although the attribute of critical thinking may have similar elements across disciplines, it will likely have particularities to the discipline. For example, Korkmaz and Karakuş (2009, p. 53) commented about the 'distinct position' of geography regarding critical thinking skills, arguing that geographers need to be able to analyse and synthesise information collected in the context of human–natural environment interaction. Another generic attribute is ethical thinking (and acting), and as Boyd et al. (2008) pointed out, often ethics are invisible in curricula. In their study of teaching ethics in geography, they emphasised the need to teach ethics through specific geographical content, paying attention to both normative ethics (solutions to moral problems) and metaethics (analysis of moral concepts) (Boyd et al., 2008, p. 40). Healey and Ribchester (2016) reported on using a tutorial-based approach to develop ethical thinking in geographers. Whalley et al. (2011) linked together the attributes of ethics and sustainability, arguing that developing ethical thinking in geographers should include not just knowing about sustainability, but also acting in a sustainable way.

Less visible perhaps on institutional graduate profiles are personal attributes such as interpersonal skills, though possibly these are implicit in an attribute such as teamwork. Flexibility, adaptability and resilience are further characteristics that are highly valued by employers (for example Arrowsmith et al., 2011; Le Heron and Hathaway, 2000), and are likely of increased importance in a world of work that involves 'portfolio careers', with periods of employment (in varying roles), unemployment and self-employment (Henderson and Robertson, 1999, p. 236). To operate in such a dynamic work environment, it is important that graduates have dispositions such as openness to experience, agreeableness, sociability, self-confidence and initiative (Bridgstock, 2009, p. 37). Such dispositions, Bridgstock (2009) argued, underpin career management skills, yet they are seldom given enough attention by universities. The career management skills she identified included self-management skills (for example values, abilities, attitudes, interests, work/life balance), career-building skills (for example finding and using information about labour markets, locating and applying for work and learning opportunities, creating professional relationships), and the acquisition, display and use of both discipline-specific and generic attributes required for work (Bridgstock, 2009, p. 36). She discussed the need for career management skills to be developed in disciplinary contexts, since knowledge and skills will have discipline-based variability.

Table 31.2 provides a summary of key attributes that are desirable to foster in geographers (sub-disciplines may have a further set of attributes), and the next section discusses how to embed these attributes in geography curricula. As well as geographical knowledge and skills, Whalley et al. (2011) listed written communication, critical thinking and making decisions on incomplete information as necessary skills for geographers. In addition to these skills, should be ethical thinking, teamwork, time management, career management, flexibility and adaptability, resilience, openness to experience, agreeableness, sociability, self-confidence and initiative.

Table 31.2   Examples of knowledge, skills and attributes that are desirable to foster in geography students

Knowledge	Skills or Attributes
Climate change – impacts, socio/political implications	Making a decision with limited information
Uncertainty	Self-efficacy
Sustainability	
Hazard management and risk assessment	
Social justice	Information and new media literacy
Equity	Presentation and communication
Social responsibility	Critical thinking and metacognition
Social inequality/exclusion	
Citizenship	
Spatial context/connection	Social competence
Awareness/understanding connections	Citizenship
	Fluency: technical, numerical, information and writing
Consequences of human action on environment	Cultural understanding of maps
Awareness of another culture	Effective written communication
Awareness of how global processes affect local spaces	Skill: ability to work with and analyse spatial data
	Attribute: curiosity in local/world affairs and connections
Cultural coherence (local to global)	Writing
Population/settlement patterns	Map creation/GIS spatial cognition
Environmental/human impacts	Oral communication
Relevance of geographical understanding of world events	Independent thinking
	Self-motivated
Human–environment dependency/relationship	Communication skills
Contribution of geographers to public life	
Global dynamics of specialty area	Interdisciplinary collaboration
Familiarity with one cognate field	Public advocacy for geography
Awareness of geography in international context	Mentoring
Cultural diversity	Conflict resolution
Models of community engagement	Decision-making
Ethical practice	Cross-cultural communication skills

Source: Adapted from Whalley et al. (2011, p. 382).

DESIGNING GEOGRAPHY CURRICULA TO FOSTER GRADUATE ATTRIBUTES

When embedding graduate attributes in curricula, there are several steps in the process. Spronken-Smith et al. (2016) generated a toolkit to assist geography programme coordinators with implementation of graduate attributes. The first three steps they identified were:

1. Deciding who is going to be responsible for driving curriculum renewal around graduate attributes
2. Developing contextualised graduate profiles for geography degrees
3. Gaining leverage from enablers of engagement with graduate attributes
    a. Drawing on external drivers
    b. Creating the context for curriculum renewal
    c. Ensuring enabling structures and processes are in place (note that curriculum mapping is a key procedural enabler)
    d. Ensuring developmental enablers are in operation
    e. Activating achievement enablers (Spronken-Smith et al., 2016, pp. 259–260).

The fourth step involved monitoring the progress of embedding graduate attributes, and this is considered in the next section.

The first two steps above concern who is going to drive curriculum renewal (if this is required), and the need to develop a contextualised graduate profile for the geography programme. Research on implementing curriculum change is in agreement about one key factor – the need for ownership of the initiative by those involved in implementing change. Thus, even if the move to embed graduate attributes in curricula is being led by a champion or a small working group, it is important for this person or group to closely consult and communicate with other academics in the department. The development of a contextualised graduate profile is a significant and important undertaking. There should be widespread consultation with stakeholders including students, academics, alumni, employers and professional associations. If there is an institutional graduate profile, each attribute should be considered and defined in a geographical context, to sit alongside the discipline-specific attributes generated. Discussion concerning possible graduate attributes should include consideration of knowledge (particularly threshold concepts as mentioned above and in Chapter 6), skills and values.

There may be a core set of attributes that are applicable to all geographers, with further attributes according to the sub-discipline. In a curriculum development session run several years ago with a geography department, I witnessed debates amongst geography academics about how the attributes for physical geographers, for example, are very different to those for cultural geographers. Yet, interestingly, when both groups were asked to generate the core attributes for geographers, there was remarkable agreement.

Once a graduate profile has been generated, there is a need to ensure that the profile becomes a 'lived experience' through teaching and learning activities, and the assessment regime. To help embed graduate attributes in curricula, Spronken-Smith et al. (2016) discuss the importance of drawing on external drivers, creating the context for curriculum renewal, ensuring enabling structures and processes are in place, ensuring developmental enablers are in operation, and activating achievement enablers. These enablers are described in detail in Table 31.3, but three of them deserve further mention as they are key to successful implementation of a graduate attribute agenda: curriculum mapping; using high impact educational practices; and teaching using signature pedagogies; and they are considered below.

The phrase 'curriculum mapping' has been attributed to English (1984, p. 50, cited in Harden, 2001), who said: 'The real genius of mapping is to give a broad picture of the taught curriculum'. Harden (2001), in an article on the use of curriculum mapping in

Table 31.3   Strategies to promote embedding graduate attributes in geography curricula

Enablers	Mechanisms to help embed graduate attributes in curricula
External – forces to which institutions were required to respond or perceived they were responding, or should respond	• Mandate from audit and quality processes and professional bodies, e.g. geographical associations • Stakeholder involvement in developing graduate attributes (employers, professional associations, alumni, students)
Structural and procedural – those that facilitated or engaged staff and communities within the institution to become aware of, or work towards, change in practice in regard to graduate attributes	• Supportive middle managers responsible for teaching and learning • Promoting a team focus to curriculum development • Having people familiar with regulatory and structural aspects of qualifications • Developing a contextualised programme graduate profile for geography • Requiring clear links between the programme graduate profile (i.e. set of attributes) and the institutional graduate profile (if there is one) • Requiring strong links between graduate attributes, learning outcomes and assessment (curriculum mapping)
Developmental – those that assisted staff/ groups/departments to introduce and develop graduate attributes and embed them in curricula, or undertake some curriculum development	• 'Translation' or 'enabling' beliefs about the role of graduate attributes and teaching and learning (see Barrie, 2006) • Champions • Recognising and supporting staff ownership of their programme • Engaging and valuing all staff in curriculum renewal • Provision of academic development support for the process and particularly for developing learning outcomes • Provision of teaching resources and planning tools such as curriculum mapping • Instigating formal and informal conversations about teaching and curriculum • Having good communication of the process and outcomes
Achievement – those that were related to assisting students to achieve the graduate attributes	• Having clear educational and employment pathways • Using contemporary/flexible delivery methods • Ensuring curricula focus on students • Having strong links between graduate attributes, learning outcomes and assessment • Scaffolding of skills – to gradually develop graduate attributes • Including high impact educational experiences (e.g. service learning, inquiry; see Kuh, 2008) and signature pedagogies in geography (see Komoto, 2009; Spronken-Smith, 2013) • Requiring ePortolios or similar • Involvement of students in developing graduate attributes
Contextual – generic institutional and/or individual cultural/ affective qualities that crossed other enablers and made them more or less effective	• High staff morale • Good communication • A departmental culture that focuses on teaching • Creating time and space for discussions for curriculum renewal • Having an alertness to the context of lecturers

Source: Adapted from Spronken-Smith et al. (2016, p. 260).

Table 31.4   *Example of a simple curriculum map in geography for selected attributes in a three-year degree*

Attribute	1st year	2nd year	3rd year
Cartographic skills	GEOG101 – two lectures and two laboratories; skills assessed in lab reports and mid-term examination	GEOG203 – dedicated course; skills assessed in two assignments and in a final examination	GEOG301, 302, 306 and 310 – skills taught in elements of these papers; some assessment in 306 and 310
Teamwork	GEOG101 – group work in tutorials (not assessed)	GEOG201 – working in teams taught in a tutorial; group project work and assessment of resulting posters as well as peer assessment of contribution to the group	GEOG303, 305 – group project work including assessment of group report/ presentation
Ethics	GEOG102 – principles of ethics taught in tutorials		GEOG302 – ethics taught as part of research methodology course; minor component of assessment

Note: Such 'maps' can be used to identify areas of overlap (which may be important), as well as gaps.

medical education, discussed how curriculum mapping makes elements of the curriculum more transparent, and enables the linkages and connections between different components of the curriculum to be seen. As such, curriculum mapping is a useful tool to help achieve 'constructive alignment' (Biggs, 1996), in which the learning outcomes are well aligned with the teaching and learning methods, and the assessment regime. Curriculum maps at their simplest can be in tabular form (for example see Table 31.4), but there is now sophisticated software available for more complex mapping, that allow an extensive range of curriculum components to be included. Irrespective of the tool used, it is important that each graduate attribute is considered, with a map showing where in the curriculum this attribute is both taught and assessed.

Although simple in idea, the task of curriculum mapping is not straightforward. It is certainly easier for new programmes, when an outcomes-based approach can be taken, starting with each attribute and determining at which level (or levels), and in which topics, the attribute can be fostered. However, for existing programmes, often the learning outcomes are implicit, and possibly not well connected to a graduate profile. The process of curriculum mapping therefore requires conversations with course or paper coordinators to determine what is being taught and how, and what the assessment regime entails. It is even more complicated when courses involve teaching teams since rarely is this actually 'team' teaching, and academics may not realise what their colleagues are teaching. Research has shown that academics come to value these conversations as they promote collegiality, make teaching less isolating, and often uncover areas of inefficiency, such as many academics teaching the same knowledge and/or skill, or worse, areas of deficiency whereby no-one is teaching a particular attribute (for example Spronken-Smith et al., 2013).

Another key enabler to embedding graduate attributes in curricula is the use of 'high impact educational practices' (Kuh, 2008). These practices stem from research involving nine years of data from national surveys of student engagement in higher education in the USA. Analysis of student feedback resulted in 10 high impact educational practices being identified. As noted by Spronken-Smith (2013, p. 323), five of these commonly occur in geography curricula: collaborative assignments and projects; undergraduate research and inquiry; diversity/global learning; service and community learning; and capstone courses and projects. The other five high impact educational practices are first-year seminars and experiences, common intellectual experiences (for example core courses), learning communities, writing-intensive courses and internships; again many geography programmes would include some of these elements. As well as getting students highly engaged in their learning, participation in these high impact educational experiences is likely to develop several graduate attributes – both discipline-specific and generic. This is because these experiences are not solely focused on content, but involve building transferable skills. For example, collaborative assignments foster interpersonal and teamwork skills, while internships develop a host of workplace skills.

Alongside using high impact educational experiences to foster graduate attributes, Spronken-Smith (2013) advocated the use of 'signature pedagogies' (Shulman 2005, p. 52). These are teaching techniques that are characteristic to the discipline and, in geography, may include fieldwork, visualisation, map-making and map interpretation (Komoto, 2009), or integrative learning, learning through inquiry, and service and community-based learning (Spronken-Smith, 2013). Fieldwork, and its potential for fostering graduate attributes in geographers, is explored through three articles in a *Journal of Geography in Higher Education* 'Symposium on Graduate Attributes' (see Couper and Porter, 2016; France et al., 2016; Fuller and France, 2016). Following Healey's early research on inquiry-based learning (Healey, 2005), other geographers have examined using problem and inquiry-based approaches in geography (for example Spronken-Smith, 2005; Pawson et al., 2006; Spronken-Smith et al., 2008). McEwen (2013) discussed the possibilities of community-based learning in geography in an introduction to a symposium on this topic in the *Journal of Geography in Higher Education* (also see other articles in this issue), and Houston and Lange (2017) argued for global/local community engagement as a way to promote integrative learning in geographers.

While I have been arguing that graduate attributes should be embedded in curricula, some attributes can also be developed through extra-curricular activities. For example, Hill and Walkington (2016) reported on the experiences of Geography, Earth and Environmental Sciences students participating in the annual British Conference of Undergraduate Research. They found that through participation in the conference, students honed their communication skills, developing the ability to present their research to a non-specialist audience, and improving their oral delivery skills. They also developed personal and intellectual autonomy, demonstrating self-regulation and self-confidence.

ASSURING LEARNING – MONITORING ATTAINMENT OF GRADUATE ATTRIBUTES

Many programmes now have graduate profiles and, increasingly, have embedded graduate attributes in their curriculum, yet there is a still a lack of monitoring of the attainment of graduate attributes. As Hill et al. (2016) discuss, evaluation of the attainment of graduate attributes is difficult. Ideally, attributes should be assessed in courses, but, as they point out, some more affective attributes are difficult to measure. Hill et al. (2016) promote triangulating data from sources such as curriculum documentation, student perception surveys, longitudinal studies, and input from employers. They also recommend the use of 'integrated frameworks' to develop attributes from undergraduate to postgraduate levels (Hill et al., 2016, p. 157). In any process of evaluating the attainment of graduate attributes, the findings should be fed back to academics and students to close the feedback loop and improve the learning experience for students (Spronken-Smith et al., 2016).

Although recommendations have been made regarding how to embed graduate attributes in curricula, some research on the success of implementation is quite sobering. For example, Green et al. (2007) reported that universities (and academics) were not well equipped with teaching and learning strategies to foster graduate attributes. They said that implementing a graduate attribute agenda required a whole-of-university approach (see also de la Harpe and David, 2012; Bond et al., 2017), and that each discipline should be responsible for contextualising, implementing and assessing graduate attributes. Yet, as de la Harpe and David (2012) noted, a key obstacle for implementing graduate attributes is academics themselves. In a study of over 1000 academics across 16 universities in Australia, they found that while many academics may have a strong belief in the importance of graduate attributes, they may not always translate this into practice. Willingness and confidence levels were the main predictors of whether academics would engage with teaching and assessing graduate attributes, and these factors were mainly positively influenced by gender (being female), industry experience and having a teaching qualification. To help overcome some of these difficulties, it is important for academics to draw on colleagues who are experienced student-centred teachers, and to seek the support of educational developers – drawing in particular on the developmental enablers outlined in Table 31.3.

CONCLUSION

Geography educators should be paying attention to graduate attributes and using them in curriculum design. It is important to develop graduates who are able to think and practise as geographers, as their knowledge and skill set will be of value to them in future careers. This chapter has discussed the need for academics to adopt student-centred approaches in their teaching, focussing on what students should know and be able to do by the time they graduate. With a student-centred approach, academics are more likely to hold a translation or enabling conception of graduate attributes, meaning that their teaching will include consideration of graduate attributes and how to foster them in the curriculum. An outcomes-based approach to curriculum and course design should be used to ensure the focus of learning is on developing desirable knowledge and skills as geographers.

Importantly, the desirable knowledge and skills sets should not be stagnant, but should be revisited periodically to ensure that graduate attributes are fit for contemporary society, particularly given the rapid and transformative changes occurring through advances in technology.

Having identified a set of desirable attributes for geography graduates, the chapter outlined some practical guidelines regarding how to realise this profile through embedding the attributes in teaching, learning and assessment. Key mechanisms to embed graduate attributes in geography curricula include curriculum mapping to ensure all attributes are taught and assessed, and the use of high impact educational practices and signature pedagogies to develop the attributes. However, as discussed, implementing graduate attributes can be challenging, so it is important to seek support from colleagues and educational developers. Finally, the chapter highlighted the importance of determining whether geography graduates are indeed obtaining the desired set of graduate attributes. Alongside direct assessment of attributes, tools such as alumni surveys, longitudinal studies and feedback from employers can help evaluate the success of implementing a graduate attribute agenda.

USEFUL RESOURCES

- Donert, K. (2007) *Aspects of the State of Geography in European Higher Education TUNING Geography: A Report of Findings and Outcomes.* Available at: http://tunin gacademy.org/wp-content/uploads/2014/02/HERODOT_Tuning-Geography.pdf.
- Spronken-Smith, R., Bond, C., McLean, A., Frielick, S., Smith, N., Jenkins, M. and Marshall, S. (2013) *Toolkit for Heads of Department and Programme Directors to Engage with Graduate Outcomes.* Wellington, New Zealand: Ako Aotearoa. Available at: https://ako.ac.nz/knowledge-centre/graduate-outcomes/?destination=node%252F 5324.
- Spronken-Smith, R., Bond, C., McLean, A., Frielick, S., Smith, N., Jenkins, M. and Marshall, S. (2013). *Toolkit for Lecturers to Engage with Graduate Outcomes.* Wellington, New Zealand: Ako Aotearoa. Available at: https://ako.ac.nz/knowledge -centre/graduate-outcomes/?destination=node%252F5324.

REFERENCES

Arrowsmith, C., Bagoly-Simo, P., Finchum, A., Oda, K. and Pawson, E. (2011) 'Student employability and its implications for geography curricula and learning practices', *Journal of Geography in Higher Education*, 35, pp. 365–377.

Barr, R.B. and Tagg, J. (1995) 'From teaching to learning – a new paradigm for undergraduate education', *Change: The Magazine of Higher Learning*, 27(6), pp. 12–26.

Barrie, S.C. (2006). 'Understanding what we mean by the generic attributes of graduates', *Higher Education*, 51, pp. 215–241.

Biggs, J.B. (1996) 'Enhancing teaching through constructive alignment', *Higher Education*, 32(1), pp. 1–18.

Biggs, J. and Tang, C. (2011) *Teaching for Quality Learning at University.* New York: The Society for Research into Higher Education & Open University Press.

Bond, C., Spronken-Smith, R., McLean, A., Smith, N., Frielick, S., Jenkins, M. and Marshall, S. (2017) 'A framework for enabling graduate outcomes in undergraduate programmes', *Higher Education Research and Development*, 36(1), pp. 43–58.

Bowden, J., Hart, G., King, B., Trigwell, K. and Watts, O. (2000) *Generic Capabilities of ATN University Graduates*. Sydney: University of Technology.

Boyd, W., Healey, R.L., Hardwick, S.W., Haigh, M., Klein, P., Doran, B., Trafford, J. and Bradbeer, J. (2008) '"None of us sets out to hurt people": the ethical geographer and geography curricula in higher education', *Journal of Geography in Higher Education*, 32, pp. 37–50.

Bridgstock, R. (2009) 'The graduate attributes we've overlooked: enhancing graduate employability through career management skills', *Higher Education Research and Development*, 28(1), pp. 31–44.

Couper, P. and Porter, S. (2016) '"Environmental awareness" and rock climbing: changing pedagogies to enhance pro-environmental graduate attributes', *Journal of Geography in Higher Education*, 40(2), pp. 207–221.

de la Harpe, B. and David, C. (2012) 'Major influences on the teaching and assessment of graduate attributes', *Higher Education Research & Development*, 31(4), pp. 493–510.

de St Jorre, T. and Oliver, B. (2018). 'Want students to engage? Contextualise graduate learning outcomes and assess for employability', *Higher Education Research & Development*, 37(1), pp. 44–57.

France, D., Powell, V., Mauchline, A.L., Welsh, K., Park, J., Whalley, B. and Rewhorn, S. (2016) 'Ability of students to recognize the relationship between using mobile apps for learning during fieldwork and the development of graduate attributes', *Journal of Geography in Higher Education*, 40(2), pp. 182–192.

Fuller, I.C. and France, D. (2016) 'Does digital video enhance student learning in field-based experiments and develop graduate attributes beyond the classroom?', *Journal of Geography in Higher Education*, 40(2), pp. 193–206.

Green, W., Hammer, S. and Star, C. (2007) 'Facing up to the challenge: why is it so hard to develop graduate attributes?', *Higher Education Research and Development*, 28(1), pp. 17–29.

Haigh, M. and Clifford, V.A. (2011) 'Integral vision: a multi-perspective approach to the recognition of graduate attributes', *Higher Education Research & Development*, 30, pp. 573–584.

Harden, R.M. (2001) 'AMEE Guide No. 21: Curriculum mapping: a tool for transparent and authentic learning and teaching', *Medical Teacher*, 23, pp. 123–137.

Hay, I. (2012) 'Over the threshold – setting minimum learning outcomes (benchmarks) for undergraduate geography majors in Australian universities', *Journal of Geography in Higher Education*, 36, pp. 481–498.

Healey, M. (2005) 'Linking research and teaching to benefit student learning', *Journal of Geography in Higher Education*, 29(2), pp. 183–201.

Healey, R.L. and Ribchester, C. (2016) 'Developing ethical geography students? The impact and effectiveness of a tutorial-based approach', *Journal of Geography in Higher Education*, 40(2), pp. 302–319.

Henderson, R. and Robertson, M. (1999). 'Who wants to be an entrepreneur? Young adult attitudes to entrepreneurship as a career', *Education + Training*, 41, pp. 236–245.

Hill, J. and Walkington, H. (2016) 'Developing graduate attributes through participation in undergraduate research conferences', *Journal of Geography in Higher Education*, 40(2), pp. 222–237.

Hill, J., Walkington, H. and France, D. (2016) 'Graduate attributes: implications for higher education practice and policy', *Journal of Geography in Higher Education*, 40(2), pp. 155–163.

Hounsell, D. and McCune, V. (2002) *Teaching–Learning Environments in Undergraduate Biology: Initial Perspectives and Findings* (ETL Occasional Reports, no. 2). Universities of Edinburgh, Durham and Coventry, ETL Project.

Houston, S.D. and Lange, K. (2017) '"Global/local" community engagement: advancing integrative learning and situated solidarity', *Journal of Geography in Higher Education*, https://doi.org/10.1080/03098265.2017.1331425.

Kalfa, S. and Taksa, L. (2015) 'Cultural capital in business higher education: reconsidering the graduate attributes movement and the focus on employability', *Studies in Higher Education*, 40(4), pp. 580–595.

Komoto, C. (2009) 'Moving toward a signature pedagogy in geography', in Gurung, R.A.R., Chick, N.L. and Haynie, A. (eds), *Exploring Signature Pedagogies: Approaches to Teaching Disciplinary Habits of Mind*, Sterling, VA: Stylus, pp. 121–138.

Korkmaz, Ö. and Karakuş, U. (2009) 'The impact of blended learning model on student attitudes towards geography course and their critical thinking dispositions and levels', *Turkish Online Journal of Educational Technology*, 8(4), pp. 51–63.

Kuh, G. (2008) *High-Impact Educational Practices: What They Are, Who Has Access to Them, and Why They Matter*. Available online at: https://secure.aacu.org/PubExcerpts/HIGHIMP.html. Accessed 26 February 2018.

Le Heron, R. and Hathaway, J.T. (2000) 'An international perspective on developing skills through geography programmes for employability and life: narratives from New Zealand and the United States', *Journal of Geography in Higher Education*, 24(2), pp. 271–276.

Mager, S. and Spronken-Smith, R. (2014) 'Graduate attribute attainment in a multi-level undergraduate geography course', *Journal of Geography in Higher Education*, 38(2), pp. 238–250.

McCune, V. and Entwistle, N.J. (2011) 'Cultivating the disposition to understand in 21st century university education', *Learning & Individual Differences*, 21, pp. 303–310.

McCune, V. and Hounsell, D. (2005) 'The development of students' ways of thinking and practicing in 3 final-year biology courses', *Higher Education*, 49(3), pp. 255–289.

McEwen, L. (2013) 'Geography, community engagement and citizenship: introduction', *Journal of Geography in Higher Education*, 37(1), pp. 5–10.

Meyer, J. and Land, R. (2005) 'Threshold concepts and troublesome knowledge (2): epistemological considerations and a conceptual framework for teaching and learning', *Higher Education*, 49, pp. 373–388.

Oliver, B. and de St Jorre, T. (2018) 'Graduate attributes for 2020 and beyond: recommendations for Australian higher education providers', *Higher Education Research and Development*, DOI: 10.1080/07294360.2018.14 46415.

Pawson, E., Fournier, E., Haigh, M., Muniz, O., Trafford, J. and Vajoczki, S. (2006) 'Problem-based learning in geography: towards a critical assessment of its purposes, benefits and risks', *Journal of Geography in Higher Education*, 30(1), pp. 103–116.

Richardson, J. (2005). 'Students' approaches to learning and teachers' approaches to teaching in higher education', *Educational Psychology*, 25(6), pp. 673–680.

Shulman, L. (2005) 'Signature pedagogies in the professions', *Dædalus*, 134, pp. 52–59.

Solem, M., Cheung, I. and Schlemper, M. (2008) 'Skills in professional geography: an assessment of workforce needs and expectations', *The Professional Geographer*, 60, pp. 356–373.

Spronken-Smith, R.A. (2005) 'Implementing a problem-based learning approach for Teaching Research Methods in Geography', *Journal of Geography in Higher Education*, 29(2), pp. 203–221.

Spronken-Smith, R. (2013) 'Towards securing a future for geography graduates', *Journal of Geography in Higher Education*, 37(3), pp. 315–326.

Spronken-Smith, R., Bond, C., McLean, A., Darrou, M., Frielick, S., Smith, N., Jenkins, M. and Marshall, S. (2013) *Graduate Outcomes: Are they Driving Learning?* Wellington, New Zealand: Ako Aotearoa. Available online at: https://akoaotearoa.ac.nz/graduate-outcomes. Accessed 26 February 2018.

Spronken-Smith, R.A., Bullard, J., Ray, W., Roberts, C. and Keiffer, A. (2008) 'Where might sand dunes be on Mars? Engaging students through inquiry-based learning in geography', *Journal of Geography in Higher Education*, 32(1), pp. 71–86.

Spronken-Smith, R., McLean, A., Smith, N., Bond, C., Jenkins, M., Marshall, S. and Frielick, S. (2016) 'A toolkit to implement graduate attributes in geography curricula', *Journal of Geography in Higher Education*, 40(2), pp. 254–266.

Whalley, W., Saunders, A., Lewis, R., Buenemann, M. and Sutton, P. (2011) 'Curriculum development: producing geographers for the 21st century', *Journal of Geography in Higher Education*, 35(3), pp. 379–393.

32. Teaching geography students about careers
Michael Solem, Niem Tu Huynh and Joseph Kerski

INTRODUCTION

Educating students about career opportunities in geography is in many ways a unique challenge. It is rather uncommon for an employer to advertise an opening for a 'geographer' per se, even in cases where a job entails applications of geographic knowledge, skills, and technologies (Adams et al., 2013). At the same time, many employers are simply unfamiliar with what a person with a geography degree knows and is able to do (Kneale, 2010). While this may at first glance seem to put geography students at a disadvantage, the good news is that the professional possibilities awaiting them are extensive, and very likely to remain so well into the future (Solem et al., 2008, 2013). Though methods of preparation vary, geography students overall benefit from an integrative perspective and skill-set that bridges human and physical systems, often aided and enhanced by geographic information systems (GIS) and other geospatial technologies. Our responsibility as educators and academic advisers in this context is to engage students in a process of thinking about the significance and potential of their academic preparation in geography and what it means to be and become a professional 'geographer'.

As a crucial component of this process, we believe geography educators need to be mindful of the broader purposes of education and learning in their discipline. Often the discourse on employability, careers, and workforce development assumes a neoliberal tenor and runs the risk of defining and evaluating educational practice, and what disciplines contribute to higher learning, in the language of managerialism, credentialism, and vocationalism (Walkington et al., 2018). Indeed, many academic institutions in the US and elsewhere are feeling pressures to produce 'human capital' of service to various industries. Academic geography departments are not immune to these forces and, in fact, many programs are rebranding and renaming themselves in efforts to project a more modern and appealing identity, in some cases dropping 'geography' altogether in favor of 'geoscience', 'geospatial science', and other interdisciplinary and hybrid names that are perceived to have greater cache from the perspective of students and university administrators (Frazier and Wikle, 2016).

We are in no doubt that many geographers feel these changes are necessary to address local needs, boost student enrollments, and satisfy administrators seeking to reduce costs by merging or eliminating 'unproductive' departments and programs. At the same time, there is no broader understanding of what these changes mean for the geography discipline over the longer term. Until we have research that produces evidence of the impact of these changes, we are only left to speculate about the potential impacts on the discipline. It seems reasonable to suggest that there is significant potential for loss in the epistemic quality of geography in higher education if educators and administrators begin to evaluate curricula solely in terms of the skills and competencies that have the most currency in an era where academic programs often have to justify their existence in terms of whether their graduates find employment. The danger, as we and others see it, is a neglect of the 'powerful' disciplinary knowledge that geography adds to the education of all young people (Lambert and Solem, 2017).

Powerful geographic knowledge refers to the substantive, conceptual, and procedural knowledge of the discipline that advances human capability, well-being, and agency in life, and which has significance that cannot be understood solely in terms of its economic and labor market values. Many examples of powerful geographic knowledge, and what makes it significant for individuals and society, are available on the GeoCapabilities website (www.geocapabilities.org). As we proceed in this chapter to introduce resources and approaches to teaching students about career opportunities in geography, we encourage readers to never lose sight of what it is that geography adds beyond preparation for work and career life.

GEOGRAPHY, EMPLOYABILITY, AND CHANGE IN HIGHER EDUCATION

Teaching about geography careers is a longstanding tradition within geography. The goal of much of the instruction has been to equip students with the geographic skills, perspectives, and content knowledge to make them employable. Approaches have included the introduction of enterprise and employability modules (Maguire and Guyer, 2007), hands-on work with geographic tools (such as GIS, GPS, and remote sensing), field trips to workplaces where people using geography skills are hired (such as a city planning and zoning office), guest lectures by public and private sector geographers, and participation in special events such as GIS Day (www.gisday.com). Bridgstock (2009, p. 31) argued that:

> In the context of a rapidly changing information and knowledge-intensive economy, employability involves far more than possession of the generic skills listed by graduate employers as attractive. Rather, for optimal economic and social outcomes, graduates must be able to proactively navigate the world of work and self-manage the career-building process.

Le Heron and Hathaway (2000) argued the quality of geography education can be improved by closing the gap between the perceived social usefulness of the subject (suggested by evidence to be relatively low) and the realities of what a subject offers as preparation for workplace roles (suggested by evidence to be relatively high). Spronken-Smith (2013) stated that the goal of career education in geography was to empower students to cope with an uncertain future. The evolving economy and continuous emergence of new jobs that do not yet exist (Hallett and Hutt, 2016) make it challenging to prepare students for their future career.

Today's students will begin their careers in an era of massive global change driven by human activity. The unprecedented scale of anthropogenic change to the environment has prompted some scholars to refer to this period as the Anthropocene (Dalby, 2016; Kress and Stine, 2017). Scientific agencies such as the US National Science Foundation and the US National Research Council have issued many high-profile reports and assessments of future workforce needs in relation to these contemporary social and environmental challenges, including calls for more interdisciplinary training to support emerging research areas that help address problems at the human-Earth system interface (National Science Foundation, 2009; National Research Council, 2010). Meanwhile, there have been repeated calls for change in the academy and graduate education to encourage the broadening of career paths to include non-traditional and non-academic careers (Bowness, 2015; UBC Faculty of Graduate and Postdoctoral Studies, 2017).

Along with these changes has been the rise of professionalism in society, first noted by sociologists over 40 years ago (Larson, 1977), and the subsequent rise in credentialism and certification in the workplace. The past decade has seen a rapid rise in the number of universities offering a professional science master's degree (Laredo, 2007), including in geography and environmental studies, aimed at students who want to pursue a non-academic career (Monk and Foote, 2015). Professional doctorates are also appearing (Wildy et al., 2014), such as one at Concordia University which supports placements in the government or non-profit sector. These professional graduate degrees tend to include a greater amount of fieldwork, networking and internships with professionals, independent 'capstone' projects rather than a traditional research thesis, and are designed to be completed in a shorter period of time (for example the Masters of the Environment Program at the University of Colorado requires just 17 months to complete). Some universities have formed a membership organization called the Professional Science Masters (https://www.professionalsciencemasters.org) designed to maintain rigor and establish standards for what constitutes such a degree over a 'regular' master's degree. Alongside these programs have risen a great number of certificate programs (Kawabata et al., 2010), which in geography is most evident in certificates involving geotechnologies such as GIS, remote sensing or, more recently, web map coding or programming.

In order to support these changes and the shift in academic culture they imply, the educational system will need the proper tools, such as student-to-professional career educational resources that provide detailed information on how disciplinary knowledge, skills, and perspectives are applied in different professional sectors and how students' educational and career pathways are likely to develop over time. It is with this information that academic geography programs can accurately assess the current rate at which students are entering careers and practicing geography in different industries.

Many of the programmatic changes sweeping higher education come in the wake of governmental assessments warning of looming workforce shortages in both the geoscience and geographical professions. Geography's professional societies have also increasingly sounded the alarm about the prospect of workforce shortages over the next decade as geoscience workforce demographics have indicated an impending wave of retirements juxtaposed against a persistent low supply of new graduates entering the profession (Freeman, 2006, 2008; Powers, 2008). In addition, the development of connections between business sectors and academia is a key for ensuring that geography students obtain the education and skill-sets that prepare them for careers in both 'traditional' and emerging and non-traditional areas that expand the application and influence of the geographical sciences (Groat, 2008; Manduca et al., 2008).

As academic departments continue to face budget cuts and increasing pressure from reviews and assessments by university administrations, many programs are in need of help with educating students and potential majors about the value of a geography degree for the job market. In Canada, the leaders who are addressing this need are often found in university career centers or graduate studies units and professional associations. For example, Wilfrid Laurier University (Waterloo, Ontario in Canada) hosts lunchtime career webinars as well as an online networking platform called 'ten thousand coffees' for alumni and current students. At Queen's university, the careers centre developed a 'majors map' of a four-year undergraduate itinerary to the workplace. As a final example, the Canadian Association of Geographers (CAG) developed a comprehensive report of careers resources across geography departments. The authors of this report highlighted exemplary resources and called for an immediate need for developing more resources of this nature (Quinn and Huynh, 2016). In response, the association invested money to produce profiles of professional geographers who represent the diverse demographic face of the nation as well as the sectors in the workforce. These have been shared on social media and showcased at various geography events (for example, Geography Day, GIS Day) (See the Useful Resources section of this chapter for additional examples of careers resources).

A survey of first-year university students in Canada found that one of the primary reasons they pursue post-secondary education is to advance their career prospects (Canadian University Survey Consortium, 2016). The return on investment in a post-secondary education is often questioned by parents, students taking undergraduate courses, and scholars pursuing graduate studies. This discussion has prompted creative ways in graduate recruitment to spotlight alumni and highlight careers outcomes. For example, the 'career outcomes' tab featured on the geography program page at the University of British Columbia targets prospective students.

The expectation of linking higher education to a career is another driver for the creation of careers-oriented programs and resources. In Canada, there is increasing dialogue, studies, and leadership on alternative academic (also known as alt-ac) options and resources beneficial to the social sciences generally, and to geography more specifically. Some players include the Canadian publication *University Affairs* (equivalent to *The Chronicle of Higher Education* in the US), which hosts a blog called 'Beyond the Professoriate' to illuminate career paths of graduate degree holders. Recently, a collaborative project, borne between US and Canadian universities, launched *Imagine PhD*. This website offers a range of free employment-related resources for doctoral and post-doctoral scholars in the social sciences and humanities.

BUILDING CAPACITY FOR CAREERS EDUCATION IN GEOGRAPHY

Over the past decade, the American Association of Geographers (AAG) has developed a variety of strategies and curriculum resources to teach geography students, high school through to post-secondary and graduate studies, about issues of professional ethics, career planning, networking strategies, work–life balance, lifelong learning, and relationships between theory and applied practice in geography. Geography is such a wide-ranging field that it can be hard to know what one wants to do without gaining first-hand experiences about current and future options. In the following sections of this chapter, we highlight three particular activities that have been featured for several years in workshops held in the Jobs and Careers Center during the AAG Annual Meeting. The first activity we present is a data-based approach to teaching students how to evaluate their professional qualifications using a 'gap analysis'. Next, we discuss an activity that illustrates ways of using geography's interdisciplinary characteristics to help students of diverse backgrounds map their geographic interests onto different career fields. GIS technology provides the context for the third activity, which asks students a series of probing questions about the knowledge and skill-sets required to perform spatial analysis using GIS in an authentic career context.

In each of these cases, the pedagogical approach we advocate goes beyond the technical 'nuts-and-bolts' of helping students write cover letters, format resumes, design portfolios, and improve their interviewing skills. Instead, the activities demonstrate ways of preparing students to think analytically about the broader industry trends shaping the future economy, what it means for them to be a geographer, and how disciplinary expertise in geography connects to the evolving needs of business, government, and nonprofit employer organizations.

The activities presented in this chapter take different approaches to teaching students how they can gain knowledge and skills to enhance their employability. Cognizant of rapid changes in the workplace and continuously emerging geography-related career opportunities, these activities also encourage 'elastic thinking' (Cook, 2018) to adapt to changes by way of active explorations of information gathering. There are no correct responses, only insights, about the range of professional possibilities that apply to geography, and in relation to each student's individual career interests. From this approach, students stand to gain valuable research skills and a newfound appreciation of the broader value of geography in a wide array of professional settings.

THREE MODEL ACTIVITIES

Below we introduce a set of activities that are designed to help students identify and understand the range of career options available to geographers. These activities, developed by academics doing research in geography careers in collaboration with professional geographers, were first introduced at the 2013 AAG Annual Meeting. Since that time, the authors have refined the activities based on feedback from over 60 participants who represented primarily college/university professors and high school teachers. Attendees commented on several immediate benefits stemming from their participation, one of which is showing where educators can access geography careers material. The second is that participants report more confidence, after the workshop, to incorporate careers materials into the curriculum. Overall, the feedback, from the perspective of instructors rather than students, has been positive and strengthens the argument for more work and resources to support the dissemination of geography careers information.

The activities may be further tailored to different educational settings by incorporating elements such as assigning a graded value to the activity, joint instruction between educators and career advisors, and soliciting student feedback to inform refinement and revision of the activities. The activities may be used to raise career awareness among students as soon as they are ready to think about their future employment. We suggest that they be implemented at multiple points in the duration of a student's academic career, rather than solely in the last year of high school or college/university. While the activities focus on careers, each makes a strong case that content knowledge in geography is critical to the application of skills. For example, to most effectively use spatial analysis to analyze watersheds or water quality, knowledge of the interaction between watersheds, terrain, land use, zoning, weather patterns, and land cover is essential. Otherwise, the application is often reduced to 'button-pushing', or only knowing how to operate software.

Activity 1: Evaluating Professional Qualifications Using a Gap Analysis

This assignment was originally created by Dr Joy K. Adams, former Senior Researcher at the American Association of Geographers, and since modified by Dr Michael Solem. The activity is designed to help students identify a potential occupation, based on an area of personal interest or selected from among the profiles of professional geographers in the AAG book *Practicing Geography* (Solem et al., 2013), the AAG's Jobs and Careers website, or external sources.

Once an occupation has been selected, students assess their previous knowledge of this occupation, including its educational requirements, required skills and abilities, estimated salary and hiring outlook, and other considerations. They record this information in the 'My Initial Perceptions' column of Table 32.1(a). Next, students conduct research to verify, refute, and/or refine their initial perceptions using the information provided in the *Bureau of Labor Statistics Occupational Outlook Handbook* (http://www.bls.gov/ooh/), O*Net (http://www.onetonline.org/), and/or the online salary and labor information available on the AAG Jobs and Careers website (www.aag.org/salarydata). This information is recorded by students in the 'What the Data Show' and 'Sources Cited' columns of Table 32.1(a).

Students then use the results to perform a gap analysis to assess their preparation to work in this occupation and identify areas where further training, education, or experience is necessary or advantageous (Table 32.1(b)). A gap analysis is defined by Greneir and Wikle (2013, p. 9) as:

> a systematic process for comparing a job seeker's qualifications with those specified in a position advertisement. Missing elements or 'gaps' can be identified by making a list of skills or competencies desired or required by employers in one column and creating a second column

Table 32.1(a)   Sample career exploration worksheet

Job title: _____

	My initial perception(s)	What the data show	Source(s) cited
Median salary			
Educational requirements			
Occupational outlook			
Major knowledge areas			
Key skills/technologies used			
Primary duties/job tasks			
Top industries for this occupation			

Table 32.1(b)   Sample gap analysis matrix

Job requirement	My qualifications	Gaps identified	Strategies for addressing gaps

to show the job seeker's corresponding skills and competencies. The final step in a gap analysis is comparing employer needs to personal skills and competencies. Deficiencies or 'gaps' should be shown in a third column together with a plan describing what will be done to address the deficiency. For example, a gap involving experience with a specific remote sensing software package could be addressed by taking an additional course or a training seminar.

As an optional assessment, students can submit their gap analysis matrix with a brief paper about their gap analysis that demonstrates: 1) their ability to conduct basic research related to employment prospects and career opportunities; 2) clear and effective written communication; and 3) critical thinking about their own skills and qualifications relative to the demands of the job market. Papers should also include a reflective component in which students discuss the accuracy of their preconceived ideas about a specific occupation and how this exercise might influence their approach to future professional development, job searches, and educational activities.

This activity is suitable for any student, but especially those students at transitional points of their academic career, such as towards the end of high school or when they are declaring a major in college. In the former case, students could research the available courses offered at various colleges/universities that would support their skill/knowledge development, making an informed decision on where they invest in their post-secondary studies.

Activity 2: Transcending Boundaries: Applying Geography Knowledge, Skills, and Practices Across Disciplines

This assignment was created by Niem Huynh, former Senior Researcher at the American Association of Geographers. The activity, like the previous gap analysis exercise, uses profiles of professional geographers to illustrate to learners the interdisciplinary nature of geography and how that can be leveraged to formulate a comprehensive education plan for students.

Students are provided with a list of geography employment titles and an interdisciplinary diagram of geography. As examples and a starting point, job titles from profiles developed by professional organizations can be explored:

● American Association of Geographers Jobs and Careers website: http://www.aag.org/careerprofiles

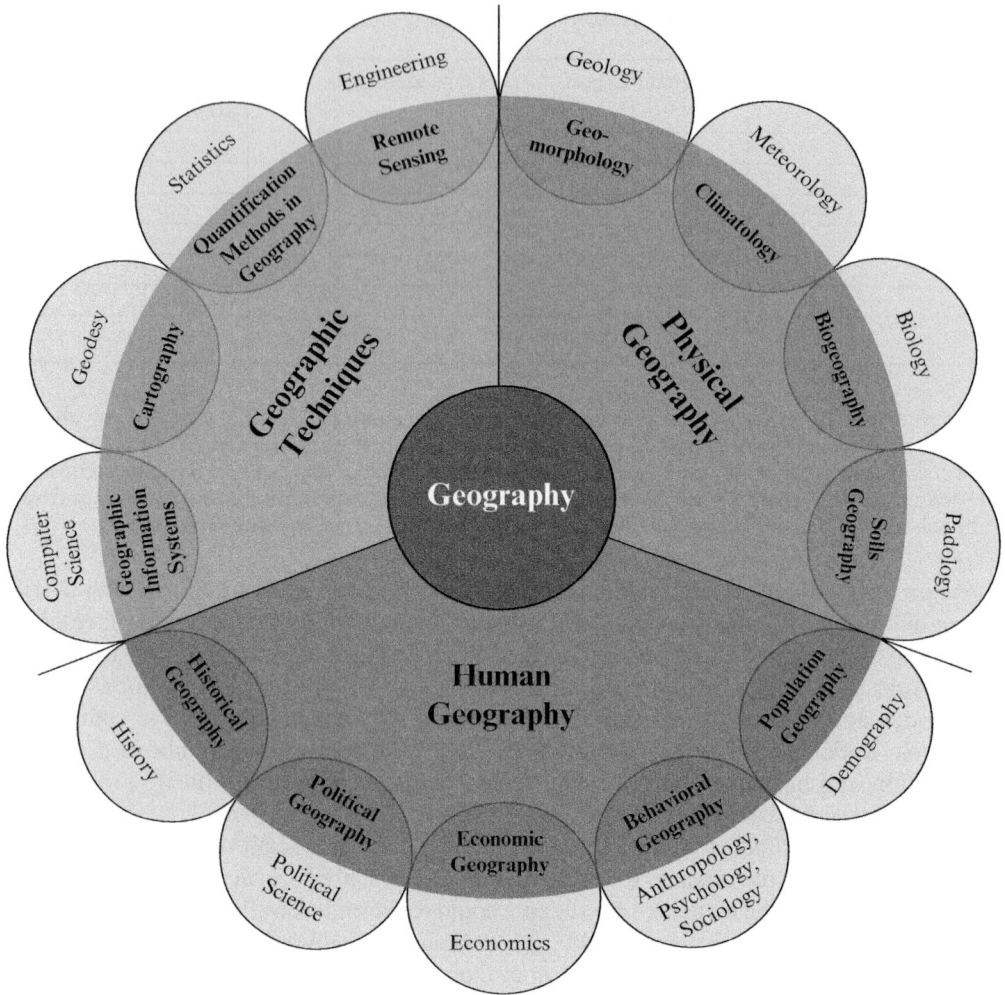

Source: de Blij and Muller (2006).

Figure 32.1 Interdisciplinary geography diagram

- Canadian Association of Geographers profiles of professional geographers: https://www.cag-acg.ca/profiles-of-geographers
- Geomatics Association of Nova Scotia: https://www.gans.ca/Geospatial-Careers

Using the provided list of geography employment titles (or profile), students select a position from each of four categories (business, education, government, and nonprofit sectors). They write each position title on the interdisciplinary diagram (Figure 32.1) near the areas from which it is most likely to draw geography and related disciplinary content knowledge, skills, and perspectives.

Reading the selected profiles in the above sources or from research, students note the education level these positions require (for example high school, college, university). In small groups or in a pair, students discuss and identify on the diagram core elements of geography (geographic techniques, physical geography, and human geography) and cross-cutting concepts that may be helpful for one of the job titles selected (for example economic geography, economics, population geography, demography, and planning are useful to be a real estate market researcher).

Finally, the students investigate, based on the diagram, what current course(s) they can take at their institution (or another organization) to prepare for one of the selected job titles or what experiential opportunities to pursue before graduation. An example of an end product is a diagram with geography in the center, and extending out in individual spokes are jobs available from studying geography or a related field, education prerequisites for each position, and concepts (core or cross-cutting) helpful to the job.

As an optional assignment, students can be asked to seek an informational interview from a professional geographer in order to gain employment insight and advice. This is also a chance for students to learn the importance of professional conduct (for example how to address the professional or make the initial request for an interview), as well as interviewing skills (for example have a list of questions prepared, keep track of time, send a thank-you note after the interview to the participating geographer).

On completion of this assignment, students have developed networking skills and the know-how to accomplish this within their local, state, or national agencies. AAG offers contact information of geographers working in a range of fields (http://www.aag.org/ask_a_geographer) who are open to sharing their experiences, connect with people on LinkedIn, or ask for an introduction from a mutual contact.

To enhance this activity, resources could be leveraged in the local community to engage with professional geographers. Educators could create a list of contacts by searching for job titles (as provided in the websites above) through social media (e.g. LinkedIn) or word-of-mouth. In creating this contact list, the importance of diversity should be kept in mind, both demographic and professional work. The contacts collected by each cohort could be compiled to generate an on-going list of professional geographers for future use.

Activity 3: Examining Career Skills Necessary to Apply Geography to Solve Problems Using GIS

The third activity was created by Joseph Kerski of Esri and University of Denver. It asks students to think purposefully about careers in applying geography to solve problems through the use of GIS, using the Esri Map Books series as a basis for discussion and investigation.

The activity invites students to think about career pathways, skill building, and work environments while examining maps produced using GIS to solve specific problems. Each year, thousands of GIS professionals and scientists from around the world submit paper and digital maps to be featured in the map gallery at the Esri User Conference. During the week that the map gallery is open, the maps are viewed by 18,000 conference attendees, plus thousands more online. These maps represent the application of GIS to address and solve geographic problems at local to global scales. Authors of the maps include local, regional, national, and international government agencies, nonprofit organizations, private companies, individual consultants, and university and school instructors and students. The maps cover a large variety of themes, including energy, water quality and quantity, natural hazards, transportation, sustainable agriculture, tourism, land use, weather and climate, city planning, health, business, economics, wildlife biology, public safety, criminal justice, cartography, and many more. A subset of the maps submitted each year are chosen for the Esri Map Book. The maps are chosen for the book because they address a unique issue, because they use GIS tools in innovative ways, because their subject matter has wide appeal, or because the cartography is compelling.

To prepare the activity, a facilitator should obtain one or more print copies of the Esri Map Books, either from Esri Press (www.esri.com/books) or the online version on the MapMuseum (www.esri.com/mapmuseum). For greater variety, facilitators should ideally choose map books representing several different years (see Figure 32.2). The books should be distributed to the students or they should be asked to visit the website. In introductory comments and discussion, the facilitator should focus on these three key elements:

1. GIS is a manifestation of applied geography. It represents a way of addressing geographic problems in a systematic way, by applying tools, data, and procedures to solve those problems.
2. The fields, themes, and scales that GIS can be applied to continue to expand as the technology itself becomes easier to use, migrates to a web-based platform, and the spatial data behind GIS becomes more open and available. The chief reasons are because the intensifying complex issues of the 21st century are increasingly affecting our everyday lives and the health of the planet, and because these complex issues are inherently geographic. To deal with these issues and to build resilient communities, more and more organizations are asking, and will continue to ask, the 'where' question, and the 'whys of where' question.
3. As the application of geography continues to expand, so too do the career opportunities wherein workers can and will make use of GIS. Some of these career opportunities will be in job titles that include GIS, such as 'GIS analyst' or 'GIS manager', but most will have job titles that make no reference to GIS, such as 'transportation engineer' or 'wildlife biologist'. In those latter cases, GIS will still be a fundamental skill necessary for success in that position.

After introducing the activity, gather students into a classroom configuration that fosters conversation, such as around a common table or with chairs arranged in a circle. Foster an interactive sharing of ideas by asking students to choose three maps that interest them for some reason, and then engage them in a dialogue using the following questions:

● Is the symbology and layout of the maps you have chosen appealing? Is the problem that the maps address related to your own interests or background? Is the location addressed one you are interested in visiting, have already visited, or near where you live? Or, is there another reason for your interest in the maps?
● Why does the first of your three maps interest you? Encourage the students responding to this question to show the rest of the group the map that they have identified by holding up and passing the page in the map book around the room or by showing the digital version of the map on their own device or on a screen or wall via a projector.

Figure 32.2   Section of Esri Map Books that shows the application of geographic thinking to solve problems through GIS

- What is the problem(s) or issue(s) to which GIS is being applied? Why does the problem or issue matter? Who are the people affected by the problem or issue, where do they live, and how does the problem or issue affect them?
- What field(s) or disciplines are home to this problem or issue? How is geography important, even if the home discipline to the problem identified is from the field of human health, business marketing, emergency management, or another discipline?
- What is the scale of this problem; neighborhood, city, regional, national, or global? Or, does the problem have multiple scales that are equally important? How might the problem, and the spatial patterns and relationships being examined, change if the scale of analysis for this problem is changed?
- What organization(s) were involved in grappling with this problem? Do some research on the organization. What is the mission of the organization? How many people work for the organization? What sort of other work, outside the issue identified by the map, do you think these individuals do?
- Could you envision yourself working for this organization? Do you know someone working for this organization? Do you know of another organization with a similar mission? How could you connect with that person or with that organization to find out more about it?
- What sort of work environment do you think the people working on this map have? Does any of their work take place in the field? If so, what percentage? What are the field conditions for these workers? How much of the work do you think is in teams versus working independently?
- How much of a typical week's time do you think the people who worked on this map spend on GIS analysis, versus communicating the results of their work, versus other tasks?
- How does GIS and the geographic perspective help solve the problem represented by this map? What is the value added to the organization, to the community, and to society by using GIS and the geographic perspective?
- Introduce the following statement and discuss: 'A good map teaches us to ask a better question'. What is your reaction to this statement? Can you think of an additional question about the problem based on your chosen map? What additional data, procedures, or tools might be used to address the problem?
- What skills in technology, multimedia, data, cartography, communications, GIS, critical thinking, and spatial thinking are required to use GIS to solve the problem presented in your chosen map?
- What content knowledge (such as water quality and quantity, land use change, ocean currents, animal behavior, crop health, planning and zoning, and so on) is required to solve this problem?
- How can the skills and content knowledge that you just identified be obtained? Are they best obtained on the job, at a technical college, at a university, at a private company, through an online set of courses, or through some other means?
- What course(s) would you need to take at your technical or community college, or university so that you could gain the skills necessary to solve the problems in the ways that are presented in this map? What courses or training could you take outside the university to enhance your skills?

After this activity is completed, wrap up the session by completing the following two steps:

1. Summarize the importance of GIS in applying geography to solve problems. At the same time, focus on the fact that the effective use of GIS depends not only on technical skills, but also communication skills, geographic content knowledge, and the geographic perspective.
2. If print editions of the map books are available, consider posting selected pages on the classroom wall. Each page is large and makes an intriguing poster. In this way, students are seeing a wide variety of maps and are physically surrounded by examples of geography in action through GIS when they come to class.

CONCLUSION

In countries like the US, with limited time in the school curriculum for geography instruction, most students enter higher education knowing little about geography careers or what they could do with a career in geography. Therefore, career education in geography will most likely always require ongoing and creative efforts to communicate the value of the discipline to parents, students, and employers. Dialogue and engagement are needed to dispel misunderstandings about the nature of geography as a field of study and what its practitioners actually do. Despite the ubiquity of geospatial technologies in everyday life (Couclelis et al., 2011), the use of maps and geo-visualizations in media, and the rise of location-based services, there will always be a need for geographers to articulate clearly and argue persuasively for the knowledge and skills geography graduates can contribute to business, government, and nonprofit organizations. Similarly, there will be a continued need for geographers to contribute their knowledge of complex earth systems and skills for solving problems at the human-Earth system interface (Gewin, 2004; Kerski, 2008).

As academic institutions, the nature of work, and the ways in which geography can be applied all continue to evolve at an accelerated pace, a critical need exists to evaluate the effectiveness of instruction about careers. A research opportunity involving the activities presented in this chapter might include a study with a large number of students across multiple institutions, to explore research questions such as: How effective are these activities in terms of how students understand the breadth of career opportunities in geography? Are these activities influential in students deciding to keep geography as their primary field of study? Are these activities influential in students' choices on pursuing internships and jobs?

As geography general education courses are often students' first encounter with disciplinary geography, including these activities in such courses could be instructive in terms of assessing whether they influence students' decisions to choose a geography major. We also advocate that other career resources, some of which we have identified below, are evaluated in terms of their effectiveness. In an era of unprecedented resources from which to choose, the results of these evaluations would be helpful for instructors who seek the maximum return on investment in terms of which resources they should teach with.

USEFUL RESOURCES

The activities presented in this chapter are only some of the diverse resources for careers education that can help address disciplinary educational challenges. Below are some exemplars of freely available resources for learners, student advisers, educators and anyone looking to transition to professional work in the field of geography.

- Activities to pursue for career discovery (Queens University, Canada): http://careers. queensu.ca/students/wondering-about-career-options/major-maps.
- Academic research repository on careers identity (McGill University, Canada): https://www.mcgill.ca/doc-work/.
- Geography careers posters (Geomatics Association of Nova Scotia): https://www. gans.ca/Geospatial-Careers.
- Geography career videos (Esri): https://www.virtualjobshadow.com/vs3/partners/ esri/.
- Professional geographer profiles:
  - o   American Association of Geographers: http://www.aag.org/careerprofiles;
  - o   AAG Esri GeoMentor program: http://www.aag.org/cs/geomentors/connect/ geomentor_spotlight;
  - o   Canadian Association of Geographers: https://www.cag-acg.ca/profiles-of-geo graphers.
- *Directions Magazine* GeoInspirations column by Joseph Kerski: https://www.direc tionsmag.com/playlist/6651.

REFERENCES

Adams, J.K., Huynh, N.T., Kerski, J.K. and Hall, G.B. (2013) 'Geography education and career readiness', in M. Solem, K. Foote and J. Monk (eds), *Practicing Geography: Careers for Enhancing Society and the Environment.* Upper Saddle River, NJ: Pearson Education, pp. 15–26.

Bowness, S. (2015) *What's Up With Alt-Ac Careers.* Available online at: https://www.universityaffairs.ca/features/ feature-article/whats-up-with-alt-ac-careers/.

Bridgstock, R. (2009) 'The graduate attributes we've overlooked: Enhancing graduate employability through career management skills', *Higher Education Research and Development*, 28 (1), pp. 31–44.

Canadian University Survey Consortium (2016) *2016 First-Year University Student Survey.* Available online at: http://www.cusc-ccreu.ca/publications/CUSC_2016-First-Year-Report-EN.pdf.

Cook, G. (2018) *The Power of Flexible Thinking.* Available online at: https://www.scientificamerican.com/article/ the-power-of-flexible-thinking/.

Couclelis, H., Nyerges, T. and McMaster, R. (eds) (2011) *The SAGE Handbook of GIS and Society.* London: Sage.

Dalby, S. (2016) 'Framing the anthropocene: The good, the bad and the ugly', *The Anthropocene Review*, 3 (1), pp. 33–51.

de Blij, H.J. and Muller, P.O. (2006) *Geography, Realms, Regions, and Concepts* (12th edition). Wiley.

Frazier, A. and Wikle, T. (2016) 'Renaming and Rebranding within U.S. and Canadian Geography Departments, 1990–2014', *The Professional Geographer*, 69 (1), pp. 12–21.

Freeman, L.W. (2006) *Careers, Competencies (and Compensation): Human Resource Crisis in the Minerals Industry.* Paper presented at the Geological Society of America Annual Meeting, Philadelphia, PA.

Freeman, L.W. (2008) *Perspectives on an Emerging Workforce Crisis in Geology: Assessing a Looming Irony – the Mining Perspective: Carpe Diem.* Paper presented at the 2008 Joint Annual Meeting ASA-CSSA-SSSA, Pittsburgh, PA.

Gewin, V. (2004) 'Mapping opportunities', *Nature*, 427, pp. 376–377.

Greneir, A. and Wikle, T. (2013) 'Part strategy, part serendipity: A candid guide to career planning for geographers', in M. Solem, K. Foote and J. Monk (eds), *Practicing Geography: Careers for Enhancing Society and the Environment.* Upper Saddle River, NJ: Pearson Education, pp. 1–14.

Groat, C.G. (2008) *Perspectives on the Future Unconventional Geoscience Workforce. 2008.* Paper presented at the 2008 Joint Annual Meeting ASA-CSSA-SSSA, Pittsburgh, PA.

Hallett, R. and Hutt, R. (2016) *10 Jobs that Didn't Exist 10 Years Ago.* Available online at: https://www.weforum.org/agenda/2016/06/10-jobs-that-didn-t-exist-10-years-ago/.

Kawabata, M., Thapa, R.B., Oguchi, T. and Tsou, M.-H. (2010) 'Multidisciplinary cooperation in GIS education: A case study of US colleges and universities', *Journal of Geography in Higher Education*, 34 (4), pp. 493–509.

Kerski, J. (2008) 'The role of GIS in digital earth education', *International Journal of Digital Earth*, 1 (1), pp. 326–346.

Kneale, P. (2010) 'Careers for geography graduates', *Journal of Geography in Higher Education*, 3, pp. 405–412.

Kress, W. and Stine, J. (eds) (2017) *Living in the Anthropocene: Earth in the Age of Humans.* Washington, DC: Smithsonian Books.

Lambert, D. and Solem, M. (2017) 'Rediscovering the teaching of geography', *Geographical Education*, 30, pp. 8–15.

Laredo, P. (2007) 'Revisiting the third mission of universities: Toward a reviewed categorization of university activities?', *Higher Education Policy*, 20 (4), pp. 441–456.

Larson, M.S. (1977) *The Rise of Professionalism: A Sociological Analysis.* Berkeley: University of California Press.

Le Heron, R. and Hathaway, J. (2000) 'An international perspective on developing skills through geography programmes for employability and life: Narratives from New Zealand and the United States', *Journal of Geography in Higher Education*, 24 (2), pp. 271–276.

Maguire, S. and Guyer, C. (2007) 'Preparing geography, earth and environmental science (GEES) students for employment in the enterprise culture', *Journal of Geography in Higher Education*, 28 (3), pp. 369–379.

Manduca, C.A., Macdonald, R.H., Feiss, P.G., Richardson, R.M., Bralower, T.J., Eyles, C.H. and Ormand, C.J. (2008) *Geoscience Departments and the Workforce: Bringing Together Student Interests and Industry Needs.* Paper presented at the 2008 Joint Annual Meeting ASA-CSSA-SSSA, Pittsburgh, PA.

Monk, J. and Foote, K. (2015) 'Directions and challenges of master's programs in geography in the United States', *The Professional Geographer*, 67 (3), pp. 472–481.

National Research Council (2010) *Understanding the Changing Planet: Strategic Directions for the Geographic Sciences.* Washington, DC: The National Academics Press.

National Science Foundation (2009) *GeoVision Report.* Available online at: http://www.nsf.gov/geo/acgeo/geovision/start.jsp.

Powers, R. (2008) *The Future GeoEnvironmental Workforce – Will there be Enough Talent?* Paper presented at the 2008 Joint Annual Meeting ASA-CSSA-SSSA, Pittsburgh, PA.

Quinn, R. and Huynh, N.T. (2016) *Where, What, and How do Geography Students find Geography Careers Information?* Available online at: https://www.cag-acg.ca/career-resources.

Solem, M., Cheung, I. and Schlemper, B. (2008) 'Skills in professional geography: An assessment of workforce needs and expectations', *The Professional Geographer*, 60 (3), pp. 1–18.

Solem, M., Foote, K. and Monk, J. (eds) (2013) *Practicing Geography: Careers for Enhancing Society and the Environment.* Upper Saddle River, NJ: Pearson Education.

Spronken-Smith, R. (2013) 'Toward securing a future for geography graduates', *Journal of Geography in Higher Education*, 37 (3), pp. 315–326.

UBC Faculty of Graduate and Postdoctoral Studies (2017) *UBC PhD Career Outcomes.* Available online at: http://outcomes.grad.ubc.ca/docs/UBC_PhD_Career_Outcomes_April2017.pdf.

Walkington, H., Dyer, S., Solem, M., Haigh, M. and Waddington, S. (2018) 'A capabilities approach to higher education', *Journal of Geography in Higher Education*, 42 (1), pp. 7–24.

Wildy, H., Peden, S. and Chan, K. (2014) 'The rise of professional doctorates: Case studies of the doctorate in education in China, Iceland and Australia', *Studies in Higher Education*, 40 (5), pp. 761–774.

33. Exploring pedagogic tensions in final year programme design
Pauline E. Kneale

INTRODUCTION

What is the purpose of the final undergraduate year, making it distinctive pedagogically and as a capstone experience that provides professional experiences with lasting benefits? Questions that arise in considering the curriculum include: whose space is it; what are the most effective learning and assessment styles; what experiences will yield the greatest long-term relevance; how do we move towards long-term capabilities (Walkington et al., 2018), and who makes the decisions? Is the final year designed as an exciting event in its own right, as a closing down space, or a transition year to higher degrees or professional employment (Gardner et al., 1998)? What are the components that will inspire, enthuse and engage this generation of students so they see their activities, their research, having impact in the workplace, community and other spheres?

We can articulate tensions between a programme's vision of the final year involving a space of freedom (Freire, 1998), challenge, disruption (Higgitt, 2014), liminality (Hill et al., 2019), unfinished thinking, and a confusion of ideas, many of which remain unresolved on graduation (Scott, 2015), versus a controlled space for analysis, synthesis, reflection, defined project delivery and calm surety. This sets up tensions between those faculty preferring to work in a creative, dynamic, student-centred environment at one end of the spectrum and those preferring calm, controlled delivery with limited student–student and student–staff interaction at the other. With teacher-centred approaches, the focus is on a lecturer's performance and presentation of material, essentially transferring information to the class. In student-centred approaches, involving active and experiential pedagogies, learning is prioritised and supported (Scheyvens et al., 2008), assessment is authentic (see Chapter 27 in this volume by Hill and Worth), and delivery is inclusive, supporting learners with diverse backgrounds and learning needs (Gibbs and Simpson, 2005; Biggs and Tang, 2007).

This chapter will explore key issues to consider when (re-)designing programmes, presenting them deliberately in an oppositional style to provoke discussion between colleagues (Figueira et al., 2018), but recognising that stark versus/or/rather than statements hide the reality of many shades of grey in a system that is constantly evolving. The chapter builds on these debates to present an argument for increasing team-based, large scale research challenges in the final undergraduate year.

EXPLORING PEDAGOGIC TENSIONS

The Millennial Student Tension

Understanding how today's students learn successfully is essential. Ebert (2016) bluntly calls for educators to change their methods in order to reach today's millennial student. Similarly, NIU (2014) state 'Millennials are the most diverse generation we have had to teach, thus our approaches to teaching must be diverse . . . Millennials expect to be engaged in their learning, they do not do well being passive learners'. Stevens and Nies (2018) maintain that these students embrace technology, lose interest during lectures, and enjoy the challenges and experience of taking part in interactive learning activities. Likewise, Phillips and Joseph's (2015, p. 526) study includes some points made by students which are worth foregrounding: 'Don't read from PowerPoint . . . I zoned out before the second slide. Try to relate the material to the real world or explain how it would be applied to actual tasks. Try to engage students in the material by answering questions, rather than consistent lecturing'. This preference for authentic action learning, with class time used to encourage student understanding, underpins the use of flipped classroom pedagogies (Graham et al., 2017), and supports consistent use of RASE pedagogy (Resources, Activities, Support and Evaluation) in all modules (Churchill et al., 2014; UNSW, 2017). Research by Maxwell-Stuart et al. (2018, p. 1401) shows that 'fee-paying students are more engaged in co-creation activities in comparison to non-fee-paying students', engaging actively in both academic and wider student and professional experiences.

Tensions arise from teachers adopting traditional lecture and assessment practices which suited learning in the pre-digital age, whereas today's students are not primarily book-led learners and are evidentially different from previous generations (Howe and Strauss, 2007). Millennial students have always had the mobile technologies to listen, search, chat, text, video, network, write and publish when and where they choose. Monaco and Martin (2007) indicate that, as a generation, they assume they will have immediate feedback, possess a sense of entitlement, have some unrealistic expectations and are used to significant parental involvement. They expect to be guided to succeed in learning and other aspects of life. In addition, these students know that digital solutions and automation of jobs is changing the workplace (Autor, 2015; Frey and Osborne, 2017).

Howe and Strauss's (2007, p. 46) vision for the millennial generation offers some further prompts for programme level design:

> Millennials will be more confident, trusting, and teachable in the workplace than their Boomer and Gen X colleagues. They will also be viewed as more pampered, risk averse, and dependent. Many employers are already complaining about their need for constant feedback and their weakness in basic job skills such as punctuality and proper dress – though most employers who manage large numbers of them agree that they *can perform superbly when given clear goals and allowed to work in groups.* Millennials will have more of a knack for cooperation and organization than for out-of-the-box initiative. They will tend to treat co-workers as partners rather than rivals. (emphasis added)

Although contemporary students frustrate some faculty, they are proficient with social media, the technologies to research online at any time, and are comfortable learning by doing (Kneale, 2018; Stevens and Nies, 2018). Logically, we should design curricular and learning outcomes to align with this generation's characteristics: technologically proficient, confident, team-oriented, pressured, achieving people who expect to have what they need to succeed academically and in life. While comment about attention spans being shorter abound, maybe it is attention in the lecture theatre where this is obvious in a generation preferring collaboration with peers. Working in teams with authentic assessments that mimic workplace practices are ideal, because they mirror academic research processes. Knowledge acquisition, or 'learning for its own sake', will possibly re-emerge in the future, but for now the ability to research easily online means that knowledge can be discovered and discussed by teams in short timeframes, evaluated and used there and then. Arguably, final year deep learning is more about being comfortable, confident and 'expert' with the processes of research and reporting in a very professional manner, gained through relevant professional practice.

Meeting the needs and expectations of the millennial generation makes sense because these are features of academic research in practice: alignment of learning outcomes that promote team work; clear goals, self-organising, group management and leadership opportunities; workplace relevance and a focus on partnership work inside and outside the academy. Developing curricula in this manner is a potential win–win.

Who Designs Modules and Programmes?

It is nearly 30 years since Apple (1981, p. 115) pointed out that 'there exists in curriculum development . . . something of a failure of nerve. We are willing to prepare students to assume only some responsibility for their own learning'. Ask yourself, do your students have a real, active, valued place in your programme design and evaluation, and could you do more to achieve this? Following the United Nations Convention on the Rights of the Child (UNCRC, 1989), which recognised children's right to express their views and to be taken seriously in all matters affecting them (Lansdown, 2005), pupils have been increasingly involved in school governance, including committee experience on school councils, governing bodies and in the appointment of staff and governors. While experiences vary, most students are aware of committee and governance processes. It should be expected that undergraduates are effective members of committees and interested in how teaching is developed and managed (Mitra and Gross, 2009; Brasof, 2015; Mayes, 2017; Charteris and Smardon, 2018).

Geography encourages research involving undergraduates, postgraduates, professors, professional staff and external stakeholders. The current paradigm encourages students to be responsible for their learning, making decisions, developing autonomy, understanding their learning processes, feeding back on all parts of their degree, which collectively equips them to play a significant part in the teaching development discourse. Students as agents of their own learning in partnership is advocated and deserves implementation (Czerniawski and Kidd, 2011; Matthews, 2017; and see Chapter 23 in this volume by Moore-Cherry). This chapter advocates programme design conversations that involve all stakeholders (Bovill and Bulley, 2011; Willis and Gregory, 2016); students, professional services staff, faculty, alumni, and external partners. It argues against the lone academic creating a module with minimal reference to a wider programme team. Arguably, the papers and chapters cited in this paragraph should be considered by all programme designers.

Who Creates Teaching Materials and Decides the Learning Outcomes?

Excellent advice on programme design and module development tackles core components (Biggs and Tang, 2007; Race, 2014), but for final year it is as important to understand that students can be more involved in the selection of content and the creation of support and activity materials (Carey, 2013; Brooman et al., 2015). Adopting the RASE pedagogy (Churchill et al., 2013, 2014; Fox, 2017; UNSW, 2017), regardless of the module topic and style, provides consistency across a programme, and encourages all module designers to be creative in structuring learning materials. Involving students in developing resources and activities, in contributing to module support, and seeing how evaluation is incorporated into the process is part of valuing students as co-researchers and co-creators (see, for example, McHugh et al., 2016; Money et al., 2016; Whiley et al., 2017).

There is insufficient space here to explore in detail the RASE model for designing student-centred curricula (see UNSW, 2017), but a short discursion into the Activity component shows how this process for learning support aligns with millennial student preferences. RASE 'activities' are available for personal exploration and in-class use to: test ideas; generalise models, ideas and equations to other circumstances, data sets or conditions; and to check on understanding and confidence in working with new ideas. All activities: focus on what students will do to learn; are worked on by students in groups with staff as facilitators; and create tangible artefacts that demonstrate learning processes and the acquisition of new literacies. Activities usually involve ill-defined, academic research or workplace problems or case studies, because geographical problem-solving is normally a messy business with multiple possible outcomes. The aim is to mirror professional practice, using the methods and equipment that are used by professional geographers to produce videos, posters, software, role-play scenarios, fieldwork plans, laboratory protocols, reports, presentations, or blogs that demonstrate professional competencies (UNSW, 2017).

In the workplace, as in academia, any product is subject to peer review and revision before submission. Building in time for review by peers, lecturers and external experts, so that students gain confidence in responding to feedback, is important to develop these professional competencies (see Chapter 27 in this volume by Hill and Worth). Through this adaptive process, the final product demonstrates development and a more effective achievement of learning outcomes.

Tensions in Programme Progression and Module Choice

Geography programme design is underpinned in general by the concepts of progression and exploring and researching contemporary issues. It is relatively usual for there to be limited or no module choice in early undergraduate years, blossoming into considerable choice in the final year. Limited choice promotes cohorts of students with a common understanding of specific research approaches, technical skills and understanding of applications. Students understand what they need to do to be successful. These courses are promoted as providing a well thought through, balanced diet of knowledge and skills.

Interestingly, students who have extensive choice are often more dissatisfied because they retain an inherent uncertainty about having selected the 'right combination' and are afraid they might miss out on content. Choice is a contested area with some students welcoming it, while others feel that staff do not care enough about them to direct them in particular ways. As Toohey (1999, p. 15) notes:

> Choice helps to promote ownership and responsibility. It is unlikely that students will take responsibility for their own learning when all the decisions about what topics or skills are more relevant, and what evidence of learning might be presented, have already been made by someone else. Where the unit is prescribed, where there is little or no choice in assessable work and all of the assessment requires a similar response, students are more likely to opt for a surface approach in order to meet requirements that they feel little commitment to.

I suggest that curriculum design across a three-year programme needs to focus on how to foreground progression, revisiting topics and skills in increasing depth to drive deeper understanding, while giving students opportunities to pursue their own (not necessarily staff) interests.

Inclusivity Tensions: the Diverse Curriculum and Classroom

The diversity of student backgrounds in higher education means that inclusive learning must be at the forefront of programme design (see Chapter 13 in this volume by Hughes and McDuff). Addressing unconscious bias is a serious matter for classroom practice in all years, but no matter how well managed in the earlier undergraduate years, diversity issues do not disappear in the final year (Cotton et al., 2013, 2017; Muneer et al., 2015). Programme design strategies should be explicitly conscious of:

- *Variety in learning activity and teaching delivery styles* because students learn in many different ways (Turner et al., 2017).
- *Group activities and assignments* enabling student–student conversations and action, to break down barriers, and challenge assumptions and stereotypical thinking. There is a tension between permitting group self-selection that might subdue difference versus enforcing group diversity while sensitively taking account of off-campus (commuter student, single parent) time constraints.
- Collecting and processing *feedback regularly and anonymously; reporting back* to students swiftly to resolve immediate issues, and explain how next year's module will change or not change as a result of comments. Well-advertised, bookable office hours for individual or group support delivered face-to-face, online or by phone ensures students are appropriately supported.
- *Peer review* of assignments in class, ensuring everyone has equality of access.
- *Blind marking* of all work, followed by *conversations* with all students to encourage and support their development. Misunderstanding of what is required is so often at the root of low grades (Price et al., 2010). Peer-to-peer conversations can be helpful, less demanding of faculty time, and less daunting for students lacking confidence (Nicol, 2010).
- *Communicating across years*; Milsom et al. (2014) discuss the challenge of stepping up to second year, but for many the step to third year is a similar gulf. Design support sessions to remove final year mythologies where second year students talk to final year students. Make final year module materials visible to second year students

six months in advance, particularly the resources, activities, videos and frequently asked questions (FAQs), to support everyone's learning.

International students are generally expected to settle into new pedagogic practices with very little induction and limited ongoing support (Griffiths et al., 2001). In this section the focus is exemplified with the international student but national, religious, equality of access and intersectionality are similarly important considerations for design. The unbiased classroom is a utopia but designing learning to support specific groups benefits the whole class. Solutions usually involve thoughtful preparation and sensitive delivery (Killick, 2017).

The spatial breadth of module content leads to interesting content discussions, especially when students are drawn from many nationalities. The absurdly parochial: 'My research is on tourism in the Pyrenees, that's what the Geography of the Pyrenees module covers, all answers must focus on the Pyrenees' is unlikely. But at a less blatant level there is a real issue in designing learning sessions and assessments to ensure that all students can put material into personally relevant contexts. Traditionally, geographers have approached this design issue by concentrating class teaching on theory, processes and methodology and steered students to *research* the practice examples and case studies that provide context and relevance. Being specific, every time, about this expectation is critical. Stating, for example:

I expect you to use the 10 hours active learning time allocated for this session to think, read, analyse . . . There are two starter case studies on the reading/resources list but what else can you find? The examples are four years old and are USA-based. What has happened more recently and in the rest of the world? Use the (RASE) Resources and Activities on the module web pages. Please make sure I am surprised when I read your assignments.

This level of clarity, expressed repeatedly, is tremendously helpful to all. It reminds everyone of expectations and encourages international students to explore and cite cases and literature from their home countries.

There may be tension when examiners query the merit of case examples evidenced by papers in different languages. But why not? An internationally open curriculum should encourage such engagement, especially where students want to complete their research projects using field sites near to home, and home is 3000 miles away. This raises the dissertation location tension: 'You can work anywhere in the world' versus 'How do I as supervisor/examiner know that the field sites are suitable and the results are valid?' In practice, almost every location in the world has a university nearby. The network of geographers is global and many collaborative projects have developed from fieldwork meetings with research undertaken by students. We must recognise that students choosing to study abroad are influenced by costs and national and international events. Ideally, we should encourage programmes to explicitly support individuals to learn using materials that have relevance whether they choose to stay in their new country or return home after study.

In designing curricula that support international students, and which are inclusive for all, consideration needs to be given to faculty awareness of students' background knowledge; building content around 'international' examples; using language that clearly states expectations; indicating opportunities for follow-up projects to be undertaken in international settings and involving relevant international staff, face-to-face or through video and conferencing. All students benefit hugely from inclusive teaching approaches: materials on the web in advance; clear introduction and closing elements in classroom sessions that emphasise the relevance of the learning; signposting to further activity resources with clear expectations that autonomous learning will be completed and recognised; ensuring resources are rich with pre-reading, visual materials, answers to student FAQs and activities.

The Employability Tension

There is not necessarily a tension between providing students with the skills to be effective researchers in geography versus a curriculum that delivers the professional skills which are sought after by employers (Artess et al., 2017), but it needs thinking through. The curriculum design issue concerns how employability skills are explicitly embedded in modules, and where extra-curricular developments can be promoted. Yorke (2006, p. 23) defines employability as: 'A set of achievements – skills, understanding and personal attributes – that makes graduates more likely to gain employment and be successful in their chosen occupations, which benefits themselves, the workforce, the community and the economy.' This clarifies the difference between the university curricular employability offer as developing ability, skills and understanding, and acquiring a graduate job on graduation which universities cannot guarantee (Yorke, 2006).

For international students, commuter students (Thomas and Jones, 2017) and carers, amongst others, engaging with extra-curricular activities can be challenging. Stevenson and Clegg (2012) find those involved tend to be full-time students, financially secure and with the social and cultural capacities to find positions. They are generally fit and well, living on or around the campus, not involved in paid employment and unencumbered by domestic responsibilities. Finding space in the final year programme to level the playing field for all, through places to acknowledge, reflect and value the skills gained from paid employment, caring and managing extensive daily travel, is important for developing the professional employability skills of all students.

Of the nine skills AGR (2016) employers identified as important for employability and on-the-job performance, at least six are core to 'doing geography' but are not necessarily explicitly visible and reinforced as learning outcomes with students. 'Teamwork', 'interpersonal skills', 'problem-solving', 'self-awareness', 'negotiating' and 'dealing with conflict' are enhanced through active learning, problem-based learning, enquiry-based learning, and expedition and fieldwork pedagogies, all of which frequently involve group-based project work. 'Managing up' is unconsciously part of daily life for every young person. Linked with negotiating, this is key to project or dissertation management especially in external, community, workplace and international settings. 'Business communication' and 'commercial awareness' may be explicitly developed in the human geography curriculum and by students involved in developing their own enterprises. The importance of internships and work experience in developing business communication and commercial awareness is evident but the AGR research acknowledges that all these skills are gained as part of university courses (AGR, 2016).

The tension for final year programme design sits alongside the concept of the final year student as an autonomous operator. Where excellent practice in personal development planning (PDP), CV development and reflection have been established in earlier years, faculty expect that students will continue to use these resources, tactics and strategies. From the student perspective the PDP and other processes are too easily seen as a box successfully ticked, assessed and put away. Final year skills development needs reflection to be valued by students, and that means promoted by the people that they value; their tutors and module leaders. The tension here is that by final year these are embedded processes, valued in their own right but not necessarily assessed. Student engagement, however, is motivated by assessment so programme design must consider how reflection and evaluation of skills is captured. Arguably, self-reflection, particularly assessment of personal progress through a project, should be incorporated into summative assessment.

The Group Work Tension

Fieldwork, laboratory and IT practicals in the initial years of most geography degrees involve group work which provides safety, support and community of practice opportunities for the discussion and development of ideas (Wenger, 1998). These group practices can then be in tension with a final year ethos of students demonstrating what they can do alone, through individual research projects, dissertations and assignments. There is an argument that students find this change in ethos confusing and it disrupts their developmental preparation to be effective, team-based researchers with improving leadership capability in workplace or academic settings. Team work has the additional advantage of providing support and building confidence. It is a sustainable and inclusive approach that supporting students with well-being concerns.

Consider how building activities around challenging group-based projects, extending over a semester or year, would be appropriately developmental, demonstrate 'progression', enable deeper thinking and embed research and reporting skills through serious practical experience. It would enable exploration and research into contemporary issues in geography that are relevant, exciting, and motivating. Such an approach reinforces the value of the research–teaching nexus and should enable groups of undergraduates to engage more actively in the research areas which may otherwise be privileged to a higher degree and research students (Griffiths, 2004; Jenkins and Healey 2009; Brennan et al., 2019). Holton's (2018) analysis of students' responses on field classes distinguishes difference in skills and learning outcomes when comparing reflections on student-led and staff-led project days suggesting that both have value in different ways, while Carnell and Fung (2017) include multiple examples of research in practice.

Dissertation Tensions

The final year dissertation, extended project or capstone experience, has been developed to embrace an ethos of integrating learning from previous years and demonstrating the ability to research independently (Boyer Report, 1998; Hill et al., 2011; Kinzie, 2013) (see Chapter 28 in this volume by Hovorka and Wolf). In some countries the final project is an individual piece grounded in the discipline, but elsewhere it can be multi-disciplinary, based in the community, industry, field or laboratory as suits local circumstances (Kuh, 2008). Generally, solo research is found in final year, although Guo et al. (2018) introduce individual research projects in first year geography demonstrating that this improves average grades. Final year curriculum design needs to consider whether evolving the nature of the culminating project is timely. Arguably, we should move from the status quo unless there is compelling evidence that all (circa 90 per cent) alumni from the past five years affirm that their project was challenging, transformational, relevant and rewarding with employability benefits. Progressive design considerations should include:

Solo or team activity: teamwork is a core workplace skill, and undergraduate field and laboratory work is generally undertaken by teams, particularly in the first two years. Co-authored dissertations and PhDs are still rare but recognised by a number of higher education institutions (Gale and Wyatt, 2009). The contemporary focus on creating global citizens has prompted interdisciplinary and inter-university project work (Bishop, 2009; Clark and Wilson, 2017; Simm and Marvell, 2017). Over the next ten years how relevant will it be for students to be forced to work alone? Many interesting projects require input from more than one person, so we should anticipate and welcome the opportunity for teams to tackle more complex issues. Will the typical project or PhD thesis declaration: '*This thesis and the work presented in it are my own and has been generated by me as the result of my own original research*', become increasingly inappropriate? As more students have access to multidisciplinary modules and these are seen positively (Spelt et al., 2009; Hall et al., 2018), joint project work pairing geography students with sociology, business, geology, engineering and other disciplines is a logical next step. The usual barrier to group work, '*it's too big a risk because the team may fall apart*', needs to be challenged in the context of professional workplace behaviours. '*Yes, there will be problems, but it's for mature 20 plus year olds to manage and resolve*', it is part of the process and there is coaching and advice available. The lifecycle of project behaviour (norming, storming, forming, performing) will occur, but groups can manage difficulties (Tuckman and Jensen, 1977).

Topic development: students relatively unguided personal choice versus faculty promoting: opportunities to address fundamental research questions working alongside academics; community-led and community-identified problem-solving (Owen and Hill, 2011; NCCPE, 2019); employer-defined work to resolve contemporary workplace issues; projects that align to the university or department mission exploring policy and society issues. In essence, topics should inspire dedicated enjoyment and deep engagement.

Research support: characterised by mentoring throughout the project in an active and engaged manner because this is how academics research. Is it time to stop 1:1 supervision? Consider establishing community of practice groups of six to ten students who will review early drafts of each other's work, present early results, refine the process as research progresses and engage throughout with those who will use the output (community, industry, academic researchers) so that the final product has been tested, developed and finessed to meet the user's needs. Two products may be required; the report for the commissioning community group, employer or researcher and the academic report providing greater depth on methodology, process, results and critique, including the 'what next' section.

These three dissertation considerations raise practical questions in curriculum design about resources, safety and about the relative value (credits) of the work to be completed. Time is needed for every student, individually or as part of a team, to tackle a substantial issue and work through a number of drafts and analyses. If the final year project really is the capping experience, allowing time for research in varied locations and with external partners, what should it be worth in terms of time and credits for the year? Arguably 50 per cent of the credits, possibly more?

Staff Tensions

The temptation is to continue along well-trodden paths as long as results are 'good enough'. A significant question is whether geographers are ready and able to move into new ways of doing, and accessing support for changing approaches? Design discussions need to acknowledge that developing new learning materials and moving to new ways of delivery takes time, and people need the confidence to overcome barriers and adopt new approaches to learning facilitation and support (Walder, 2015; Lattuca and Pollard, 2016; Hasanefendic et al., 2017).

External influences on higher education mean change is the normal *modus operandi.* It is challenging for everyone, so responding flexibly and speedily is important. And herein lies a major tension: (Mis-understood) notions of academic freedom versus imposed internal and external requirements: 'It's my classroom where I teach what I wish' versus 'the Dean/University/Office for Students requires ...' versus 'this programme offers a cohesive curriculum that delivers ...'. External and internal governance matters because it frames university structures and provides assurance for standards and quality. National quality oversight standards cannot be ignored (for example Council of Ministers Canada, 2007; Australian Qualifications Authority, 2014; New Zealand Qualifications Authority, 2017; QAA, 2017). They provide useful frameworks for programme planning. Departments establish programmes with modules that align to deliver programme learning outcomes. This does not constrain modules from addressing radical, sensitive, risky material in exciting and innovative ways; the curriculum and learning outcomes just need to align and acknowledge the approaches. External metrics should not push staff towards pedagogic frailty (Kinchin et al., 2016; Kinchin and Francis 2017) and learning, teaching and assessment conservatism.

Finally, there are tensions around recognition and reward for innovation in teaching. Although many universities have recognised pathways for promotion for excellent scholars, the rewards are not consistent across the sector (HEA, 2009; Dobele and Rundle-Theile, 2015; Locke et al., 2016; Kok and McDonald, 2017). While this is not directly pertinent to curriculum design, being sensitive to staff thinking on this is important when bringing a team together for whole programme re-design.

WHAT WOULD YOU LIKE YOUR STUDENTS TO BE DOING IN FIVE YEARS' TIME?

This chapter has raised questions and explored tensions in programme design. There remains the personal question of 'what do I want to see my students doing in the next five years that will enhance their and my life, their and my research?' Four geographers provide some intriguing answers, which could be core to curriculum re-design:

Following a personalised path of learning that links academic skills with potentialities of the workplace, where dialogue and empathic relationships/partnerships are at the core and students self-regulate and reflect, driving their own development. They are assessed in authentic ways including a professionalised way of receiving a grade/judgement post-feedback (as with academic journal papers).

Finding genuine satisfaction in tackling serious contemporary issues, increasing understanding while appreciating that the timescales for finding solutions are lengthy and largely unresolvable. Making an impact through exploring community and wider practical problems in multi-disciplinary groups including academics and external influencers. Developing the confidence and practice in making a difference, becoming global citizens.

A team of eight or ten people who are really interested in my research who can work closely with me for a whole year. We would achieve so much. The opportunity to trial ideas, get away from safe options. Putting the same data into three different types of models and genuinely testing, comparing and evaluating would be magic. We could cover in a year what would otherwise take three or more.

Knowing that my former students, who are no longer in higher education, are now out in the world working in an ethically-considered manner. An example would be that they embody the vision of the UK's National Union of Students 'to see all students leaving formal education with the knowledge, skills and attributes to create a more just and sustainable future' (NUS, 2018). I'd like to think that this is genuinely possible with an inclusive, critical and values-explicit programme.

Each university and department has its own traditions, expectations and ecology of learning. The solution for one department will not translate without thought and tailoring to another institution, but the core ambitions can be consistent. Progressive curriculum design allows students to build confidence and experience through deepening practice across three years of exciting, relevant contemporary action research activities, where everyone feels they are making a contribution to significant issues, with enough time for deep learning experiences.

Race (2014) emphasises the need to reinforce WIIFM (what's in it for me?) with students. By consciously addressing reasons to learn, students are encouraged to want to learn. But he warns that 'However strong the *want* or *need* to learn may be, nothing happens unless some *learning by doing* happens next' (Race, 2014, p. 41). A similar point is made by Hattie and Donoghue (2016) in their study of over 400 learning strategies. In their Model for Learning, the elements of skill, will and thrill are key to motivating effective learning.

To provide deeply immersive, motivated and thrilling learning let us consider a final year involving two all year (60 credit or equivalent) projects running in parallel. These might involve:

- A significant challenge where 6–10 people progress a contemporary issue with group reporting, leadership and project management skills explicitly developed. The group is 'timetabled' to work immersively together for two days each week, mimicking research and workplace practices. This would enable the team to capture developments, discuss, track, refine and action tasks, and undertake literature searches, field and laboratory analysis. Making regular presentations to update the stakeholders is key, seeking informed guidance on successive stages so the final outcomes are relevant and potentially very different from those anticipated at the start; and
- A tighter, smaller scale project, tackled by 3–6 people in different ways, producing

distinct projects, again meeting weekly, working, sharing and developing as a self-supporting community of practice (Wenger, 1998).

Both of these projects could be framed by external bodies, be embedded in community action or follow an academic research path (Owen and Hill, 2011; NCCPE, 2019). We know immersive learning is effective pedagogy, and at the core of geography fieldwork. Students really appreciate the benefits of focusing on one topic without distraction (Ferguson et al., 2017; Turner et al., 2017), developing resilience (Cassidy, 2015; Cotton et al., 2017; Ein-Gar and Steinhart, 2017). Two all-year modules would provide the flexibility for extended fieldwork in term-time, enabling teams to collect significant datasets for analysis. The leadership and management involved with many brains concentrating together provides professional research and work-relevant experience.

CONCLUSION

This chapter has explored some key issues in programme design and presented the argument for increasing team-based, larger scale research challenges in the final undergraduate year. Although expressed here as tensions, practice exists across every continuum. Every programme is shaped and nuanced in different ways. The chapter aimed to highlight relevant literature and examples of practice to prompt mature conversations about final year curricula. The impact of the arrival of the internet and World Wide Web in the mid-1990s has worked through to the millennial generation; it is timely to evolve curricula to their interests and styles of learning. Module and programme designers need to be conscious of building motivation to learn. What will work for, energise, enthuse and thrill students now? It certainly is not what worked in the 1960s. Change is very unsettling, but clinging to known patterns is risky; better to be flexible, adopt, adapt and flourish. The argument here is that it is time to shake up and evolve curricula to prepare students for 21st century competencies, with 'The inclusion of essential twenty-first century skills such as learning how to solve difficult, ill-defined problems and learning how to collaborate' (Scott, 2015, p. 2).

Useful resources

- Churchill, D., King, M. and Fox, B. (2014) *About RASE Pedagogical Model.* In Moodle and pedagogical design workshop. Available online at: https://sites.google.com/site/hkumoodle/pedagogical-model. Accessed 23 February 2019.
- Ferguson, R., Barzilai, S., Ben-Zvi, D., Chinn, C.A., Herodotou, C., Hod, Y., Kali, Y., Kukulska-Hulme, A., Kupermintz, H., McAndrews, P., Rienties, B., Sagy, O., Scanlon, E., Sharples, M., Weller, M. and Whitelock, D. (2017) *Innovating Pedagogy 2017*. Open University Innovation Report 6. Milton Keynes: The Open University.
- Hattie, J.A.C. and Donoghue, G.M. (2016) 'Learning strategies: a synthesis and conceptual model', *npj Science of Learning*, 1, 16013. Available online at: https://www.nature.com/articles/npjscilearn201613#f1. Accessed 14 December 2018.
- HEA CPD Toolkit. Available at: https://www.plymouth.ac.uk/research/institutes/pedagogic/hea-cpd-framework. Accessed 23 February 2019.

- Kneale, P.E., Winter, J., Turner, R., Spowart, L. and Muneer, R. (2016) *Evaluating Teaching Development Activities in Higher Education: A Toolkit*. Project report for HE Academy Measuring impact of CPD. Available online at: https://www.plymouth.ac.uk/research/institutes/pedagogic/measuring-impact. Accessed 23 February 2019.

REFERENCES

AGR (Association of Graduate Recruiters) (2016) *The AGR 2016 Annual Survey*. Available online at: https://www.justoncampus.co.uk/wp-content/uploads/2016-AGR-Annual-Survey-2.pdf. Accessed 23 February 2019.

Apple, M.W. (1981) 'On analysing hegemony', in H.A. Giroux, A.N. Penna and W.F. Pinar (eds), *Curriculum and Instruction Alternatives in Education*. Berkeley, CA: McCutchen Publishing.

Artess, J., Hooley, T. and Mellors-Bourne, R. (2017) *Employability: A Review of the Literature 2012 to 2016*. York: HEA. Available online at: https://www.heacademy.ac.uk/knowledge-hub/employability-review-literature-2012-2016. Accessed 23 February 2019.

Australian Qualifications Authority (2014) *Australian Qualifications Framework*. Available online at http://www.aqf.edu.au/aqf/in-detail/aqf-levels/. Accessed 23 February 2019.

Autor, D.H. (2015) 'Why are there still so many jobs? The history and future of workplace automation', *The Journal of Economic Perspectives*, 29, pp. 3–30.

Biggs, J. and Tang, C. (2007) *Teaching for Quality Learning at University*. Maidenhead: Open University Press.

Bishop, M.P. (2009) 'International multidisciplinary research and education: a mountain geography perspective', *Journal of Geography*, 108, pp. 112–120.

Bovill, C. and Bulley, C.J. (2011) 'A model of active student participation in curriculum design: exploring desirability and possibility', in C. Rust (ed.), *Improving Student Learning* (18). Oxford: The Oxford Centre for Staff and Educational Development, pp. 176–188.

Boyer Report (1998) *Reinventing Undergraduate Education: A Blueprint for America's Research Universities*. Stony Brook, NY: Boyer Commission on Educating Undergraduates in the Research University. Available online at: http://naples.cc.sunysb.edu/Pres/boyer.nsf/673918d46fbf653e852565ec0056ff3e/d955 b61ffddd590a 852565ec005717ae/$FILE/boyer.pdf. Accessed 23 February 2019.

Brasof, M. (2015) *Student Voice and School Governance: Distributing Leadership to Youth and Adults*. London: Routledge.

Brennan, L., Cusack, T., Delahunt, E., Kuznesof, S. and Donnely, S. (2019) 'Academics' conceptualisations of the research–teaching nexus in a research-intensive Irish university: a dynamic framework for growth and development', *Learning and Instruction*, 60, pp. 301–309.

Brooman, S., Darwent, S. and Pimor, A. (2015) 'The student voice in higher education curriculum design: is there value in listening?', *Innovations in Education and Teaching International*, 52, pp. 663–674.

Carey, P. (2013) 'Student as co-producer in a marketised higher education system: a case study of students' experience of participation in curriculum design', *Innovations in Education and Teaching International*, 50, pp. 250–260.

Carnell, B. and Fung, D. (2017) *Developing the Higher Education Curriculum: Research-based Education in Practice*. London: UCL Press.

Cassidy, S. (2015) 'Resilience building in students: the role of academic self-efficacy', *Frontiers in Psychology*, 6, p. 1781. Available online at: https://www.frontiersin.org/articles/10.3389/fpsyg.2015.01781/full. Accessed 14 December 2018.

Charteris, J. and Smardon, D. (2018) 'Assessment and student participation: 'choice and voice' in school principal accounts of schooling territories', *Teaching Education*, DOI: 10.1080/10476210.2018.1462311.

Churchill, D., King, M., Webster, B. and Fox, B. (2013) 'Integrating learning design, interactivity, and technology', in H. Carter, M. Gosper and J. Hedberg (eds), *Proceedings of 30th Ascilite Conference 2013*, Sydney, Australia, pp. 139–143.

Churchill, D., King, M. and Fox, B. (2014) *About RASE Pedagogical Model*. In Moodle and pedagogical design workshop. Available online at: https://sites.google.com/site/hkumoodle/pedagogical-model. Accessed 14 December 2018.

Clark, C.H. and Wilson, B.P. (2017) 'The potential for university collaboration and online learning to internationalise geography education', *Journal of Geography in Higher Education*, 41, pp. 488–505.

Cotton, D., George, R. and Joyner, M. (2013) 'Interaction and influence in culturally-mixed groups', *Innovations in Education and Teaching International*, 50, pp. 272–283.

Cotton, D.R.E., Nash, T. and Kneale, P. (2017) 'Supporting the retention of non-traditional students in higher education using a resilience framework', *European Education Research Journal*, 16, pp. 62–79.

Council of Ministers Canada (2007) *The Canadian Degree Qualifications Framework – A Ministerial Statement on Quality Assurance of Degree Education in Canada.* Available online at: http://www.cicic.ca/docs/cmec/QA-Statement-2007.en.pdf. Accessed 23 February 2019.

Czerniawski, G. and Kidd, W. (2011) *The Student Voice Handbook: Bridging the Academic/Practitioner Divide.* Bingley, WA: Emerald Group Publishing Limited, pp. 89–96.

Dobele, A.R. and Rundle-Theile, S. (2015) 'Progression through academic ranks: a longitudinal examination of internal promotion drivers', *Higher Education Quarterly*, 69, pp. 410–429.

Ebert, K. (2016) 'Teaching techniques. Classroom strategies for millennial learners', *Radiation Therapist*, 25, pp. 201–204.

Ein-Gar, D. and Steinhart, Y. (2017) 'Self-control and task timing shift self-efficacy and influence willingness to engage in effortful tasks', *Frontiers in Psychology*, 8, Article 1788. Available online at: https://www.frontiersin.org/articles/10.3389/fpsyg.2017.01788/full.

Ferguson, R., Barzilai, S., Ben-Zvi, D., Chinn, C.A., Herodotou, C., Hod, Y., Kali, Y., Kukulska-Hulme, A., Kupermintz, H., McAndrews, P., Rienties, B., Sagy, O., Scanlon, E., Sharples, M., Weller, M. and Whitelock, D. (2017) *Innovating Pedagogy 2017.* Open University Innovation Report 6. Milton Keynes: The Open University.

Figueira, C., Theodorakopoulos, N. and Caselli, G. (2018) 'Unveiling faculty conceptions of academic risk taking: a phenomenographic study', *Studies in Higher Education*, 43, pp. 1307–1320.

Fox, B. (2017) *RASE Model.* UNSW elearning. Available online at: https://www.youtube.com/watch?v=U2B8i8ldqZo&feature=youtu.be. Accessed 14 December 2018.

Freire, P. (1998) *Pedagogy of Freedom: Ethics, Democracy and Civic Courage.* Lanham, MD: Rowman and Littlefield.

Frey, C.B. and Osborne, M.A. (2017) 'The future of employment: how susceptible are jobs to computerisation?', *Technological Forecasting and Social Change*, 114, pp. 254–280.

Gale, K. and Wyatt, J. (2009) *Between the Two: A Nomadic Inquiry into Collaborative Writing and Subjectivity.* Newcastle, UK: Cambridge Scholars Publishing.

Gardner, J., Van der Veer, G. and Associates (1998) *The Senior Year Experience: Facilitating Integration, Reflection, Closure and Transition.* San Francisco, CA: Jossey-Bass.

Gibbs, G. and Simpson, C. (2005) 'Conditions under which assessment supports students' learning', *Learning and Teaching in Higher Education*, 1, pp. 3–31.

Graham, M., McLean, J., Read, A., Suchet-Pearson, S. and Viner, V. (2017) 'Flipping and still learning: experiences of a flipped classroom approach for a third-year undergraduate human geography course', *Journal of Geography in Higher Education*, 41, pp. 403–417.

Griffiths, R. (2004) 'Knowledge production and the research–teaching nexus: the case of the built environment disciplines', *Studies in Higher Education*, 29, pp. 709–726.

Griffiths, S., Wisker, G., Waller, S., Illes, K. and Wu, S. (2001) 'The learning experience of postgraduate students: matching methods to aims', *Innovations in Education and Teaching International*, 38, pp. 292–308.

Guo, X., Loy, K. and Banow, R. (2018) 'Can first-year undergraduate geography students do individual research?', *Journal of Geography in Higher Education*, 42, pp. 412–426.

Hall, T., McGuinness, M., Parker, C. and Toms, P. (2018) 'Student experiences of multidisciplinarity in the undergraduate geography curriculum', *Journal of Geography in Higher Education*, 42, pp. 220–237.

Hasanefendic, S., Birkholz, J.M., Horta, H. and van der Sijde, P. (2017) 'Individuals in action: bringing about innovation in higher education', *European Journal of Higher Education*, 7, pp. 101–119.

Hattie, J.A.C. and Donoghue, G.M. (2016) 'Learning strategies: a synthesis and conceptual model', *npj Science of Learning*, 1, p. 16013. Available online at: https://www.nature.com/articles/npjscilearn201613#f1. Accessed 14 December 2018.

HEA (2009) *Reward and Recognition in Higher Education: Institutional Policies and Their Implementation.* York: Higher Education Academy. Available online at: https://www.heacademy.ac.uk/system/files/rewardandrecognition_2_2.pdf. Accessed 14 December 2018.

Higgitt, D. (2014) 'Editorial: disruptive moments', *Journal of Geography in Higher Education*, 38, pp. 1–6.

Hill, J., Kneale, P., Nicholson, D., Waddington, S. and Ray, W. (2011) 'Re-framing the geography dissertation: a consideration of alternative, innovative and creative approaches', *Journal of Geography in Higher Education*, 35, pp. 331–349.

Hill, J., Walkington, H. and Kneale, P. (2019) 'Borderland spaces: moving towards self-authorship', in T. Bilham, C. Hamshire, M. Hartog and M. Doolan (eds), *Reframing Space for Learning: Excellence and Innovation in University Teaching.* London: UCL/IoE Press (in print).

Holton, M. (2018) 'Traditional or non-traditional students? Incorporating UK students' living arrangements into decisions about going to university', *Journal of Further and Higher Education*, 42, pp. 556–569.

Howe, N. and Strauss, W. (2007) 'The next 20 years: how customer and workforce attitudes will evolve', *Harvard Business Review.* Available online at: https://hbr.org/2007/07/the-next-20-years-how-customer-and-workforce-attitudes-will-evolve. Accessed 14 December 2018.

Jenkins, A. and Healey, M. (2009) 'Developing the student as a researcher through the curriculum', *Innovations in Practice*, 2, pp. 3–15.

Killick, D. (2017) *Developing Intercultural Practice: Academic Development in a Multicultural and Globalizing World*. SEDA Series. London: CRC Press.

Kinchin, I.M. and Francis, R.A. (2017) 'Mapping pedagogic frailty in geography education: a framed autoethnographic case study', *Journal of Geography in Higher Education*, 41, pp. 56–74.

Kinchin, I.M., Alpay, E., Curtis, K., Franklin, J., Rivers, C. and Winstone, N. (2016) 'Charting the elements of pedagogic frailty', *Educational Research*, 58, pp. 1–23.

Kinzie, J. (2013) 'Taking stock of capstones and integrated learning', *Peer Review*, 15, pp. 27–30.

Kneale, P.E. (2018) 'Where might pedagogic research focus to support students' education in a REF-TEF world', *Journal of Geography in Higher Education*, 42, pp. 487–497.

Kok, S.K. and McDonald, C. (2017) 'Underpinning excellence in higher education – an investigation into the leadership, governance and management behaviours of high-performing academic departments', *Studies in Higher Education*, 42, pp. 210–231.

Kuh, G.D. (2008) *High-impact Educational Practices: What They Are, Who Has Access to Them, and Why They Matter*. Washington, DC: Association of American Colleges and Universities.

Lansdown, G. (2005) *The Evolving Capacities of the Child*. Florence: UNICEF Innocenti Research Centre. Available online at: https://www.unicef-irc.org/publications/pdf/evolving-eng.pdf. Accessed 14 December 2018.

Lattuca, L.R. and Pollard, J.R. (2016) 'Towards a conceptualization of faculty decision-making about curricular and instructional change', in L. Leisyte and U. Wilkesmann (eds), *Organizing Academic Work in Higher Education: Teaching, Learning and Identities*. New York: Routledge, pp. 89–108.

Locke, W., Whitchurch, C., Smith, H.J. and Mazenod, A. (2016) *Shifting Landscapes: Meeting the Staff Development Needs of the Changing Academic Workforce*. York, UK: The Higher Education Academy. Available online at: https://www.heacademy.ac.uk/knowledge-hub/shifting-landscapes. Accessed 14 December 2018.

Matthews, K.E. (2017) 'Five propositions for genuine students as partners practice', *International Journal for Students as Partners*, 1, pp. 1–9.

Maxwell-Stuart, R., Taheri, B., Paterson, A.S., O'Gorman, K. and Jackson, W. (2018) 'Working together to increase student satisfaction: exploring the effects of mode of study and fee status', *Studies in Higher Education*, 43, pp. 1392–1404.

Mayes, E. (2017) 'Reconceptualizing the presence of students on school governance councils: the a/effects of spatial positioning', *Policy Futures in Education*, November, pp. 1–17.

McHugh, R., Bilous, R., Grant, C. and Hammersley, L. (2016) 'PACE at a glance: case studies of the student experience', in J. Sachs and L. Clark (eds), *Learning Through Community Engagement*. New York: Springer, pp. 153–169.

Milsom, C., Stewart, M., Yorke, M. and Zaitseva, E. (2014) *Stepping up to the Second Year at University: Academic, Psychological and Social Dimensions*. London: Routledge.

Mitra, D. and Gross, S. (2009) 'Increasing student voice in high school reform: building partnerships, improving outcomes', *Educational Administration Quarterly*, 37, pp. 522–543.

Monaco, M. and Martin, M. (2007) 'The millennial student: a new generation of learners', *Athletic Training Education Journal*, 2, pp. 42–46.

Money, J., Dinning, T., Nixon, S., Walsh, B. and Magill, C. (2016) 'Co-creating a blended learning curriculum in transition to higher education: a student viewpoint', *Creative Education*, 7, pp. 1205–1203.

Muneer, R., Cotton, D. and Winter, J. (2015) *7 Steps to: Mitigating Unconscious Bias in Teaching and Learning*. Plymouth University: 7 Steps Series, Teaching and Learning Support. Available online at: https://www.plymouth.ac.uk/your-university/teaching-and-learning/guidance-and-resources/7-step-series. Accessed 23 February 2019.

NCCPE (2019) *Why Does Public Engagement Matter?* National Co-ordinating Centre for Public Engagement. Available online at: https://www.publicengagement.ac.uk/about-engagement/why-does-public-engagement-matter. Accessed 23 February 2019.

New Zealand Qualifications Authority (2017) *New Zealand Qualifications Framework*. Available online at http://www.nzqa.govt.nz/qualifications-standards/. Accessed 23 February 2019.

Nicol, D. (2010) 'From monologue to dialogue: improving written feedback processes in mass higher education', *Assessment and Evaluation in Higher Education*, 35, pp. 501–517.

NIU (2014) *Millennials: Our Newest Generation in Higher Education*. DeKalb, IL: Northern Illinois University, Faculty Development and Instructional Design Center. Available online at: https://www.niu.edu/facdev/_pdf/guide/students/millennials_our_newest_generation_in_higher_education.pdf. Accessed 23 February 2019.

NUS (National Union of Students) (2018) *Responsible Futures*. Available online at https://sustainability.nus.org.uk/sdgteachin/home. Accessed 23 February 2019.

Owen, D. and Hill, S. (2011) *Embedding Public Engagement in the Curriculum: A Framework for the Assessment of Student Learning from Public Engagement*. Bristol: National Coordinating Centre for Public Engagement.

Available online at: https://www.publicengagement.ac.uk/sites/default/files/publication/assessing_student_learning_from_pe.pdf. Accessed 23 February 2019.

Phillips, C.R. and Joseph, E. (2015) *Millennial Students and the Flipped Classroom*. Proceedings of ASBBS Annual Conference: Las Vegas, 21, pp. 519–530. Available online at: http://asbbs.org/files/ASBBS2014/PDF/P/Phillips_Trainor(P519-530).pdf. Accessed 23 February 2019.

Price, M., Handley, K., Millar, J. and O'Donovan, B. (2010) 'Feedback: all that effort, but what is the effect?', *Assessment and Evaluation in Higher Education*, 35, pp. 277–289.

QAA (Quality Assurance Agency) (2017) *UK Quality Code for HE*. Available online at http://www.qaa.ac.uk/assuring-standards-and-quality/the-quality-code. Accessed 23 February 2019.

Race, P. (2014) *Making Learning Happen*. London: Sage Publications.

Scheyvens, R., Griffin, A.L., Jocoy, C.L., Liu, Y. and Bradford, M. (2008) 'Experimenting with active learning in geography: dispelling the myths that perpetuate resistance', *Journal of Geography in Higher Education*, 32, pp. 51–69.

Scott, C.L. (2015) *The Futures of Learning 3: What Kind of Pedagogies for the 21st Century?* ERF Working Papers Series, No. 15. Paris: UNESCO Education Research and Foresight. Available online at: http://unesdoc.unesco.org/images/0024/002431/243126e.pdf. Accessed 23 February 2019.

Simm, D. and Marvell, A. (2017) 'Creating global students: opportunities, challenges and experiences of internationalizing the geography curriculum in higher education', *Journal of Geography in Higher Education*, 41, pp. 467–474.

Spelt, E., Biemans, H., Tobi, H., Luning, P. and Mulder, M. (2009) 'Teaching and learning in interdisciplinary higher education: a systematic review', *Educational Psychological Review*, 21, pp. 365–378.

Stevens, K.P. and Nies, M.A. (2018) 'Transforming nursing education in a 140-character world: the efficacy of becoming social', *Journal of Professional Nursing*, 34, pp. 31–34.

Stevenson, J. and Clegg, S. (2012) 'Who cares? Gender dynamics in the valuing of extra-curricular activities in higher education', *Gender and Education*, 24, pp. 41–55.

Thomas, L. and Jones, R. (2017) *Student Engagement in the Context of Commuter Students*. London: NUS.

Toohey, S. (1999) *Designing Courses for Higher Education*. Buckingham: SRHE and Open University Press.

Tuckman, B.W. and Jensen, M.A.C. (1977) 'Stages of small group development revisited', *Group and Organization Studies*, 2, pp. 419–427.

Turner, R., Morrison, D., Cotton, D., Child, D., Stevens, S., Nash, P. and Kneale, P.E. (2017) 'Easing the transition of first year undergraduates through an immersive induction module', *Teaching in Higher Education*, 22, pp. 805–821.

UNCRC (1989) *United Nations Convention on the Rights of the Child*. Available online at: https://downloads.unicef.org.uk/wp-content/uploads/2010/05/UNCRC_united_nations_convention_on_the_rights_of_the_child.pdf. Accessed 23 February 2019.

UNSW (2017) *Course Design Model – RASE Learning Design and Student Engagement*. Sydney: University of New South Wales. Available online at: https://teaching.unsw.edu.au/course-design-model-rase. Accessed 23 February 2019.

Walder, A.M. (2015) 'Obstacles to innovation: the fear of jeopardising a professorial career', *British Journal of Education*, 3, pp. 1–16.

Walkington, H., Dyer, S., Solem, M., Haigh, M. and Waddington, S. (2018) 'A capabilities approach to higher education: geocapabilities and implications for geography curricula', *Journal of Geography in Higher Education*, 42, pp. 7–24.

Wenger, E. (1998) *Communities of Practice, Learning, Meaning and Identity*. Cambridge: Cambridge University Press.

Whiley, D., Witt, B., Colvin, R.M., Arrue, R.S. and Kotir, J. (2017) 'Enhancing critical thinking skills in first year environmental management students: a tale of curriculum design, application and reflection', *Journal of Geography in Higher Education*, 41, pp. 166–181.

Willis, P. and Gregory, A. (2016) *Making the Road While Walking: Co-creation, Teaching Excellence and University Leadership*. Leadership Foundation Report. Available online at: https://www.lfhe.ac.uk/en/components/publication.cfm/WillisST33. Accessed 23 February 2019.

Yorke, M. (2006) *Employability in Higher Education: What It Is and What It Is Not*. Learning and Employability Series 1. York: ESECT/Higher Education Academy. Available online at: http://www.heacademy.ac.uk/assets/documents/employability/id116_employability_in_higher_education_336.pdf. Accessed 23 February 2019.

34. Teaching, learning and assessing in geography: a foundation for the future
Jennifer Hill, Helen Walkington and Sarah Dyer

INTRODUCTION

Throughout this edited collection the authors demonstrate that a geographical education offers a synthesising framework that helps us to make sense of the world's diversity and dynamism, and to understand ourselves relationally in this world. Being geographically literate can help us to understand contemporary patterns, challenge popular assumptions about environment and society and help solve some of the most pressing social and environmental challenges of the Anthropocene (an era of substantial global change driven by human activity). These challenges are beset with uncertainty, require multiple perspectives and a range of approaches to appreciate them fully, and have a number of possible answers that necessitate informed judgement. As such, geography educators must draw on a range of teaching, learning and assessment approaches to develop in their students the requisite knowledge, skills, attitudes and values.

Our assembled authors make clear that the landscape in which geography higher education is delivered and assessed has shifted immensely over the last decade under neoliberal market forces, manifesting themselves through massification, consumerism, vocationalism and precarity (see also Erickson, 2012; Dyer et al., 2016; Nellis, 2017; Kneale, 2018). Around the world, reductions in public funding and resource constraints mean delivering an excellent quality student experience has never been more challenging for higher education institutions. National policies focus on enhancing graduate employability and economic productivity across a diversity of students, measured annually using performance indicators that feed into published institutional league tables. In tandem, student cohorts continue to evolve and diversify. It has become important to consider how we encourage our students to assume greater responsibility for their learning at a time when they are paying higher tuition fees than ever before, and might thereby assume a passive consumerist mentality.

The teaching, learning and assessment approaches highlighted in this volume sit firmly within the social constructivist learning paradigm (Vygotsky, 1978). Social constructivism contends that students learn best by 'co-constructing' knowledge around shared goals, developing their views via dialogue with each other and their teacher, and connecting new knowledge to what they already believe or understand. This view considers learning to be a deliberate, progressive construction and deepening of meaning, rather than a passive process of receiving information. Students and academic staff work together to build knowledge as part of a social process, in which both play a dynamic and salient role. The social constructivist approach allows alternative viewpoints to be negotiated and developed, enabling misconceptions to be overturned. It is learner-centred and well suited, as many of our chapters testify, to the discipline's signature pedagogy (Shulman,

2005) of fieldwork, where students, guided by academic staff, co-discover knowledge and understanding and connect theoretical concepts with real-world scenarios.

ESTABLISHING A FOUNDATION FOR THE FUTURE

Drawing on the 32 chapters that comprise our edited collection, we identify four principles that, when actioned by individual faculty members, course teams and institutional administrators, build a solid foundation for successful teaching, learning and assessment of geography in higher education. We define these as:

1. Entering the pedagogic borderlands.
2. Embracing partnership working.
3. Acknowledging the whole student.
4. Adopting courageous pedagogy.

1. Entering the Pedagogic Borderlands

Many of the chapters in this collection contextualise their arguments within what we term the pedagogic borderlands. Borderland spaces of learning in higher education can be defined as unfamiliar physical or metaphorical territories whose novelty and ambiguity offer challenge to students and faculty (Hill et al., 2016). They can be novel spaces, such as a virtual world, or a familiar undergraduate space in which an unfamiliar pedagogy is adopted, such as student-led teaching during fieldwork. They can exist within curricula or as co-curricular spaces, such as student research conferences and dedicated online student research journals, which allow students to open up their work for critique to a broader and unknown audience. The concept of borderland spaces offers a powerful means for representing and reframing educational practices (Hill et al., 2019a). Borderland spaces are liminal, operating as a transition between secure knowledge and new understanding, and they thereby foreground a sense of becoming. Entering them creates a sense of displacement, resulting in initial discomfort and uncertainty for both faculty and students as they encounter the vulnerability of 'not knowing' (Thomas, 2010). However, crossing a threshold into the borderland permits new and previously inaccessible ways of thinking and practising (Meyer and Land, 2006). This makes borderland spaces potentially transformative (Mezirow, 2000). Ultimately, there can be a reformulation of the learner's frame of meaning as prevailing views are discarded and alternative forms of personal understanding are accepted (Land et al., 2014).

Borderland spaces of learning can destabilise traditional academic power hierarchies (Freire, 1970). Students work with peers and faculty, and draw more freely on their own experiences, which can prompt the construction of new identities (Giroux, 1992). The division between teaching and learning becomes blurred as students adopt the role of tutor and tutors become facilitators, each gaining a greater understanding of themselves and each other. Borderland spaces are fluid and un-prescribed, remaining open to being shaped by the processes of learning experienced by their participants.

Importantly, the permissive spaces of the borderland allow genuine dialogue to take place, offering opportunities for co-inquiry and reflection amongst students and between students and faculty (Lodge, 2005). In such spaces, students can be empowered to participate in their learning so that they might actively shape their own learning experiences and possibly those of succeeding cohorts. Borderland spaces can therefore be viewed as 'contact zones' for creative possibility (Askins and Pain, 2011), in which people and ideas can be brought into uneasy but transformative interaction. Perhaps the most important result for students is a movement towards self-authorship; the ability to know oneself, to know what one knows, to reflect upon it and to base judgements on it (Baxter Magolda, 2004). Self-authorship is a personally-referenced way of knowing that draws on experience, knowledge and values related to learner identity, and how that relates to others. Self-authorship develops skills of critical thinking, development of mature working relationships, embracing and valuing of diversity and consideration of multiple perspectives. It increases learner self-efficacy and self-regulation (Ritchie, 2016), and thereby enhances student learning and development (Gutman and Vorhaus, 2012).

Learning spaces in higher education are not automatically borderland spaces – they have to be used as such ontologically, epistemologically and practically. Hill et al. (2016) identify three spaces that have been used as borderland spaces for undergraduate geography teaching and learning: the field, online digital space and peer-mentoring space. They demonstrate how these spaces 'have been used to challenge student understanding, identities and perspectives, by engaging students in partnership with one another and with faculty' (Hill et al., 2016, pp. 389–390). In our edited collection, we see a reiteration of these ideas. Matt Finn and Carrie Mott (Chapter 4), for example, discuss how they consciously work to disrupt the dynamics of power and authority in large classes, re-imagining learning in these spaces by adopting flexible and creative pedagogies, and engendering different modes of interaction and encounter. Erin Fouberg (Chapter 6) comments that the goal of geography educators should not be to rush undergraduate students through borderland spaces to being an expert in the discipline. Rather, the goal should be to help students to apply and personalise concepts, to think deeply and recursively, and to be comfortable and curious in liminal space. Helen Walkington (Chapter 14) describes reciprocal elucidation between conference participants when students are challenged to present their work in a professional and novel space. Niamh Moore-Cherry (Chapter 23) notes how borderland spaces support partnership practice in geographical pedagogy, and Jennifer Hill and Nancy Worth (Chapter 27) identify that actively engaging students in assessment to build their skills of self-regulation and self-efficacy can take them into borderland spaces for learning. In these spaces, the faculty–student relationship becomes more reciprocal as knowledge, understanding and standards are jointly explored and goals are co-constructed. Hill and Worth evidence that these discursive borderland spaces of assessment and feedback have the potential to enhance learner behaviour and achievement. Finally, Pauline Kneale (Chapter 33) identifies tensions in final year programme design involving creating spaces of challenge, growth, disruption and liminality, versus controlled spaces for synthesis, collation, reflection and defined project delivery. She concludes that it is timely to evolve curricula to suit the learning styles of the millennial generation.

Our chapter authors, and the wider literature, acknowledge that there are challenges to teaching, learning and assessing in the pedagogic borderlands. Students and faculty can feel anxiety and insecurity as they enter these spaces and assume new roles. They let go of familiar ways of learning and place their trust in a process that is unpredictable.

Thus, borderland spaces can be messy and confusing for participants. Additionally, they are personal and emotional spaces (an issue returned to below). As a consequence, there must be appropriate guidance and institutional support available for students and faculty to ensure the successful navigation of more than a confident minority into and out of the borderland (Felten et al., 2013; Moore-Cherry et al., 2016).

2. Embracing Partnership Working

Developing a 'partnership' approach has become an aspirational goal in higher education around the world, with efforts to shift from faculty-centred to student-centred pedagogies (Healey et al., 2014). Many of our chapters refer to partnership work across and between students and faculty (for example, Chapters 9, 10, 15, 23 and 27 by Amy Griffin, Sarah Dyer, Richard Hodgkins and Joanna Bullard, Niamh Moore-Cherry, and Jennifer Hill and Nancy Worth respectively) and between faculty/students and external partners (see Chapters 25, 29 and 30 by Shauna Brail and Kate Whalen, Ifan Shepherd, and Colin Arrowsmith and William Cartwright respectively). Our contributors frame partnership as a process of meaningful engagement in learning, teaching and assessment, where students, faculty and external partners work together to foster engaged learning in curricular and co-curricular environments.

Meaningful partnership working can be transformative for all involved (Johansson and Felten, 2014). Evidence demonstrates that partnership between students and faculty can enhance student (as well as faculty) motivation, confidence and sense of intellectual agency, both within the immediate process and in wider academic settings (Bovill et al., 2011; Cook-Sather et al., 2014). It can also assist in building a sense of academic identity and belonging, critical to retention, successful progression and achievement (Moore-Cherry et al., 2016). As geography is fundamentally about understanding environment and society, for learning to be authentic it should ideally be connected with professional contexts beyond the classroom. Partnership working between students and external clients exposes students to the complexities and uncertainties of practice situations, which cannot be duplicated in the classroom. Students tend to develop high-level skills in inquiry, time management and effective communication. More recently, studies have shown that such partnerships, when adopted critically, can help students to develop the skills and dispositions of reciprocity, reflexivity, resilience and interdependent knowledge production (McEwen, 2013).

In Chapter 29, Ifan Shepherd introduces a useful framework for undergraduate student engagement with work and the workplace. He suggests that preparing geography students for work can be undertaken by bringing the workplace into the classroom and/or by taking students out into the workplace. He makes three important points about this process. Firstly, students must learn how to transfer skills, both during their acquisition, and when they apply them to new contexts. This implies that the emphasis in geography curricula should shift from 'the transferability of skills and knowledge' to the 'transfer ability of students'. Secondly, Shepherd notes the need for students to understand the distinctive 'ways of working' within individual workplaces if they are to become truly effective in applying their knowledge and skills beyond the classroom. Thirdly, he comments that work-related capabilities have rarely been subjected to formal evaluation and that there is a particular need for research that tracks geography students after graduation to determine the effectiveness of their degrees in enabling successful application of their prior learning in work environments.

As noted earlier in this chapter, higher education institutions are increasingly being held accountable against metrics of educational outputs, including the development of graduate attributes (Hill and Walkington, 2016; Walkington et al., 2018). But as Michael Solem, Niem Tu Huynh and Joseph Kerski suggest in Chapter 32, there is potential with such a focus to lose the epistemic quality of geography if faculty begin to evaluate curricula solely in terms of skills and competencies. The danger, as these authors express, is a neglect of 'powerful' disciplinary knowledge (Lambert and Solem, 2017), the substantive, conceptual, and procedural knowledge of the discipline that advances human capability, well-being, and agency in life, and which has significance that cannot be understood solely in terms of its labour market values. Solem and colleagues encourage us not to lose sight of what geography adds beyond preparation for careers. This has led geographers to favour a 'capabilities approach' to education, which considers the broader purposes and values of disciplinary knowledge in contributing to human welfare, and in developing the capabilities of learners to make and act upon ethically informed personal choices. Walkington et al. (2018) propose five geocapabilities: geographical imagination; ethical subjecthood; integrative thinking about society and environment; spatial thinking; and a structured exploration of place. The capabilities approach broadens the dialogue about the role of universities and emphasises the crucial role of disciplinary knowledge in the holistic development of an effective and informed global citizenry.

Many of the pedagogic implications of developing geocapabilities in undergraduate students are identified across the chapters in our edited collection. These include: embedding study skills as part of student transition, progressing to advanced geographic and epistemic skills in later years (Chapter 2 by Simon Tate and Peter Hopkins, Chapter 3 by Graham Butt, and Chapter 25 by Shauna Brail and Kate Whalen); active and relational participation in problem-based learning related to fieldwork (Chapter 22 by Ian Fuller and Derek France, and Chapter 26 by Lisa Mol, Michael Horswell and Lucy Clarke), interdisciplinary thinking and doing (Chapter 9 by Amy Griffin), ethical debate (Chapter 11 by Ruth Healey and Chris Ribchester) and issues-based inquiry (Chapter 16 by Phil Klein, Karen Barton, Jessica Salo, Jieun Lee and Timothy Vowles); research-based learning within and beyond curricula (Chapter 14 by Helen Walkington); authentic learning and assessment (Chapter 5 by Bradley Rink, Chapter 19 by Zoe Robinson, and Chapter 27 by Jennifer Hill and Nancy Worth); and curriculum design to embed geography graduate capabilities (Chapter 31 by Rachel Spronken-Smith).

There are a number of challenges, however, that need to be overcome if the true potential of partnership working in higher education is to be realised (Bovill et al., 2016). With student–faculty partnerships, both parties need to develop skills to take part effectively in the new educational arenas and changed power relationships. Tutors leave behind the security of transmission-based pedagogies, becoming more personally involved in their students' learning, and this can demand significant investments of time. Students, with their identities in flux between learner and teacher, can feel confused about their role and behaviour with different tutors across a variety of learning contexts. An important challenge of working in pedagogic partnership relates to how a multiplicity of contested/marginalised voices can be made audible in these relationships (Felten et al., 2013; Moore-Cherry et al., 2016). There is a responsibility for faculty to encourage and support inclusivity in learning partnership, particularly for those lacking confidence and cultural capital. Attention also needs to be paid to the physical and virtual spaces required for participants to engage in meaningful informal social interactions and dialogue (Hill et al., 2016). Finally, there should be adequate supporting infrastructure, promotion of co-creative approaches in academic development fora, and personal development opportunities and recognition for students and faculty to engage successfully in partnership (Healey et al., 2014).

Critiques of partnerships between academia and industry/communities emphasise the disjunction between short-term student projects and long-term needs of community organisations and work places, coupled with resource and funding shortages (Pain et al., 2013). Stakeholder expectations must be managed concerning the amount of time, as well as the knowledge and skills, which students have to complete their projects. Equally, students must accept unpredictability and open themselves up to feelings of discomfort. Success in community-engaged and work-integrated learning requires managing the complexities of open-ended, real world situations while helping students navigate their requirements and ambiguities.

3.   Acknowledging the Whole Student

Many authors in our edited collection acknowledge an important role for geography educators beyond the cognitive development of their students. This is the case throughout the higher education learning journey, from student transition into higher education (for example, Chapter 2 by Simon Tate and Peter Hopkins, and Chapter 7 by Kamalini Ramdas), through the middle years that strive to develop autonomous learning (Chapter 8 by David Conradson, and Chapter 18 by Avril Maddrell and Edward Wigley), to the final year that focuses on capstone and bridging pedagogies (for example, Chapter 23 by Niamh Moore-Cherry, and Chapter 28 by Alice Hovorka and Peter Wolf). The affective domain in education engages students with their emotions, feelings and values (Krathwohl et al., 1964). Emotions are fundamental to learning, influencing an individual's approach to any learning experience (Felten et al., 2006). Acknowledging the emotions of students can motivate them to engage meaningfully in more reflective and self-directed learning (Niemiec and Ryan, 2009), ultimately leading to better performance (Boyle et al., 2007). It is equally important to acknowledge the 'emotional labour' of teaching (as Matt Finn and Carrie Mott call it in Chapter 4) and a role for co-pedagogy (Chapter 10 by Sarah Dyer) in enabling faculty to share negative feelings aroused through processes of education. Co-pedagogy might provide a supportive framework for tutors to explore negative affect, helping them to face discomfort without being overwhelmed (Haynes and Macleod-Johnstone, 2017).

Engaging with the affective as well as the cognitive, the personal and the academic, has become increasingly important in higher education as universities across the globe have expanded their student body from traditional groups straight from school to more diverse cohorts (Jacklin and Robinson, 2007). These students experience the challenges of living independently, autonomous learning and comparisons between themselves and their peers. Alongside this, they face significant pressures including competition for graduate jobs and financial challenges established by high tuition and living fees (Anthoney et al., 2017). These factors have meant that student stress and mental health problems in higher education continue to rise internationally (Ferguson, 2017). There is evidence that university students now experience situations that negatively impact on their wellbeing at rates higher than their peers, and this is more so with respect to minority groups (Stallman, 2010; Ibrahim et al., 2013; Beiter et al., 2015).

Resonating with the many references to emotions and wellbeing across our contributions, Hill et al. (2019b) have recently presented a model, evidenced by findings from the discipline, which highlights that engaging students in partnership with faculty enables academic staff to guide students through the emotions they experience in challenging learning environments. These authors demonstrate that consciously encountering emotion in the relational engagement of student–faculty pedagogic partnership can move students from negative feelings towards positive emotions, attitudes and learning behaviours, building their resilience and wellbeing. Through open dialogue with students, academic staff can expose their own struggles with learning and normalise the emotions that attend the development of knowledge. To realise this process, academic staff must be willing to encourage students into the borderland spaces of partnership identified above (Hill et al., 2016, 2019a) and students must also be willing to enter and work in them, becoming comfortable with uncertainty and challenge, changing their ideas and behaviours, and becoming more responsible and resilient in their learning. In short, transformative learning (irreversibly changing knowledge, emotions, attitudes and behaviour) comes in the struggles that are exposed and shared through dialogue in partnership.

The chapters in this book demonstrate the importance of developing curricula based on positive strategies to encourage wellbeing, situated in relational interaction, community and industry engagement and authentic research and project work. These strategies favour active student-centred and social pedagogic approaches (Doyle, 2008; Wiemer, 2013) such as fieldwork, group work, inquiry-based learning, research-based learning and authentic assessment, integrated across the learning journey from first to final year. Our contributions show that academics should not divorce the affective realm of learning from the cognitive, but instead use the emotional resonance of the subject for effective teaching through student engagement, being sensitive to the emotional aspects of subject content and learner development (see Chapter 18 by Avril Maddrell and Edward Wigley, and Chapter 27 by Jennifer Hill and Nancy Worth). Working in partnership, encountering emotion and collaboratively developing our students' positive feelings, learning behaviours and wellbeing, we can maximise the potential for sustainable learning and academic success.

Unmasking emotion links with a broader pedagogy of compassion (Vandeyar, 2013), where students recognise distress and/or disadvantage to themselves or others and commit to take action to reduce it. Waddington (2016, p. 3) implores higher education faculty to release the shackles of instrumental relations emerging from sector regulation to 'foster a culture where compassion is honoured'. Research in the UK (Gilbert, 2016) has shown that students are inclined to increase efforts over time to enhance their own and others' social and learning experiences in seminars through compassionate behavioural interventions during discussions.

Compassion-focussed pedagogy requires a willingness to co-create, to explore and share excitement, insight, passion, vulnerability, pain and joy (Arai and Tepylo, 2016). It embraces the idea of hospitality in teaching and learning (Nouwen, 1975), a sentiment taken up by David Conradson (Chapter 8), who highlights the need to consider how faculty can relate to students in ways that are welcoming, hospitable and attuned to them as individuals in classrooms, and through group work and fieldwork. A hospitable and compassionate pedagogy argues for geography faculty to engage in reflexive dialogue with their students to elicit new insights and create meaning together. This can help foster personalised and inclusive learning environments, which is a strong message emerging from our contributions. In such supportive environments, students are known by their peers and teachers, they feel welcomed, recognised and valued, and their aspirations to learn are encouraged and facilitated. We do, however, recognise that a commitment to this pedagogy, with growing class sizes, is a resourcing challenge.

Our contributions (notably Chapter 13 by Annie Hughes and Nona McDuff, Chapter 17 by James Esson and Angela Last, and Chapter 20 by Ash Parton and Martin Haigh), allude to a need to challenge the reproduction of inequality and injustice within the Academy and to afford any student a sense of legitimacy and belonging in their course/ institution. It is important to create courses that counteract the perpetuation of hegemonic discourses and identities, delivering new ways of learning, teaching and being that are based upon coexistence and respect, and allowing all students to see themselves reflected in the curriculum. Such inclusive curricula are crucial in ensuring that all students are connected to their learning and therefore more likely to achieve successful outcomes. In the classroom, contemplative pedagogy can help to give students equal voice (see the useful resources section). Contemplative pedagogy aims to connect students to the lived, embodied experiences of their learning (Barratt, 2016). Students are encouraged to become more aware of their internal world and to connect their learning to their own values and sense of meaning which, in turn, enables them to form richer deeper, relationships with their peers, their communities and the world around them. By incorporating classroom activities such as student–faculty and peer–peer dialogue, deep listening and reflection, all of which create space for encountering emotion and meaning, academic staff can help students to become more open to transformation as they explore and challenge social and personal values and preconceptions. Developing attitudes and values enables students educated *in* and *through* geography to understand the diverse, complex and changing world from alternative perspectives. In this way, the experience of geography in higher education should engender reflexivity, ensuring that due consideration is given to the impact of unequal social relations, whether of gender, sexuality, race, religion or belief, socio-economic status, age or disability, and to the risks of reproducing relations of exploitation or disempowerment within and beyond the university.

4.   Adopting Courageous Pedagogy

In Chapter 4, Matt Finn and Carrie Mott express a need for 'courage, wisdom and humility' in the classroom and we believe this is true for geography educators in higher education generally. The authors throughout this edited collection acknowledge increasing pressures of regulatory oversight, which challenge innovative teaching and learning. Within this environment, we nevertheless encourage geography faculty to be adventurous in their pedagogic approaches rather than 'play it safe' under the weight of increasingly demanding national governance and quality structures. We should be mindful to rise to the challenge of 'pedagogic frailty' (Kinchin et al., 2016; Kinchin and Francis, 2017). This is a situation in which faculty find the cumulative pressures of academia inhibiting their capacity to change practice in response to an evolving teaching environment, leading them to maintain conservative pedagogic approaches. Pedagogic frailty can curtail creative teaching, learning and assessment practices. But, the outward-looking and critically reflective nature of the discipline should help us to reflect upon and challenge this frailty. Letting go of academic surety is essential if we are to challenge our students with inclusive, engaging, innovative and relevant teaching, learning and assessment in an era of reductionist metrics and external accountability.

Three ways forward have been identified by Waddington (2016, p. 6) to counter-balance market-driven reforms in higher education through the promotion of challenging, creative and compassionate teaching, learning and assessment practice:

1. 'Challenge the "objectification and measurement" of students and staff, which reduces people to faceless resources to be manipulated and managed;
2. "Walk the line" between challenging established norms and upholding them, by walking in the company of colleagues and students who share the values and practice of appreciative inquiry;
3. Be more attentive to the language and representations of compassion in everyday experience.'

Many authors in this volume echo our call to reveal to students our disciplinary ways of knowing the world, acting positively to help solve its problems through learning and working collaboratively in critical forms of community. We consider that entering the pedagogic borderlands as spaces in which to legitimate emotions and caring as part of meaningful academic exploration, and working in partnership to understand complexity, may help us to achieve this. Being courageous in our pedagogy, taking calculated risks, and working creatively within time constraints and workload pressures, we can ultimately establish more meaningful connections and deeper ways of knowing in the classroom, over our campuses, in local communities and across the world.

CONCLUSIONS

The contributions to our edited collection highlight that geographers in higher education are employing innovative pedagogic approaches including: partnership and participatory pedagogies; inquiry- and problem-based learning; research-based learning; experiential/embodied learning; outcomes-focused pedagogy; ethical pedagogy; community-engaged and work-integrated learning; technology-enhanced learning; and assessment as pedagogy. Applying our four over-arching principles to these teaching, learning and assessment approaches moves us from performativity to authenticity, a process supported by the sustained development of information and communication technologies (ICT), especially in relation to wireless connectivity and mobile technologies. As some of our chapters evidence (for example, Chapter 5 by Bradley Rink, Chapter 22 by Ian Fuller and Derek France), improved ICT is facilitating the movement of geography learning and teaching beyond formal classroom space, allowing technology enhanced learning to take place seamlessly across multiple contexts. Students can employ technology in a wide array of settings; public and private, shared and individual. In addition to enhancing fieldwork learning in a variety of ways, notably by supporting geospatial functionality, improving connectivity between student groups within and beyond the field and developing graduate attributes (Fuller and France, 2016), students are increasingly able to access resources from around the world in preparing their assessments, as well as being able to make online connections with peers, professionals and employers.

But whilst digital technologies can be seen as a democratisation of resources for students, they can also establish individual, institutional and national inequalities. Computer and broadband access is not only uneven globally, but also nationally and regionally, and this differentially influences personal learning experiences (Higgitt, 2008). A further concern noted in our collection (Chapter 12 by Richard Waller, Gill Miller and David Schultz) is the ability of students to critically evaluate the veracity and reliability of information retrieved online. As such, encouraging equitable access to technology and enhancing digital literacy might be areas of pedagogic development for geographers going forward.

Geographic pedagogies must continue to evolve in order to maintain their relevance and to respond to contemporary and future socio-economic, cultural, environmental and geopolitical challenges. As editors, we reiterate the message communicated by many of our chapter authors – geographic pedagogies should challenge students to become 'border crossers', moving them beyond the familiar pedagogic contexts of their undergraduate experience to situate them in novel learning environments that compel them to consider new conceptions of self and personally-referenced ways of knowing. The chapters in this volume have shown that borderland spaces of learning (Hill et al., 2016, 2019a) can be created at the heart of the curriculum or in the less formal, co-curricular spaces in between. Transition into the borderland may involve entry into a novel learning space, such as students writing for an undergraduate journal or presenting at a multi-disciplinary research conference (Chapter 14 by Helen Walkington), or students becoming teaching and learning consultants (Chapter 15 by Richard Hodgins and Joanna Bullard). Equally, entry into the borderland can be gained through adopting an unfamiliar pedagogy in a familiar space, such as students leading inquiry-based seminars (Chapter 16 by Phil Klein and colleagues), ethical debate (Chapter 11 by Ruth Healey and Chris Ribchester), student-led field activities (Chapter 26 by Lisa Mol and colleagues) and non-western teaching (Chapter 20 by Ash Parton and Martin Haigh).

Moving into the borderland can also help to develop in our students the skills of self-determined learning, or heutagogy (see Chapter 21 by Michael DeMers, and Chapter 24 by Eric Pawson and Mark Poskitt). This metacognitive form of pedagogy requires 'double-loop' learners who are capable not only of reaching a goal, but also reflecting on the learning process and considering how to become more proficient learners (Hase and Kenyon, 2013). When faced with situations in the future, such students have the personal capabilities to find new approaches or fresh information, and they are able to apply these in an effective manner. Many authors in our edited collection note the need to support metacognition or 'learning to learn' within geography programmes, through a combination of discussion, reflection and practice, in order to help students to diagnose their learning needs, set goals, find appropriate resources, choose learning strategies, reflect on progress and evaluate learning outcomes. Indeed, the transitions that students go through as they enter into higher education, which allow them to develop more autonomous learning and prepare them for lifelong learning and real-world application, have been the organising framework for this book.

Many contributors to this collection note the importance of geographers engaging beyond their subject boundaries, applying their diverse epistemologies, methodologies and perspectives within multi- and interdisciplinary contexts (for example, Chapter 9 by Amy Griffin, Chapter 14 by Helen Walkington and Chapter 19 by Zoe Robinson). Interdisciplinary inquiry may be the answer to addressing complex societal and environmental questions, although tensions can arise as theoretical frameworks, perspectives and skills must be integrated from different disciplines over the lifespan of projects. As such, it would be useful to introduce undergraduate students to interdisciplinarity at an early stage of their learning to ensure that its meaning and consequences are understood. Within this, it is important to develop communicative competence (Sharp, 2015) as a pathway to successful interdisciplinary learning because it casts critical attention upon the abilities and cultural sensitivities that are the hallmarks of interdisciplinary collaboration – from negotiating meaning to critical disciplinary awareness.

The future for higher education geographical teaching, learning and assessment might focus less on individual elements of our practice and more on how to integrate emerging pedagogies into an effective process for future-facing lifelong learning. This might be achieved by focusing on heutagogy in borderland spaces of learning; bringing together a multiplicity of geography and other disciplinary students over diverse spaces and times to co-construct understanding through dialogue, guided by peers, academic colleagues and external partners. Producing geography graduates who can transcend disciplinary boundaries, work collaboratively, and learn from complexity will help us to manage 'wicked problems', the messy real-world problems that defy complete resolution. Drawing on the mass of knowledge presented in this collection, we hope that colleagues feel more supported in working with students to develop the geocapabilities for responsible global citizenship, now and into the future.

USEFUL RESOURCES

- Contemplative pedagogy network: https://contemplativepedagogynetwork.com.

REFERENCES

Anthoney, J., Stead, R. and Turney, K. (2017) 'Making connections and building resilience: developing workshops with undergraduates', *Knowledge Management & E-Learning*, 9, pp. 404–418.

Arai, S.M. and Tepylo, H. (2016) 'Compassionate pedagogy for reflexive community practices', in E. Sharpe, H. Mair and F. Yuen (eds), *Community Development: Applications for Leisure, Sport and Tourism*. State College, PA: Venture Publishing, pp. 143–154.

Askins, K. and Pain, R. (2011) 'Contact zones: participation, materiality, and the messiness of interaction', *Environment and Planning D: Society and Space*, 29, pp. 803–821.

Barratt, C. (2016) 'Exploring the potential of contemplative pedagogy in health professional education', *Focus on Health Professional Education: A Multi-Professional Journal*, 17, pp. 20–31.

Baxter Magolda, M.B. (2004) 'Preface', in M.B. Baxter Magolda and P.M. King (eds), *Learning Partnerships: Theory and Models of Practice to Educate for Self-Authorship*. Sterling, VA: Stylus Publishing, pp. xvii–xxvi.

Beiter, R., Nash, R., McCrady, M., Rhoades, D., Linscomb, M., Clarahan, M. and Sammut, S. (2015) 'The prevalence and correlates of depression, anxiety, and stress in a sample of college students', *Journal of Affective Disorders*, 173, pp. 90–96.

Bovill, C., Cook-Sather, A. and Felten, P. (2011) 'Students as co-creators of teaching approaches, course design, and curricula: implications for academic developers', *International Journal for Academic Development*, 16, pp.133–145.

Bovill, C., Cook-Sather, A., Felten, P., Millard, L. and Moore-Cherry, N. (2016) 'Addressing potential challenges in co-creating learning and teaching: overcoming resistance, navigating institutional norms and ensuring inclusivity in student–staff partnerships', *Higher Education*, 71, pp.195–208.

Boyle, A., Maguire, S., Martin, A., Milsom, C., Nash, R., Rawlinson, S., Turner, A., Wurthmann, S. and Conchie, S. (2007) 'Fieldwork is good: the student perception and the affective domain', *Journal of Geography in Higher Education*, 31, pp.299–317.

Cook-Sather, A., Bovill, C. and Felten, P. (2014) *Engaging Students as Partners in Learning & Teaching: A Guide for Faculty*. San Francisco, CA: Jossey-Bass.

Doyle, T. (2008) *Helping Students Learn in a Learner-Centred Environment. A Guide to Facilitating Learning in Higher Education*. Sterling, VA: Stylus Publishing.

Dyer, S., Williams, R., Walkington, H., Morton, K. and Wyse, S. (2016) 'Shifting landscapes: from coalface to quicksand? Teaching geography, earth and environmental sciences in higher education', *Area*, 48, pp.308–316.

Erickson, R.A. (2012) 'Geography and the changing landscape of higher education', *Journal of Geography in Higher Education*, 36, pp.9–24.

Felten, P., Gilchrist, L. and Darby, A. (2006) 'Emotion and learning', *Michigan Journal of Community Service Learning*, 12, pp.38–46.

Felten, P., Bagg, J., Bumbry, M., Hill, J., Hornsby, K., Pratt, M. and Weller, S. (2013) 'A call for expanding inclusive student engagement in SoTL', *Teaching and Learning Inquiry*, 1, pp.63–74.

Ferguson, D. (2017) 'The rise in student mental health problems. "I thought my tutor would say: deal with it"', *The Guardian*, 29 August 2017.

Freire, P. (1970) *Pedagogy of the Oppressed*. New York: Continuum.

Fuller, I.C. and France, D. (2016) 'Does digital technology enhance student learning in field-based experiments and develop graduate attributes beyond the classroom?', *Journal of Geography in Higher Education*, 40, pp.193–206.

Gilbert, T. (2016) 'Assess compassion in higher education? Why and how would we do that?', *LINK*, 2 (1). Available online at: https://www.herts.ac.uk/link/volume-2,-issue-1/assess-compassion-in-higher-education-how-and-why-would-we-do-that. Accessed 3 November 2018.

Giroux, H.A. (1992) *Border Crossings: Cultural Workers and the Politics of Education*. New York: Routledge.

Gutman, L.M. and Vorhaus, J. (2012) *The Impact of Pupil Behaviour and Wellbeing on Educational Outcomes. Research Report of the Institute of Education*. London: University of London, Childhood Wellbeing Research Centre.

Hase, S. and Kenyon, C. (eds) (2013) *Self-Determined Learning: Heutagogy in Action*. London: Bloomsbury Academic.

Haynes, J. and Macleod-Johnstone, E. (2017) 'Stepping through the daylight gate: compassionate spaces for learning in higher education', *Pastoral Care in Education*, 35, pp.179–191.

Healey, M., Flint, A. and Harrington, K. (2014) *Engagement through Partnership: Students as Partners in Learning and Teaching in Higher Education*. York: HEA.

Higgitt, D. (2008) 'Editorial: geography, technology and society', *Journal of Geography in Higher Education*, 32, pp.1–5.

Hill, J. and Walkington, H. (2016) 'Developing graduate attributes through participation in undergraduate research conferences', *Journal of Geography in Higher Education*, 40, pp.222–237.

Hill, J., Walkington, H. and Kneale, P. (2019a) 'Borderland spaces: moving towards self-authorship', in T. Bilham, C. Hamshire, M. Hartog and M. Doolan (eds), *Reframing Space for Learning: Excellence and Innovation in University Teaching*. London: UCL/IoE Press, pp.88–101.

Hill, J., Healey, R.L., West, H. and Déry C. (2019b) 'Pedagogic partnership in higher education: encountering emotion in learning and enhancing student wellbeing', *Journal of Geography in Higher Education*, https://doi.org/10.1080/03098265.2019.1661366.

Hill, J., Thomas, G., Diaz, A. and Simm, D. (2016) 'Borderland spaces for learning partnership: opportunities, benefits and challenges', *Journal of Geography in Higher Education*, 40, pp.375–393.

Ibrahim, A.K., Kelly, S.J., Adams, C.E. and Glazebrook, C. (2013) 'A systematic review of studies of depression prevalence in university students', *Journal of Psychiatry Research*, 47, pp.391–400.

Jacklin, A. and Robinson, C. (2007) 'What is meant by "support" in higher education? Towards a model of academic welfare', *Journal of Research in Special Educational Needs*, 7, pp.114–123.

Johansson C. and Felten P. (2014) *Transforming Students: Fulfilling the Promise of Higher Education*. Baltimore, MD: Johns Hopkins Press.

Kinchin, I.M. and Francis, R.A. (2017) 'Mapping pedagogic frailty in geography education: a framed autoethnographic case study', *Journal of Geography in Higher Education*, 41, pp.56–74.

Kinchin, I.M., Alpay, E., Curtis, K., Franklin, J., Rivers, C. and Winstone, N. (2016) 'Charting the elements of pedagogic frailty', *Educational Research*, 58, pp.1–23.

Kneale, P.E. (2018) 'Where might pedagogic research focus to support students' education in a REF-TEF world', *Journal of Geography in Higher Education*, 42, pp. 487–497.

Krathwohl, D.R., Bloom, B.S. and Bertram, B.M. (1964) *Taxonomy of Educational Objectives. The Classification of Educational Goals, Handbook II: Affective Domain*. New York: David McKay.

Lambert, D. and Solem, M. (2017) 'Rediscovering the teaching of geography', *Geographical Education*, 30, pp. 8–15.

Land, R., Rattray, J. and Vivian, P. (2014) 'Learning in the liminal space: a semiotic approach to threshold concepts', *Higher Education*, 67, pp. 199–217.

Lodge, C. (2005) 'From hearing voices to engaging in dialogue: problematising student participation in school improvement', *Journal of Educational Change*, 6, pp. 125–146.

McEwen, L. (2013) 'Geography, community engagement and citizenship: introduction', *Journal of Geography in Higher Education*, 37, pp. 5–10.

Meyer, J.H.F. and Land, R. (eds) (2006) *Overcoming Barriers to Student Understanding: Threshold Concepts and Troublesome Knowledge*. London: Routledge.

Mezirow, J. (ed.) (2000) *Learning as Transformation: Critical Perspectives on a Theory in Progress*. San Francisco, CA: Jossey-Bass.

Moore-Cherry, N., Healey, R., Nicholson, D.T. and Andrews, W. (2016) 'Inclusive partnership: enhancing student engagement in geography', *Journal of Geography in Higher Education*, 40, pp. 84–103.

Nellis, D. (2017) 'Transitions in U.S. higher education: implications for geography learning', *Journal of Geography in Higher Education*, 41, pp. 155–165.

Niemiec, C. and Ryan, R. (2009) 'Autonomy, competence, and relatedness in the classroom. Applying SDT to educational practice', *Theory and Research in Education*, 7, pp. 133–144.

Nouwen, H.J.M. (1975) *Reaching Out: The Three Movements of the Spiritual Life*. New York: Doubleday.

Pain, R., Finn, M., Bouveng, R. and Ngobe, G. (2013) 'Productive tensions – engaging geography students in participatory action research with communities', *Journal of Geography in Higher Education*, 37 pp. 28–43.

Ritchie, L. (2016) *Fostering Self-Efficacy in Higher Education Students*. London: Palgrave.

Sharp, E. (2015) 'Interdisciplinary experiences: a postgraduate geographer's perspective', *Journal of Geography in Higher Education*, 39, pp. 220–225.

Shulman, L. (2005) 'Signature pedagogies in the professions', *Daedalus*, 134, pp. 52–59.

Stallman, H.M. (2010) 'Psychological distress in university students: a comparison with general population data', *Australian Psychologist*, 45, pp. 249–257.

Thomas, H. (2010) 'Learning spaces, learning environments and the dis"placement" of learning', *British Journal of Educational Technology*, 41, pp. 502–511.

Vandeyar, S. (2013) 'Teaching a class act of human compassion', *Mediterranean Journal of Social Sciences*, 5, pp. 57–61.

Vygotsky, L.S. (1978) *Mind in Society*. Cambridge, MA: Harvard University Press.

Waddington, K. (2016) 'The compassion gap in UK universities', *International Practice Development Journal*, 6 (1). Available online at: https://www.fons.org/library/journal/volume6-issue1/article10. Accessed 3 November 2018.

Walkington, H., Dyer, S., Solem, M., Haigh, M. and Waddington, S. (2018) 'A capabilities approach to higher education: geocapabilities and implications for geography curricula', *Journal of Geography in Higher Education*, 42, pp. 7–24.

Weimer, M. (2013) *Learner-Centred Teaching. Five Key Changes to Practice* (Second edition). San Francisco, CA: Jossey-Bass.

Index

'3M' model 146

A Level Content Advisory Board (ALCAB) 36
A levels
    curriculum revision 37–8
    information literacy and independent learning 153–4, 155
    and transition to degree 39
academic and social transitions to undergraduate geography 16–17
    academic transition, student perspectives on 17–20
    and information literacy 152–5, 161
    social transition, student perspectives on 20–27
    transitions map 24, 25–6, 27
    see also fieldwork as transition pedagogy (promoting collaborative learning amidst uncertainty); school and university geography, bridging divide between; supportive learning environments, and transition to university
accessibility 171–2
accreditation 12, 37, 134, 139, 271, 415
active learning 63, 199–201, 202, 214, 300–301
    see also taking ownership (active learning and student engagement)
adult learning (andragogy) 287–9
adulthood, transition to 21
American Library Association (ALA) 151
analysis, as conceptual knowledge 212–13
'analytical-predictive' approach 300, 301
Anthropocene, learning for 337–8, 444–5
assessment
    diagnostic, surveys for 64–5
    and liminal space 372
    non-examination assessments (NEAs) 155
    peer learning and assessment 67–8, 380
    self-assessment 106
    summative 372–3, 377
    and supportive learning 105–6
    see also authentic assessment and feedback, to develop lifelong learning; formative assessment; large classes, strategies for assessment of learning
'assimilator' learning style 241

Association of College and Research Libraries (ACRL) 152, 153, 156–7, 160
Association of Graduate Recruiters (AGR) 464
attainment and attainment gaps 168–9, 175, 176–8, 231, 334
attributes, graduate *see* graduate attributes
attunement 103, 104
Australia, information literacy 153, 157, 159–60
authentic assessment and feedback, to develop lifelong learning 371–2
    challenges of authentic assessment and ways forward 379–82
    conclusions and recommendations for practice 382
    developing authentic assessment 372–6
    integrating authentic assessment 379
    iterative dialogic feed-forward assessment 376–9
authentic learning 63, 64–5, 67, 477
authorship, politics of 338–9
A–Z Geography Student Handbook 20

Barrie, S.C. 430–31
Barrow, R. 402
Basu, P. 35
Baxter Magolda, M. 146, 183, 191, 314, 317, 324, 476
Bednarz, S.W. 404–5
bibliographic software/websites 163
Biddle, D. 39, 40
black and minority ethnic (BME) staff 231–2
black and minority ethnic (BME) students 168–9, 172, 173, 174, 175–8, 231
blind marking 462
Bonnett, A. 32, 231
borderland spaces 318, 325, 372, 379, 475, 476, 477, 480, 483, 484
boundary spaces 336
Bovill, C. 316, 321, 324, 325
Bowden, J. 430
Boyle, A. 345
Boys, J. 333
Bridgstock, R. 433, 444
Bringle, R.G. 262
British Conference of Undergraduate Research (BCUR) 190–92, 438